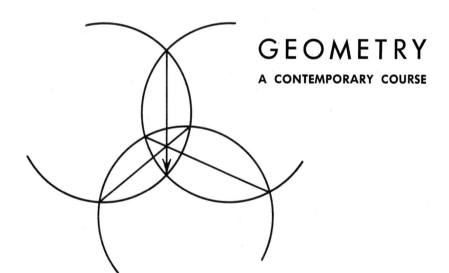

GEOMETRY

A CONTEMPORARY COURSE

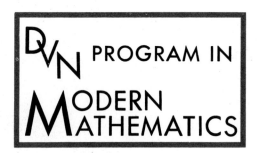

D**v**N **PROGRAM IN**
MODERN **M**ATHEMATICS

GEOMETRY

A CONTEMPORARY COURSE

Second Edition

HARRY LEWIS

D. Van Nostrand Company, Inc.

PRINCETON, NEW JERSEY   TORONTO   LONDON   MELBOURNE

Dr. Harry Lewis is principal of Arts High School, Newark, New Jersey. He was formerly the chairman of the Mathematics Department of East Side High School of Newark, having taught mathematics for many years in the Newark Public School System. He is the coauthor of textbooks on business mathematics and has taught at the New York University School of Education.

VAN NOSTRAND REGIONAL OFFICES: *New York, Chicago, San Francisco*

D. VAN NOSTRAND COMPANY, LTD., *London*

D. VAN NOSTRAND COMPANY (Canada), LTD., *Toronto*

D. VAN NOSTRAND COMPANY AUSTRALIA PTY. LTD., *Melbourne*

Library of Congress Catalog Card No. 67-31126

01681b150

PRINTED IN THE UNITED STATES OF AMERICA

Preface

GEOMETRY—*A Contemporary Course* reflects the influence of a number of sources. Not the least of these is the weight of the experimentation conducted in the teaching of geometry during the past twenty-five years by both the author and his colleagues. The data collected over this period strongly indicated the need for both the arrangement and the development of elementary mathematical concepts as presented in this text. Further evidence that this presentation appears to be desirable is the fact that the most frequent comment of teachers using the first edition is that a much larger percent of students understand the nature of proof than have ever done so in the past.

Even a cursory examination of this text reveals that the author has leaned heavily on the geometry program prepared by the School Mathematics Study Group. The symbolism—the distinction between line, line segment, and ray—the emphasis on the concept of "betweenness" as related to points or to rays—the use of congruence rather than equality—and on and on, all indicate a very apparent attempt to adhere to certain broad and desirable aspects of the SMSG proposals. Similarly, the blending of synthetic, coordinate and three-space geometries gives ample evidence that the report of the Commission on Mathematics of the College Entrance Examination Board has left its impact on the writer.

Distinctive Features

1. The introductory concepts on definitions and postulates are totally separated from one another.

(a) The first chapter is devoted to the need for definitions in any discussion, the methods of formulating a definition, and the outgrowth of undefined terms as a consequence of the structure of the connotative definition.

(b) The second chapter dwells only on the definitions of a relatively few geometric terms and their application to geometric figures. Distinction is made between reasoning from a definition as against reasoning from the reverse of the definition.

(c) The third chapter is wholly devoted to justifying the need for postulates in any discussion and in particular to the field of geometry. Great pains are taken to apply the operational postulates to geometric situations rather than algebraic ones. It has been shown

v

that many students, although disinterested in algebra, seem "to come to life" when exposed to the nature of proof in geometry. In view of this, examples involving excessive algebraic manipulation have been omitted from the early chapters of the book.

2. The indirect proof has been presented both slowly and carefully by making use of Aristotle's second and third laws of logic. Experience indicates that the student has difficulty in expressing himself when attempting to develop an indirect proof in the "Two-Column" form, hence the "Paragraph" proof is introduced, and this format is required for all problems calling for an indirect proof. To establish a feeling for this proof, a section containing many problems ranging from those that are almost obvious to others that will challenge the brightest students are included. From this point on in the text there appear problems requiring the indirect proof in almost every set of exercises.

3. The narrative problem does not appear in the text until the technique of expressing a proof has been firmly established. Only then are the conditional and categorical statements introduced, and, again, a large number of problems are available to the student so that he can achieve some skill in handling this segment of the course.

4. The chapters on coordinate geometry are both extensive and thorough. They were not included merely to pay lip service to the Commission's Report. The concept of locus as a "set of points" in coordinate geometry helps pave the way for an understanding of locus in synthetic geometry. In addition to the usual loci problems involving equalities, there are many that are devoted to inequalities. In keeping with the current trend, set notation is used to describe these loci.

5. It was felt that introducing elements of three dimensional geometry at the very outset would only add to the burden of learning too many unfamiliar terms too early in the work. It is only after the properties of perpendicularity in a plane have been established that we find any reference to space geometry. By this time the student should feel secure in his understanding of the subject matter and be ready to extend some of the notions he has learned to a "broader" space.

6. The book is designed so that the teacher who prefers to restrict the course to topics related only to synthetic plane geometry can do so without fear that she may be assigning problems in either three dimensional or coordinate geometry.

7. Each chapter contains a test or review of that chapter. In addition there is often a short section pertaining to an interesting and unusual problem that frequently has some historical significance.

8. In addition to a very careful grading of the problems within each set of exercises, the narrative problems are kept distinct from those wherein the diagram, Given Data, and Conclusion are given to the student, and these, in turn, are separated from the numerical problems.

Every effort has been made to gear the level of the writing to students in the tenth and eleventh grades. In fact, our experience has shown that it is possible for students to read and comprehend the explanations without the aid of a teacher.

Second Edition

In this, the second edition, the definition of the interior of an angle was revised to overcome certain inconsistencies. This was achieved by establishing more rigorous definitions of "betweenness" as related to points and as related to rays. By these changes, a disturbing loophole was closed in the proof of the theorem on perpendicularity of lines—Theorem 15. Largely affected was the content of Chapter 3 of the earlier edition— and little else.

A number of teachers who had used the first edition suggested that material be included in the current revision covering the circumference and area of a circle, the volume and surface area of a sphere, the volume and surface area of a cylinder, and, of course, the volume and surface area of a cone. In view of this, these topics were added to those of Chapters 17 and 18. The postulates used in the development of the theorems pertaining to these concepts are quite different from those frequently found at this level. They are, however, far more in keeping with the interpretation of a "limit" as used in advanced courses in mathematics than the vague symbolism normally employed when this topic is developed in secondary school mathematics classes.

I would like to express my gratitude to Mr. Sidney Flamm, Mr. Angelo Rosamilia, and Mrs. Laura Schefter—all of East Side High School, Newark, New Jersey—who offered valuable criticism after having taught this material in mimeographed form. And, by all means, I am thankful for and deeply touched by the many moving and sincere letters that I have received from teachers and students across the nation. This is the heady wine on which an author nourishes.

HARRY LEWIS

January, 1968

Contents

LIST OF SYMBOLS

$\overset{\frown}{AB}$	Arc AB
⊙	Circle
◉	Circles
△	Triangle
△	Triangles
▱	Parallelogram
$\overline{AB}$	Segment AB
$\overset{\leftrightarrow}{AB}$	Line AB
$\overset{\rightarrow}{AB}$	Ray AB
$\angle A$	Angle A
$m\ \overline{AB}$	Measure of $\overline{AB}$
$m\ \angle A$	Measure of $\angle A$
$\angle A{-}BC{-}D$	Dihedral angle $A{-}BC{-}D$
⊥	Perpendicular
⊥̸	Not perpendicular
∥	Parallel
∦	Not parallel
≅	Congruent
≇	Not congruent
~	Similar
=	Equal
≠	Not equal
>	Greater than
<	Less than
≥	Greater than or equal to
≤	Less than or equal to
≯	Not greater than
≮	Not less than
$\sqrt{\ \ }$	Square root
{ }	Set
|	Such that
∩	Intersection
Δy	Delta y
$\lvert a \rvert$	Absolute value of a
∴	Therefore
$A \leftrightarrow H$	A corresponds to H
$p \rightarrow q$	If p then q
$\sim p$	Not p

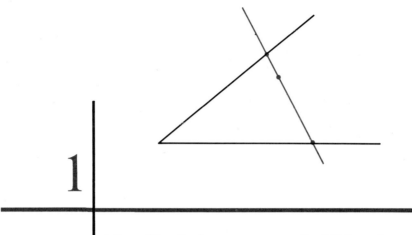

1

Definitions and Their Place in a Proof

THE ARGUMENT HAD REACHED A STALEMATE.
Finally, in disgust, the taller and heavier man shouted, "If you don't believe me, I'll prove it for you!" With that, he took off his jacket, rolled up his sleeves, clenched his fist, and laid his opponent low.

Well, you may not want to consider this a "proof," but certainly the argument was forceful and, needless to say, the conclusion was no longer in doubt. Yes, this is one of many ways in which decisions are arrived at or "arguments" are "proved." Though most intelligent people would prefer not to resort to violence in order to prove their point, with many primitive people, with young children, and even with some nations, this seems only too often to be a way of imposing ideas on a weaker opponent. This method of proof is frequently referred to as *proof by force*.

It is very likely that during the many discussions you have had with friends, you may have tended to use various appeals to convince them of the correctness of your cause. In some cases you may have sought their pity. In others, if you were certain they were unfamiliar with the topic at hand, you may have deliberately used their ignorance to drive your point home. And in still others, perhaps you clinched your argument by an appeal to authority such as, your teacher, your clergyman, your parent, your doctor, or, in desperation, possibly an advertisement on TV. All these methods of "proof" rely heavily on an appeal to the emotions of the listeners or to their respect for authority.

Mathematical proofs, on the other hand, are designed so that the conclusions drawn by mathematicians are but an outgrowth of a relatively few statements that they have agreed upon. During the coming year you will learn several methods employed by mathematicians for proving statements. This understanding will also enable you to determine those circumstances for which it is better to apply one method rather than another. In addition, the shortcomings of each of these patterns of proof will be shown.

■ Need for Definitions

Most of us rarely think twice about the words we hear during the course of the day. Perhaps this is as it should be. There are times, however, when a slight reflection on our part may cause us to wonder what in the world was meant by what we have just heard. To illustrate, consider the incident, oft used by comic strip writers, of the mother asking her five-year-old son to wash himself. Within a few moments the boy appears, proudly displaying his "clean" fingers, but only to be met by the indignant outburst from his parent insisting that he return to the bathroom to *wash* himself. To the boy, *washing* meant cautious dipping of the finger tips in water and removal of the water as quickly as possible by rubbing vigorously with a towel. To the mother, on the other hand, *washing* implied the application of soap from elbows to finger tips—from neck through forehead— certainly a grossly different interpretation of *washing* than had been given to it by her offspring!

In a more serious vein, a great deal has been said recently about the nature of our education. Were we confronted with the statement that

"Most people receive an adequate education"

we would very likely declare, "Why, of course it is so!" Yet, were we to reflect for but a moment, we would soon realize that there are several words in the statement that are a bit vague. Thus, the word *education* means many things to many people.

To some, education means occupying a seat in a building where there are other students and a teacher. To others, this word implies having a thorough understanding of mathematics, physics, chemistry, and at least two foreign languages. Removing the word education from the original sentence and replacing it with each of the interpretations just stated, we obtain these two sentences:

(1) Most people occupy (or have occupied) a seat in a building where there are other pupils and teachers.
(2) Most people have a thorough understanding of mathematics, physics, chemistry, and at least two foreign languages.

In all likelihood we would agree with the accuracy of the first sentence but question that of the second. Yet both are merely a rewording of the sentence, *Most people receive an adequate education*, wherein the word "education" has been replaced by two of its definitions.

EXERCISES

1. Why did we reach two completely opposite conclusions concerning the truth or falsity of the statement *Most people receive an adequate education?*
2. Which of the definitions of education would you say is the correct one?
3. Make up your own definition of the word "education" that would make the sentence true.
4. What other words in the statement *Most people receive an adequate education* need clarification?
5. State one reason why people may have completely contradictory views about simple statements.

■ Who Determines the Definitions of Words?

From the illustration in the preceding section we should have learned that one of the reasons why people arrive at different conclusions is because they attach different meanings to the key words in the discussion. But who is to say whose definition is the *correct* one? Frankly, no one person can say. The people participating in any discussion must agree on the meanings of the terms in question. Once they have reached an understanding, however, it is important that no one change the definitions of these terms without notifying the others. Not to notify the others would be quite foolish, for then this person would arrive at conclusions based on private definitions that would be meaningless to the others.

So, too, will be the case with the many, many words that will be considered in geometry. Once the definitions of terms have been agreed upon (they will be those that appear in this textbook), we can not be fickle and change them to suit ourselves as we might change our clothes. On the other hand there is nothing sacred about which definition has been agreed upon. What is important is that we do not change horses in midstream. What would happen if part way through the course several students in the class, without consulting the others, decided to go back and change the definitions of all the words they had learned to date?

Briefly, we can now say

(1) Definitions are made to suit the needs of the people involved in any discussion.

(2) Once a definition has been agreed upon, it can not be changed by any single member without consulting the others of the group.

EXERCISES

Define the underlined words in two ways: (*a*) to make the sentence true and (*b*) to make it false.

1. A television set is a piece of <u>furniture</u>.
2. A dog is man's best <u>friend</u>.
3. A refrigerator is an <u>icebox</u>.
4. The school nurse is a <u>teacher</u>.
5. A magazine is a <u>textbook</u>.
6. George Washington was an <u>intellectual</u>.
7. A candy bar is <u>food</u>.
8. Climbing the school stairs is <u>participating in gymnastic activities</u>.

■ Constructing a Definition

Although we have been discussing the need for clearly defined terms, in addition to the fact that we have been called upon to define several words, nothing, absolutely nothing, has been said concerning *how* to construct a good definition. This may appear as an oversight. Yet, on the other hand, it provided an opportunity to formulate several definitions that can now be examined carefully. In this way we will be able to select the special ingredients from which definitions are brewed. These ingredients are frequently called the *characteristics* or *properties* of a definition.

If each of us had written the definition of a teacher called for in Problem 4 of the preceding *Exercises*, one of these would probably be

"A teacher is a person who imparts information to her students."

There are two features of this definition that must be emphasized:

(1) The subject of the sentence is the word being defined.
(2) The verb is some form of the verb "to be."

Equally as important, though, is the fact that the word following the verb pertains to a collection of objects which have similar traits. In this situation the collection is the word *person*. Other things that would have similar traits to the word *teacher* that would also belong to the collection of things called *person* would be: policeman, fireman, engineer, man, woman, taxi driver, and many, many more. Can you name at least six other things that belong to the collection of *person?* Should you examine some of the other definitions you made for the preceding *Exercises*, you may find that the collections to which each of the first three words belonged were

(1) A piece of furniture is a *household article.* . . .
(2) A friend is a *person.* . . .
(3) An icebox is a *piece of furniture.* . . .

Quite apparently our definition did not end when we placed the word being defined into the collection of articles that had similar features. Returning to the definition of *teacher*, you will notice that a modifying clause was placed after the word *person*. What is the purpose of this clause? Why is it that the definition could not have ended with the word person? If it had ended with the word person, name several other words whose meaning would be identical to that of the word teacher.

From your answers to the last four questions it should be clear that every good definition must contain a clause or phrase modifying the collection of objects. The purpose of this clause is to show how the word being defined differs from all the other words in the collection to which it belongs. If the modifying clause were not added, then all the words in the collection would have identical meanings. Thus, in the case of teacher, the modifying clause is

". . . who imparts information to her students."

Were this clause not in the definition, then the words teacher, policeman, fireman, engineer, man, woman, and all the other words classified as person would have the same meaning. In each of the definitions that you wrote for the underlined words in the *Exercises* on page 4, how did you distinguish the word you defined from the other words in that collection?

A third important property of a definition can be illustrated by asking you to criticize the following "definition":

"A teacher is a person who teaches."

This definition certainly complies with the first two properties of a definition:

(1) The word is placed into a collection (persons) that contains objects having similar features.

(2) The word is distinguished from the other objects in the collection by the modifying phrase *who teaches*.

But yet there is something confusing in this definition. The person who did not know the meaning of the word *teacher* would certainly not know the meaning of the word *teaches*. Thus, he would be no closer to an understanding of the word *teacher* after he heard the definition than before he had heard it. Hence, what relationship should exist between the words in the definition and the word being defined?

The fourth and last property of a definition is not quite as apparent as the earlier three. Return again to the definition of a teacher:

"A teacher is a person who imparts information to her students."

Were we to reverse this sentence—that is, interchange the predicate nominative with the subject of the sentence—it would become

"A person who imparts information to her students is. . . ."

Quite apparently, it would be best if this person was a *teacher*, not a fireman, nor a doctor, nor a lawyer.

Thus, our definition of teacher is reversible. Every definition must be reversible. By this we mean that when the predicate nominative and the subject of a definition are interchanged, the new sentence will be true. This is not so with all sentences. To illustrate, the reverse of

"All kings are men"

is

"All men are kings."

Although most men would prefer to believe that the latter sentence is true, most women know all too well that it is not! Can you make up five other statements that are not reversible?

Thus, we can now say that the properties of a definition are

(1) The word being defined must be placed into its nearest class. Earlier this *class* was referred to as a collection of words having similar properties.

(2) It is necessary to show how the word being defined differs from the other words in its class. This was done by adding the modifying clause or phrase.

(3) The words in the definition must be simpler than the word being defined.

(4) The definition must be reversible.

EXERCISES

1. Which of the properties of a definition are not complied with in each of the following "definitions"?

(a) An automobile is a vehicle.

(b) A desk is that which is used to write on.

(c) A history book is a book that contains history.

(d) An instrument used for keeping time is a clock.

(e) If a rectangle is a square, then it has four equal sides.

2. Rewrite each of the sentences in Problem 1 so that they will conform with the properties of a definition.

3. Using the properties of a definition, define each of the following words:

(a) running shoes   **(b)** biography   **(c)** football helmet

(d) writing paper   **(e)** chair   **(f)** garage

■ Need for Undefined Terms

The method we have used for defining words is certainly not the only way to formulate definitions. By reflecting a moment, you would realize that no dictionary gives a definition in sentence form. The definitions that you find in a dictionary are called *synonymous definitions*. Why was this name chosen?

A very common type of definition is the one used when teaching a baby how to speak. It would be a bit absurd to say to a young child:

"A table is an article of furniture upon which food is placed."

Not only would this approach be nonsense, but by insisting upon defining words in this manner to an infant we would probably retard his ability to speak by many years! A parent would normally point to the object and repeat its name many times. In due course the child would begin to mumble something that vaguely resembled the word. No, this is not a scientific definition, but a definition nevertheless, as any proud parent would vouch for. Definitions of this variety are called *demonstrative definitions*. When pointing to a table and repeating the word "table," we never know whether the child may be thinking only of the four legs rather than the entire object. Hence, to him, every desk, every chair, every stool, in fact every four-legged object might be a table!

The type of definition whose properties were listed on page 6 is called a *connotative definition*. This method for defining terms is used in most areas of elementary mathematics, including geometry. Without realizing it, in your study of algebra you defined such words as term, monomial, binomial, trinomial, and polynomial by employing the properties of the connotative definition. If you are now studying biology, you will find that all the words in this science are defined in terms of the connotative definition. Similarly, if you study physics and chemistry, here, too, application will be made of the connotative definition.

The fact that we insist upon the use of the connotative definition in geometry leads us squarely into a rather nasty predicament. Let us suppose that we did not understand the meaning of the word "person" at the time we were writing a definition of the word "teacher." Were we to look for the word "person" in the dictionary, it would lead us to the classification of "human beings." Again, assuming that this phrase meant little or nothing to us, we moved on undaunted to seek its meaning in the dictionary also. And so we continued to investigate the meaning of each new class that we encountered until finally our array of words resembled the picture below:

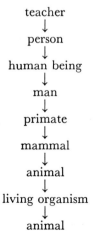

teacher
↓
person
↓
human being
↓
man
↓
primate
↓
mammal
↓
animal
↓
living organism
↓
animal

What criticism would you have of a dictionary that led us from "animal" to "living organism" and from "living organism" back to "animal"? Which of the properties of the connotative definition was not complied with by a dictionary that would lead us into a "circular definition" such as this?

Unfortunately, were we to trace words from class to class, we would find that the authors of most dictionaries will lead us in circles as in the case above. They do, however, have another choice. At some point in this process of "back stepping," the authors can call a halt saying, "I think that this word is so elementary that its meaning is known to all. Since there are no simpler words in my language with which to define this word, I will not define it at all." Words such as this are referred to as *first words*. The mathematician would call them *primitive terms*, or *elemental terms*, or simply *undefined terms*. In the diagram on page 7 "living organism" should have been considered as an undefined term, for in this case there appeared to be no word in the language in which to classify it.

Were we permitted to use the demonstrative definition, it would have been possible to have pointed to the object and in that way "defined" it. In geometry, however, we insist that the connotative, and only the connotative, definition be used. Hence, in order to define a word, it *must* be classified. Since we must begin our language—and our language will be the language of geometry—with some words, these first words will have no prior words by which they can be classified. *They must, therefore, of necessity remain undefined.*

EXERCISES

1. Prepare a diagram in which the word being defined is led from class to class to the undefined term that appears at the very end. Use the following group of words, where the first word is the undefined term: living organism, animal, person, citizen, teacher, mathematics instructor, Mr. Clark.

2. Draw a similar diagram for the following terms where the undefined term is the last one: rhombus, parallelogram, quadrilateral, polygon.

3. In each of the following problems rearrange the terms in their proper order, then draw a diagram similar to that found on page 7.

   (a) number, improper fraction, fraction, nine-fifths

   (b) furniture, moveable article, desk, table

4. Using a dictionary, trace each of the following words to their original source. Draw a diagram similar to the one on page 7, showing the class into which each word fell.

   (a) fable   **(b)** gold   **(c)** rose   **(d)** carpet   **(e)** brick

5. Will it be possible to define the first word you learn in the subject of geometry? Justify your answer.

■ The Language of Geometry

Point

The language of geometry is frequently opened with a discussion of the term *point*. It goes without saying that this word, of all words in geometry, can not be defined as it is the very first word in our language. Although it is not possible to define† this term, we are still faced with the problem of how to make its meaning clear to all. This is done by listing some of the properties, or characteristics, of the word without classifying it. Whenever a word can not be defined, that word is *described*. Fundamentally, the difference between a description and a definition lies only in the fact that

(1) When a word is defined, it is *classified*.
(2) When a word is described, properties of the word are given *without classifying it*.

To get some idea of why the properties of a point were so chosen, try to visualize the very fine end of a needle or a pin. Although you may consider that it is extremely pointed in its present condition, imagine what this end would be like if the refining or sharpening process were to continue indefinitely. It is just such a notion that the mathematician would like us to keep in mind when we think of a point. He wants the point to indicate some fixed position such as the end of the needle or pin. And yet he does not want it to occupy any space as the needle end does! Hence, he asks us to consider this needle end in the process of refinement at the moment it is vanishing. At that time, it represents a point to him. Thus, we obtain the properties of a point.

A point has neither length nor width but indicates position.

Line

When trying to define a *line*, we have two avenues of attack open to us. If the word is definable, there exists only one class into which it can be placed. Why? If it is not definable, it will be the second of our undefined terms. The mathematician prefers that it be undefined. There are a number of ways, though, in which we can visualize a line:

(1) The fine edge of a formica counter.
(2) The fine thread by which a spider lowers itself.
(3) The crease made by folding a piece of paper.
(4) The "line of sight" of a gun.
(5) A piece of elastic stretched to the breaking point.
(6) The edge of a ruler.

† Whenever the word "define" appears henceforth in this book, it will imply the use of the connotative definition.

Perhaps one of the better ways of picturing what the mathematician conceives of as a line is the piece of elastic mentioned above. Assume that it will never break. As it is stretched more and more, it becomes thinner and thinner. Should this process be continued indefinitely, the elastic would become minutely narrow and yet extend infinitely far in either direction. It is with this view in mind that the properties of a line were established.

A line has no width but can be extended as far as desired in either direction.

At this stage of our work we have come to a roadblock. We can not proceed with our work unless we recall some of the things we learned in algebra. Of great importance to us now is an understanding of the term *set*.

Set

■■■■■■■■■ The word *set* will be third of our undefined terms. As in the case of the other two words we will try to make its meaning clear by describing it. Thus,

A set is a "well-defined" collection.

Emphasis is placed on the words "well-defined," for

(1) If the *members* or *elements* of the set are known to us, we should be able to describe how they were found.

(2) Should we be given a description of a set of elements, it will be possible for us to list the members of this set.

To illustrate, given the set of elements

$$\{a, e, i, o, u\}$$

it is possible for us to describe this set by saying that it consists of all the vowels in the alphabet. Notice that the letters a, e, i, o, and u are the *elements* or *members* of this set and that they are enclosed in braces $\{\ \}$.

Now, secondly, were the members of a set described to us, this description would have to be such that we could list these members. Thus, consider the description

"The set of elements consisting of the names of the
days of the week beginning with the letter S."

This would be a "well-defined" collection, for from this description it is possible to list the elements in this set:

$$\{Saturday, Sunday\}$$

Relative to the background that we will need, there are three concepts yet to be recalled. These are **(1)** subsets, **(2)** intersection of sets, and **(3)** union of sets.

(1) *Subsets:* A set A is said to be a subset of the set B if every element of A is an element of B.

As an example, if the set of elements B is given as

$$B = \{2, 3, 4, 5\}$$

then, if

$$A = \{2, 3\}$$

A would be a subset of B. Other subsets of B are

$$\{3, 4, 5\} \quad . \quad \{3, 5\} \quad \quad \{5\}$$

Can you name at least four other subsets of B?

(2) *Intersection of Sets:* The intersection of two sets A and B is the set of all elements that are members of both A and B.

As an example consider the sets

$$A = \{1, 3, 5, 7, 9\}$$
$$B = \{3, 4, 5, 6, 7\}$$

The intersection of A and B is the set

$$\{3, 5, 7\}$$

for this set consists of all elements that are members of both A and B.

If the two sets have no elements in common, then the set representing their intersection will have no members. Thus, the intersection of the sets

$$C = \{1, 3, 5, 7, 9\}$$
$$D = \{2, 4, 6, 8, 10\}$$

will be the empty set or null set $\{\ \}$, for there are no elements that are common to both C and D.

(3) *Union of Sets:* The union of two sets A and B is the set of all elements that are members of either A or B.

As an example consider the sets

$$A = \{1, 2, 3, 4\}$$
$$B = \{2, 4, 6, 8\}$$

The union of A and B is the set

$$\{1, 2, 3, 4, 6, 8\}$$

for the members of this set are in either A or B.

EXERCISES

1. From the description given below, list the elements of each of the following sets:

(a) The set of all integers greater than 10 and less than 20.

(b) The set of all odd numbers greater than 2 and less than 10.

(c) The set of all multiples of 4 that are greater than 20 and less than 30.

(d) The set of all prime numbers greater than 10 and less than 20.

(e) The set of all the names of the days of the week that begin with the letter "M."

(f) The set of all one digit integers greater than 9.

(g) The set of all numbers greater than 0 and less than 10 that consist of the cubes of integers.

(h) The set of all multiples of 9 that are greater than 12 and less than 15.

(i) The set of all proper fractions whose numerator and denominator are members of $\{1, 2, 3, 4\}$.

2. What is the description of each of the sets below?

(a) $\{2, 4, 6, 8\}$

(b) $\{5, 10, 15, 20, 25\}$

(c) $\{3, 6, 9, 12, 15, 18\}$

(d) $\{$Tuesday, Thursday$\}$

(e) $\{a, b, c, d, \ldots, x, y, z\}$

(f) $\{1, 3, 5, 7, 9, 11, \ldots, 2n + 1, \ldots\}$

(g) $\{\frac{1}{2}, \frac{1}{3}, \frac{1}{4}, \frac{1}{5}, \ldots, 1/(n + 1), \ldots\}$

3. (a) List three subsets of $\{a, b, c, d, e\}$.

(b) List all the subsets of $\{1, 2\}$. (Both the original set and the null set should be included among the subsets of any set.)

(c) List all the subsets of $\{1, 2, 3\}$.

(d) By analyzing problems (b) and (c) can you state how many subsets there will be for $\{1, 2, 3, 4\}$ without listing them?

4. If $K = \{a, b, c, d\}$ and $M = \{c, d, e, f\}$, find at least two sets of elements that will be subsets of both K and M.

5. If $S = \{1, 2, 3, 4, 5\}$ and $T = \{2, 4, 6, 8\}$, find

(a) The intersection of S and T.

(b) The union of S and T.

6. If $R = \{a, e, i, o, u\}$ and $Y = \{a, b, c, d, e\}$, find

(a) The intersection of R and Y.

(b) The union of R and Y.

7. If $A = \{1, 3, 5, 7\}$ and $B = \{2, 4, 6, 8\}$, then find the intersection of A and B.

8. If A is the set of integers greater than 2 and B is the set of integers less than 10, then find the intersection of A and B.

9. A "geometric figure" is often described as a set of points. Draw diagrams similar to the ones at the top of page 13 and, in color, mark those elements that represent the intersection of the two sets in each situation.

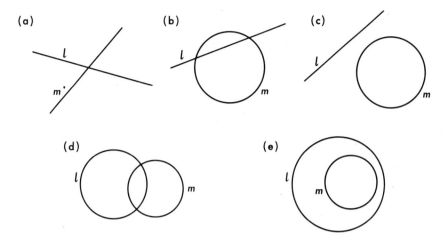

10. Draw diagrams similar to the ones below and, in color, mark those elements that represent the union of the sets shown in each situation.

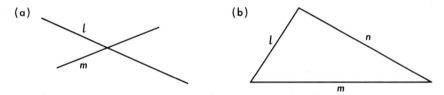

11. (a) Is the intersection of two sets a subset of either of the two sets? Illustrate by using the sets S and T in exercise 5.
    (b) Is the union of two sets always a subset of either set? Illustrate by using the sets S and T in exercise 5.
    (c) Give an illustration where the union of two sets is a subset of one of these sets.

12. Sentences 2 and 3 concerning the intersection and union of sets that appear on page 11 are actually the definitions of these terms. In what way were these definitions made to comply with the properties of the connotative definition?

Betweenness

Until recently mathematicians showed little concern about the term "between," although they had used it quite often. Currently, however, efforts are being made to indicate precisely what this term shall mean when used in a geometric discussion. If you are wondering why any-one would be confused by the use of the word "between," consider the diagrams in Figure 1-1. Is A, in each case, "between" B and C; or is B "between" A and C; or is C "between" A and B?

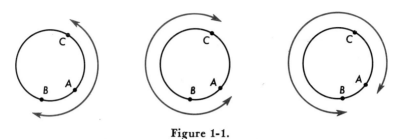

Figure 1-1.

Although "between" will be another of our undefined terms, confusion of the nature shown above will not exist, for at no time shall we ever use this term *unless the three points are points of the same line.* At this time it would be well to state that points are named by using a single capital letter. In the diagrams of Figure 1-1 the three points were named by the capital letters *A*, *B*, and *C*. Furthermore, *by considering a line to be a set of points* the expression that points "fall on" a line will merely imply that these points are members of the set that comprise the points of the line.

Before we can speak of arranging things, it seems essential that these things be distinct. Thus, we would not think of "arranging" a single book on a shelf, for there is no other book with reference to which it can be arranged. However, had we two books, we would have our choice of placing one first and the other second or in the reverse order. Should we be arranging three books—a history, an English, and a science book—on the shelf, then one of three situations might arise:

(1) The history book will be between the English and the science books.
(2) The English book will be between the history and the science books.
(3) The science book will be between the English and the history books.

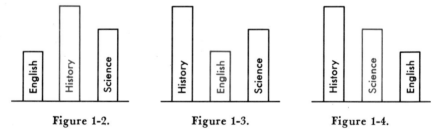

Figure 1-2.   **Figure 1-3.**   **Figure 1-4.**

It would make no difference to us were the order in Figure 1-2 English, history, science or science, history, English, for in either event the history book would be between the other two.

So, too, is the case when referring to *three points on a line.* Were their order on the line either *A*, *B*, *C* or *C*, *B*, *A*, we would speak of *B* as being between *A* and *C*. As seen in the diagrams of Figure 1-5, it would make very little sense to speak of the order of the points as the first point in question, the second, and the third, for how we numbered the points would depend on

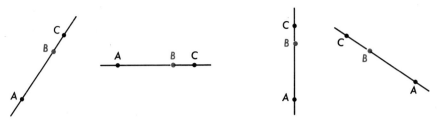

Figure 1-5.

the manner in which we approached them on the line. In all four cases, however, B is between A and C, for the order in which they appear on the line, no matter how we approach them on the line, is either A, B, C or C, B, A.

In general, for any three points on a line one and only one of the following orders must exist:

$$A, B, C \qquad A, C, B \qquad B, A, C$$

Remember, of course, that the order A, B, C is no different than C, B, A, for in each case B is between A and C.

Line Segment

We are now in a position where we can define the very first term in the language of geometry: line segment. As the word itself implies, we would like this term to denote a segment or piece of a line and exclude from it the remaining points of this line. To do this, we make the following definition:

DEFINITION 1: A line segment AB is a set of points of a line consisting of the points A and B and all the points between them.

In Figure 1-6 the points A and B and all the points of the line between them is said to comprise the line segment AB. The points A and B themselves

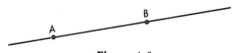

Figure 1-6.

are called the *endpoints* of the segment. Oddly enough, the line of which A and B are points can also be named by the same two capital letters and, hence, be called the line AB. To distinguish the line AB from the segment AB, the following symbols are used:

$$\text{line } AB\colon \overleftrightarrow{AB}$$

$$\text{segment } AB\colon \overline{AB}$$

The double arrowhead over the AB helps to recall the property that the line can be extended infinitely far in either direction.

Although a line segment must be named by using only those letters at its endpoints, a line may be named by referring to any two points of that line. Thus, in Figure 1-7 this line may be called $\overleftrightarrow{AB}$, $\overleftrightarrow{BA}$, $\overleftrightarrow{AD}$, $\overleftrightarrow{DA}$, or any

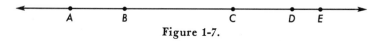

Figure 1-7.

one of a number of other ways. Can you name this line in at least ten ways not already given?

Ray

We have often heard people speak of sun rays, or moon rays, or a ray of light. So, too, in geometry we would like to speak of a ray from a similar point of view. We can picture a ray by visualizing the thread of light that would be seen if a flashlight were placed behind a dark sheet of paper that had been punctured by a pin. As shown in Figure 1-8 the ray

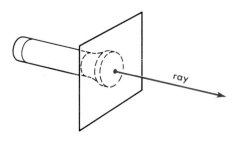

Figure 1-8.

would start at the paper and go off to the right. No part of this ray would exist to the left of the paper.

This description is clear, but it is far from being mathematically precise. To make it so, we will have to clarify what is meant by the statement that two points are on the same side of a third point. Thus, if B and C are on the *same* side of A, then either B is between A and C as in Figure 1-9 or C is between A and B as in Figure 1-10. Were A between B and C, then B and C are said to be on *opposite* sides of A as in Figure 1-11.

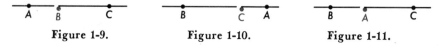

Figure 1-9.   Figure 1-10.   Figure 1-11.

DEFINITION 2: A ray is a set of points consisting of the union of a fixed point of a line and all the points of that line on the same side of the fixed point.

The fixed point is called the *endpoint* of the ray, while the ray itself is named by using two capital letters. The first of these must be the letter at the endpoint, while the second is the name of any other point of the ray. To illustrate, the ray in Figure 1-12 is ray AB, written $\overrightarrow{AB}$; Figure 1-13 is

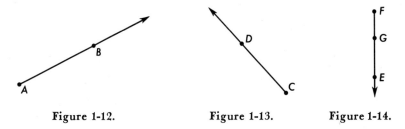

Figure 1-12.   Figure 1-13.   Figure 1-14.

the ray CD $(\overrightarrow{CD})$; while Figure 1-14 is the ray FE $(\overrightarrow{FE})$ or ray FG $(\overrightarrow{FG})$. Notice that only single headed arrows are placed over the two capital letters. This is to indicate that a ray can be extended in one direction only. Why is it not possible to name the ray with endpoint F in Figure 1-14 as $\overrightarrow{GE}$?

DEFINITION 3: Opposite rays are two distinct rays of the same line that have a common endpoint.

In Figure 1-15 $\overrightarrow{AB}$ and $\overrightarrow{AC}$ are opposite rays, for they are

  (1) distinct
  (2) of the same line $(\overleftrightarrow{EF})$
  (3) have a common endpoint (A)

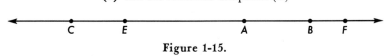

Figure 1-15.

On the other hand $\overrightarrow{AB}$ and $\overrightarrow{AF}$ would not be opposite rays, although they have a common endpoint and are on the same line, for $\overrightarrow{AB}$ and $\overrightarrow{AF}$ are merely two different names for the same ray!

Angle

Much of geometry concerns itself with relationships that exist among line segments and among angles. It is unlikely that this is the very first time that the word angle has come to your attention. However,

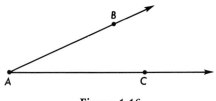

Figure 1-16.

as you realize by now, vague notions of what this word may mean can lead to difficulties. Hence, by examining Figure 1-16 see if you can formulate a clear definition of an angle. After having done this, compare your definition with that given here.

DEFINITION 4: An angle is the set of points consisting of the union of two rays that have a common endpoint.

The common endpoint is called the *vertex of the angle*, while the two rays are referred to as the *sides of the angle*. An angle is named by using three capital letters. The letter naming the vertex must *always* appear as the middle letter. The other two letters are names of two points, one from each of the sides. Thus, in Figure 1-17 the angle may be named either angle *ACE*,

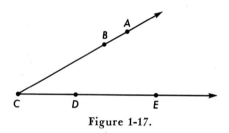

Figure 1-17.

written as ∠*ACE*; or angle *ECA* (∠*ECA*); or ∠*BCE*; or any one of a number of other ways wherein *C* is always the middle letter. How would you name this angle in at least four ways not already given?

EXERCISES

1.

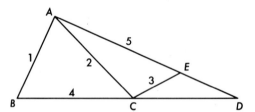

(a) Name the line marked 1 in two different ways.
(b) Name the line marked 3 in two different ways.
(c) Name the line marked 4 in six different ways.
(d) Name the line marked 5 in six different ways.
(e) Name the line segment marked 1 in two different ways.
(f) Name the line segment marked 2 in two different ways.

2. (a) In the diagram in Problem 1, at what point do the lines *BA* and *DA* intersect?

(b) In the diagram in Problem 1, what is the intersection of $\overleftrightarrow{BD}$ and $\overleftrightarrow{AC}$?

3.

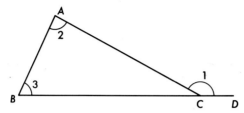

(a) Name the angle marked 1 in two different ways.
(b) Name the angle marked 2 in two different ways.
(c) Name the angle marked 3 in four different ways.

(d) Name the angle whose sides are $\overrightarrow{AB}$ and $\overrightarrow{AC}$.

(e) Name the angle whose sides are $\overrightarrow{CB}$ and $\overrightarrow{CA}$.

(f). Name the two sides of $\angle ACB$; of $\angle ACD$; of $\angle BCD$.

4.

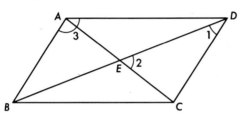

(a) Name the angle marked 1 in four different ways.
(b) Name the angle marked 2 in two different ways.
(c) Name the angle marked 3 in two different ways.
(d) Give two other names for the line BD.
(e) Give four other names for the line AE.
(f) At what point do the lines AC and BD intersect?

(g) Name the intersection of $\overleftrightarrow{AB}$ and $\overleftrightarrow{EC}$.

5.

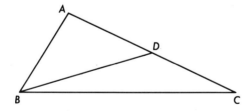

(a) Name the angle formed by $\overrightarrow{AB}$ and $\overrightarrow{AC}$.
(b) Name the rays that form the angle whose vertex is C.
(c) Name two angles that have a common ray as a side of each of the angles.
(d) Name an angle whose sides are a pair of opposite rays.

(e) What is the intersection of $\overleftrightarrow{AC}$ and $\overleftrightarrow{BD}$?

6. Using the properties of a connotative definition, explain why a line can not be defined as: "A line is a set of points."

7. Using the diagram below, how might it be possible to describe $\overline{AB}$ in terms of $\overrightarrow{AC}$ and $\overrightarrow{BD}$?

8. Illustrate how two rays can have a point in common and yet their union will not be an angle.

9. The set of points of a line on one side of a given point is called a *half-line*. How does a half-line differ from a ray?

10. (a) What is the intersection of $\overline{AB}$ and $\overrightarrow{AB}$?

  (b) What is the intersection of $\overleftrightarrow{AB}$ and $\overrightarrow{AB}$?

  (c) What is the union of $\overleftrightarrow{AB}$ and $\overline{AB}$?

■ Test

1. Explain why it is not possible to define the first word when building the language of a new science.

2. How is a "definition" distinguished from a "description"?

3. Which of the properties of a connotative definition were not complied with when each of the following definitions was made?
   (a) A newspaper informs its readers of events that have recently occurred.
   (b) An Englishman is a person.
   (c) An isosceles triangle is a triangle that is isosceles.

4. From the descriptions given below, list the elements of each of the following sets:
   (a) The set of all one-digit integers that are multiples of 3.
   (b) The set of numbers that are the squares of the first five odd numbers.
   (c) The set of all prime numbers that are greater than 23 and less than 29.
   (d) The set of all fractions whose numerator comes from the set {1, 2, 3} and whose denominator comes from the set {5, 7}.

5. Give a description for each of the sets below.
   (a) {4, 8, 12, 16, 20}
   (b) {2, 3, 5, 7, 11, 13, 17, 19}

(c) {January, June, July}

(d) {1, 4, 9, 16, 25}

6. Find the intersection of the two sets in each of the following problems:

   (a) {Mary, Betty, Jane} and {Doris, Mary, Jane}

   (b) {1, 3, 5, 9} and (2, 4, 6, 8}

7. (a) Explain what the conditions would have to be so that the intersection of $\overleftrightarrow{AB}$ with $\overleftrightarrow{CD}$ was $\overleftrightarrow{AB}$.

   (b) Explain what the conditions would have to be so that the intersection of $\overleftrightarrow{AB}$ with $\overleftrightarrow{CD}$ was the null set.

   (c) Explain what the conditions would have to be so that the union of $\overleftrightarrow{AB}$ with $\overleftrightarrow{CD}$ was $\overleftrightarrow{AB}$.

8. a is the set of points of one line, b the set of points of a second line, and c the set of points of a third line.

   (a) Draw a diagram in which the intersection of a and b is an element of c.

   (b) Draw a diagram in which the intersection of a and b, the intersection of a and c, and the intersection of b and c are three distinct elements.

9. Each of the problems below should be answered in terms of this diagram.

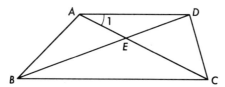

   (a) Name the angle marked 1.

   (b) Name the rays that form the sides of $\angle AED$.

   (c) Name the angle whose sides are $\overrightarrow{BE}$ and $\overrightarrow{BA}$.

   (d) Name a pair of opposite rays.

   (e) Name the intersection of $\overleftrightarrow{BE}$ and $\overleftrightarrow{CD}$.

   (f) Name the intersection of $\overline{AC}$ and $\overline{AE}$.

10. (a) If two rays intersect, will their point of intersection be the vertex of an angle of which the rays are the sides of that angle? Justify your answer.

    (b) Two rays have a common endpoint and they are subsets of the same line. Does this imply that they are opposite rays? Justify your answer.

    (c) The intersection of $\overline{XY}$ and $\overline{RS}$ is $\overline{RY}$. Draw a diagram illustrating this situation.

2

Definitions of Geometric Terms

THE TERMS THAT WE WILL CONSIDER IN THIS chapter will enable us to examine the relationships that exist between angles and between line segments. These relationships concern themselves with the notion of equality—a concept that was examined quite thoroughly by you during your course in algebra.

As you recall, the equality

$$a = b$$

was a means that was used to express the fact that a and b were but different symbols representing the *same* "thing." And, to a large extent, these "things" in algebra were simply numbers. Thus, the equality

$$3 + 4 = 5 + 2$$

expressed the fact that the symbols on the right of the equality sign and the symbols on the left were merely two different ways of representing the number seven.

In view of this, it would be both inconsistent and unwise to state at any time that

$$\overline{AB} = \overline{CD}$$

for $\overline{AB}$ and $\overline{CD}$ are the names of two *different* line segments and, as such, are not symbols representing the *same* "thing." Similarly, to say that

$$\angle XYZ = \angle RST$$

would be mathematically inaccurate, for the left member of the equation is the name of one angle, while the right member is the name of a completely different angle. Yet, there does exist an equality of some nature that can be examined between line segments and between angles. Of what character this equality is will be our concern for much of this chapter.

■ The Measure of a Line Segment

An important unit of your study of algebra centered around the "one-to-one" correspondence that exists between the points on a line and the real numbers. Rather briefly, the real numbers consist of all the numbers you examined during that course except for the imaginary numbers such as $\sqrt{-5}$. Specifically, these numbers did include positive and negative integers, positive and negative fractions, plus irrational numbers of the form $\sqrt{2}$, $\sqrt[3]{68}$, and π. Furthermore, the term "one-to-one" correspondence as used here merely implies that for each point on the number line there exists but one real number naming that point and, moreover, for every real number there exists but one point to represent it on the number line.

Such a correspondence is called a *coordinate system*. In addition, the number naming any particular point of the number line is called the

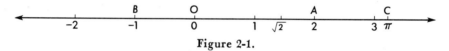

Figure 2-1.

coordinate of that point. For the number line in Figure 2-1 the coordinate of A is 2. What are the coordinates of B and C? In the study of geometry, we are interested only in that part of the number line consisting of the $\overrightarrow{OA}$; that is, the point zero and all the positive points on the number line.

What we have tried to do is make the number line resemble an infinitely long ruler. By varying the position of the point named "1" we can in turn make the number line appear to be either the "inch" ruler, the "centimeter"

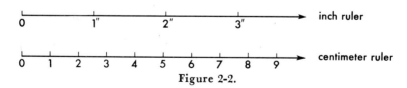

Figure 2-2.

ruler, the "foot" ruler, in fact any dimension ruler we care to make it. Changing the position of the 1 changes the unit of measure. Whether we use the inch, the centimeter, the foot, the yard, the meter, or any one of a multitude of other units in creating the number line, is not important. What is of great importance, however, is that we do *not* change the unit on the number line when part way through a problem. In fact, to avoid any misunderstanding, we will agree that the number lines encountered in any single problem will have identically the same unit.

We are now in a position where we can formulate a very important concept. Starting with any given line segment, we can establish a coordinate system on the line containing that segment. By making the coordinate of one endpoint of that segment 0, *the coordinate of the other endpoint will be called the measure of the line segment.*

2-3) we create a coordinate system whereby the coordinate of *A*, one end-

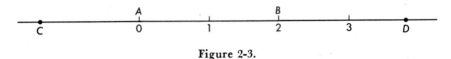

Figure 2-3.

point of $\overline{AB}$, is 0. Since the coordinate of the other endpoint, *B*, is 2, the number 2 is said to be the measure of $\overline{AB}$. Using symbols, this is expressed as

$$m\,\overline{AB} = 2 \qquad\qquad (1)$$

Quite apparently, we are saying no more here than

If a ruler is placed on line segment AB to determine its length, this length would be 2.

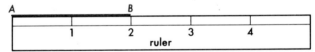

Figure 2-4.

Note that when we referred to the measure of $\overline{AB}$ in (1) above, we did not state that it was 2 centimeters, or 2 inches, or 2 feet, or 2 of any unit whatsoever. This is so since the measure of a line segment is the *coordinate* of one of its endpoints (when its other endpoint is 0). And as a coordinate, it is simply a real number and nothing else!

With the establishment of the measure of a line segment, we have overcome the difficulty raised in the opening paragraphs of this chapter. It was pointed out that it would be improper to say that

$$\overline{AB} = \overline{CD}$$

for $\overline{AB}$ and $\overline{CD}$ are the names of two different line segments. Now, however, to say that

$$m\,\overline{AB} = m\,\overline{CD}$$

will simply imply that the symbols on the left of the equality sign and the symbols on the right represent identically the same coordinate.

Midpoint of a Line Segment

█████████ Since we have a means of expressing equality, we would like to examine several situations in which this will occur. The first of these is with reference to the midpoint of a line segment.

DEFINITION 5: The midpoint of a line segment is a point of that line segment such that the two segments formed have equal measures.

To illustrate, if C is the midpoint of $\overline{AB}$, then by definition the measure

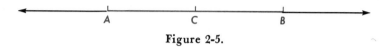

Figure 2-5.

of $\overline{AC}$ will be equal to the measure of $\overline{CB}$. This is expressed as

$$m\ \overline{AC} = m\ \overline{CB}$$

There are many, many lines that contain the midpoint of a line segment. Each of these, other than the one of which the line segment is a subset, is called the *bisector of the line segment*.

DEFINITION 6: The bisector of a line segment is a line that intersects the line segment at the midpoint of the line segment.

If, in Figure 2-6, $\overleftrightarrow{AB}$ is the bisector of $\overline{CD}$, it will imply that B must be the midpoint of $\overline{CD}$. Pursuing this further: since B is the midpoint of $\overline{CD}$, then as before

$$m\ \overline{CB} = m\ \overline{BD}$$

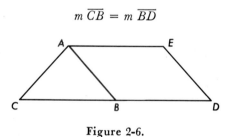

Figure 2-6.

Frequently, information in problems will be given as
Line segment XY is the bisector of line segment RS (Figure 2-7).

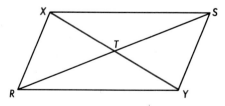

Figure 2-7.

This may appear to be an inconsistency, for the bisector of a line segment was defined as a line, not a line segment. It is not in error, however, for the segment XY is merely a subset of the line XY. Hence, if $\overline{XY}$ contains the midpoint of $\overline{RS}$, then so too must $\overleftrightarrow{XY}$.

One more point to be noted is the fact that the following two statements are equivalent:

(1) $\overleftrightarrow{XY}$ is the bisector of $\overline{RS}$.

(2) $\overleftrightarrow{XY}$ bisects $\overline{RS}$.

Statements such as these will be used interchangeably, for they will have the same meaning.

EXERCISES

1. What conclusion can be drawn from the data given in each of the problems below?

(a) D is the midpoint of $\overline{AC}$.

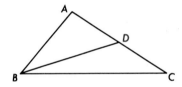

(b) $\overleftrightarrow{VT}$ is the bisector of $\overline{SW}$.

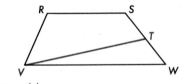

(c) F is the midpoint of $\overline{AE}$.

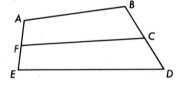

(d) $\overleftrightarrow{AC}$ bisects $\overline{BE}$.

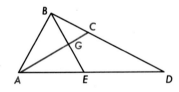

(e) F is the midpoint of $\overline{AB}$.

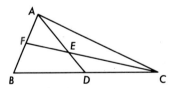

(f) $\overleftrightarrow{DE}$ bisects $\overline{AB}$.

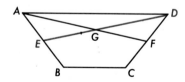

(g) $\overline{AC}$ and $\overline{BD}$ bisect each other. (Draw two conclusions.)

(h) $\overline{AB}$ and $\overline{CD}$ bisect each other.

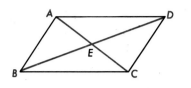

2. Based on the property of a line, explain why it would not be possible for a line to have a midpoint.

3. If, in the diagram at the right,
$$m\ \overline{BC} = m\ \overline{CD} = m\ \overline{DE}$$
then C and D are called the *trisection* points of $\overline{BE}$. How would you define the "trisection points of a line segment"?

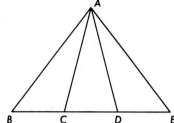

4. In the diagram in Problem 3 where $m\ \overline{BC} = m\ \overline{CD} = m\ \overline{DE}$, then $\overleftrightarrow{AC}$ and $\overleftrightarrow{AD}$ are called the trisectors of $\overline{BE}$. How would you define the "trisectors of a line segment"?

5. "If $m\ \overline{EF} = m\ \overline{FG}$, this will not necessarily imply that F is the midpoint of $\overline{EG}$."

(a) Draw a diagram justifying this statement.

(b) Under what conditions will F be the midpoint of $\overline{EG}$?

6. What is the name of the point of intersection of the bisector of a line segment and the segment itself? Justify your answer.

■ The Measure of an Angle

In trying to express an equality between angles we run into the same difficulty as we did with line segments. That is, to say that in Figure 2-8

$$\angle ABC = \angle DEF$$

Figure 2-8.

would not be correct, for the name on the right of the equality refers to an angle that is different from the angle that is referred to by the name on the left. By now we realize that the equality sign can be used only if the symbols on both sides of it are names for the same thing. Thus, we are forced into a position of having to create a measure for an angle as we had created a measure for a line segment.

Whereas the number line, or infinitely long ruler, was used to enable us to express the measure of a line segment, to express the measure of an angle we fall back upon the protractor. Ignoring the instrument itself and thinking only of its outline, we obtain Figure 2-9. To point A at the right

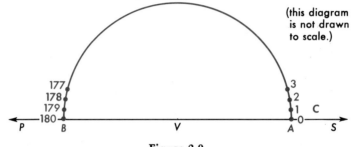

Figure 2-9.

we assign the number 0, while to the end point, B, of the red figure—NOT the segment AB—we assign the number 180. For later information, it is important to notice that the outline of the protractor begins at point A on ray $\overrightarrow{VS}$ and ends at point B on the ray opposite $\overrightarrow{VS}$; that is, $\overrightarrow{VP}$. This outline is then divided into 180 equal parts. The point C at the end of the first of these equal parts is marked "1." In the same way, each of the succeeding endpoints of every one of the equal parts is marked with the consecutive integers 2, 3, 4, ... The last of which, of course, is 180.

As a matter of fact, in a manner similar to that used on the number line, we establish a pairing off, or one-to-one correspondence, between every point on this red outline of the protractor and the real numbers from 0 to 180 inclusive. Where will the point representing the number $1\frac{1}{2}$ appear? The point representing the number .25? The point representing the number 179.99? Notice that once again we have created a *coordinate system*. This time, though, the points lie on the outline of the protractor, while the coordinates

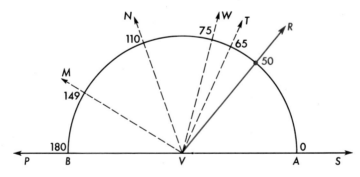

Figure 2-10.

are the real numbers greater than or equal to 0 and less than or equal to 180.

Now, were we to place the vertex of an angle at the point V and one of the sides along the ray VA, the other side of the angle will intersect the arc at some point. The *coordinate* of this point is called the *measure of the angle*.

In Figure 2-10 the measure of $\angle RVS$ is 50, for the side $\overrightarrow{VR}$ intersects the outline of the protractor at the point whose coordinate is 50. With symbols, this is expressed as

$$m \angle RVS = 50$$

And, in the same way as you had interpreted this in previous work in mathematics, we do say that $\angle RVS$ is an angle of 50 degrees (50°). Just as the inch and the foot are names for units of measure for a line segment, so the degree is the name for the unit of measure of an angle.

Returning to Figure 2-10, we notice that

$$m \angle WVS = 75$$

and

$$m \angle MVS = 149$$

What is the measure of $\angle NVS$? Of $\angle TVS$? Of $\angle PVS$?

Before we leave this topic, two features must be stressed. The first of these is the fact that the measure of an angle is merely the coordinate of the point on the arc. As such it is a number and no more. Hence, we should *never express the measure* of an angle as, let us say, 15 *degrees*, for the coordinate of a point is the number itself without the word "degree." Secondly, by limiting the outline of the protractor we drew, we have restricted ourselves to angles whose measure can be no greater than 180. This will exclude angles such as the one ($\angle CBA$) pictured in Figure 2-11. Although angles of

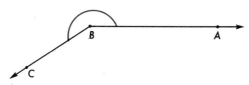

Figure 2-11.

this nature—and others much larger, too—occur in more advanced courses in mathematics, they do not arise in our work. We shall, therefore, ignore them.

With the understanding of the measure of an angle at our disposal, we are in a position to define a great many new terms.

Right Angle and Straight Angle

The angles discussed most frequently in the study of geometry are the angles about to be defined. They have further importance since many other terms are defined in terms of these angles.

DEFINITION 7: A right angle is an angle of 90 degrees.

Equally as often, a right angle is referred to as being an angle whose measure is 90. This, too, is correct, for the statement that

"The measure of an angle is 90"

is equivalent to the statement that

"A certain angle is an angle of 90 degrees."

To help fix this in your mind, these statements will be used interchangeably in this book.

DEFINITION 8: A straight angle is an angle of 180 degrees.

How might this definition have been worded if the word "measure" appeared in the definition?

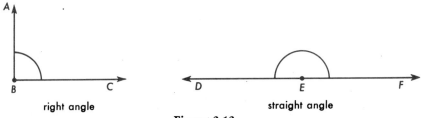

right angle   straight angle

Figure 2-12.

There is a very important property that follows from this definition that must not be overlooked. In the discussion of the measure of an angle on page 28 it was implied that an angle whose measure was 180 would be such that its sides would form a pair of opposite rays. Being opposite rays, it is possible to say that the sides of such an angle fall on the same line. Hence, it follows that

The sides of a straight angle fall on a line.

This, of course, gave rise to the use of the word *straight* in the name *straight angle*.

Acute Angle and Obtuse Angle

▬▬▬▬ At present we have names for angles whose measure is either 90 or 180. It is quite apparent that it would be impossible to have different names for every angle as there are infinitely many angles of different measures. Why is this so? To simplify this naming process, angles other than the right or straight are grouped so as to belong either to the set whose measures fall between 0 and 90 or to the set whose measures fall between 90 and 180.

DEFINITION 9: An acute angle is an angle whose measure is greater than 0 and less than 90.

DEFINITION 10: An obtuse angle is an angle whose measure is greater than 90 and less than 180.

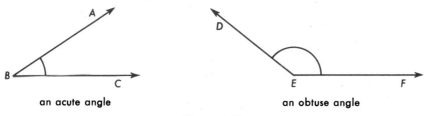

an acute angle   an obtuse angle

Figure 2-13.

With these two definitions we have completed the process of naming all angles whose measures are greater than 0 but less than or equal to 180. You may have noticed that no name was given to the angle of 0 measure. This was done deliberately, for reference to this angle does not occur in the study of geometry. What can be said concerning the sides of an angle of 0 measure?

Complementary and Supplementary Angles

Throughout the study of mathematics we often find reference to quantities being treated in pairs. The first illustration of this nature that occurs in geometry is the pairing of two angles wherein the sum of their measures is 90. Two such angles would be those whose measures are 63 and 27, or 15 and 75, or 89 and 1. Pairs of angles such as these are called *complementary angles*.

DEFINITION 11: Complementary angles are two angles the sum of whose measures is 90.

When two angles are complementary, one is said to be the *complement* of the other. Thus, an angle whose measure is 10 is the complement of one whose measure is 80; an angle of 40 degrees is the complement of one of 50 degrees. What is the complement of an angle of 70°? 25°? 1°? 54°? $\frac{1}{2}$°?

It must have been apparent to you that if a special name was given to a pair of angles the sum of whose measure was 90, that a special name would also be given were the sum 180. Two angles having this property are called *supplementary angles*.

DEFINITION 12: Supplementary angles are two angles the sum of whose measures is 180.

If one of two supplementary angles has a measure of 150, what is the measure of the other? Each of these angles is said to be the *supplement* of the other. In this illustration the angle whose measure is 150 is the supplement of the angle whose measure is 30. What is the supplement of an angle of 25°? 40°? 2°? 179°?

Since the measure of a straight angle is also 180, the definition of supplementary angles might have been stated as

DEFINITION 12A: Supplementary angles are two angles the sum of whose measures is *the measure of a straight angle.*

This statement is equivalent to that of Definition 12, for *the measure of a straight angle* and *180* are the same number, the number 180!

Similarly, the definition of complementary angles is equivalent to the statement

DEFINITION 11A: Complementary angles are two angles the sum of whose measures is the measure of a right angle.

EXERCISES

1. Classify each of the following angles as to whether they are acute, right, obtuse, or straight angles.

    (a) 124°   (b) 56°   (c) 90°

    (d) $12\frac{1}{2}°$ (e) 180°   (f) $179\frac{1}{4}°$

2.

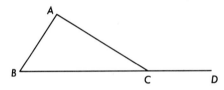

    (a) On the basis of your observation, what would you judge the measure of ∠ABC to be? In view of its measure, what name can be given to ∠ABC?

    (b) Angle ACD is an angle of approximately how many degrees?

    (c) Approximately what is the measure of ∠BAC? Were this so, by what name should ∠BAC be called?

    (d) If $\overrightarrow{CD}$ and $\overrightarrow{CB}$ are a pair of opposite rays, what is the name of ∠BCD? What is the measure of ∠BCD?

3.

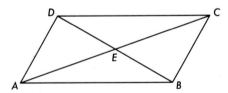

    (a) Approximately what is the measure of ∠DCB? What is the name of this angle?

    (b) Approximately what is the measure of ∠ADC? What is the name of this angle?

    (c) Name two straight angles in this figure.

(d) Name four angles that appear to be acute angles.

(e) Name two angles that appear to be obtuse angles.

4. (a) What is the complement of an angle of

$$15°, \quad 48°, \quad 1°, \quad 5\tfrac{1}{2}°, \quad x°$$

(b) What is the supplement of an angle whose measure is

$$126, \quad 57, \quad 38\tfrac{1}{2}, \quad 129\tfrac{1}{2}, \quad A + B$$

5. If the measures of an angle and its supplement are equal, what is the measure of each?

6. If the measure of an angle is five times as large as its supplement, what are the measures of the angle and its supplement? (Hint: Let x equal the measure of the supplement, then $5x$ will be the measure of the angle.)

7. If the measure of an angle is 46 more than its supplement, then what is the measure of this angle?

8. (a) When a right angle was defined, into what classification was this figure placed?

(b) How was a right angle distinguished from the other members of its class?

9. Criticize the following statements as "definitions."

(a) The measure of a straight angle is 180.

(b) A right angle is the union of two rays having a common endpoint.

10. If the number 200 had been assigned to point B in Figure 2-10 on page 28 rather than 180, how would each of the following terms have been defined?

(a) right angle   (b) straight angle

(c) acute angle   (d) obtuse angle

11. State your answer and then justify it for each of the following questions:

(a) Is it possible for two obtuse angles to be supplementary?

(b) Is it possible for an obtuse angle to be complementary to an acute angle?

(c) Can a right angle be one of two supplementary angles?

(d) Can a right angle be one of two complementary angles?

Perpendicular Lines

▬▬▬▬▬ When two lines intersect, the measures of the angles formed may be any real numbers between 0 and 180. Thus, in Figure 2-14, $\angle DBC$ appears to be acute, while $\angle ABD$ is apparently obtuse. If, however, at least one of the angles formed when two lines intersect is a right angle, then the lines are said to be *perpendicular*.

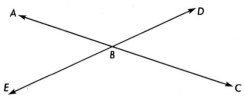

Figure 2-14.

DEFINITION 13: Perpendicular lines are two lines that intersect and form right angles.

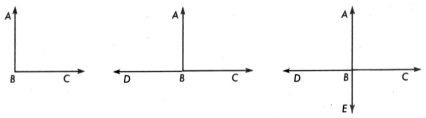

Figure 2-15.   **Figure 2-16.**   **Figure 2-17.**

In Figure 2-15 the rays BA and BC form a right angle, $\angle ABC$. Hence, these rays are said to be perpendicular. Being rays, however, they are subsets of lines, and as such, their opposite rays can be drawn. If in Figure 2-15 the ray opposite to $\overrightarrow{BC}$ is drawn, then two right angles will be formed as in Figure 2-16. Can you justify why $\angle ABD$ will have to be a right angle? If in Figure 2-15 the rays opposite both $\overrightarrow{BA}$ and $\overrightarrow{BC}$ were drawn, then four right angles would be formed as in Figure 2-17. Since angles ABC and ABD are right angles, can you justify why angles DBE and EBC should be right angles also?

The symbol used to represent the word "perpendicular" is $\perp$. In view of this, the expression $\overleftrightarrow{AB} \perp \overleftrightarrow{CD}$ is read as, $\overleftrightarrow{AB}$ is perpendicular to $\overleftrightarrow{CD}$.

EXERCISES

Using the information given, name the right angles in each of the figures below.

1. $\overleftrightarrow{AB} \perp \overleftrightarrow{BD}$ $\overleftrightarrow{RT} \perp \overleftrightarrow{ST}$ **2.**

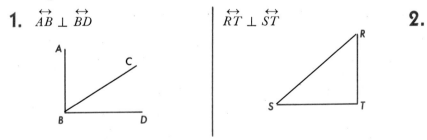

3. $\overleftrightarrow{AC} \perp \overleftrightarrow{BD}$

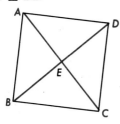

4. $\overleftrightarrow{RS} \perp \overleftrightarrow{RW}$

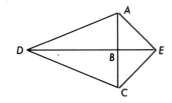

5. $\overleftrightarrow{AC} \perp \overleftrightarrow{BD}$

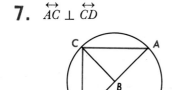

6. $\overleftrightarrow{AE} \perp \overleftrightarrow{CE}$

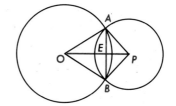

7. $\overleftrightarrow{AC} \perp \overleftrightarrow{CD}$

8. $\overleftrightarrow{OP} \perp \overleftrightarrow{AB}$

Bisector of an Angle

Earlier we learned that it was possible to have a point, the midpoint, forming two line segments of equal measure on a given line segment. So, too, is it possible to have a ray whose endpoint is the vertex of an angle and creating two angles of equal measure from this angle. A ray such as this is called the *bisector of an angle*.

DEFINITION 14: The bisector of an angle is a ray such that its endpoint is the vertex of the angle and it forms two angles of equal measure with the sides of the angle.

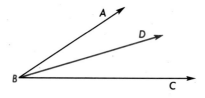

Figure 2-18.

Were we given the information for Figure 2-18 that $\overrightarrow{BD}$ is the bisector of (or bisects) $\angle ABC$, the definition of an angle bisector would permit us to conclude that $m \angle ABD = m \angle DBC$.

Frequently, students beginning their study of geometry find it a bit difficult to select the two angles of equal measure when an angle has been bisected. This is particularly true when the figure contains many lines. Should this occur to you, the following points may help clear up your difficulty.

(1) The vertex of the angle that has been bisected and the vertices of the angles of equal measure are identically the same point.

(2) The bisector of the angle will be a side of each of the two new angles that have been formed.

(3) Each side of the bisected angle will be a side in each of the new angles that have been formed.

As a last resort, ignore everything in the diagram other than the three rays consisting of the angle bisector and the two sides of the angle that has been bisected. Thus, in Figure 2-19 with the data given, think only of these rays: $\overrightarrow{RW}$, $\overrightarrow{RS}$, $\overrightarrow{RT}$. By so doing, it should soon become apparent that the angles of equal measure must be $\angle WRS$ and $\angle TRS$.

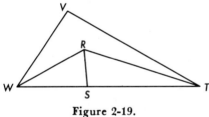

$\overrightarrow{RS}$ is the bisector of $\angle WRT$.

Figure 2-19.

EXERCISES

In Problems 1 through 8 what conclusion can be drawn in terms of the data given?

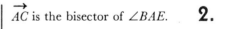

1. $\overrightarrow{DB}$ is the bisector of $\angle ADC$. $\overrightarrow{AC}$ is the bisector of $\angle BAE$.   **2.**

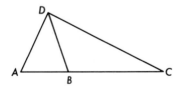

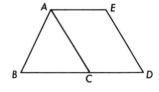

3. $\overrightarrow{BE}$ bisects $\angle ABC$.

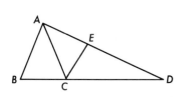

$\overrightarrow{BD}$ bisects $\angle ABC$.   **4.**

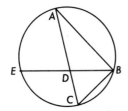

5. $\overrightarrow{CE}$ bisects $\angle DCA$.

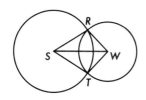

$\overrightarrow{DC}$ is the bisector of $\angle ADB$.   **6.**

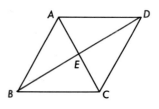

7. $\overrightarrow{WS}$ is the bisector of $\angle RWT$.

$\overrightarrow{BD}$ bisects $\angle EBF$.   **8.**

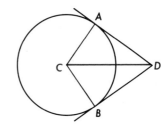

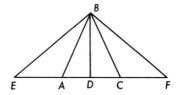

9.

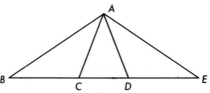

If in the diagram above $m \angle BAC = m \angle CAD = m \angle DAE$, then $\overrightarrow{AC}$ and $\overrightarrow{AD}$ are said to be the trisectors of $\angle BAE$. How would you define the trisectors of an angle?

Congruency of Angles and Line Segments

▬▬▬▬ The symbols that we have used in expressing the equality of measures between line segments or between angles have been found to be rather cumbersome. To overcome this feature, a new symbol was invented, this being ≅. It is read as the word "congruent" and appears in relations such as

and

(1) $\overline{AB} \cong \overline{CD}$

(2) $\angle XYZ \cong \angle RST$

These relations are read as

and

(1) $\overline{AB}$ is congruent to $\overline{CD}$.

(2) $\angle XYZ$ is congruent to $\angle RST$.

To make this symbol operational, the following two definitions are necessary:

DEFINITION 15: Congruent line segments are line segments having equal measures.

DEFINITION 16: Congruent angles are angles having equal measures.

In view of these definitions, where formerly we spoke of the equality of the measures of line segments, now we can refer directly to the congruence of these segments. And a similar relation will hold with angles. Hence, the following statements are said to be equivalent:

$m\ \overline{AB} = m\ \overline{CD}$ is equivalent to $\overline{AB} \cong \overline{CD}$.

$m\ \angle XYZ = m\ \angle RST$ is equivalent to $\angle XYZ \cong \angle RST$.

Furthermore, the definitions of the midpoint of a line segment and bisector of an angle can be restated in terms of *congruence* rather than in terms of *equal measures*. Thus,

The midpoint of a line segment is a point on that segment such that the two segments formed are congruent.

Compare this definition with the definition of the midpoint that appears on page 25. Can you write a similar definition for the bisector of an angle?

The following problem will illustrate the manner in which conclusions will henceforth be made.

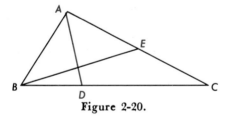

Figure 2-20.

$\overrightarrow{AD}$ bisects $\angle BAC$.

On the basis of the data given, we shall say that

$$\angle BAD \cong \angle DAC$$

and justify our conclusion by quoting the revised definition of the bisector of an angle:

The bisector of an angle is a ray such that its endpoint is the vertex of the angle and it forms two congruent angles with the sides of the given angle.

Had E in Figure 2-20 been given as the midpoint of $\overline{AC}$, the conclusion drawn would be

$$\overline{AE} \cong \overline{EC}$$

Justification for this conclusion lies in the revised definition of the midpoint of a line segment.

EXERCISES

What conclusion about congruence can be drawn from the data given in each of the problems below?

1. D is the midpoint of $\overline{AC}$.

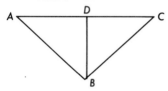

$\overrightarrow{DB}$ bisects $\angle ADC$. **2.**

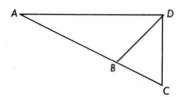

3. $\overleftrightarrow{BD}$ bisects $\overline{AC}$.

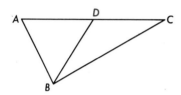

$\overrightarrow{AE}$ is the bisector of $\angle DAB$. **4.**

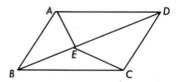

5. E is the midpoint of $\overline{BD}$.

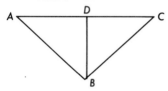

$\overrightarrow{EC}$ bisects $\angle AEB$. **6.**

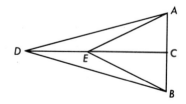

7. $\overleftrightarrow{DB}$ is the bisector of $\overline{EG}$.

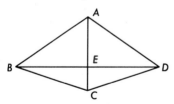

M is the midpoint of $\overline{AB}$. **8.**

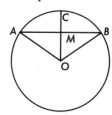

9. $\overleftrightarrow{AC}$ bisects $\overline{DE}$. | $\overrightarrow{BE}$ bisects $\angle ABC$. | **10.**

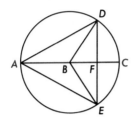

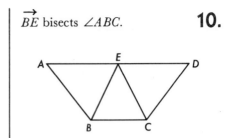

■ Drawing a Conclusion Based on the Reverse of a Definition

You may recall that the fourth property given to a connotative definition was the fact that it was reversible. This was interpreted as

If the subject and predicate nominative of a definition are interchanged, then the new sentence will be a true statement.

Thus, the reverse of the definition of the bisector of an angle will be

A ray whose endpoint is the vertex of an angle and that forms congruent angles with the sides of the angle is the bisector of the angle.

What is the reverse of the definition of the bisector of a line segment? Of the midpoint of a line segment? Of perpendicular lines? Of a right angle? Of a straight angle?

To illustrate how the reverse of a definition can be applied, let us suppose that $\angle ABD \cong \angle DBC$ in Figure 2-21. In order that this can be so, $\overrightarrow{BD}$

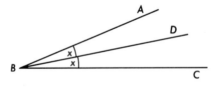

Figure 2-21.

will have to be the bisector of $\angle ABC$. Hence, we say that $\overrightarrow{BD}$ is the bisector of $\angle ABC$. To justify this conclusion we merely refer to the reverse of the definition of the bisector of an angle that appears in red above.

You may be questioning this procedure by saying, "Why isn't it possible to justify this conclusion by simply referring to the definition of the bisector of an angle rather than the reverse?". The definition of the bisector of an angle can be used as justification of a conclusion only if the data given stated that the ray was the bisector. In this problem, however, this was not stated. You knew only that there were two congruent angles, and from this *you, yourself,* concluded that the ray BD must be the bisector of the angle. When such a conclusion is made, it is justified by quoting the reverse of the definition. This is so since it is the reverse of the definition that states that

the ray-that forms congruent angles with the sides of the angle is the bisector of the angle.
As another illustration, in Figure 2-22 $\overline{AD} \cong \overline{DC}$. From this it can be

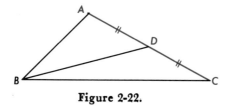

Figure 2-22.

concluded that D is the midpoint of $\overline{AC}$. To justify the conclusion, we would say

"A point on a line segment that forms two congruent line segments is the midpoint of that line segment."

The reverse of the definition is given since it is known that point D forms two congruent line segments on $\overline{AC}$. The definition of the midpoint of a line segment was not given as the reason, for the fact that D is the midpoint was not known to us at the outset of the problem.

EXERCISES

What conclusion can be drawn on the basis of the data given in each of the problems below? Justify your conclusion by stating the reverse of one of the definitions you have had. In order that your work will follow the pattern that will be used throughout the year, arrange your conclusion and reason as it is shown below.

Illustration:

Given: $\angle ABC$ is a straight angle.

CONCLUSION	REASON
$\angle ABD$ and $\angle DBC$ are supplementary angles.	Two angles the sum of whose measures is the measure of a straight angle are supplementary angles.

1. Given: $\angle BAD \cong \angle DAC$ ⏐ Given: $\angle ACB$ is a right angle. **2.**

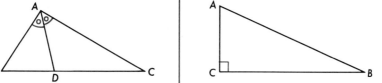

3. Given: $\overline{AD} \cong \overline{DC}$

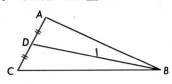

Given: $\angle ABC$ is a right angle. **4.**
(Give two conclusions.)

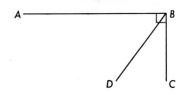

5. Given: $m \angle ABC = 62$

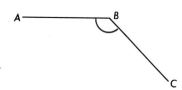

Given: $\angle ABC$ is a straight **6.**
angle.

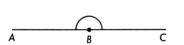

7. Given: $m \angle ABC = 134$

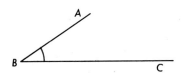

Given: $m \angle ABC = 180$ **8.**

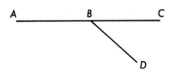

9. Given: $\angle ACB \cong \angle ACD$

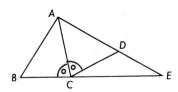

Given: $\angle ADB$ is a right **10.**
angle.

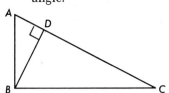

11. Given: $\angle ABC$ is a straight
angle.

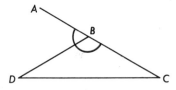

Given: $\overline{AE} \cong \overline{EC}$ **12.**

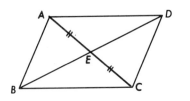

■ Drawing Conclusions on the Basis of Definitions and the Reverse of Definitions

At the outset of this text it was pointed out that there are a great many ways in which arguments can be "proved." Our objective this year is to show how the mathematician justifies the conclusions that he makes. Thus far, you have learned that he can justify these conclusions through one of two ways:

(1) He can refer to the accepted definitions of the words that appear in the data that have been given.

(2) He can refer to the reverse of the definitions that have been agreed upon.

Our attitude toward mathematics is determined largely on how well we understand the work we are called upon to do. The following set of problems is designed to help you gain confidence in drawing conclusions and then justifying these conclusions through either the definitions of terms or the reverse of the definitions. Arrange your work as illustrated in the problem below.

Illustration:

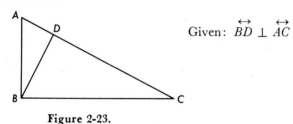

Given: $\overleftrightarrow{BD} \perp \overleftrightarrow{AC}$

Figure 2-23.

CONCLUSION	REASON
∠ADB and ∠CDB are right angles.	Perpendicular lines are two lines that intersect and form right angles. (Def.)

EXERCISES

Draw a conclusion in each of the problems below. Your conclusion should be based *only* on the data that has been given, *not* on what you believe the diagram may imply. Immediately following your reason, indicate whether this reason is a definition (Def.) or the reverse of a definition (Rev. of Def.).

1. Given: *E* is the midpoint of $\overline{AC}$.

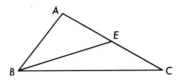

Given: $\overrightarrow{CA}$ bisects ∠*DCB*.   **2.**

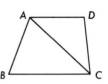

3. Given: ∠*ACB* is an acute angle.

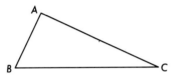

Given: ∠*ABC* and ∠*CBD* are **4.** supplementary angles.

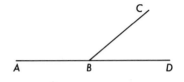

5. Given: $\overline{AB} \cong \overline{BC}$

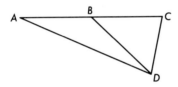

Given: $\overrightarrow{CE}$ bisects ∠*ACD*.   **6.**

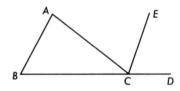

7. Given: *A* is the midpoint of $\overline{BC}$.

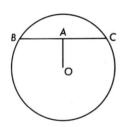

Given: ∠*FHE* ≅ ∠*KHE*   **8.**

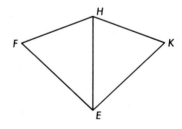

9. Given: ∠*ABC* is a right angle.

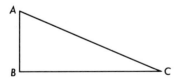

Given: ∠*ABD* and ∠*DBC* **10.** are complementary angles.

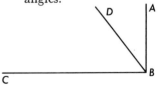

11. Given: $\overleftrightarrow{AB}$ bisects $\overline{CD}$.

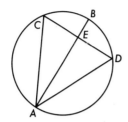

Given: $\overleftrightarrow{AD} \perp \overleftrightarrow{BC}$ **12.**

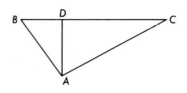

13. Given: $\angle ABC$ is a right angle. (Give two conclusions.)

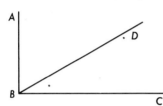

Given: $m \angle CAB = 55$; $m \angle CBA = 35$ **14.**

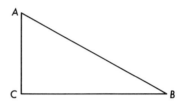

15. Given: $\angle RVS$ is a straight angle. (Give two conclusions.)

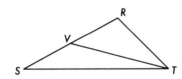

Given: $\overleftrightarrow{AC}$ is the perpendicular bisector of $\overline{BD}$. (Give two conclusions.)   **16.**

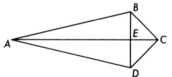

17. Given: $\overline{AB} \cong \overline{BC}$

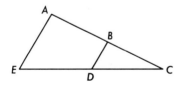

Given: $\overleftrightarrow{BD} \perp \overleftrightarrow{AC}$ **18.**

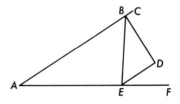

19. Given: $\overleftrightarrow{FC}$ bisects $\overline{BE}$.

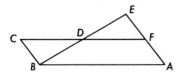

Given: $\angle CBA$ is a right angle.   **20.**

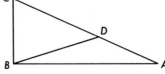

21. Given: B and C are the trisection points of $\overline{AD}$ (See page 27, Problem 3.)

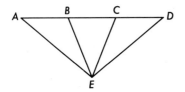

Given: $\overleftrightarrow{ZY} \perp \overleftrightarrow{XY}$ **22.**

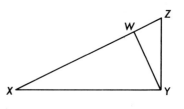

23. Given: $\angle ACB$ and $\angle BCD$ are complementary angles.

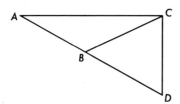

Given: $\overline{RT}$ and $\overline{SW}$ bisect   **24.** each other. (Give two conclusions.)

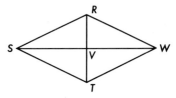

25. Given: $\angle ADC$ is a right angle.

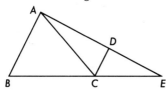

Given: $\angle BEC \cong \angle DEC$ **26.**

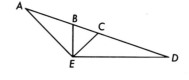

■ **Test**

1. **(a)** What is meant by the measure of a line segment?
   (b) Is it possible for the same line segment to have two different measures? Justify your answer.

2. **(a)** What is meant by the measure of an angle?
   (b) Is it possible for the same angle to have two different measures?

3. If $\overrightarrow{VR}$ and $\overrightarrow{VS}$ are subsets of $\overleftrightarrow{RS}$, then what are the two possibilities concerning the measure of $\angle RVS$?

4. If $\angle ABC$ is an acute angle, what can be said concerning the measure of its supplement?

5. (a) If $\overline{AB} \cong \overline{BC}$, does this imply that B is the midpoint of $\overline{AC}$? Justify your answer.

   (b) If $\angle ABC \cong \angle CBD$, does this imply that $\overrightarrow{BC}$ is the bisector of $\angle ABD$? Justify your answer.

6. Under what conditions only would it be possible to write the following equality?

$$\overline{AB} = \overline{CD}$$

7. Classify each of the following angles as to whether they are acute, right, obtuse, or straight.
   (a) 90°   **(b)** 156°   **(c)** 84°

8. (a) What is the measure of an angle if the measure of its complement is 82?

   (b) What is the measure of an angle if its supplement is an angle of y degrees?

9. (a) What is the measure of an angle that is four times as large as its complement?

   (b) The measure of an angle is 15 more than twice its supplement. How large is the angle?

10. The definition of a reflex angle is

> A reflex angle is an angle whose measure
> is greater than 180 and less than 360.

Answer the following questions in terms of this definition:
(a) What is the reverse of this definition?
(b) Explain why a reflex angle is not discussed in plane geometry?
(c) How was a reflex angle classified?
(d) How was a reflex angle distinguished from the other members of its class?
(e) What can be said concerning the supplement of a reflex angle?

B

   Draw a conclusion in each of the problems below. Immediately following your reason for this conclusion, indicate whether this reason is a definition or the reverse of a definition.

1. Given: F is the midpoint of $\overline{AE}$.

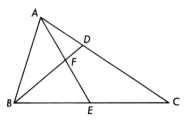

Given: $\overleftrightarrow{AD} \perp \overleftrightarrow{ED}$ **2.**

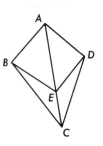

3. Given: $\angle DAE \cong \angle CAE$

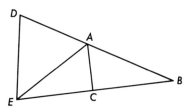

Given: $\angle BDA$ is a right angle.   **4.**

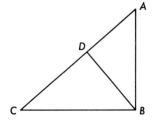

5. Given: $\overline{BE} \cong \overline{CE}$

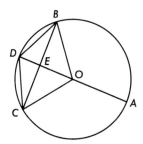

Given: $\overleftrightarrow{FJ}$ bisects $\overline{AC}$.   **6.**

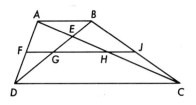

7. Given: $\angle CDE$ and $\angle ADE$ are complementary angles.

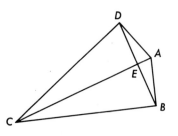

Given: $\angle ABC$ is a straight angle.   **8.**

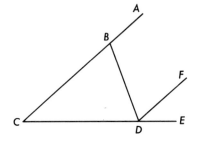

9. Given: $\overrightarrow{DE}$ bisects $\angle BDG$.

Given: $\overleftrightarrow{BD}$ is the $\perp$ bisector **10.**
of $\overline{AC}$. (Give two
conclusions.)

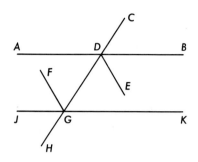

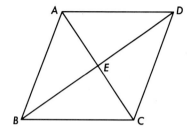

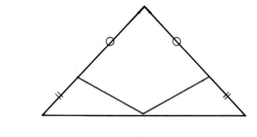

3

Assumptions and Their Place in a Proof

EARLIER WE DISCUSSED THE IMPORTANT role definitions play in helping to mold the decisions we make each day of our lives. There are, however, factors other than the interpretation of words that lead us to the conclusions we make or the acts we do. The decision of whether John or Bill is the better candidate for president of the student council frequently has little bearing on how terms are defined. Our attitude toward questions such as this is shaped more by the convictions we hold about these young men than by the clarification of terms they may have used. This chapter is devoted to showing at least a few of the ways in which convictions are born and, when related to mathematics, their significance to the development of this subject.

■ How Do the Blind Draw Conclusions?

Among the poems you may have read and enjoyed is the one below about the blind men and the elephant. As you read it through now, ask yourself why a poem such as this should appear in a geometry book. Is there any connection between this poem and the basis for conclusions that we, as human beings, reach each day of our lives?

50

THE BLIND MEN AND THE ELEPHANT
by John Godfrey Saxe

It was six men of Indostan,
　　To learning much inclined,
Who went to see the elephant
　　(Though each of them was blind,)
That each by observation
　　Might satisfy his mind.

The first approached the elephant,
　　And happening to fall
Against his broad and sturdy side,
　　At once began to bawl:
"God bless me! but the elephant
　　Is very much like a wall!"

The second, feeling of the tusk,
　　Cried: "Ho! what have we here
So round, and smooth, and sharp?
　　To me 'tis very clear
This wonder of an elephant
　　Is very like a spear!"

The third approached the animal,
　　And happening to take
The squirming trunk within his hands,
　　Thus boldly up he spake:
"I see," quoth he, "the elephant
　　Is very much like a snake!"

The fourth reached out his eager hand,
　　And fell upon the knee:
"What most this wondrous beast is like,
　　Is very plain," quoth he;
" 'Tis clear enough the elephant
　　Is very like a tree!"

The fifth who chanced to touch the ear
　　Said: "E'en the blindest man
Can tell what this resembles most:
　　Deny the fact who can,
This marvel of an elephant
　　Is very like a fan!"

The sixth no sooner had begun
　　About the beast to grope,
Then, seizing on the swinging tail
　　That fell within his scope,

"I see," quoth he, "the elephant,
  Is very like a rope!"

And so these men of Indostan
  Disputed loud and long,
Each in his own opinion
  Exceeding stiff and strong,
Though each was partly in the right,
  And all were in the wrong!

Upon what evidence did the first blind man draw his conclusion that the elephant resembled a wall? Why did the second blind man arrive at the decision he had made? What had led each of them to the conclusion he had drawn?

Are We So Different from the Blind?

████████████ You were probably a little amused as you read the poem, for you knew that each "saw" but a small part of the elephant. Were these men capable of seeing the animal in its entirety, they would not have come to such completely different points of view. And yet, perhaps we should not treat this poem too lightly. We normal human beings may be wearing blinders without realizing it. In terms of one interpretation that some scientists give to light rays, the graph below presents a picture of the relative sizes of the wavelengths of "light" coming from the sun.

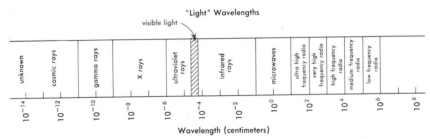

To be exact, a wavelength of light that can be seen by the human eye ranges from 4 hundred-thousandths to 7 hundred-thousandths of a centimeter! The length of each "wave" is the length of the line segment joining

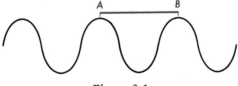

Figure 3-1.

two peaks such as *A* and *B*. The centimeter itself is a very small distance, while 4 hundred-thousandths of a centimeter is far, far smaller than the naked eye might ever see. Thus, it appears that of all the "light" waves that strike the earth, only a very small fraction of these are visible to the human eye. Hence, we may be just a little removed from the blind men of the poem. Were we suddenly granted the ability to observe "light" whose wavelengths varied between 1 millionth of a centimeter in length and 1 hundredth of a

$$\vdash\!\!\!\!\!\rule{2cm}{0.8pt}\!\!\!\!\!\dashv$$
1 centimeter

centimeter, then the things that seem "obvious" to us now might appear rather silly under our newly found "vision." Many of the things we say and many of the ideas we have are based on the observation of things as we see them. And this vision of ours may not only be faulty but is certainly limited!

The Faulty Eyesight of Man

Since man first began to think, his eye-sight led him to create many beliefs that he felt were justifiable. At the present we realize that a great number were completely groundless. Among these was the notion that the earth was flat. For, so it was reasoned, if the earth was round, how might a man stand at the south pole without tumbling off into nothingness! Yes, there were some scientists who realized that the earth was "round." In fact, an early Greek mathematician gave a rather close approximation for the circumference of the earth. These men, however, were in the minority, a very small minority at that. The great multitude of people "realized" that the earth had to be flat, for did not their eyes tell them so!

EXERCISES

1. List three beliefs in the field of aviation that had been held for many years yet now have been discarded.
2. List three beliefs in the field of medicine that were discarded because of medical research.
3. List five beliefs in general that people held for many years but now feel that they are probably not so.

Postulates in Geometry

The early Greek mathematician laid the foundation for his work on certain "beliefs" that he referred to as "self-evident truths," for to him they reflected the world about him as he saw it. The more sophisticated modern mathematician, however, recognizes the principles from which he evolves his subject for what they really are; that is, no more than *a set of mutually agreed upon properties about figures that he himself has created*. To illustrate, he created the line and the real number system; he then linked the two together by the property that to every real number there exists one and only one point on this line and further, that to every point there exists one and only one real number. A statement such as this the mathematician accepts in order to lay the foundation for further discussion. This discussion can not take place without some core of ideas or frame of reference from which to begin. These fundamental principles from which mathematics springs are the *postulates* or, as they are often called, *axioms* or *assumptions*.

Current interpretation of mathematics has divorced a postulate from its original interpretation as a "belief." When considering a belief, we are sometimes left with a feeling of vagueness as to the truth or falsity of the statement. On the other hand, a postulate carries with it no such squeamishness; it is like asking, "Are the rules of baseball true or false?" The question, obviously, makes little sense. These are the rules established to create the game; they are neither true nor false! So, too, are the postulates, the "rules" to create the subject of mathematics.

It would be inaccurate to leave you with the impression that creating mathematics is comparable to creating a game where the rules are established at the whim of the creator. Far from this! Mathematicians frequently formulate their postulates as a model of what they perceive in the world that exists about them. It is true that some aspects of modern mathematics appear to bear no remote resemblance to any practical application. However, as has happened almost always in the past, future scientists will very likely discover a need for these branches of mathematics in their work.

In view of the foregoing analysis, it would seem wise if we, too, placed our cards face up on the table and admitted to a number of postulates we had failed to establish in Chapters 1 and 2, although we had made use of them. Briefly, they were concerned with these points:

(1) The possibility of extending a line as far as desired in either direction.
(2) The notion of "betweenness" that implied that between any two points on a line there existed a third point.
(3) The existence of a pairing between the points on a line and the real numbers.

These principles we will now state formally as our first three postulates:

POSTULATE 1: A line may be extended as far as desired in either direction.
POSTULATE 2: For any two points on a line, there exists a third point that is between them.
POSTULATE 3: There exists a one-to-one correspondence between the points on a line and the real numbers.

The last of the principles concerning a line that we want to consider at this time is one that you have used each time you drew a margin on a piece of paper. In drawing a "half-inch" margin, it is likely that you placed a point $\frac{1}{2}$ inch from the edge near the top of the paper and repeated this process at the bottom. After which you laid the ruler along these two points and drew the line. In so doing, you were using the principle stated here:

POSTULATE 4: There exists one and only one line through two points.

The combination of Postulate 3 and the interpretation we have given to the measure of a line segment as being the coordinate of one endpoint when the coordinate of the other endpoint is zero is but a modified form of two postulates that are often called The Ruler Postulate and The Ruler Placement Postulate. Had these two postulates been at our disposal earlier, we could have created a more formal definition of "betweenness." Thus,

Point B being between points A and C means that the three points are different elements of the same line and,

$$m\ \overline{AB} + m\ \overline{BC} = m\ \overline{AC}$$

By examining Figure 3-2 it becomes evident that in a rather elaborate way this definition says no more than if it so happens that when the "distance" from A to B is added to the "distance" from B to C the sum turns

Figure 3-2.

out to be the "distance" from A to C, then B is *between* A and C.

At the time we established the measure of a line segment we in some ways trapped ourselves into an awkward position. Consider the coordinate system below. There would be no problem in determining the measure of

Figure 3-3.

$\overline{PA}$ for the coordinate of P is zero and hence, the coordinate of A which is 5 represents the measure of $\overline{PA}$. Similarly, finding the measures of $\overline{PB}$, $\overline{PC}$, and $\overline{PD}$ also presents no difficulty for in each case the coordinate of one of the endpoints, P, is zero. However, finding the measure of $\overline{AB}$ does create a problem for the coordinate of neither A nor B is zero. Hence, either we set up a new coordinate system with A or B as the zero point or we develop another device for determining the measure of a line segment. The latter of these alternatives frees us from constantly having to shift the zero point.

By simply counting the number of units from A to B we can see that $m\ \overline{AB} = 3$. Doing the same for the number of units from B to C, we discover that $m\ \overline{BC} = 7$ and, similarly $m\ \overline{RP} = 2$ while $m\ \overline{RB} = 10$. Obviously, counting the units between the two endpoints of a line segment is not very practical and by now you must certainly have discovered that the 3 which is the measure of $\overline{AB}$ can be determined by subtracting the coordinate, 5, of A from the coordinate, 8, of B. In the same way,

$$m \ \overline{BC} = 15 - 8 = 7$$
and
$$m \ \overline{AD} = 17 - 5 = 12$$

How would you find the measure of $\overline{BD}$? The measure of $\overline{CD}$? We do run into a slight difficulty, though, in determining the measure of $\overline{RA}$ for the coordinate of R is a negative number. By recalling the technique for computing the difference between two *signed* numbers, this problem is easily eliminated. Thus,

$$m \ \overline{RA} = \ \ 5 - (-2) = 7$$
and
$$m \ \overline{SD} = 17 - (-1) = 18$$

What would happen, however, if we inadvertently interchanged the positions of the coordinates in finding the difference? Then,

$$m \ \overline{AB} = 5 - \ \ \ 8 = -3$$
$$m \ \overline{BC} = 8 - 15 = -7$$
and
$$m \ \overline{AD} = 5 - 17 = -12$$

Hence it appears that each of the answers turns out to be the negative of what we would want it to be. To eliminate this from occurring we make use of the concept of the *absolute value of a number* that we had learned in our study of algebra.

$$|12 - 3| = |9| \ \ \ \ = 9$$
$$|3 - 12| = |-9| = 9$$

Recall that the absolute value of either a positive or a negative number was the number itself devoid of its sign. Thus, in the situations above we will say,

$$m \ \overline{BC} = |8 - 15| \ \ \ \ \ = |-7| \ \ = 7$$
and
$$m \ \overline{AD} = |5 - 17| \ \ \ \ \ = |-12| = 12$$
Similarly,
$$m \ \overline{RB} = |-2 - 8| \ \ \ \ = |-10| = 10$$
and
$$m \ \overline{CR} = |15 - (-2)| = |17| \ \ \ = 17$$

Now we are in a position where we can conceive of the measure of a line segment:

> The measure of a line segment is the absolute value of the difference of the coordinates of its endpoints.

EXERCISES

1. Express each of the following in terms of a single numeral.

(a) $|8 - 2|$ (b) $|15 - 6|$ (c) $|12 - 5|$
(d) $|3 - 7|$ (e) $|5 - 6|$ (f) $|0 - 2|$
(g) $|-2 - 5|$ (h) $|-6 - 3|$ (i) $|-1 - 7|$
(j) $|6 - (-2)|$ (k) $|5 - (-4)|$ (l) $|8 - (-9)|$
(m) $|-2 - (-3)|$ (n) $|-7 - (-7)|$ (o) $|0 - (-5)|$

2. The coordinates of points A and B are given in each of the problems below. Find the measure of $\overline{AB}$.

(a) A: 10; B: 7   (b) A: 26; B: 5   (c) A: 8; B: −1
(d) A: 6; B: −5   (e) A: 0; B: −8   (f) A: −2; B: 6
(g) A: −5; B: 8   (h) A: −3; B: 3   (i) A: −1; B: −5

3.

```
         A     B  C       D  E       F       G       H
 ←─┼──┼──┼──┼──┼──┼──┼──┼──┼──┼──┼──┼──┼──┼──┼──→
   -6  -5  -4  -3  -2  -1   0   1   2   3   4   5   6   7   8   9
```

Using the coordinate system above, determine the measure of each of the following line segments.

(a) $\overline{DE}$ (b) $\overline{DG}$ (c) $\overline{DH}$
(d) $\overline{EF}$ (e) $\overline{EG}$ (f) $\overline{FH}$
(g) $\overline{HG}$ (h) $\overline{FC}$ (i) $\overline{BG}$
(j) $\overline{EA}$ (k) $\overline{AD}$ (l) $\overline{DB}$

4. Given the information that B is between A and C, determine the answer to each of the following problems.

(a) $m\,\overline{AB} = 6$, $m\,\overline{BC} = 2$, $m\,\overline{AC} = \,?$
(b) $m\,\overline{AB} = 5$, $m\,\overline{BC} = 9$, $m\,\overline{AC} = \,?$
(c) $m\,\overline{AC} = 9$, $m\,\overline{BC} = 2$, $m\,\overline{AB} = \,?$
(d) $m\,\overline{AC} = 16$, $m\,\overline{BC} = 1$, $m\,\overline{AB} = \,?$
(e) $m\,\overline{AB} = 5$, $m\,\overline{AC} = 12$, $m\,\overline{BC} = \,?$
(f) $m\,\overline{AB} = a$, $m\,\overline{BC} = b$, $m\,\overline{AC} = \,?$

5. If $m\,\overline{PQ} = 7$, $m\,\overline{QR} = 12$, and $m\,\overline{PR} = 5$, and P, Q and R are points of the same line, then which of these points is between the other two?

6. (a) The coordinate of A is 4 while $m\,\overline{AB} = 15$. If the coordinate of B is a positive number, what is that number?

(b) In a coordinate system the coordinate of A is 2 while the coordinate of B is 7. If the same unit is used for a coordinate system where the coordinate of A is changed to 0, then what is the coordinate of B in this system?

■ The Sum and Difference of Two Line Segments

The postulates used most often in geometry are called the "operational" postulates, for they are concerned with the operations of addition, subtraction, multiplication, and division. Before they are investigated, it is apparent that we will have to interpret these operations with reference to geometric figures.

DEFINITION 17: The sum of two line segments, $\overline{AB}$ and $\overline{BC}$, is $\overline{AC}$ if, and only if, B is between A and C.

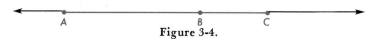

Figure 3-4.

By using symbols this relationship will be expressed as

$$\overline{AB} + \overline{BC} = \overline{AC}$$

Having used the equality sign, we mean to imply no more or no less than that the name used on the left $(\overline{AB} + \overline{BC})$ and the name used on the right $(\overline{AC})$ are but two different names for the same segment $(\overline{AC})$. This situation is similar to saying that $4 + 3 = 7$ for both the $4 + 3$ and the 7 are merely two different names for the number *seven*.

The definition, furthermore, states that the sum of two line segments exists only if the two line segments lie on the same line and their intersection is one and only one point. In Figure 3-4 $\overline{AB}$ and $\overline{BC}$ lie on line AC, while B is the only point they have in common.

With reference to the definition explain why the sums given below can not be found.

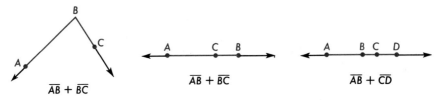

Figure 3-5.

The diagrams we will encounter will frequently have many, many lines in them. When trying to find the line segment that represents the sum of two line segments, direct your attention to that line on which the two segments fall. All other lines will have no importance at that time. Thus, if you are looking in Figure 3-6 for $\overline{AF} + \overline{FE}$, focus your attention on $\overleftrightarrow{AE}$ and ignore

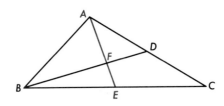

Figure 3-6.

all other lines. The definition enables you to say that

$$\overline{AF} + \overline{FE} = \overline{AE}$$

In this same diagram what is the sum of $\overline{BE}$ and $\overline{EC}$? $\overline{AD}$ and $\overline{DC}$? $\overline{BF}$ and $\overline{FD}$? Explain why the sum of $\overline{AF}$ and $\overline{FD}$ does not exist.

DEFINITION 18: The difference between two line segments, $\overline{AB}$ and $\overline{BC}$, is $\overline{AC}$ if, and only if, C is between A and B.

Figure 3-7.

By using symbols this relationship will be expressed as

$$\overline{AB} - \overline{BC} = \overline{AC}$$

Here, as in the addition of line segments, the use of the equality sign signifies merely that the two names $(\overline{AB} - \overline{BC})$ and $(\overline{AC})$ are but different names for the same segment $(\overline{AC})$. Also, as before, subtraction of line segments can exist only if the two segments are subsets of the same line and their intersection is one of these segments. In the diagram above, $\overline{AB}$ and $\overline{BC}$ are subsets of line AB, while their intersection consists of all the points of one of these segments $(\overline{BC})$.

EXERCISES

In each of the problems below, you are asked to find the sum or difference of two line segments. If it is not possible to find this line segment, simply write "no answer" after the problem number.

1. (a) $\overline{AB} + \overline{BC} = ?$
(b) $\overline{AC} - \overline{BC} = ?$

2. (a) $\overline{ED} + \overline{DC} = ?$
(b) $\overline{EC} - \overline{DC} = ?$
(c) $\overline{AB} + \overline{BC} = ?$
(d) $\overline{CE} - \overline{ED} = ?$

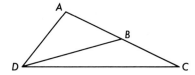

3. (a) $\overline{AE} + \overline{EC} = ?$
(b) $\overline{AC} - \overline{EC} = ?$
(c) $\overline{BC} + \overline{CD} = ?$
(d) $\overline{BD} - \overline{BE} = ?$
(e) $\overline{BE} + \overline{DE} = ?$
(f) $\overline{AD} - \overline{DC} = ?$

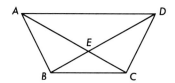
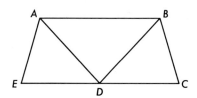

■ The Sum and Difference of Two Angles

In the same way that we defined a point as being between two points so, too, is it possible to define a ray as being between two rays. Thus,

DEFINITION 19: The ray PB being between two rays PA and PC means that,

$$m \angle APB + m \angle BPC = m \angle APC$$

And here again we seem to be saying no more than that we want the sum of the measures of ∠APB and ∠BPC to be the same as the measure of ∠APC. In Figure 3-8 this would imply that when the measures of 30

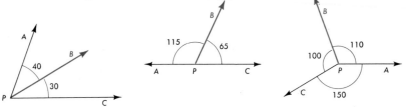

Figure 3-8.   Figure 3-9.   Figure 3-10.

and 40 of the two smaller angles are added, their sum of 70 must be the measure of ∠APC. In Figure 3-9 we see that this definition holds equally well where the ray PB happens to be between the pair of opposite rays PA and PC.

As seen in Figure 3-10, $\overrightarrow{PB}$ is not considered to be between $\overrightarrow{PA}$ and $\overrightarrow{PC}$ for the sum of the measures of ∠APB and ∠BPC does not equal the measure of ∠APC.

With Definition 19 at our disposal, defining the sum or difference of two angles will present little difficulty.

DEFINITION 20: The sum of two angles, ∠ABC and ∠DBC, is ∠ABD if, and only if, $\overrightarrow{BC}$ is between $\overrightarrow{BA}$ and $\overrightarrow{BD}$.

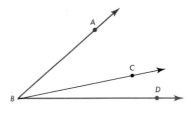

Figure 3-11.

By using symbols this relationship can be expressed as

$$\angle ABC + \angle DBC = \angle ABD$$

Here again, the equality sign is used to imply the fact that although the name that appears on the left (∠ABC + ∠DBC) is different from the name appearing on the right (∠ABD), both represent the same angle (∠ABD).

In Figure 3-12 the sum of ∠BAD and ∠CAD is ∠BAC. In this figure, $\overrightarrow{AD}$ is between $\overrightarrow{AB}$ and $\overrightarrow{AC}$. What is the sum of ∠ABD and ∠CBD? How would you express ∠ACD + ∠BCD by naming a single angle?

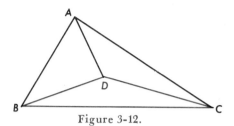

Figure 3-12.

DEFINITION 21: The difference of two angles, $\angle ABD$ and $\angle ABC$, is $\angle CBD$ if, and only if, $\overrightarrow{BC}$ is between $\overrightarrow{BA}$ and $\overrightarrow{BD}$.

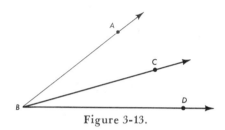

Figure 3-13.

Symbolically we express this as

$$\angle ABD - \angle ABC = \angle CBD$$

where the two names ($\angle ABD - \angle ABC$) and ($\angle CBD$) are but different names representing the same angle ($\angle CBD$).

EXERCISES

In each of the problems below, you are asked to find the sum or difference of two angles. If it is not possible to find this angle, simply write "no answer" after the problem number.

1.
(a) $\angle EAD + \angle DAB = ?$
(b) $\angle ABD + \angle CBD = ?$
(c) $\angle ADE + \angle ADB = ?$
(d) $\angle AED + \angle BCD = ?$
(e) $\angle EAB - \angle DAB = ?$
(f) $\angle ABC - \angle CBD = ?$
(g) $\angle AEC - \angle BCE = ?$
(h) $\angle EDC - \angle ADC = ?$

(a) $\angle BAC + \angle CAE = ?$ **2.**
(b) $\angle ACB + \angle ACE = ?$
(c) $\angle CAE + \angle BEA = ?$
(d) $\angle BDC + \angle EDC = ?$
(e) $\angle ABC - \angle ABE = ?$
(f) $\angle BCE - \angle BAE = ?$
(g) $\angle BAE - \angle CAE = ?$
(h) $\angle ADC - \angle ADE = ?$

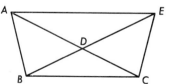

■ The Addition Postulate

Having defined what is meant by the "sum" and "difference" with reference to line segments and angles, we are now prepared to introduce the first of the "operational" postulates. These are the postulates that were needed in determining the solution set, or roots, of an equation at the time you studied algebra. As an example,

If   **(1)** $x - 2 = 7$

then   **(2)** $x - 2 + 2 = 7 + 2$

The reason enabling you to write step (2) based on the information given in step (1) was the "law" stating that

$$
\begin{aligned}
\text{If} \qquad\qquad & a = b \\
\text{then} \qquad\qquad & a + c = b + c
\end{aligned}
\qquad\text{(A)}
$$

In the illustration above, $a = x - 2$, $b = 7$, while $c = 2$. Perhaps you learned this postulate as

"If equals are added to equals, the sums are equal."

rather than with the symbols given in (A). In either event, we shall need this postulate, and the other operational postulates, as a foundation for the geometry work. Hence, it will be repeated here, in a slightly different form.

POSTULATE 5: The Addition Postulate

$$
\begin{aligned}
\text{If} \qquad\qquad & a = b \\
\text{and} \qquad\qquad & c = d \\
\text{then} \qquad\qquad & a + c = b + d
\end{aligned}
$$

Or as a statement:

If equals are added to equals, the sums are equal.

When this postulate was applied in algebra, the symbols a, b, c, and d were placeholders for numbers. Furthermore, the statement $a = b$ implied that the symbol a and the symbol b were merely different names for the same number. This will still be true in our work in geometry. Now, however, we must realize that since the statements

$$m\,\overline{AB} = m\,\overline{CD} \quad\text{and}\quad \overline{AB} \cong \overline{CD}$$

are equivalent, we can and will treat the congruence symbol ($\cong$) in identically the same way as we had treated the equality symbol ($=$) in algebra. Hence, were we to apply the Addition Postulate in the following situation:

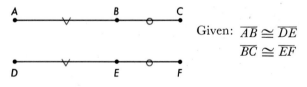

Given: $\overline{AB} \cong \overline{DE}$

$\overline{BC} \cong \overline{EF}$

Figure 3-14.

we could conclude that

(1) $\overline{AB} + \overline{BC} \cong \overline{DE} + \overline{EF}$

Moreover, since $\overline{AB} + \overline{BC}$ is but another name for $\overline{AC}$, while $\overline{DE} + \overline{EF}$ is another name for $\overline{DF}$, it is preferable to write (1) as

$$\overline{AC} \cong \overline{DF}$$

This can be expressed in quite an elementary way as follows:

If the measure of $\overline{AB}$ is 9 (inches), then $\overline{DE}$ must have a measure of 9 (inches), for the two segments by being congruent have the same measure. Similarly, if the measure of $\overline{BC}$ is 5 (inches), then the measure of $\overline{EF}$ must

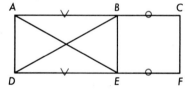

Figure 3-15.

be 5 (inches). The conclusion that $\overline{AC} \cong \overline{DF}$ can be interpreted here as merely implying that both segments have a measure of 14 (inches).

It frequently happens that there are many lines in the diagram that are completely irrelevant to the data given. Try to ignore these lines. To illustrate, Figure 3-15 might have been drawn as

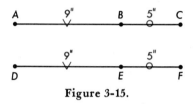

Given: $\overline{AB} \cong \overline{DE}$
$\overline{BC} \cong \overline{EF}$

Figure 3-16.

As before, the conclusion would still be $\overline{AC} \cong \overline{DF}$ and for the reason stated; that is, the Addition Postulate. Name five lines in the diagram that are in no way related to the information stated.

The Addition Postulate as applied to angles would occur under conditions such as the following:

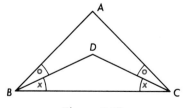

Given: $\angle ABD \cong \angle ACD$
$\angle DBC \cong \angle DCB$

Figure 3-17.

What conclusion can be drawn on the basis of the given data? The use of numbers may help make the picture a little clearer to you. If $\angle ABD$ has a measure of 20, then $\angle ACD$ will also have the measure of 20, for as stated in the given data, these two angles are congruent. So, too, if the $m \angle DBC = 30$, what can be said of $\angle DCB$? What is the measure of $\angle ABC$? Of $\angle ACB$? Since the measure of both is 50, what conclusion should follow?

This same conclusion could have been arrived at by resorting to the Addition Postulate rather than to specific numbers. The formal arrangement of the problem is identical to that used on page 41. This time, however, the reason that justifies the conclusion is a postulate rather than a definition or the reverse of a definition.

CONCLUSION	REASON
$\angle ABC \cong \angle ACB$	The Addition Postulate: If congruent angles ($\angle ABD$ and $\angle ACD$) are added to congruent angles ($\angle DBC$ and $\angle DCB$), their sums will be congruent angles ($\angle ABC$ and $\angle ACB$).

EXERCISES

By using the Addition Postulate only, what conclusion can be drawn in each of the following problems? State your conclusion and reason exactly as shown above.

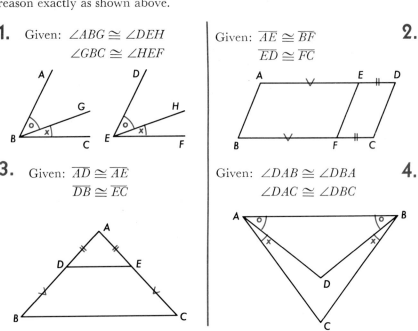

1. Given: $\angle ABG \cong \angle DEH$
          $\angle GBC \cong \angle HEF$

Given: $\overline{AE} \cong \overline{BF}$ **2.**
          $\overline{ED} \cong \overline{FC}$

3. Given: $\overline{AD} \cong \overline{AE}$
          $\overline{DB} \cong \overline{EC}$

Given: $\angle DAB \cong \angle DBA$ **4.**
          $\angle DAC \cong \angle DBC$

most frequent application. Situations calling for its need would be those in
which the bisector of an angle, the bisector of a line segment, or the midpoint
of a line segment were found in the problem. Let us illustrate by using the
midpoint of a line segment. This point will separate the segment into two
congruent segments. The measure of each of these segments will be half of
the original segment. Thus,

A ———————————•——————————— B   Given: M is the midpoint of $\overline{AB}$.
                M

Figure 3-19.

$$m\ \overline{AM} = \tfrac{1}{2}m\ \overline{AB}$$

also

$$m\ \overline{MB} = \tfrac{1}{2}m\ \overline{AB}$$

Similarly, if $\overrightarrow{BD}$ is the bisector of $\angle ABC$, then by definition

$$\angle ABD \cong \angle DBC$$

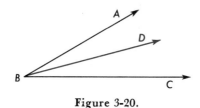

Figure 3-20.

Or this relation can be stated as

$$m\ \angle ABD = \tfrac{1}{2}m\ \angle ABC$$

and

$$m\ \angle DBC = \tfrac{1}{2}m\ \angle ABC$$

Two illustrations of the application of Postulate 8 appear below. What
conclusion based on all the given data can be drawn in each case?

Illustration 1:

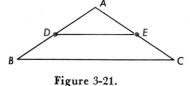

Given: $\overline{AB} \cong \overline{AC}$
       D is the midpoint of $\overline{AB}$.
       E is the midpoint of $\overline{AC}$.

Figure 3-21.

CONCLUSION	REASON
$\overline{AD} \cong \overline{AE}$	Division postulate: Halves ($\overline{AD}$ and $\overline{AE}$) of congruent segments ($\overline{AB}$ and $\overline{AC}$) are congruent.

To avoid confusion, it might be well to point out that the term "halves" as used in these examples refers to the fact that the measures of both $\overline{AD}$ and $\overline{AE}$ are halves of the measures of $\overline{AB}$ and $\overline{AC}$. The Division Postulate will also enable us to conclude that $\overline{BD} \cong \overline{CE}$, for their measures, too, are halves of those of the congruent segments $\overline{AB}$ and $\overline{AC}$. What two other conclusions can be drawn in this problem?

Illustration 2:

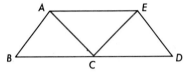

Given: $\angle BAE \cong \angle DEA$

$\overrightarrow{AC}$ bisects $\angle BAE$.

$\overrightarrow{EC}$ bisects $\angle DEA$.

Figure 3-22.

CONCLUSION	REASON
$\angle BAC \cong \angle DEC$	Division postulate: Halves ($\angle BAC$ and $\angle DEC$) of congruent angles ($\angle BAE$ and $\angle DEA$) are congruent.

EXERCISES

In each of the following problems draw a single conclusion based on *all* the data given. Do your work as shown in the two illustrations above.

1. Given: $\overline{AB} \cong \overline{DC}$

E is the midpoint of $\overline{AB}$.

F is the midpoint of $\overline{DC}$.

Given: $\overline{AB} \cong \overline{AC}$ **2.**

$\overleftrightarrow{DE}$ bisects $\overline{AB}$.

$\overleftrightarrow{DF}$ bisects $\overline{AC}$.

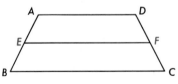

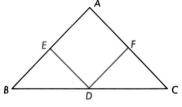

3. Given: $\angle ADC \cong \angle BCD$

$\overrightarrow{DF}$ bisects $\angle ADC$.

$\overrightarrow{CE}$ bisects $\angle BCD$.

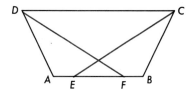

Given: $\overline{CA} \cong \overline{CB}$ **4.**

$\overleftrightarrow{DE}$ bisects $\overline{CA}$ and $\overline{CB}$.
(Hint: Write these
data as two pieces of
information.)

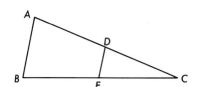

5. Given: $\angle ABE \cong \angle DCE$

$\overrightarrow{BG}$ bisects $\angle ABE$.

$\overrightarrow{CF}$ bisects $\angle ECD$.

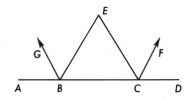

Given: $\overline{AC} \cong \overline{BD}$ **6.**

$\overline{AC}$ and $\overline{BD}$ bisect each
other. (Hint: Write
these data as two
pieces of information.)

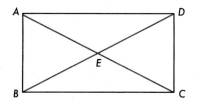

7. Given: $\angle ADB \cong \angle BCA$

$\overrightarrow{DE}$ bisects $\angle ADB$.

$\overrightarrow{CE}$ bisects $\angle BCA$.

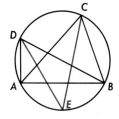

Given: $\overline{PB} \cong \overline{PC}$ **8.**

A is the midpoint
of $\overline{PB}$.

D is the midpoint
of $\overline{PC}$.

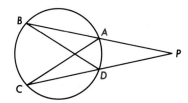

9. Given: $\overleftrightarrow{OF}$ bisects $\overline{DC}$.

$\overleftrightarrow{OE}$ bisects $\overline{AB}$.

$\overline{AB} \cong \overline{DC}$

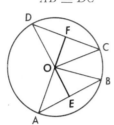

Given: $\overrightarrow{AC}$ bisects $\angle BAD$.   **10.**

$\overrightarrow{CA}$ bisects $\angle BCD$.

$\angle BAD \cong \angle BCD$

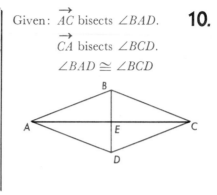

■ The Postulates of Equality

We have been making some rather vague references to the fact that in the relation

$$a = b$$

the symbol on the left and the symbol on the right are but two different names for the same "thing," where most frequently this "thing" has been a number. To express this concept formally, the mathematicians created three postulates setting forth what they call the **properties of an equality**.

POSTULATE 9: Reflexive Property of Equality

$$a = a$$

POSTULATE 10: Symmetric Property of Equality

If $a = b$
then $b = a$

POSTULATE 11: Transitive Property of Equality

If $a = b$
and $b = c$
then $a = c$

The first of these properties has a very long history, having been first noted by the Greek philosopher Aristotle. He referred to it by saying that a quantity must be identically equal to itself and noted this as his first law of logic. It was called the **Law of Identity**. There are two other laws of logic that Aristotle established. Both of these will play an important role in our work later in the course.

The Symmetric Property establishes the idea that an equality between numbers will hold in both directions. That is, if a is equal to b, then so, too, must b be equal to a. Finally, the third, or transitive, property of equality enables us to discover two numbers that are equal by showing that they are equal to the same third number. Although the information in the Transitive Property was given as

$$a = b$$

and

$$b = c$$

by applying the Symmetric Property to the second of these equalities, it can be written as

$$c = b$$

Thus, Postulate 11 can be written as

If $\qquad\qquad a = b$
and $\qquad\qquad c = b$
then $\qquad\qquad a = c$

When stated in this way, we can easily recognize that both a and c are equal to b. Then by the Transitive Property we will conclude that

$$a = c$$

The equivalence of the following statements was noted several times in the past:

$$m\,\overline{AB} = m\,\overline{CD} \text{ is equivalent to } \overline{AB} \cong \overline{CD}.$$

Since it follows from the Symmetric Property that

if $\qquad\qquad m\,\overline{AB} = m\,\overline{CD}$
then $\qquad\qquad m\,\overline{CD} = m\,\overline{AB}$

Therefore, it can be said that

if $\qquad\qquad \overline{AB} \cong \overline{CD}$
then $\qquad\qquad \overline{CD} \cong \overline{AB}$

The same relations will hold with reference to the Reflexive Property and the Transitive Property. That is, henceforth,

> The Reflexive, Symmetric, and Transitive Properties of Equality will also be interpreted as Reflexive, Symmetric, and Transitive Properties of Congruence of line segments and Congruence of angles.

■ Applications of the Properties of Equality

The reflexive property of equality has some very special applications when used in conjunction with the addition and subtraction postulates. The four illustrations below will help point up those situations under which this occurs. Before reading the "Conclusion" and "Reason" that appear for each problem, try to draw your own conclusion and justify it in terms of the postulates.

Illustration 1:

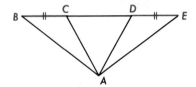

Given: $\overline{BC} \cong \overline{DE}$

Figure 3-23.

CONCLUSION	REASON
$\overline{CD} \cong \overline{CD}$	Reflexive property of congruent segments.
$\overline{BD} \cong \overline{CE}$	Addition postulate: If congruent segments ($\overline{CD}$ and $\overline{CD}$) are added to congruent segments ($\overline{BC}$ and $\overline{DE}$), the sums will be congruent segments ($\overline{BD}$ and $\overline{CE}$).

Illustration 2:

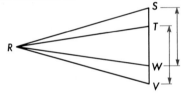

Given: $\overline{SW} \cong \overline{TV}$

Figure 3-24.

CONCLUSION	REASON
$\overline{TW} \cong \overline{TW}$	Reflexive property of congruent segments.
$\overline{ST} \cong \overline{WV}$	Subtraction postulate: If congruent segments ($\overline{TW}$ and $\overline{TW}$) are subtracted from congruent segments ($\overline{SW}$ and $\overline{TV}$), the differences will be congruent segments ($\overline{ST}$ and $\overline{WV}$).

Illustration 3:

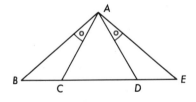

Given: $\angle BAC \cong \angle DAE$

Figure 3-25.

CONCLUSION	REASON
$\angle CAD \cong \angle CAD$ $\angle BAD \cong \angle CAE$	Reflexive property of congruent angles. Addition postulate: If congruent angles ($\angle CAD$ and $\angle CAD$) are added to congruent angles ($\angle BAC$ and $\angle DAE$), the sums will be congruent angles ($\angle BAD$ and $\angle CAE$).

Illustration 4:

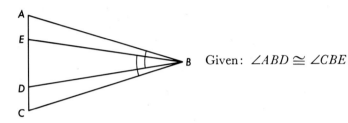

Given: $\angle ABD \cong \angle CBE$

Figure 3-26.

CONCLUSION	REASON
$\angle EBD \cong \angle EBD$ $\angle ABE \cong \angle CBD$	Reflexive property of congruent angles. Subtraction postulate: If congruent angles ($\angle EBD$ and $\angle EBD$) are subtracted from congruent angles ($\angle ABD$ and $\angle CBE$), the differences will be congruent angles ($\angle ABE$ and $\angle CBD$).

An illustration of the transitive property of congruence is given below. Before reading the conclusion and reason that appears for the problem, try to formulate your own.

Illustration 5:

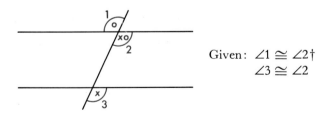

Given: $\angle 1 \cong \angle 2$†
$\angle 3 \cong \angle 2$

Figure 3-27.

† Angles are frequently named with numbers rather than with three capital letters.

CONCLUSION	REASON
$\angle 1 \cong \angle 3$	Transitive property of congruence: If two angles ($\angle 1$ and $\angle 3$) are congruent to the same angle ($\angle 2$), then they are congruent to each other.

EXERCISES

In each of these problems, state one conclusion and the reason justifying this conclusion. Do your work as shown in the five illustrations above.

1. Given: $\overline{AG} \cong \overline{FE}$

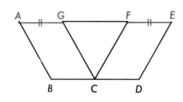

Given: $\angle ABC \cong \angle BAC$
$\angle ACB \cong \angle BAC$ **2.**

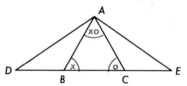

3. Given: $\angle 1 \cong \angle 2$

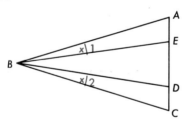

Given: $\angle 1 \cong \angle 2$
$\angle 2 \cong \angle 3$ **4.**

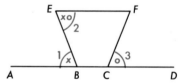

5. Given: $\overline{AD} \cong \overline{EC}$

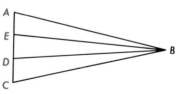

Given: $\angle AEC \cong \angle DEB$ **6.**

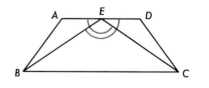

7. Given: $\angle 1 \cong \angle 2$
$\qquad\quad \angle 3 \cong \angle 2$

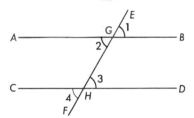

Given: $\overline{BE} \cong \overline{FC}$ **8.**

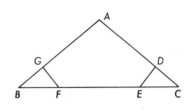

9. Given: $\overline{BC} \cong \overline{AE}$
$\qquad\quad \overline{AE} \cong \overline{CD}$

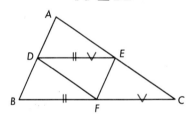

Given: $\angle RYT \cong \angle WYS$ **10.**

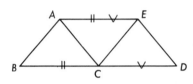

11. Given: $\overline{DE} \cong \overline{BF}$
$\qquad\quad\; \overline{FC} \cong \overline{DE}$

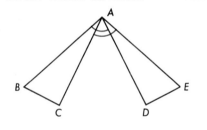

Given: $\angle BAD \cong \angle EAC$ **12.**

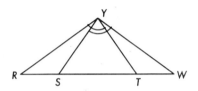

■ Applications of the Postulates of Geometry

Though we will learn other postulates throughout the year, the few we have studied in this chapter have wider application than any of the others. If you understand these thoroughly, there is little likelihood that you will encounter any great difficulty with the work that follows. On the other hand, should you still feel unsure of yourself with the application of these postulates, it would be best to go back and redo each of the sets of exercises in this chapter. To help you decide whether this review is necessary, do all the problems in the exercises that follow. If you have no difficulty in determining which postulate should be used to justify each conclusion, then it is very likely that you understand how and when to apply the operational postulates.

EXERCISES

Unless otherwise stated, draw only one conclusion on the basis of the data given in each of the following problems. To the right of each of your conclusions, state the postulate you have used to justify this conclusion.

1. Given: $m \angle 1 = 35$
$m \angle 2 = 35$

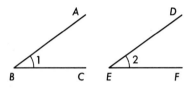

Given: $\overline{AB} \cong \overline{DE}$
$\overline{BC} \cong \overline{EF}$ **2.**

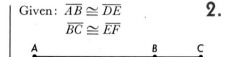

3. Given: $\angle 1 \cong \angle 3$
$\angle 2 \cong \angle 4$

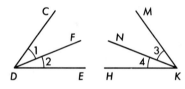

Given: $\overline{MN} \cong \overline{OP}$ **4.**

5. Given: $\angle 1 \cong \angle 4$
$\angle 2 \cong \angle 3$

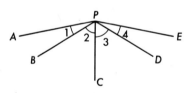

Given: $\angle 1 \cong \angle 2$ **6.**

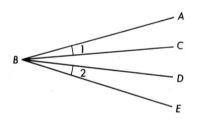

7. Given: $\angle CAD \cong \angle CBD$
$\angle DAB \cong \angle DBA$

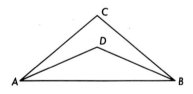

Given: $\overline{LN} \cong \overline{PR}$ **8.**
$\overline{MN} \cong \overline{PQ}$

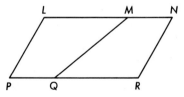

9. Given: $\overline{EA} \cong \overline{EC}$
$\overline{EF} \cong \overline{ED}$

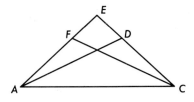

Given: $\angle ABC \cong \angle ACB$ **10.**
$\angle 1 \cong \angle 2$

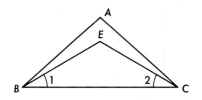

11. Given: $\overline{BC} \cong \overline{BD}$
$\overline{BE} \cong \overline{BF}$

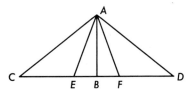

Given: $\angle CEA \cong \angle BED$ **12.**

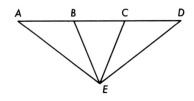

13. Given: $\angle 3 \cong \angle 2$
$\angle 1 \cong \angle 2$

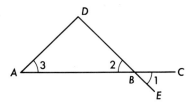

Given: $\angle 1 \cong \angle 3$ **14.**
$\angle 2 \cong \angle 4$

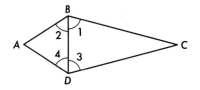

15. Given: $\angle 1 \cong \angle 2$
$\angle 1 \cong \angle 3$

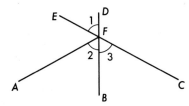

Given: $\overline{AB} \cong \overline{CD}$ **16.**

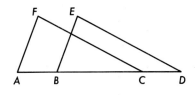

17. Given: $\angle 3 \cong \angle 2$
$\angle 4 \cong \angle 2$

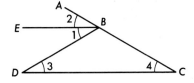

Given: $\angle 1 \cong \angle 2$ **18.**
$\angle GCD \cong \angle FDC$

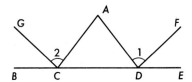

19. Given: $\angle ABC \cong \angle ACB$
$\angle 1 \cong \angle 2$

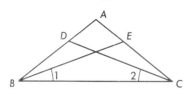

Given: $\angle ABC \cong \angle DCB$
$\overrightarrow{BE}$ bisects $\angle ABC$.
$\overrightarrow{CE}$ bisects $\angle DCB$.   **20.**

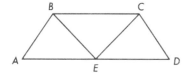

21. Given: $\angle 1 \cong \angle 2$
$\angle 2 \cong \angle 3$

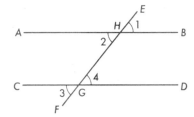

Given: $\overline{AB} \cong \overline{DC}$
$\overline{AF} \cong \overline{DE}$ **22.**

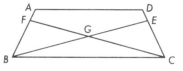

23. Given: $\overline{AB} \cong \overline{DC}$
E is the midpoint of $\overline{AB}$.
F is the midpoint of $\overline{CD}$.

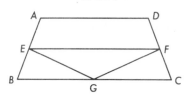

Given: $\overline{AC} \cong \overline{BD}$ **24.**

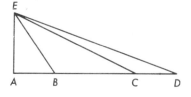

25. Given: $\angle ABC \cong \angle ACB$
$\overrightarrow{BD}$ bisects $\angle ABC$.
$\overrightarrow{CD}$ bisects $\angle ACB$.

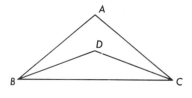

Given: $\overline{EC} \cong \overline{AB}$
$\overline{ED} \cong \overline{AB}$ **26.**

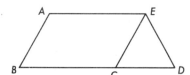

27. Given: $\overline{BF} \cong \overline{CE}$

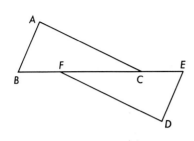

Given: $\overline{CA} \cong \overline{CB}$ **28.**
$\overleftrightarrow{DE}$ bisects $\overline{CA}$ and
$\overline{CB}$.

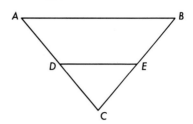

29. Given: $\angle ABC \cong \angle EFG$
$\angle 1 \cong \angle 2$

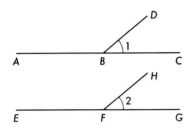

Given: $\overline{BA} \cong \overline{BC}$ **30.**
$\overline{AD} \cong \overline{CE}$

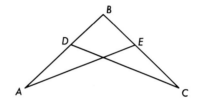

31. Given: $\angle ABC \cong \angle ADC$
$\angle 2 \cong \angle 1$

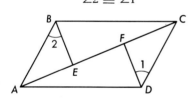

Given: $\angle AEC \cong \angle DEB$ **32.**

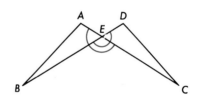

■ **Test**

$$\boxed{\text{A}}$$

1. In what way does a "postulate" differ from a "belief"?

2. Two mathematicians in different parts of the world develop subjects that they call plane geometry. The postulates used by one are completely different than those used by the other. Does this imply that one of these men is right while the other is wrong? Justify your answer.

3. State the postulate that was used in concluding Step B on the basis of the information given in Step A in each of the following problems.

(a) Step A: $3x = 12$
    Step B: $x = 4$

(b) Step A: $x + 4 = 10$
    Step B: $x = 6$

(c) Step A: $2x - 5 = 13$
    Step B: $2x = 18$

(d) Step A: $5x + 10 = 5$
    Step B: $x + 2 = 1$

4. If points A, B, and C are elements of $\overleftrightarrow{RS}$, then under what condition will $\overline{AC} + \overline{CB} = \overline{AB}$?

5. If $\overleftrightarrow{AB}$ and $\overleftrightarrow{CD}$ intersect in points X and Y, then what conclusion can be drawn?

6. Answer each of the questions below in terms of this diagram. If an answer is not possible, simply write "no answer" after the problem number.

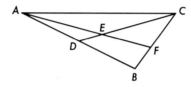

(a) $\overline{AD} + \overline{DB} = ?$

(b) $\overline{CE} + \overline{ED} = ?$

(c) $\overline{AE} + \overline{ED} = ?$

(d) $\overline{BC} - \overline{FC} = ?$

(e) $\overline{AC} - \overline{AE} = ?$

(f) $\angle BAC - \angle FAC = ?$

(g) $\angle BCD + \angle BCA = ?$

(h) $\angle AEF - \angle DEF = ?$

7. Express each of the following in terms of a single numeral.

(a) $|7 - 3|$ (b) $|4 - 9|$ (c) $|3 - (-7)|$

8. If the coordinate of A is 9 and the coordinate of B is 15, what is the measure of $\overline{AB}$?

9. If P is between R and Q, what is $m \overline{RP}$ if $m \overline{RQ} = 17$ and $m \overline{PQ} = 9$?

10. The $m \angle APB = 60$ and $m \angle BPC = 20$.

(a) If $\overrightarrow{PB}$ is between $\overrightarrow{PA}$ and $\overrightarrow{PC}$, what is the $m \angle APC$?

(b) If $\overrightarrow{PC}$ is between $\overrightarrow{PA}$ and $\overrightarrow{PB}$, what is the $m \angle APC$?

Draw a conclusion in each of the problems below. Immediately following your reason for this conclusion, indicate whether this reason is a postulate, a definition, or the reverse of a definition.

1. Given: $\overline{AD} \cong \overline{BE}$
$\overline{DC} \cong \overline{EC}$

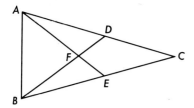

Given: $\overrightarrow{CE}$ bisects $\angle ACB$. **2.**

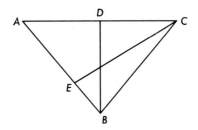

3. Given: $\angle DBA \cong \angle EBC$

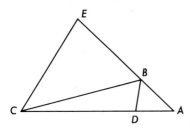

Given: $\overline{ED} \cong \overline{BC}$ **4.**
F is the midpoint of $\overline{ED}$.
G is the midpoint of $\overline{BC}$.

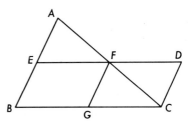

5. Given: $\overleftrightarrow{EF} \perp \overleftrightarrow{AC}$

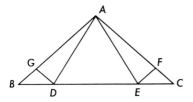

Given: $\angle EDC \cong \angle FDB$ **6.**

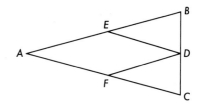

7. Given: $\overline{AD} \cong \overline{AE}$
$\overline{AB} \cong \overline{AC}$

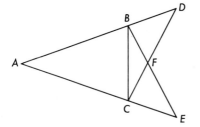

Given: $\overrightarrow{AD}$ bisects $\angle BAF$. **8.**

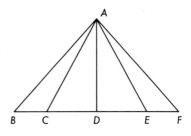

9. Given: $\overline{AC} \cong \overline{BD}$
$\overline{EC} \cong \overline{ED}$

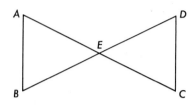

Given: $\angle BJF \cong \angle CGE$ **10.**
$\overrightarrow{JK}$ bisects $\angle BJF$.
$\overrightarrow{GH}$ bisects $\angle CGE$.

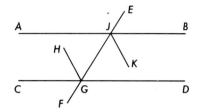

11. Given: $\overline{AB}$ and $\overline{CD}$ bisect each other.

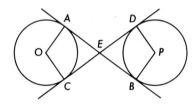

Given: $\overline{RA} \cong \overline{RC}$ **12.**
$\overline{RC} \cong \overline{RB}$

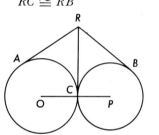

13. Given: $\overline{BE} \cong \overline{FC}$

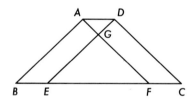

Given: $\angle AFD \cong \angle BEC$ **14.**
$\angle AFC \cong \angle CEA$

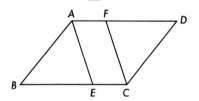

15. Given: $\overline{AE} \cong \overline{EB}$

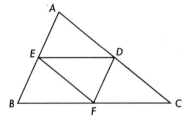

Given: $\overline{AC} \cong \overline{DB}$ **16.**
$\overleftrightarrow{EH}$ bisects $\overline{AC}$ and $\overline{DB}$.

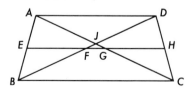
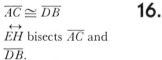

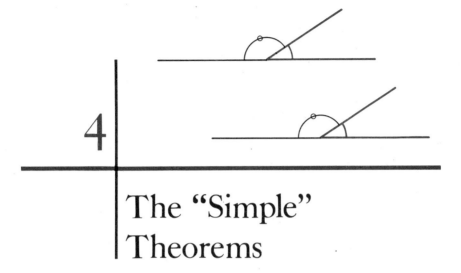

4

The "Simple" Theorems

IN THE FIRST THREE CHAPTERS WE LAID THE foundation blocks of the course in geometry. These blocks are our definitions and postulates. Now we are prepared to build a large superstructure based on these few primitive ideas. What, however, is the mortar that binds the superstructure to these definitions and assumptions? It is known either as the "Rules of Reasoning" or the "Formulas for Drawing Valid Inferences." Only one of these rules is important to us at this time.

Consider the following two statements:

(1) "If I receive a passing grade on my exam, then I shall pass for the term."

(2) "I received a passing grade on my exam."

On the basis of these two statements, what conclusion do you believe should follow? Quite apparently, by virtue of the fact that I received a passing grade on my exam, I shall pass for the term.

A statement of the form

"If I receive a passing grade on my exam,
then I shall pass for the term"

is called a *conditional statement*. That part of the statement following the word "if" is referred to as the *antecedent*, while the clause following the word "then" is the *consequent* or *conclusion*. If, as in the illustration above, we assert the truth of both the conditional statement

"If I receive a passing grade on my exam,
then I shall pass for the term"

and the antecedent

"I received a passing grade on my exam"

then it will follow that the *consequent will also be true*:

"I shall pass for the term."

If this relationship is expressed with the symbols *p* and *q* where *p* represents the antecedent and *q* the consequent, what we have just discovered would take the form of

POSTULATE 12: Accepting the conditional statement: If *p* then *q*.
            And asserting the truth of *p*: Given *p*
            Affirms the truth of *q*: Then *q* follows.

The application of Postulate 12 to geometric situations will occur as follows:

Accepting the conditional statement: If an angle is a right angle, then its
                            measure is 90.
And asserting the truth of the antecedent: ∠*ABC* is a right angle.
Affirms the truth of the consequent: The measure of ∠*ABC* is 90.

In this illustration the conditional statement is nothing more than another form of the definition of a right angle. In fact the entire problem was encountered earlier in our work as

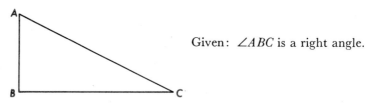

Given: ∠*ABC* is a right angle.

Figure 4-1.

The conclusion we drew was identically the same as the consequent in this illustration. Apparently, each time we drew a conclusion in the first three chapters we were accepting Postulate 12 without being aware of this!

A reasonable question to ask at this point is, "If we assert the truth of the *consequent* in a conditional statement, will this in turn affirm the truth of the *antecedent*?" To answer this question, let us examine the conditional statement

"If a person is a king, then that person is a man."

Should we assert the truth of the consequent,

"Joe Smith is a man"

it would surely *not* infer the truth of the antecedent,

"Joe Smith is a king."

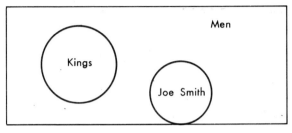

Figure 4-2.

This same situation can be illustrated rather clearly through the use of a *Venn* diagram. Here we see that both "Joe Smith" and "Kings" are subsets of the universal set called "Men." Joe Smith, however, is not necessarily a member of the set called "Kings." Thus, reasoning of the form

Accepting the conditional statement: If p, then q.
And asserting the truth of q: Given q
Affirms the truth of p: Then p follows.

is FALSE, or INCORRECT, REASONING.

Similarly, if we were to deny the antecedent, this would *not* imply the truth of a denial of the consequent. Thus, with reference to the conditional statement

"If a person is a king, then that person is a man."

if we deny the antecedent

"Joe Smith is *not* a king"

this denial does *not* imply the truth of a denial of the consequent

"Joe Smith is *not* a man"

By examining the Venn diagram above, we can see that although Joe Smith *is not* an element in the set "Kings," he *is* an element in the set "Men." Hence, reasoning following this pattern is *incorrect*.

Incorrect Reasoning

Accepting the conditional statement: If p, then q.
And asserting the truth of a denial of p: Given not-p
Affirms the truth of a denial of q: Then not-q follows.

EXERCISES

In each of the following problems state whether the reasoning is correct or incorrect. Justify your answer in either event.

1. If Mr. Strong is elected senator, then our taxes will be reduced.
   Mr. Strong was elected senator.
   ∴† Our taxes will be reduced.

2. You will have no throat irritation if you smoke Robin cigarettes.
   You smoke Robin cigarettes.
   ∴ You will have no throat irritation.

3. If it rains, we shall not go to the dance.
   It is not raining.
   ∴ We shall go to the dance.

4. If you are a good citizen, then you will vote at election time.
   You voted at election time.
   ∴ You are a good citizen.

5. If the price of goods is not increased, it will not be necessary to raise the salaries of employees.
   The price of goods was increased.
   ∴ It will be necessary to raise the salaries of employees.

6. If $\overleftrightarrow{AB} \perp \overleftrightarrow{CD}$, then ∠1 and ∠2 are right angles.
   Given: $\overleftrightarrow{AB} \perp \overleftrightarrow{CD}$
   ∴ ∠1 and ∠2 are right angles.

7. If a ray is the bisector of an angle, then two congruent angles will be formed.
   Given: $\overrightarrow{BA}$ bisects ∠B.
   ∴ Two congruent angles are formed.

8. You will be able to write quickly if you use RAPID pencils.
   You do not use RAPID pencils.
   ∴ You are not able to write quickly.

9. If $a = b$ and $c = d$, then $a + c = b + d$.
   a does not equal b, and c does not equal d.
   ∴ $a + c$ does not equal $b + d$.

† The symbol ∴ is used to represent the word "therefore."

Granting the truth of the conditional statement and the statement that follows it, what further statement will be true? If no further statement can be made by "correct" reasoning, state why this is so.

1. If a substance is an acid, it will turn blue litmus paper red.
   This substance turns blue litmus paper red.

2. If a student is not a senior, he can not run for office in the senior class.
   Fred Williams is a senior.

3. If $x = -2$, then $x^2 = 4$.
   But $x^2 = 4$.

4. If two angles are congruent to the same angle, then their measures are equal.
   $\angle A$ and $\angle B$ are not congruent to the same angle.

5. $\overline{AB} \cong \overline{BC}$ if B is the midpoint of $\overline{AC}$.
   B is the midpoint of $\overline{AC}$.

6. $\angle 1$ is not a right angle if $\overleftrightarrow{AB}$ is not perpendicular to $\overleftrightarrow{CD}$.
   $\overleftrightarrow{AB} \perp \overleftrightarrow{CD}$.

7. Two angles are supplementary if the sum of their measures is 180.
   $m\angle A + m\angle B = 180$.

8. x is an element of B if x is an element of A.
   x is an element of B.

9. If the intersection of $\overleftrightarrow{AB}$ and $\overleftrightarrow{CD}$ is the empty set, then $\overleftrightarrow{AB}$ and $\overleftrightarrow{CD}$ are not equal sets.
   The intersection of $\overleftrightarrow{AB}$ and $\overleftrightarrow{CD}$ is not the empty set.

10. If a point is the vertex of an angle, then it is a common element to each of the sides of the angle.
    P is an element common to each of two rays.

■ Theorem on Right Angles

We spoke earlier of the superstructure that we planned to build on the foundation of definitions and postulates. This superstructure consists of statements, many of them conditional, whose truth we propose to justify. To do this, we will make frequent use of Postulate 12, for it is the only means we have at our disposal for "reasoning correctly." Quite often the words "reasoning correctly" are used interchangeably with "reasoning logically" or "drawing valid conclusions." Throughout this book these three phrases will have exactly the same meaning.

To a very large extent the nature of our work will be to show why we must accept q in the statement

"If p, then q"

if we accept the truth of p. Then, *with the knowledge that both* p *and* q *are true, we will agree that the statement "If* p, *then* q" *is also true.*

Many of the statements that we *prove*—that is, justify by reasoning correctly—will have little consequence in the development of our work in geometry. Those statements that are important will be singled out and referred to as *theorems*. Theorems are used in the justification of the proofs of other statements.

All of this can be made a great deal clearer by showing an application to a specific illustration.

THEOREM 1: If two angles are right angles, then they are congruent.

At the outset we must realize that the p of this statement is
"Two angles are right angles"
while the q is
"These two angles are congruent"

Our objective now will be to accept p and show why q must also be accepted. This is done by making several applications of Postulate 12. To simplify our work, let us call the two right angles $\angle A$ and $\angle B$.

PROOF

First Application of Postulate 12

If an angle is a right angle, then its measure is 90.
$\angle A$ is a right angle.
$\therefore m \angle A = 90$

Second Application of Postulate 12

If an angle is a right angle, then its measure is 90.
$\angle B$ is a right angle.
$\therefore m \angle B = 90$

Third Application of Postulate 12

If $a = b$ and $b = c$, then $a = c$.
$m \angle A = 90$ and $m \angle B = 90$
$\therefore m \angle A = m \angle B$

Fourth Application of Postulate 12

If two angles have equal measures, then they are congruent.
$\angle A$ and $\angle B$ have equal measures.
$\therefore \angle A$ and $\angle B$ are congruent.

Thus, accepting the statement that $\angle A$ and $\angle B$ were right angles led us to the conclusion that $\angle A$ and $\angle B$ were congruent. The justification for this was based on the method of "correct reasoning" given to us by Postulate 12. In addition, we fell back upon the definition of a right angle, the reverse of the definition of congruent angles, and the transitive property of equality. Where did these three statements appear in the proof?

It is quite apparent that this method of proof is not only lengthy but also rather tedious. In view of this fact, the "Two-Column" method was developed to shorten and simplify the proof of a statement. The proof presented above will now be repeated in its "Two-Column" form.

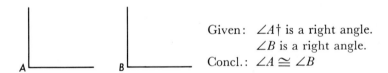

Given: $\angle A$† is a right angle.
$\angle B$ is a right angle.
Concl.: $\angle A \cong \angle B$

Figure 4-3.

PROOF	STATEMENTS	REASONS
1. $\angle A$ is a right angle.		1. Given
2. $m \angle A = 90$		2. Definition of a right angle
3. $\angle B$ is a right angle.		3. Given
4. $m \angle B = 90$		4. Same as 2
5. $m \angle A = m \angle B$		5. Transitive property of equality
6. $\angle A \cong \angle B$		6. Reverse of the definition of congruent angles

† An angle can be named with the single letter at its vertex if there are no other angles in the diagram having the same vertex.

There are several features about the preceding proof that should be called to your attention, for they will be repeated in most proofs.

(1) Notice that the *Conclusion* you are working toward is stated directly below the *Given Data*. Your objective will be to try to reach this conclusion by making a series of *Statements*. Each of these statements will have to be justified either by the fact that it is part of the Given Data or by virtue of the definitions or postulates that have been agreed upon.

(2) In developing the proof it is best not to leave any piece of the Given Data without pointing out its value in the proof. Thus, before leaving the statement that "$\angle A$ is a right angle," it was shown that because of the definition of a right angle, the measure of $\angle A$ must be 90. This was important, for arriving at our conclusion was dependent upon the fact that the measures of both $\angle A$ and $\angle B$ be shown equal to the same number, 90.

(3) Whenever the same reason appears more than once in a proof, it is unnecessary that it be repeated. In the proof illustrated, the reason for statement 4 was the same as that for statement 2. This was signified by writing, "Same as 2."

The proof of the theorem, "If two angles are right angles, then they are congruent" was based on two definitions and the postulate, the transitive property of equality. You may say, "What if we had decided not to accept this postulate?" Then, we would very likely not have been able to prove this theorem. In the same vein, should a postulate be discarded at any time during the period in which you are learning this subject, it would be necessary, too, to discard those theorems that were based upon this postulate. All is not lost, however, for an equally elegant superstructure can be built on the postulate that replaced the discarded one!

Along the same line, the question is often raised, "Which has greater 'truth,' the postulates that we have accepted or the theorems we prove?" A moment's reflection on how the theorems were justified will make you realize that the question is meaningless.

Once a theorem has been proved, it can be used thereafter as justification for statements in the same manner as definitions and postulates have been used in the past. But do, do be careful—never use them as a reason before they have been proved. As an example, refer to statement 6 in the proof on page 91. Could the reason for this statement have been given as, "If two angles are right angles, then they are congruent"? Justify your answer.

One final point may still be annoying you. Why bother to prove that right angles are congruent or, in fact, why prove any statements? Why not make things a great deal easier for ourselves by accepting this statement and all others! The answer to this lies in the nature of mathematics. Although the mathematician wants the postulates and definitions to be clearly set forth at the outset, he prefers to keep their number at a minimum. That is, he will call no new statement a postulate if it is at all possible to prove this statement in terms of the previous postulates that are already at his disposal. There will be occasions in the future when we shall make statements whose proofs are possible, and yet we shall postulate them. We do this so as not to bewilder you with small details at this early stage of your mathematical development.

Now, on to an application of Theorem 1:

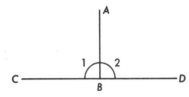

Given: $\overleftrightarrow{AB} \perp \overleftrightarrow{CD}$
Concl.: $\angle 1 \cong \angle 2$

Figure 4-4.

PROOF	STATEMENTS	REASONS
1. $\overleftrightarrow{AB} \perp \overleftrightarrow{CD}$		1. Given
2. $\angle 1$ and $\angle 2$ are right angles.		2. Definition of perpendicular lines
3. $\angle 1 \cong \angle 2$		3. If two angles are right angles, then they are congruent. (Theorem 1)

Note that we did not have to prove Theorem 1 over again in arriving at $\angle 1 \cong \angle 2$. Since the two angles were shown to be right angles, then Theorem 1 enables us to conclude that they are congruent.

EXERCISES

Show how to arrive at the conclusion in each of the following problems. Use the same method as illustrated above.

1. Given: $\angle B$ is a right angle.
$\angle D$ is a right angle.
Concl.: $\angle B \cong \angle D$

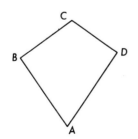

Given: $\angle B$ is a right angle.
$\overleftrightarrow{DC} \perp \overleftrightarrow{BC}$
Concl.: $\angle B \cong \angle C$ **2.**

3. Given: $\overleftrightarrow{AB} \perp \overleftrightarrow{CD}$
Concl.: $\angle ABC \cong \angle ABD$

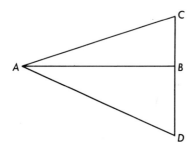

4.
Given: $\overleftrightarrow{AB} \perp \overleftrightarrow{BC}$
$\overleftrightarrow{EC} \perp \overleftrightarrow{BC}$
Concl.: $\angle B \cong \angle C$

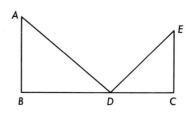

5. Given: $\overleftrightarrow{AB} \perp \overleftrightarrow{BC}$
$\overleftrightarrow{BD} \perp \overleftrightarrow{AC}$
Concl.: $\angle ABC \cong \angle ADB$

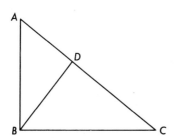

6.
Given: $\angle 1$ and $\angle 2$ are complementary angles.
$\angle DCB$ is a right angle.
Concl.: $\angle ABC \cong \angle DCB$

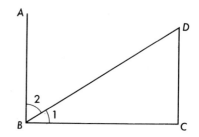

7. Given: $\angle 1$ and $\angle 2$ are complementary angles.
$\angle 3$ and $\angle 4$ are complementary angles.
Concl.: $\angle ABC \cong \angle DCB$

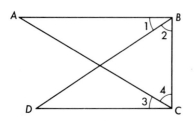

8.
Given: $\overleftrightarrow{AB} \perp \overleftrightarrow{CD}$
$\angle 2$ complementary to $\angle 3$
Concl.: $\angle ACB \cong \angle 1$

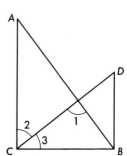

9. Given: $\overset{\leftrightarrow}{AB}$ and $\overset{\leftrightarrow}{DC} \perp \overset{\leftrightarrow}{BC}$
$\angle C \cong \angle D$
Concl.: $\angle B \cong \angle D$

Given: $\angle 1$ and $\angle 3$ are com- **10.**
plementary to $\angle 2$.
Concl.: $\angle DBF \cong \angle GBE$

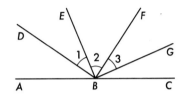

■ Theorem on Straight Angles

It should have been apparent to you that just as we had been able to prove that if two angles are right angles, then they are congruent, so, too, is it possible to prove that if two angles are straight angles, then they will be congruent.

THEOREM 2: **If two angles are straight angles, then they are congruent.**

The proof of this statement is very much the same as the one given on page 91. In what manner will the diagram have to be altered in order to conform with the information given in this theorem rather than in the one on right angles? How would you change the Given Data? What word in reason 2 will have to be changed? What other changes will have to be made in the proof? Write out the complete proof of Theorem 2.

■ Theorems on Supplementary and Complementary Angles

If $\angle B$ was supplementary to $\angle A$ and the $m \angle A$ was 20, what would be the measure of $\angle B$? What operation did you perform to arrive at 160? If $\angle C$ was also supplementary to $\angle A$, then what would be the measure of $\angle C$? In view of what you found the measures of both $\angle B$ and $\angle C$ to be, what conclusion can be drawn? How were both $\angle B$ and $\angle C$ related to $\angle A$? What relationship existed between $\angle B$ and $\angle C$ based on the fact that they were both supplementary to $\angle A$? In general then, what do you think we will be able to prove concerning two angles that are supplementary to the same angle?

THEOREM 3: **If two angles are supplementary to the same angle, then they are congruent.**

ANALYSIS: The proof will be patterned after the method used to show that two right angles are congruent. That is, we will show that both angles have the same measure; hence, they will be congruent to each other.

Since $\angle B$ and $\angle A$ are supplementary, then $m \angle B + m \angle A = 180$. If this is so, then what is the measure of $\angle B$? In a similar manner we can show that $m \angle C$ is also $180 - m \angle A$. Hence, it follows that $\angle B \cong \angle C$.

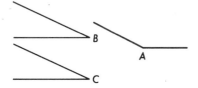

Given: $\angle B$ is supplementary to $\angle A$.
           $\angle C$ is supplementary to $\angle A$.
Concl.: $\angle B \cong \angle C$

Figure 4-5.

PROOF	STATEMENTS	REASONS
1.	$\angle B$ is supplementary to $\angle A$.	1. Given
2.	$m \angle B + m \angle A = 180$	2. Definition of supplementary angles
3.	$m \angle B = 180 - m \angle A$	3. Subtraction property of equality
4.	$\angle C$ is supplementary to $\angle A$.	4. Given
5.	$m \angle C + m \angle A = 180$	5. Same as 2
6.	$m \angle C = 180 - m \angle A$	6. Same as 3
7.	$m \angle B = m \angle C$	7. Transitive property of equality
8.	$\angle B \cong \angle C$	8. Reverse of definition of congruent angles

Before examining the theorem below, you should realize that there will be another theorem whose wording will be very much the same as that of Theorem 3. What do you think this theorem will be?

THEOREM 4: If two angles are complementary to the same angle, then they are congruent.

ANALYSIS: Refer to the proof above. Why will the diagram for the proof of this theorem have to be changed from the one used in the proof of Theorem 3? What information in the Given Data will have to be changed? Why is no change necessary in the Conclusion? Examine each step of the proof to determine which words and which numbers will have to be changed.

Using the proof above as a guide, write the complete proof of Theorem 4.

The next two theorems sound very much the same as Theorems 3 and 4. Their proofs, however, will be quite different.

THEOREM 5: If two angles are supplementary to two congruent angles, then they are congruent.

ANALYSIS: In order to arrive at our conclusion, we will try to show that both ∠1 and ∠2 are congruent and also ∡ABC and EFG must be congruent (see Figure 4-6). Once this has been accomplished, ∠ABD and ∠EFH will have to be congruent by the subtraction property of congruence.

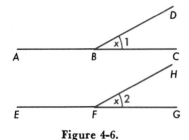

Given: ∠ABD is supplementary to ∠1.
   ∠EFH is supplementary to ∠2.
   ∠1 ≅ ∠2
Concl.: ∠ABD ≅ ∠EFH

Figure 4-6.

PROOF	STATEMENTS	REASONS
1. ∠ABD is supplementary to ∠1.	1. Given
2. ∠ABC is a straight angle.	2. Supplementary angles are two angles the sum of whose measures is the measure of a straight angle. (See Definition 12a, page 32.)
3. ∠EFH is supplementary to ∠2.	3. Given
4. ∠EFG is a straight angle.	4. Same as 2
5. ∠ABC ≅ ∠EFG	5. If two angles are straight angles, then they are congruent. (Theorem 2)
6. ∠1 ≅ ∠2	6. Given
7. ∠ABD ≅ ∠EFH	7. If congruent angles (∠1 and ∠2) are subtracted from congruent angles (∠ABC and ∠EFG), the differences will be congruent angles. (Subtraction property of congruence)

The theorem that follows differs from Theorem 5 only by the fact that the word "complementary" will replace the word "supplementary."

THEOREM 6: If two angles are complementary to two congruent angles, then they are congruent.

Using the proof of Theorem 5 as a guide, write the complete proof of Theorem 6.

The illustration that follows is an example of how Theorem 6 can be applied in the proof of a problem.

Illustration:

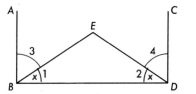

Given: $\overleftrightarrow{AB} \perp \overleftrightarrow{BD}$

$\overleftrightarrow{CD} \perp \overleftrightarrow{BD}$

$\angle 1 \cong \angle 2$

Concl.: $\angle 3 \cong \angle 4$

Figure 4-7.

PROOF	STATEMENTS	REASONS
1. $\overleftrightarrow{AB} \perp \overleftrightarrow{BD}$		1. Given
2. $\angle ABD$ is a right angle.		2. Def. of $\perp$ lines
3. $\angle 3$ is complementary to $\angle 1$.		3. Rev. of def. of complementary angles
4. $\overleftrightarrow{CD} \perp \overleftrightarrow{BD}$		4. Given
5. $\angle CDB$ is a right angle.		5. Same as 2
6. $\angle 4$ is complementary to $\angle 2$.		6. Same as 3
7. But, $\angle 1 \cong \angle 2$		7. Given
8. $\therefore \ \angle 3 \cong \angle 4$		8. If two angles are complementary to two congruent angles, then they are congruent. (Theorem 6)

There is an alternate method for arriving at the conclusion in this illustration. Since $\angle ABD$ and $\angle CDB$ were shown to be right angles, then by Theorem 1 we can conclude that they are congruent. From the Given Data we know that $\angle 1 \cong \angle 2$. Hence, why should it follow that $\angle 3 \cong \angle 4$?

EXERCISES

1. Given: $\angle 1$ is comp. to $\angle 2$.
$\angle 3$ is comp. to $\angle 2$.
Concl.: $\angle 1 \cong \angle 3$

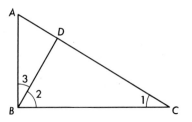

Given: $\angle 1$ is comp. to $\angle 2$.
$\overleftrightarrow{CB} \perp \overleftrightarrow{AB}$
Concl.: $\angle 3 \cong \angle 1$ **2.**

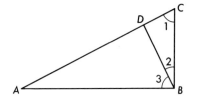

3. Given: ∠*ABC* is a straight
           angle.
           ∠*DEF* is a straight
           angle.
           ∠1 ≅ ∠2
Concl.: ∠3 ≅ ∠4

Given: $\overleftrightarrow{AB} \perp \overleftrightarrow{BC}$ **4.**
           $\overleftrightarrow{DE} \perp \overleftrightarrow{EF}$
           ∠1 ≅ ∠2
Concl.: ∠3 ≅ ∠4

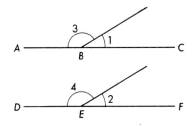

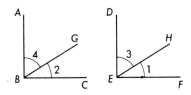

5. Given: ∠1 is supp. to ∠2.
           ∠3 is supp. to ∠2.
Concl.: ∠1 ≅ ∠3

Given: ∠3 is supp. to ∠1.   **6.**
           ∠*EFG* is a straight
           angle.
Concl.: ∠3 ≅ ∠2

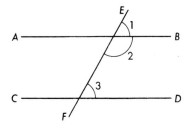

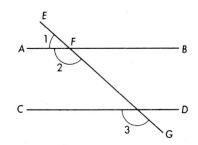

7. Given: ∠*EGH* is a straight
           angle.
           ∠*FHG* is a straight
           angle.
           ∠1 ≅ ∠2
Concl.: ∠3 ≅ ∠4

Given: *BCDE* is a straight   **8.**
           line.
           ∠1 ≅ ∠2
Concl.: ∠3 ≅ ∠4

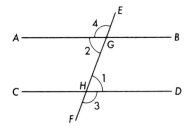

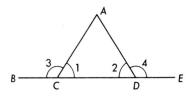

9. Given: $\angle C$ is comp. to $\angle 2$.
$\overset{\leftrightarrow}{AB} \perp \overset{\leftrightarrow}{BC}$
Concl.: $\angle C \cong \angle 1$

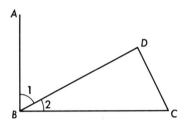

Given: $\angle 1$ is supp. to $\angle 2$.   **10.**
$\angle ABC$ is a straight
angle.
Concl.: $\angle 1 \cong \angle 3$

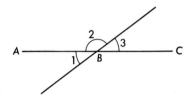

11. Given: $\overset{\leftrightarrow}{BC}$ extended to A
$\overset{\leftrightarrow}{DE}$ extended to F
$\angle 3 \cong \angle 4$
Concl.: $\angle 1 \cong \angle 2$

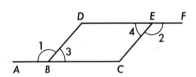

Given: $\angle 1$ is comp. to $\angle 2$.   **12.**
$\angle 3$ is comp. to $\angle 4$.
$\overset{\rightarrow}{BE}$ bisects $\angle ABC$.
Concl.: $\angle 1 \cong \angle 3$

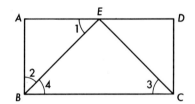

13. Given: $\overset{\leftrightarrow}{AC} \perp \overset{\leftrightarrow}{BD}$
$\angle 1 \cong \angle 2$
Concl.: $\angle 3 \cong \angle 4$

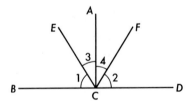

Given: $\overset{\leftrightarrow}{DB} \perp \overset{\leftrightarrow}{AC}$ **14.**
$\overset{\rightarrow}{BD}$ bisects $\angle EBF$.
Concl.: $\angle 3 \cong \angle 4$

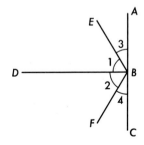

15. Given: $\overleftrightarrow{AB} \perp \overleftrightarrow{AC}$

$\qquad \overleftrightarrow{AD} \perp \overleftrightarrow{AE}$

Concl.: $\angle 2 \cong \angle 3$

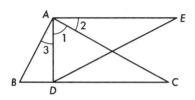

Given: AC and BD are **16.**

straight lines.

Concl.: $\angle 1 \cong \angle 2$

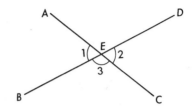

■ Vertical Angles

In doing Problem 16 of the preceding set of exercises, you have actually proved a very important theorem. The angles 1 and 2 in that diagram are called *vertical angles*. Notice that in order to obtain the sides of $\angle 2$, it was necessary to extend the sides of $\angle 1$ back through the vertex E. Similarly, had $\angle 2$ been drawn first, then to obtain the sides of $\angle 1$, it would have been necessary to have extended the sides of $\angle 2$, $\overrightarrow{ED}$ and

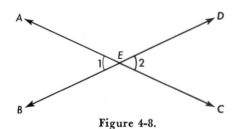

Figure 4-8.

$\overrightarrow{EC}$, through vertex E. In defining vertical angles we make use of this property. Into what class would you place vertical angles? How would you show how these angles differ from the other words in its class?

DEFINITION 22: Vertical angles are two angles such that the sides of one are rays that are opposite to those of the sides of the other.

Were Problem 16 expressed as the statement of a theorem, it would have been:

THEOREM 7: If two angles are vertical angles, then they are congruent.

ANALYSIS: The diagram in Problem 16 suggests that we make use of $\angle 3$. Since $\angle BED$ is a straight angle, then $\angle 2$ will be supplementary to $\angle 3$. Similarly, $\angle AEC$ is a straight angle. Hence, what relation exists between $\angle 1$ and $\angle 3$? If $\angle 1$ and $\angle 2$ are both supplementary to $\angle 3$, then what should follow?

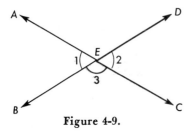

Given: ∠1 and ∠2 are vertical angles.
Concl.: ∠1 ≅ ∠2

Figure 4-9.

PROOF	STATEMENTS	REASONS
1. ∠1 and ∠2 are vertical angles.		1. Given
2. $\overrightarrow{EA}$ and $\overrightarrow{EC}$ are opposite rays.		2. Definition of vertical angles
3. ∠AEC is a straight angle.		3. Reverse of definition of a straight angle
4. ∠1 is supplementary to ∠3.		4. Reverse of definition of supplementary angles
5. $\overrightarrow{EB}$ and $\overrightarrow{ED}$ are opposite rays.		5. Same as 2
6. ∠BED is a straight angle.		6. Same as 3
7. ∠2 is supplementary to ∠3.		7. Same as 4
8. ∴ ∠1 ≅ ∠2		8. If two angles are supplementary to the same angle, then they are congruent. (Theorem 3)

There is another pair of vertical angles in the diagram above. Can you name this pair of angles? Using the same method as in the proof just given, prove that these two angles are also congruent.

Illustration of an Application of Theorem 7:

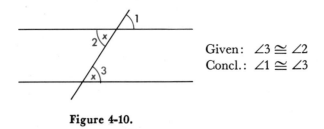

Given: ∠3 ≅ ∠2
Concl.: ∠1 ≅ ∠3

Figure 4-10.

ANALYSIS: Since ∠3 is already congruent to ∠2, if we can show that ∠1 is also congruent to ∠2, then our conclusion would follow. Why?

PROOF STATEMENTS	REASONS
1. $\angle 3 \cong \angle 2$	1. Given
2. $\angle 1 \cong \angle 2$	2. If two angles are vertical angles,† then they are congruent.
3. $\angle 1 \cong \angle 3$	3. Transitive property of congruence

A few of the problems in the next group of exercises involve the necessity of applying the transitive property of equality several times before the conclusion can be inferred. Since this same approach is found in the proofs of quite a number of the problems in the development of geometry, it seems only wise that a theorem be established now to cover this situation.

THEOREM 8: If $a = x$ (1)
           and $b = y$ (2)
           but also, $x = y$ (3)
           then $a = b$

ANALYSIS: By applying the transitive property to equations (1) and (3), we find that $a = y$. Using this information and the fact that $b = y$ (2), we discover that another application of the transitive property will enable us to say that $a = b$.

$$\text{Given: } a = x$$
$$b = y$$
$$x = y$$
$$\text{Concl.: } a = b$$

PROOF STATEMENTS	REASONS
1. $a = x$	1. Given
2. $x = y$	2. Given
3. $a = y$	3. Transitive property of equality
4. But, $b = y$	4. Given
5. $\therefore \quad a = b$	5. Same as 3

This theorem will most frequently be applied to line segments and to angles. Therefore, we will use the following statements for these special situations.

THEOREM 8a: **If two line segments are congruent to two congruent line segments, then they are congruent.**

THEOREM 8b: **If two angles are congruent to two congruent angles, then they are congruent.**

† It is unnecessary to point out in the proof that $\angle 1$ and $\angle 2$ are vertical angles.

Illustration of an Application of Theorem 8:

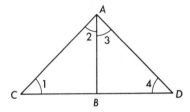

Given: $\angle 1 \cong \angle 2$
$\angle 4 \cong \angle 3$
$\overrightarrow{AB}$ bisects $\angle CAD$.
Concl.: $\angle 1 \cong \angle 4$

Figure 4-11.

ANALYSIS: If it were possible to show that $\angle 2 \cong \angle 3$, then by Theorem 8, $\angle 1$ and $\angle 4$ would also be congruent. Considering the Given Data, do you see any reason why $\angle 2$ should be congruent to $\angle 3$?

PROOF	STATEMENTS	REASONS
1. $\angle 1 \cong \angle 2$		1. Given
2. $\angle 4 \cong \angle 3$		2. Given
3. $\overrightarrow{AB}$ bisects $\angle CAD$.		3. Given
4. $\therefore$ $\angle 2 \cong \angle 3$		4. Definition of the bisector of an angle
5. Hence, $\angle 1 \cong \angle 4$		5. If two angles are congruent to two congruent angles, then they are congruent. (Theorem 8)

EXERCISES

The proofs of each of the following problems is based primarily on Theorems 7 and 8, definitions, and postulates.

1. Given: $\angle 1 \cong \angle 3$
Concl.: $\angle 1 \cong \angle 2$

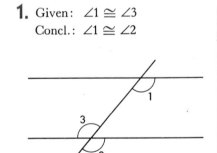

Given: $\angle D \cong \angle 2$ **2.**
Concl.: $\angle D \cong \angle 1$

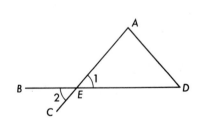

3. Given: $\angle A \cong \angle 1$
         $\angle D \cong \angle 2$
   Concl.: $\angle A \cong \angle D$

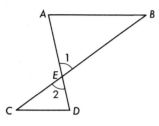

Given: $\angle B \cong \angle 1$ **4.**
         $\angle C \cong \angle 2$
Concl.: $\angle B \cong \angle C$

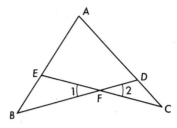

5. Given: $\angle 2 \cong \angle 3$
   Concl.: $\angle 1 \cong \angle 4$

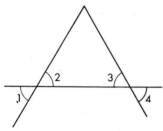

Given: $\angle 3 \cong \angle 4$ **6.**
Concl.: $\angle 1 \cong \angle 2$

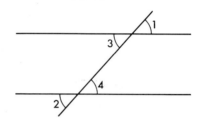

EXERCISES

Review of Theorems 1 through 8.

1. Given: $\angle 1 \cong \angle 2$
   Concl.: $\angle 3 \cong \angle 4$

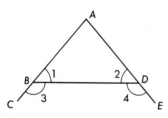

Given: $\angle 1 \cong \angle 2$ **2.**
Concl.: $\angle 3 \cong \angle 4$

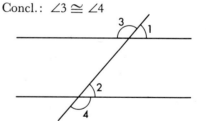

3. Given: $\angle 3$ is supp. to $\angle 2$.
   Concl.: $\angle 1 \cong \angle 2$

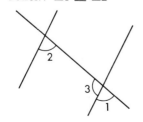

Given: $\angle 3$ is supp. to $\angle 2$.   **4.**
Concl.: $\angle 1 \cong \angle 3$

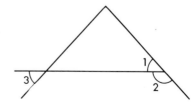

5. Given: ∠3 is comp. to ∠2.
         ∠ACB is a right angle.
Concl.: ∠3 ≅ ∠1

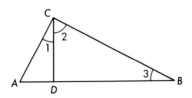

Given: ∠ABC ≅ ∠1   **6.**
         ∠DCB ≅ ∠2
Concl.: ∠ABC ≅ ∠DCB

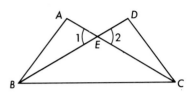

7. Given: ∠3 ≅ ∠1
         ∠4 ≅ ∠2
Concl.: ∠3 ≅ ∠4

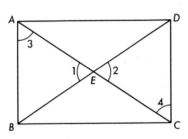

Given: ∠D is comp. to ∠2.   **8.**
         ∠E is comp. to ∠1.
Concl.: ∠D ≅ ∠E

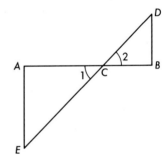

9. Given: ∠1 is supp. to ∠2.
         ∠3 is supp. to ∠4.
Concl.: ∠1 ≅ ∠3

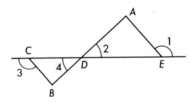

Given: ∠ABC is a right   **10.**
         angle.
         ∠DCB is a right
         angle.
         ∠1 ≅ ∠2
Concl.: ∠3 ≅ ∠4

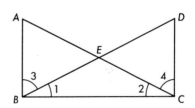

11. Given: ∠ACF ≅ ∠DBE
Concl.: ∠1 ≅ ∠2

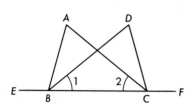

Given: $\overleftrightarrow{AB} \perp \overleftrightarrow{BC}$ **12.**
∠2 is comp. to ∠1.
Concl.: ∠2 ≅ ∠3

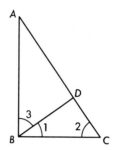

13. Given: ∠A is comp. to ∠1.
∠C is comp. to ∠2.
$\overrightarrow{BD}$ bisects ∠ABC.
Concl.: ∠A ≅ ∠C

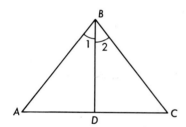

Given: ∠1 is supp. to ∠3. **14.**
Concl.: ∠2 ≅ ∠4

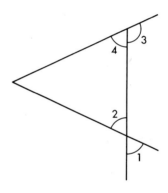

■ **Test**

1. In each of the following problems state whether the reasoning is correct
or incorrect. Justify your answer in either event.
   (a) If Joe Moran plays basketball this season, our team will win the
   pennant.
   Our team won the pennant.
   ∴ Joe Moran played basketball this season.
   (b) If I do not pass this geometry test, I shall receive a failing grade for
   this cycle.
   I passed this geometry test.
   ∴ I shall receive a passing grade for this cycle.

(c) If I brush my teeth with White Tooth Paste, my teeth will have no cavities.

I do not brush my teeth with White Tooth Paste.

∴ My teeth have cavities.

(d) If M is the midpoint of $\overline{AB}$, then $\overline{AM} \cong \overline{MB}$.

M is the midpoint of $\overline{AB}$.

∴ $\overline{AM} \cong \overline{MB}$

2. Granting the truth of the conditional statement and the statement that follows it, what further statement will be true? If no further statement can be made by "correct" reasoning, state why this is so.

(a) If the field is muddy, our team will not win today.
The field is not muddy.

(b) If a ray is not the bisector of an angle, it will not form two congruent angles with the sides of the angle.

$\overrightarrow{AB}$ does not bisect $\angle DAC$.

(c) If the measures of two angles are not equal, then the angles are not right angles.

$m \angle A = m \angle B$

(d) We will enjoy our stay in high school if we participate in the school activities.

We enjoyed the years we spent in high school.

B

Write the proof for each of the following problems:

1. Given: $\angle 1 \cong \angle 4$

Concl.: $\angle 2 \cong \angle 3$

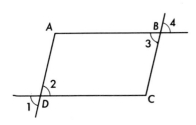

Given: $\overleftrightarrow{AB} \perp \overleftrightarrow{BC}$ **2.**

$\overleftrightarrow{AD} \perp \overleftrightarrow{DC}$

Concl.: $\angle ABC \cong \angle ADC$

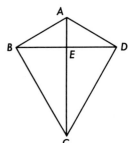

3. Given: ∠A is comp. to ∠1.
            ∠C is comp. to ∠2.
      Concl.: ∠A ≅ ∠C

Given: $\overleftrightarrow{CA}$ is extended to E.   **4.**
            ∠1 ≅ ∠2
      Concl.: ∠3 ≅ ∠4

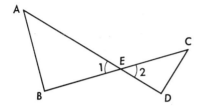

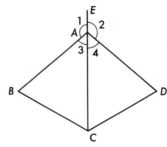

5. Given: ∠A is comp. to ∠2.
            $\overleftrightarrow{AB} \perp \overleftrightarrow{ED}$
      Concl.: ∠1 ≅ ∠A

Given: ∠C ≅ ∠1   **6.**

            ∠D ≅ ∠2

            $\overrightarrow{BA}$ bisects ∠EBF.
      Concl.: ∠C ≅ ∠D

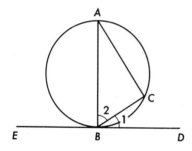

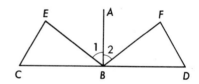

7. Given: $\overleftrightarrow{AP} \perp \overleftrightarrow{CP}$
            $\overleftrightarrow{BP} \perp \overleftrightarrow{DP}$
      Concl.: ∠1 ≅ ∠2

Given: ∠1 is supp. to ∠4.   **8.**
      Concl.: ∠2 ≅ ∠3

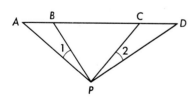

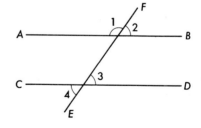

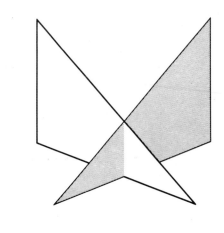

Congruence of Triangles

A VERY LARGE AND IMPORTANT UNIT OF work in geometry is concerned with the relationships that exist among triangles. Although the word "triangle" has been part of your vocabulary for some years, it should be quite apparent to you by now that launching into a discussion of this figure before clearly defining it would be foolhardy. What may seem rather odd, however, is the fact that to define this term we examine not the triangle but the much more complex figure called the *polygon*. We do this, surprisingly, not to create greater difficulty for you in learning this subject but rather to establish a general class of figures. Not only will the triangle be classified as a polygon but many other geometric figures will be so grouped too.

We would like the definition of a polygon to be so designed that Figure 5-1 will be a member of this set, while Figures 5-2, 5-3, and 5-4 will be

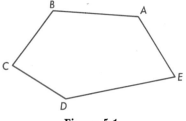

Figure 5-1.

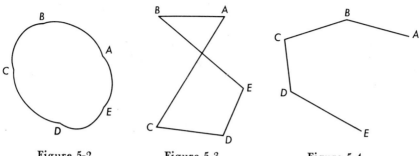

Figure 5-2.   Figure 5-3.   Figure 5-4.

excluded from the set. Notice that Figure 5-1 consists of line segments, while Figure 5-2 does not. Hence, if we insisted that the polygon consist of line segments, Figure 5-2 would be eliminated. But this still leaves us with Figures 5-3 and 5-4, since both of these consist of line segments. Note, though, that in Figure 5-3 two of the line segments ($\overline{AC}$ and $\overline{BE}$) have a point in common other than one of the points A, B, C, D, or E. Perhaps this feature will help us to eliminate Figure 5-3. Finally, the apparent difference between Figures 5-4 and 5-1 lies in the fact that the latter is "closed," while the former is "open."

These properties are now combined into the formal definition of a polygon.

DEFINITION 23: A polygon is the union of the set of points

$$P_1\dagger, P_2, P_3, \ldots, P_{n-1}, P_n$$

with the line segments

$$\overline{P_1P_2}, \overline{P_2P_3}, \ldots, \overline{P_{n-1}P_n}, \overline{P_nP_1}$$

such that if any two of these line segments intersect, their intersection will be one of the points

$$P_1, P_2, P_3, \ldots, P_{n-1}, P_n$$

and no other point.

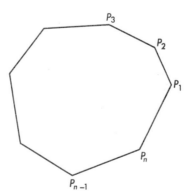

Figure 5-5.

† This is read as "P one" or "P sub-one."

Now let us examine this definition to see how Figures 5-2, 5-3, and 5-4 were eliminated.

(1) Figure 5-2 is eliminated by the fact that a polygon consists of the union of a set of points and the *line segments* joining those points.

(2) Figure 5-3 is eliminated by the fact that the line segments have no point of intersection other than the points P_1, P_2, . . . , P_n.

(3) Figure 5-4 is eliminated by the fact that a line segment must be drawn between the last point P_n and the first point P_1, thus "closing" the figure.

The set of points P_1, P_2, P_3, . . . , P_{n-1}, P_n are called the *vertices of the polygon*, while the line segments $\overline{P_1P_2}$, $\overline{P_2P_3}$, . . . , $\overline{P_{n-1}P_n}$, $\overline{P_nP_1}$ are the *sides of the polygon*. And, lastly, the angles $\angle P_1$, $\angle P_2$, . . . , $\angle P_{n-1}$, $\angle P_n$ are the *angles of the polygon*.

A polygon is named by simply referring to the letters at its vertices in either a clockwise ($\frown$) or counterclockwise order ($\frown$). Several ways of naming the polygon below are polygon *ABCDE*, or polygon *AEDCB*, or polygon *CDEAB*. Can you name this polygon in at least three other ways?

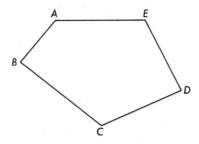

Figure 5-6.

■ Correspondence

In Chapter 2 we discussed a one-to-one correspondence when examining the points on the number line and the real numbers. At this time we would like to examine the notion of correspondence a bit more intensively. Consider the two sets of elements

{David, Harry, James}   and   {Doris, Harriet, Jane}

The boys in the first set can be paired, or matched, with the girls in the second set as follows:

David with Doris
Harry with Harriet
James with Jane

When each element of one set is matched with one and only one element of a second set, we say that a *one-to-one correspondence* exists between the elements of these two sets. And a matching such as the one above would be read as

David is matched with Doris   or   David corresponds to Doris
Harry is matched with Harriet   or   Harry corresponds to Harriet
James is matched with Jane   or   James corresponds to Jane

By using symbols this is simplified to

David ↔ Doris
Harry ↔ Harriet
James ↔ Jane

The doubleheaded arrow, however, implies two things. It is not only true that "David is matched with Doris," but also that "Doris is matched with David." That is, the matching holds in both directions.

Rather than express the matching with the three separate statements

David ↔ Doris
Harry ↔ Harriet
James ↔ Jane

it is much preferred to write this in the single form of

David   Harry   James ↔ Doris   Harriet   Jane

This will be read as either

(1) David   Harry   James   corresponds to   Doris   Harriet   Jane
or
(2) The correspondence of David   Harry   James   and   Doris   Harriet   Jane

The order in which the elements appear in a correspondence is very important, for there exists a number of correspondences, or matchings, between the elements of two sets. Thus, a correspondence of the form,

$$David \quad Harry \quad James ↔ Harriet \quad Doris \quad Jane \qquad (1)$$

is vastly different than

$$David \quad Harry \quad James ↔ Doris \quad Harriet \quad Jane \qquad (2)$$

While the first implies a matching of

$$David \ with \ Harriet \quad Harry \ with \ Doris \quad James \ with \ Jane \qquad (1)$$

the matching of the second is

$$David \ with \ Doris \quad Harry \ with \ Harriet \quad James \ with \ Jane \qquad (2)$$

Any three couples will tell you that whereby the first matching may be the ingredients for a very pleasant evening, the second may invite disaster!

EXERCISES

1. Express the correspondence

$$\text{Joe} \leftrightarrow \text{Mary} \quad \text{Fred} \leftrightarrow \text{Ann} \quad \text{Bill} \leftrightarrow \text{Carol}$$

by a single double arrow.

2. List the matchings that exist in the correspondence $a\, b \leftrightarrow x\, y$.

3. For the two sets of elements $\{a, b, c\}$ and $\{1, 2, 3\}$, there are exactly six correspondences. Two of these are $a\, b\, c \leftrightarrow 1\ 2\ 3$ and $a\, b\, c \leftrightarrow 2\ 1\ 3$. Name the remaining four.

4. "A one-to-one correspondence exists between the students in your geometry class and the seats in your geometry classroom." Interpret this statement. (Exclude the seats that are vacant.)

5. Using the replacements below for the equality $x + y = 5$, list the one-to-one correspondence that exists between the replacements of x and y such that each pair of values in this correspondence will make this equation true.

$$x \text{ replacements: } \{0, 1, 2, 3, 4, 5\}$$
$$y \text{ replacements: } \{0, 1, 2, 3, 4, 5\}$$

6. The 2, 3, and 4 of Clubs are removed from a deck of cards. If these three cards are shuffled thoroughly and then placed face up one at a time on a table, there is only one chance in six that these cards will appear in the order 2—3—4. By using correspondences can you explain why this is so?

■ Correspondence Related to Polygons

Should two polygons have the same number of vertices, then it is possible to draw up one-to-one correspondences between these

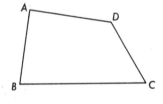 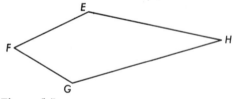

Figure 5-7.

vertices. Thus, for the two polygons in Figure 5-7 we might investigate correspondences as

(1) $ABCD \leftrightarrow EFGH$ or   (2) $ABCD \leftrightarrow HEFG$

or any one of a number of others. It is only in terms of a correspondence that such words as *corresponding sides* and *corresponding angles* can take on meaning. To illustrate, a pair of corresponding angles of two polygons will be two angles whose vertices are a pair of corresponding elements. Thus, in correspondence (1)

$$A \leftrightarrow E, \quad B \leftrightarrow F, \quad C \leftrightarrow G, \quad D \leftrightarrow H$$

$\angle A$ and $\angle E$ are considered to be corresponding angles and the same can be said of $\angle B$ and $\angle F$, $\angle C$ and $\angle G$, and $\angle D$ and $\angle H$. For correspondence (2), however, since

$$A \leftrightarrow H, \quad B \leftrightarrow E, \quad C \leftrightarrow F, \quad D \leftrightarrow G$$

then $\angle A$ will correspond to $\angle H$, $\angle B$ to $\angle E$, $\angle C$ to $\angle F$, and $\angle D$ to $\angle G$.

In the same way, a pair of corresponding sides are two sides whose end points are pairs of corresponding elements in a correspondence between the vertices of two polygons. Before retreating in despair, let us examine the meaning of this sentence in the light of correspondence (1) in the preceding paragraph. Since

$$A \leftrightarrow E \quad \text{and} \quad B \leftrightarrow F$$

then

> side AB would correspond to side EF

This can be pictured as

$$ABCD \leftrightarrow EFGH$$

Similarly,

$$A \leftrightarrow E \quad \text{and} \quad D \leftrightarrow H$$

therefore

> side AD would correspond to side EH

We can illustrate this as

$$ABCD \leftrightarrow EFGH$$

Two pairs of corresponding sides have been named in correspondence (1). Can you name the remaining two pairs of corresponding sides? What are the four pairs of corresponding sides in correspondence (2)?

DEFINITION 24: Corresponding angles of two polygons are two angles whose vertices are a pair of corresponding elements in a correspondence between the vertices of two polygons.

DEFINITION 25: Corresponding sides of two polygons are two sides whose endpoints are a pair of corresponding elements in a correspondence between the vertices of two polygons.

Before leaving this topic, it is important to clarify two more points. The first of these is concerned with the *equivalence of two correspondences*. The correspondence

$$ABCD \leftrightarrow EFGH$$

is said to be equivalent to the correspondence

$$CDAB \leftrightarrow GHEF$$

for in both

$$A \leftrightarrow E, \quad B \leftrightarrow F, \quad C \leftrightarrow G, \quad D \leftrightarrow H$$

Thus, there are a great many equivalent correspondences between the elements in two sets. *Correspondences that are equivalent are those that preserve the same one-to-one correspondence between the elements.* Can you explain why the first three correspondences below are equivalent, while the fourth is not equivalent to any one of the first three?

$$ABCD \leftrightarrow EFGH \qquad ACDB \leftrightarrow EGHF \qquad BCDA \leftrightarrow FGHE$$
$$ABDC \leftrightarrow HGFE$$

The other point to be raised is the fact that we can not select at random two pairs of vertices in a correspondence and say that they will be the end points of a pair of corresponding sides. To illustrate, again refer to the diagram on page 114 and the correspondence

$$ABCD \leftrightarrow EFGH$$

Although $A \leftrightarrow E$ and $C \leftrightarrow G$, the "side" AC does *not* correspond to the "side" EG, for neither is a side of the polygons!

EXERCISES

1. List the six different correspondences that exist between the vertices of the polygons below.

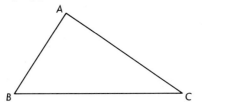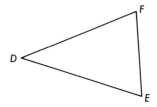

2. In the correspondence $RST \leftrightarrow YXZ$ for the two polygons below, name
   (a) The three pairs of corresponding angles.
   (b) The three pairs of corresponding sides.

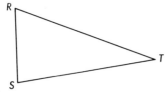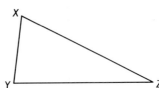

3. If in the diagram in Problem 2 the correspondence had been $RST \leftrightarrow YZX$, then
   (a) What are the three pairs of corresponding angles?
   (b) What are the three pairs of corresponding sides?

(c) Are there any corresponding sides or corresponding angles in this problem and in Problem 2 that did not change?

4. If $\angle A \cong \angle B$, $\angle C \cong \angle F$, and $\angle E \cong \angle D$, then write a correspondence between the polygons ACE and BDF so that the corresponding angles will be congruent.

5. If $\overline{RS} \cong \overline{WY}$, $\overline{ST} \cong \overline{YX}$, and $\overline{TR} \cong \overline{XW}$, then write a correspondence between polygons RST and XYW so that the corresponding sides would be congruent.

   (a) Draw a diagram for the polygons RST and XYW where the corresponding sides are congruent. Do the corresponding angles appear to be congruent also?

   (b) Draw a diagram for the polygons ACE and BDF of Problem 4 where the corresponding angles are congruent. Do the corresponding sides appear to be congruent also? If the corresponding angles are congruent, can the polygons be so drawn that the corresponding sides are not congruent?

6. For the polygons below, write a correspondence so that the corresponding angles will be congruent as marked in the diagram.

   (a) Are the corresponding sides in this correspondence also congruent?

   (b) If the corresponding angles in a correspondence between two polygons are congruent, then are the corresponding sides also congruent?

 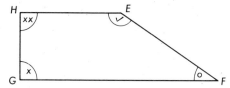

7. For the polygons below, write a correspondence so that the corresponding sides will be congruent as marked in the diagram.

   (a) Are the corresponding angles in this correspondence also congruent?

   (b) If the corresponding sides in a correspondence between two polygons are congruent, then are the corresponding angles also congruent?

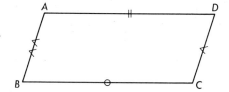 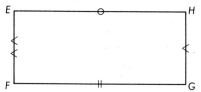

8. (a) In terms of the markings of the two polygons on page 118, write two correspondences which are not equivalent but in which the corresponding angles will be congruent.

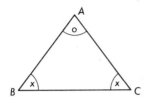
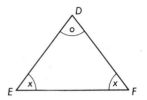

(b) In terms of the markings of the two polygons below, write two correspondences which are not equivalent but in which the corresponding sides will be congruent.

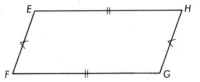

■ Congruent Polygons

One of the principal topics with which the study of geometry is concerned is the discovery of those conditions that must exist before two polygons can be placed "on top of one another and made to fit exactly." Polygons that do "fit exactly," or *coincide*, are called *congruent polygons*. Yet to use this as the definition of congruent polygons would severely handicap us, for it is difficult to prove that polygons "fit exactly." In order to develop a more usable definition of congruent polygons, it is necessary to fall back upon the concept of correspondence.

DEFINITION 26: Congruent polygons are two polygons in which there exists a one-to-one correspondence between the vertices such that

        (1) All the corresponding sides are congruent.
        (2) All the corresponding angles are congruent.

From a simple point of view this seems to say much the same as the earlier statement that congruent polygons are polygons that can be made to fit exactly when placed on top of one another. For, if they did "fit exactly," then their corresponding sides and corresponding angles would have to be congruent. In our formal definition, however, we have no need to concern ourselves with such vague terms as "fit exactly," "no overlapping," or "placed on top of one another." Furthermore, complicated as this definition may seem, it will make the development of new work far simpler than had we fallen back upon congruent polygons as meaning "to fit exactly."

For the polygons in Figure 5-8, as we know, there are many correspondences that exist between the vertices. Not all of these will lead to the

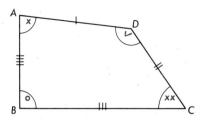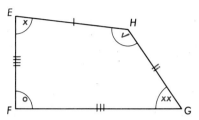

Figure 5-8.

information that the polygons are congruent. Several of these correspondences are

$$ABCD \leftrightarrow EHGF \text{ and its equivalent forms}$$

or

$$ABCD \leftrightarrow GFEH \text{ and its equivalent forms}$$

If, however, there is at least one correspondence in which all the corresponding sides are congruent and all the corresponding angles are congruent, then by the reverse of the definition of congruent polygons the polygons will be congruent. In this case, that correspondence is

$$ABCD \leftrightarrow EFGH$$

for from the markings in the diagram the corresponding sides and the corresponding angles of this correspondence are congruent.

Quite apparently, there will be many polygons for which there will exist no correspondence such that the corresponding sides and corresponding angles will be congruent. These polygons will not be congruent. This is the case with the two polygons in Figure 5-9.

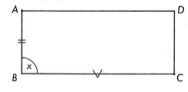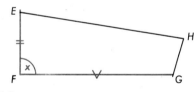

Figure 5-9.

Although there are *some* corresponding sides and *some* corresponding angles that are congruent in the correspondence

$$ABCD \leftrightarrow EFGH$$

not *all* are congruent. In fact, no correspondence exists between these two polygons in which all the corresponding parts, sides and angles, are congruent. Hence, these polygons can not be shown to be congruent.

Of the many types of polygons that exist, the most important in geometry is the one having the fewest number of sides. As you are probably aware, this polygon is the *triangle*. How would you classify a triangle? What is the fewest number of sides that a polygon may have? Why? How would you distinguish the triangle from all the other polygons?

DEFINITION 27: A triangle is a polygon that has three sides.

To prove triangles congruent by resorting to the reverse of the definition of congruent polygons would necessitate proving three pairs of corresponding sides congruent and three pairs of corresponding angles congruent. This, apparently, would require a great deal of work. Hence, the remainder of this chapter will be devoted to ways of proving triangles to be congruent without the need of showing that *all* the corresponding parts are congruent. In addition, we will also learn what conclusions will follow once the triangles are congruent.

■ Postulates for Proving Triangles Congruent

So that you might have some justification for the reasonableness of the next postulate, you will need a ruler and protractor. On a piece of paper draw a triangle similar to the one in Figure 5-10. We call this $\triangle ABC$; the symbol $\triangle$ represents the word *triangle*.

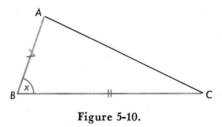

Figure 5-10.

On a second piece of paper draw a line segment whose measure is the same as that of $\overline{BC}$. Call this $\overline{DE}$.

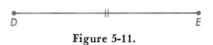

Figure 5-11.

Using your protractor, find the measure of $\angle B$ and mark off an angle at point D whose measure is the same as that of $\angle B$.

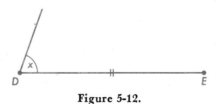

Figure 5-12.

With your ruler find the measure of $\overline{BA}$. Then by using D as one endpoint of a line segment, mark off $\overline{DF}$ so that the measure of $\overline{DF}$ will be the same as that of $\overline{BA}$.

Figure 5-13.

Now complete $\triangle FDE$ by drawing the line segment joining the points F and E.

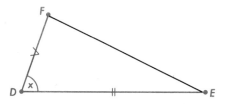

Figure 5-14.

In the correspondence $ABC \leftrightarrow FDE$ we know by our measurements that $\overline{BC} \cong \overline{DE}$, $\angle B \cong \angle D$, and $\overline{AB} \cong \overline{FD}$. From the appearance of the two triangles, what other corresponding parts do you believe will be congruent? Using your ruler, find the measure of $\overline{FE}$ and compare it with that of $\overline{AC}$. With your protractor find the measure of $\angle E$ and compare it with that of $\angle C$. Finally, find the measure of $\angle F$ and compare it with that of $\angle A$. If your drawing was accurate, you should find that $\overline{AC} \cong \overline{FE}$, $\angle A \cong \angle F$, and $\angle C \cong \angle E$. Although originally we knew of only three pairs of corresponding parts that were congruent, now it appears that all six pairs of corresponding parts are congruent. What conclusion can be drawn if the corresponding sides and the corresponding angles are respectively congruent? Why?

You will notice that the two angles that were congruent were not just *any* angles in the triangles but the angles formed between the corresponding sides whose measures were also being made congruent. Thus, $\angle B$ was formed by the sides AB and BC, while $\angle D$ was formed by the sides FD and DE. It was through our efforts that the measures of $\overline{AB}$ and $\overline{FD}$ were made equal, as were the measures of $\overline{BC}$ and $\overline{DE}$. An angle formed in this manner is referred to as an *included angle*.

In Figure 5-15 $\angle S$ is the included angle between the sides ST and SR; $\angle T$ is the included angle between the sides TS and TR. With reference to what sides would $\angle R$ be considered the included angle?

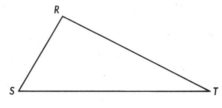

Figure 5-15.

With these terms at our disposal, we can now say

POSTULATE 13: Two triangles are congruent if there exists a correspondence between the vertices in which two sides and the included angle of one triangle are congruent respectively to those corresponding parts in the second triangle. (The symbols used to express this entire statement are S.A.S.)

What is the distinction between a theorem and a postulate? In view of the discussion presented on the preceding few pages, should we not have called Postulate 13 a theorem rather than a postulate?

Illustration:

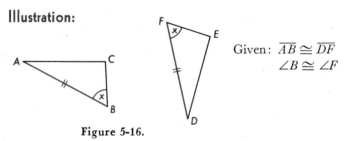

Given: $\overline{AB} \cong \overline{DF}$
$\quad\quad\quad \angle B \cong \angle F$

Figure 5-16.

In order to prove $\triangle ABC \cong \triangle DFE$† by the use of Postulate 13, what remaining parts will have to be congruent? If we knew that $\overline{BC}$ was congruent to $\overline{FE}$, why could we conclude that $\triangle ABC \cong \triangle DFE$? Rather than $\overline{BC} \cong \overline{FE}$, suppose we knew that $\overline{AC} \cong \overline{DE}$, could we still conclude that $\triangle ABC$ was congruent to $\triangle DFE$?

Assuming that the Given Data included the fact that $\overline{BC} \cong \overline{FE}$, we would know by Postulate 13 that $\triangle ABC \cong \triangle DFE$. Quite often the letters ABC and DEF are arranged in any order whatsoever. Although many mathematicians see nothing wrong in this, it would be best if we were a bit more careful. Specifically, to say that $\triangle BCA \cong \triangle DFE$ will imply the congruency correspondence of $BCA \leftrightarrow DFE$. In turn, the definition of congruent polygons enables us to say that $\overline{AB} \cong \overline{ED}$ and $\angle B \cong \angle D$. This is

† Read this as: triangle ABC congruent to triangle DFE.

so by virtue of the fact that corresponding sides and corresponding angles of congruent triangles are congruent. On the other hand, the Given Data states that $\overline{AB}$ is congruent to $\overline{DF}$, *not* to $\overline{ED}$, and that $\angle B$ is congruent to $\angle F$, *not* to $\angle D$! Hence, writing the letters carelessly in the congruence may set up a correspondence in which the corresponding parts are not congruent!

There is yet another postulate through which triangles can be proved to be congruent. Showing that this postulate is plausible can be done in the same manner as we had for Postulate 13. This will be left as an exercise for you to do.

POSTULATE 14: Two triangles are congruent if there exists a correspondence between the vertices in which two angles and the included side of one triangle are congruent respectively to those corresponding parts in the second triangle. (The symbols used to express this entire statement are *A.S.A.*)

A side is said to be included between two angles if the vertices of the angles form the endpoints of the side.

Illustration:

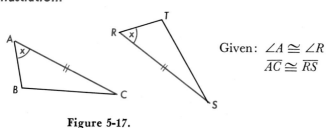

Given: $\angle A \cong \angle R$
$\overline{AC} \cong \overline{RS}$

Figure 5-17.

If we were to apply Postulate 14, what remaining parts would have to be congruent before we might conclude that $\triangle ACB \cong \triangle RST$? If $\angle C \cong \angle S$, would $\triangle ACB \cong \triangle RST$? Why or why not? If Postulate 13 were to be applied, what remaining parts would have to be shown congruent in order that $\triangle ACB$ be congruent to $\triangle RST$? Arrange the letters in the correspondence $ACB \leftrightarrow RST$ so that they will represent a correspondence equivalent to this one. Will the parts in the Given Data be corresponding parts in your correspondence? Write a correspondence in which the parts in the Given Data will not be corresponding parts.

EXERCISES

In each of the problems below, name the parts that will still have to be shown to be congruent before the triangles will be congruent by the *S.A.S.* postulate. The markings on the triangles indicate those parts that are congruent on the basis of the Given Data.

1. Concl.: $\triangle ABC \cong \triangle DFE$

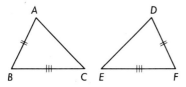

Concl.: $\triangle RST \cong \triangle YXW$ **2.**

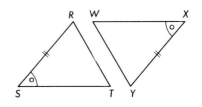

3. Concl.: $\triangle ABD \cong \triangle ACD$

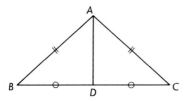

Concl.: $\triangle ADB \cong \triangle CBD$ **4.**

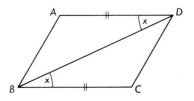

5. Concl.: $\triangle ACD \cong \triangle BCD$

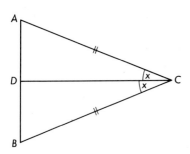

Concl.: $\triangle ABC \cong \triangle AED$ **6.**

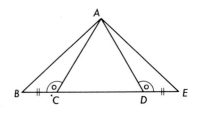

7. Concl.: $\triangle AEB \cong \triangle DEC$

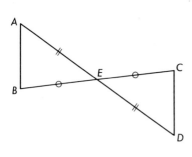

Concl.: $\triangle AEC \cong \triangle ABD$ **8.**

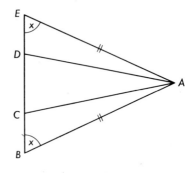

9. Concl.: $\triangle AEB \cong \angle CFD$

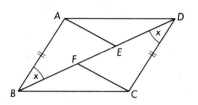

Concl.: $\triangle EAC \cong \triangle EDB$ **10.**

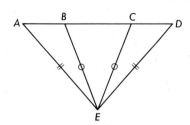

B

In each of the problems below, name the parts that will have to be congruent before the triangles can be shown to be congruent by the *A.S.A.* postulate. The markings on the triangles indicate those parts that are congruent on the basis of the Given Data.

1. Concl.: $\triangle ABC \cong \triangle FED$

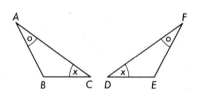

Concl.: $\triangle ABF \cong \triangle CDE$ **2.**

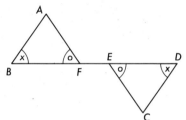

3. Concl.: $\triangle CDB \cong \triangle AEB$

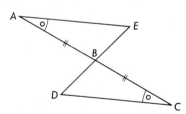

Concl.: $\triangle ABD \cong \triangle DCA$ **4.**

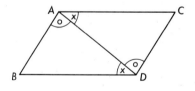

5. Concl.: $\triangle ADB \cong \triangle CDB$

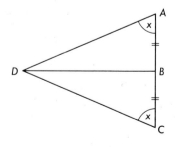

Concl.: $\triangle ACB \cong \triangle FDE$ **6.**

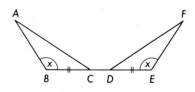

7. Concl.: $\triangle FAC \cong \triangle EDB$

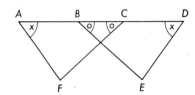

Concl.: $\triangle AEC \cong \triangle DEB$ **8.**

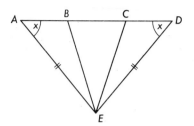

9. Concl.: $\triangle ADF \cong \triangle CBE$

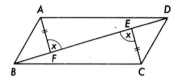

Concl.: $\triangle AGF \cong \triangle CGE$ **10.**

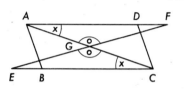

11. Concl.: $\triangle ABC \cong \triangle DCB$

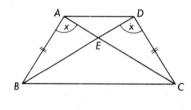

Given: $\overline{AB} \cong \overline{AE}$ **12.**
$\qquad \angle CEA \cong \angle DBA$
$\qquad ? \cong ?$
Concl.: $\triangle ADB \cong \triangle ACE$

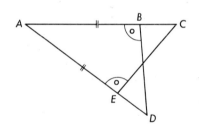

■ ## Applications of the Postulates on Congruence to Formal Proofs

We are now in a position where it is possible for us to prove that triangles are congruent by using a formal proof. As before, this will imply that each time we make a statement, we will have to justify its use by virtue of the fact that

(1) It is a piece of information stated in the Given Data.
(2) It is the property of a word as stated in the definition of that word.
(3) It is the property implied by the reverse of the definition of a word.
(4) It follows from a postulate we have made.
(5) It follows from a theorem that we have already proved.

Illustration 1

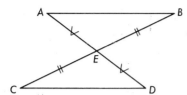

Given: $\overline{AD}$ and $\overline{BC}$ bisect each other at E.

Concl.: $\triangle AEB \cong \triangle DEC$

Figure 5-18.

ANALYSIS: The very first thing to do is to separate the Given Data into two distinct pieces of information. That is, $\overleftrightarrow{AD}$ bisects $\overline{BC}$ and $\overleftrightarrow{BC}$ bisects $\overline{AD}$. On the basis of the first piece of information, we can conclude that $\overline{CE} \cong \overline{EB}$, while the second piece tells us that $\overline{DE} \cong \overline{EA}$. This information is marked in the diagram as was done above. We note that there is still one piece of information lacking before it is possible to conclude that the triangles are congruent. From the fact that two sides in one triangle are congruent respectively to two corresponding sides in the other triangle, the apparent postulate to try to apply to show that the triangles are congruent is the *S.A.S.* postulate. Thus, the only part lacking is the included angle in each triangle.

The diagram can *not* be used to conclude that certain sides or angles may be equal because "they appear so in the diagram"! It is helpful, however, in calling our attention to the fact that

(1) There are vertical angles in the figure.
(2) The reflexive property of equality can be applied.
(3) There are pairs of supplementary angles in the figure.

In this problem we discover by examining the diagram that the angles *AEB* and *DEC* are vertical angles. Hence, from the theorem on vertical angles we can conclude that they are congruent.

PROOF STATEMENTS	REASONS
1. $\overleftrightarrow{AD}$ bisects $\overline{BC}$.	1. Given
2. E is the midpoint of $\overline{BC}$.	2. Def. of the bisector of a line segment
3. $\overline{CE} \cong \overline{EB}$ (*s*)	3. Def. of the midpoint of a line segment
4. $\overleftrightarrow{BC}$ bisects $\overline{AD}$.	4. Given
5. E is the midpoint of $\overline{AD}$.	5. Same as 2
6. $\overline{DE} \cong \overline{EA}$ (*s*)	6. Same as 3
7. $\angle AEB \cong \angle DEC$ (*a*)	7. If two angles are vertical angles, then they are congruent. (Theorem)
8. $\triangle AEB \cong \triangle DEC$	8. *S.A.S.* (Postulate)

Illustration 2

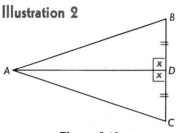

Given: $\overleftrightarrow{AD}$ is the $\perp$ bisector of $\overline{BC}$

Concl.: $\triangle ADC \cong \triangle ADB$

Figure 5-19.

ANALYSIS: As in the previous illustration, rewrite the Given Data as two pieces of information. Since the lines are perpendicular, there will be right angles at point D, and from this fact we can conclude that the angles will be congruent. Since $\overleftrightarrow{AD}$ bisects $\overline{BC}$, a side of one triangle will be congruent to a side of the other. We have exhausted the Given Data but do not yet have enough information to say that the triangles are congruent. Again we resort to an examination of the diagram. To prove the triangles congruent by the *A.S.A.* assumption would require showing that $\angle B \cong \angle C$. There is no means of doing this. To prove the triangles congruent by the *S.A.S.* assumption would require showing that $\overline{AD} \cong \overline{AD}$. This we know by the reflexive property of congruency! Hence, the conclusion follows.

PROOF	STATEMENTS	REASONS
1. $\overleftrightarrow{AD} \perp \overleftrightarrow{BC}$		1. Given
2. $\angle ADB$ and $\angle ADC$ are right angles.		2. Def. of perpendicular lines
3. $\angle ADB \cong \angle ADC$ (a)		3. If two angles are right angles, then they are congruent. (Theorem)
4. $\overleftrightarrow{AD}$ bisects $\overline{BC}$.		4. Given
5. D is the midpoint of $\overline{BC}$.		5. Def. of the bisector of a line segment
6. $\overline{BD} \cong \overline{DC}$ (s)		6. Def. of the midpoint of a line segment
7. $\overline{AD} \cong \overline{AD}$ (s)		7. Reflexive property of congruence
8. $\triangle ADC \cong \triangle ADB$		8. *S.A.S.* (Postulate)

Just a word of suggestion before you tackle the proofs of the problems in the exercises that follow. Each piece of Given Data is usually designed to lead you to a pair of congruent sides or a pair of congruent angles. In most cases, therefore, it is best not to leave any piece of information until you have shown a pair of sides congruent or a pair of angles congruent. To keep track of what you have done and where you are going, mark your diagram each time you prove a pair of sides congruent or a pair of angles congruent. Do the same for the statements in the proof by using a small (s) or a small (a).

EXERCISES†

1. Given: $\overline{AB} \cong \overline{AD}$
$\angle 1 \cong \angle 2$
Concl.: $\triangle ABC \cong \triangle ADC$

Given: $\overline{AD} \cong \overline{BC}$ **2.**
$\angle 1 \cong \angle 2$
Concl.: $\triangle ADB \cong \triangle CBD$

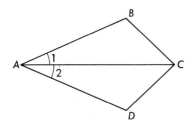

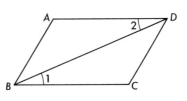

3. Given: $\overrightarrow{BD}$ is the bisector of $\angle ABC$.
$\overrightarrow{DB}$ is the bisector of $\angle ADC$.
Concl.: $\triangle ABD \cong \triangle CBD$

Given: $\overrightarrow{AC}$ bisects $\angle BAD$.   **4.**
$\overleftrightarrow{AC} \perp \overleftrightarrow{BD}$
Concl.: $\triangle ABC \cong \triangle ADC$

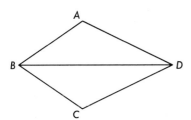

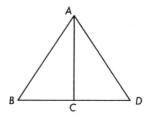

5. Given: $\overline{AC}$ and $\overline{BD}$ bisect each other at E.
Concl.: $\triangle AEB \cong \triangle CED$

Given: $\angle 1 \cong \angle 2$ **6.**
$\overline{AB} \cong \overline{FE}$
$\overline{BD} \cong \overline{CE}$
Concl.: $\triangle ABC \cong \triangle FED$

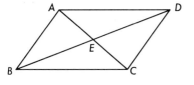

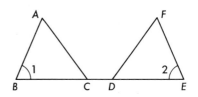

† Do not include an Analysis in the write-up of your proof.

7. Given: $\overline{AB} \cong \overline{DE}$
$\angle B \cong \angle E$
$\overline{BF} \cong \overline{CE}$
Concl.: $\triangle ABC \cong \triangle DEF$

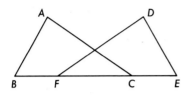

Given: C is the midpoint   **8.**
of $\overline{BD}$.
$\angle 3 \cong \angle 4$
$\angle 1 \cong \angle 2$
Concl.: $\triangle ABC \cong \triangle EDC$

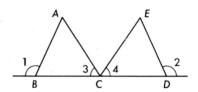

9. Given: M is the midpoint
of $\overline{BC}$.
$\angle 1 \cong \angle 2$
Concl.: $\triangle ABM \cong \triangle DCM$

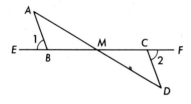

Given: $\overline{AB} \cong \overline{AE}$ **10.**
$\overline{BD} \cong \overline{EC}$
$\angle 1 \cong \angle 2$
Concl.: $\triangle ABC \cong \triangle AED$

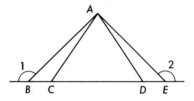

11. Given: $\overrightarrow{CA}$ bisects $\angle DCE$.
$\overrightarrow{BA}$ bisects $\angle DBE$.
Concl.: $\triangle DBC \cong \triangle EBC$

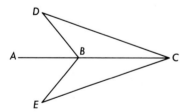

Given: $\overline{AE} \cong \overline{DE}$ **12.**
E is the midpoint
of $\overline{BC}$.
$\angle AEC \cong \angle DEB$
Concl.: $\triangle ABE \cong DCE$

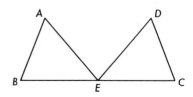

13. Given: $\overline{AB} \cong \overline{DC}$

        M is the midpoint

        of $\overline{BC}$.

        $\overleftrightarrow{AB} \perp \overleftrightarrow{BC}$

        $\overleftrightarrow{DC} \perp \overleftrightarrow{BC}$

Concl.: $\triangle ABM \cong DCM$

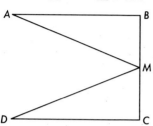

Given: $\overline{BF} \cong \overline{CE}$ **14.**

        $\angle 1 \cong \angle 2$

        $\overleftrightarrow{AB} \perp \overleftrightarrow{BE}$

        $\overleftrightarrow{DE} \perp \overleftrightarrow{BE}$

Concl.: $\triangle ABC \cong \triangle DEF$

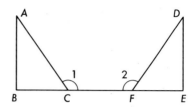

15. Given: $\overline{BE} \cong \overline{BC}$

        $\overleftrightarrow{AB} \perp \overleftrightarrow{CD}$

        $\angle 1 \cong \angle 2$

Concl.: $\triangle ABC \cong \triangle DBE$

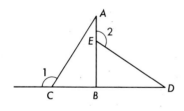

Given: $\angle 1 \cong \angle 2$ **16.**

        $\angle 3 \cong \angle 4$

        $\overrightarrow{AC}$ bisects $\angle BAD$.

        $\overline{AB} \cong \overline{AD}$

Concl.: $\triangle ABC \cong \triangle ADC$

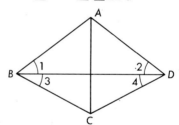

■ Proving Line Segments or Angles Congruent Through Congruent Triangles

      In view of the definition of congruent triangles, what conclusions can be drawn if $\triangle ABC \cong \triangle DEF$? Thus, it appears that if it were necessary to prove that $\angle C \cong \angle F$, one method of attack might be to find

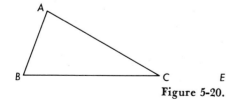
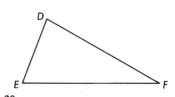

Figure 5-20.

a pair of triangles that contain these angles and prove them to be congruent. It would follow from the definition of congruent triangles that the corresponding angles were congruent.† Similarly, if we had to show that $\overline{AB} \cong \overline{DE}$, it would merely be a matter of proving $\triangle ABC \cong \triangle DEF$, and, again, from the second property of congruent polygons we would know that the corresponding sides were congruent.†

In the above diagram and in many of the problems we will encounter, it will be quite simple to select the triangles that are to be proved congruent. In other situations, however, the selection of triangles will not be quite so simple. To illustrate, examine Figure 5-21 and assume that it was

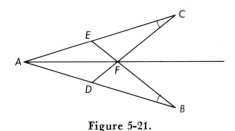

Figure 5-21.

necessary to prove $\angle B \cong \angle C$. Since there are many pairs of triangles containing $\angle B$ and $\angle C$, deciding which pair to prove congruent may be quite difficult. Name three pairs of triangles we might try to show congruent in order to prove that $\angle B \cong \angle C$.

Illustration:

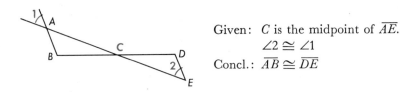

Given: C is the midpoint of $\overline{AE}$.
$\angle 2 \cong \angle 1$
Concl.: $\overline{AB} \cong \overline{DE}$

Figure 5-22.

ANALYSIS: In order to prove $\overline{AB} \cong \overline{DE}$, we will try first to prove that $\triangle ABC \cong \triangle EDC$. Once these triangles are congruent, it will follow from the definition of congruent polygons that $\overline{AB} \cong \overline{DE}$. C being the midpoint of $\overline{AE}$ will give us $\overline{AC} \cong \overline{CE}$. Angles ACB and ECD are vertical angles, hence they are congruent. Therefore, the problem simply reduces to showing that $\angle 2$ is congruent to $\angle BAC$. However, since both $\angle BAC$ and $\angle 2$ are congruent to $\angle 1$, then by the transitive property of congruence it will be possible to conclude that $\angle BAC \cong \angle 2$. Thus, the triangles are congruent by the $A.S.A.$ postulate.

† See page 118.

PROOF	STATEMENTS	REASONS
1. C is the midpoint of $\overline{AE}$.	1. Given
2. $\overline{AC} \cong \overline{CE}$ (s)	2. Def. of the midpoint of a line segment
3. $\angle 2 \cong \angle 1$	3. Given
4. $\angle BAC \cong \angle 1$	4. If two angles are vertical angles, then they are congruent. (Theorem)
5. $\angle 2 \cong \angle BAC$ (a)	5. Transitive property of congruence
6. $\angle ACB \cong \angle ECD$ (a)	6. Same as 4
7. $\triangle ABC \cong \triangle EDC$	7. A.S.A. (Postulate)
8. $\overline{AB} \cong \overline{DE}$	8. Def. of congruent polygons

EXERCISES†

1. Given: $\overleftrightarrow{CD}$ is the ⊥ bisector of $\overline{AB}$.

Concl.: $\overline{CA} \cong \overline{CB}$

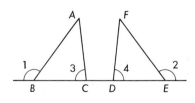

2. Given: $\overleftrightarrow{AB} \perp \overleftrightarrow{BD}$
$\overleftrightarrow{ED} \perp \overleftrightarrow{BD}$
C is the midpoint of $\overline{BD}$.
$\angle 1 \cong \angle 2$

Concl.: $\angle A \cong \angle E$

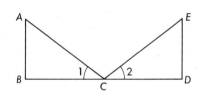

3. Given: $\angle 1 \cong \angle 2$
$\angle 3 \cong \angle 4$
$\overline{BD} \cong \overline{CE}$

Concl.: $\overline{AC} \cong \overline{FD}$

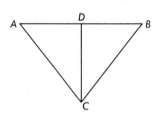

4. Given: $\angle 1 \cong \angle 2$
$\angle 3 \cong \angle 4$

Concl.: $\angle A \cong \angle C$

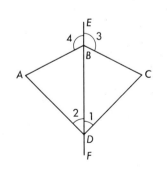

† Do not include an Analysis in the write-up of your proof.

5. Given: $\overline{AB} \cong \overline{EF}$
$\overline{AD} \cong \overline{CF}$
$\angle 1 \cong \angle 2$
Concl.: $\angle B \cong \angle E$

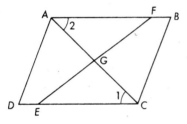

Given: $\angle 1 \cong \angle 2$
$\angle 3 \cong \angle 4$
Concl.: $\overline{AB} \cong \overline{CD}$ **6.**

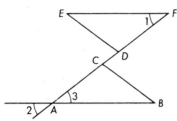

7. Given: $\angle 1 \cong \angle 2$
$\overleftrightarrow{EF}$ bisects $\overline{AC}$.
Concl.: $\overline{EG} \cong \overline{FG}$

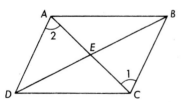

Given: $\overline{BE} \cong \overline{BF}$
$\overleftrightarrow{AB}$ is the $\perp$ bisector
of $\overline{CD}$.
$\angle 1 \cong \angle 2$
Concl.: $\overline{CE} \cong \overline{DF}$ **8.**

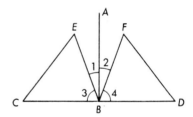

9. Given: $\overline{AC}$ and $\overline{BD}$ bisect
each other at E.
Concl.: $\angle 1 \cong \angle 2$

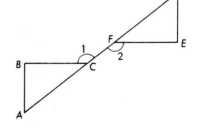

Given: $\angle 1 \cong \angle 2$
$\overline{BC} \cong \overline{EF}$
$\overleftrightarrow{AB} \perp \overleftrightarrow{BC}$
$\overleftrightarrow{DE} \perp \overleftrightarrow{FE}$
Concl.: $\angle A \cong \angle D$ **10.**

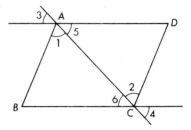

11. Given: $\angle 1 \cong \angle 2$
$\angle 3$ is comp. to $\angle 1$.
$\angle 4$ is comp. to $\angle 2$.
Concl.: $\angle A \cong \angle C$

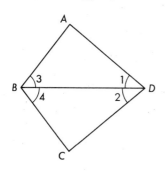

Given: $\overline{BD} \cong \overline{CE}$ **12.**
$\angle 1 \cong \angle 2$
$\angle B$ is comp. to $\angle 3$.
$\angle E$ is comp. to $\angle 4$.
Concl.: $\overline{AB} \cong \overline{EF}$

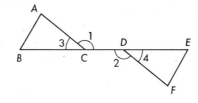

13. Given: $\overline{AC} \cong \overline{AD}$
$\overline{BD} \cong \overline{CE}$
$\angle 1 \cong \angle 2$
Concl.: $\angle 3 \cong \angle 4$

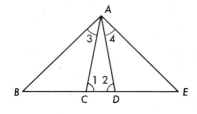

Given: F is the midpoint   **14.**
of $\overline{BC}$.
$\angle B \cong \angle C$
$\angle EFB \cong \angle DFC$
Concl.: $\overline{DF} \cong \overline{EF}$

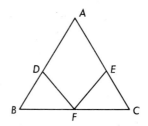

15. Given: $\angle B \cong \angle C$
E is the midpoint
of $\overline{AB}$.
G is the midpoint
of $\overline{DC}$.
$\overline{AB} \cong \overline{DC}$
$\angle 1 \cong \angle 2$
Concl.: $\overline{BF} \cong \overline{HC}$

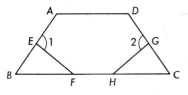

Given: $\overline{AB} \cong \overline{AD}$ **16.**
$\overline{CB} \cong \overline{CD}$
$\angle 1 \cong \angle 2$
$\angle 3 \cong \angle 4$
Concl.: $\angle 5 \cong \angle 6$

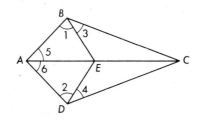

Further Conclusions That Can Be Drawn on the Basis of Congruent Triangles

Frequently it is necessary to prove that a ray is the bisector of an angle, or that a certain point is the midpoint of a line segment, or that a line is the bisector of a line segment. To illustrate, what will have to be true in Figure 5-23 before it can be concluded that $\overrightarrow{BA}$ bisects

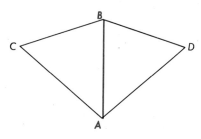

Figure 5-23.

∠CBD? What is one method of proving that ∠CBA ≅ ∠DBA? Hence, if △ABC ≅ △ABD, it will follow that ∠CBA ≅ ∠DBA. In view of this congruence and the reverse of the definition of the bisector of an angle, we can say that $\overrightarrow{BA}$ bisects ∠CBD.

Apparently, then, congruence of triangles can lead us to the congruence of certain line segments or angles, and this fact, in turn, will lead us to the conclusion we were hoping to draw.

Illustration:

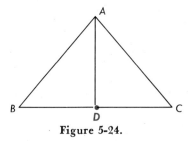

Figure 5-24.

Given: $\overrightarrow{AD}$ bisects ∠BAC.

$\overleftrightarrow{AD} \perp \overleftrightarrow{BC}$

Concl.: D is the midpoint of $\overline{BC}$.

ANALYSIS: In order to prove D to be the midpoint of $\overline{BC}$, it will be necessary to show that $\overline{BD} \cong \overline{DC}$. These line segments, however, will be congruent if △ABD ≅ △ACD. Hence, the problem reduces to one of showing that these triangles are congruent.

PROOF | STATEMENTS	REASONS
1. $\overrightarrow{AD}$ bisects $\angle BAC$.	1. Given
2. $\angle BAD \cong \angle CAD$ (a)	2. Def. of the bisector of an angle
3. $\overleftrightarrow{AD} \perp \overleftrightarrow{BC}$	3. Given
4. $\angle ADB$ and $\angle ADC$ are right angles.	4. Def. of perpendicular lines
5. $\angle ADB \cong \angle ADC$ (a)	5. If two angles are right angles, then they are congruent. (Theorem)
6. $\overline{AD} \cong \overline{AD}$ (s)	6. Reflexive property of congruence
7. $\triangle ABD \cong \triangle ACD$	7. A.S.A. (Postulate)
8. $\overline{BD} \cong \overline{DC}$	8. Def. of congruent polygons
9. D is the midpoint of $\overline{BC}$.	9. Reverse of def. of the midpoint of a line segment

EXERCISES

1. Given: $\overline{AB} \cong \overline{CB}$

$\overrightarrow{BD}$ bisects $\angle ABC$.

Concl.: $\overrightarrow{DB}$ bisects $\angle ADC$.

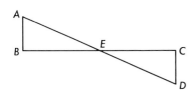

Given: $\overline{AB} \cong \overline{BC}$ **2.**

$\angle 1 \cong \angle 2$

Concl.: $\overrightarrow{DE}$ bisects $\angle ADC$.

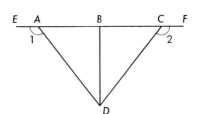

3. Given: $\overleftrightarrow{AD}$ bisects $\overline{BC}$.

$\overleftrightarrow{AB} \perp \overleftrightarrow{BC}$

$\overleftrightarrow{DC} \perp \overleftrightarrow{BC}$

Concl.: $\overleftrightarrow{BC}$ bisects $\overline{AD}$.

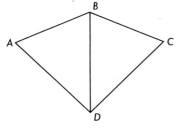

Given: B is the midpoint   **4.**
of $\overline{AC}$.

$\overleftrightarrow{BD} \perp \overleftrightarrow{EF}$

Concl.: $\angle 1 \cong \angle 2$

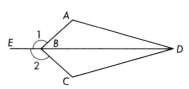

5. Given: $\angle B \cong \angle C$

$\overline{AE} \cong \overline{AD}$

$\overline{AB} \cong \overline{AC}$

$\overleftrightarrow{FE} \perp \overleftrightarrow{AC}$

$\overleftrightarrow{GD} \perp \overleftrightarrow{AB}$

Concl.: $\overline{BF} \cong \overline{GC}$

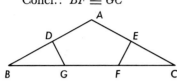

Given: $\overline{BE} \cong \overline{DE}$ **6.**

$\overleftrightarrow{CD} \perp \overleftrightarrow{AD}$

$\overleftrightarrow{AB} \perp \overleftrightarrow{BC}$

Concl.: $\angle 1 \cong \angle 2$

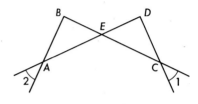

7. Given: $\overleftrightarrow{CD} \perp \overleftrightarrow{BF}$

$\angle 1 \cong \angle 2$

$\angle A \cong \angle E$

$\overline{AD} \cong \overline{ED}$

Concl.: D is the midpoint of $\overline{BF}$.

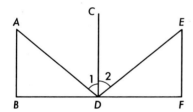

Given: $\overleftrightarrow{AB} \perp \overleftrightarrow{BC}$ and $\overleftrightarrow{AD}$ **8.***

$\overleftrightarrow{DC} \perp \overleftrightarrow{BC}$ and $\overleftrightarrow{AD}$

E is the midpoint of $\overline{BC}$.

$\angle DEB \cong \angle AEC$

Concl.: $\angle EAD \cong \angle EDA$

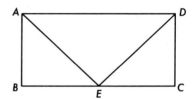

9. Given: $\overleftrightarrow{EC} \perp \overleftrightarrow{CD}$

$\overleftrightarrow{FD} \perp \overleftrightarrow{CD}$

$\overleftrightarrow{AB} \perp \overleftrightarrow{CD}$

$\overline{FD} \cong \overline{EC}$

B is the midpoint of $\overline{CD}$.

Concl.: $\overrightarrow{BA}$ bisects $\angle EBF$.

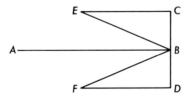

Given: $\overrightarrow{BD}$ bisects $\angle ABC$.   **10.***

$\overleftrightarrow{BD} \perp \overleftrightarrow{AC}$

$\overline{DA} \cong \overline{DB} \cong \overline{DC}$

Concl.: $\angle 1 \cong \angle 2$

(Hint: Prove $\triangle ADB \cong \triangle BDC$; then note the correspondence.)

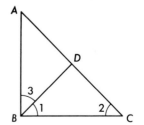

◼ Overlapping Triangles

Occasionally the difficulty of the proof is increased by the fact that the triangles to be proved congruent overlap one another. As a case in point, consider the problem below.

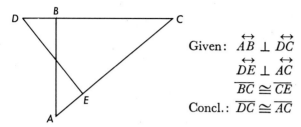

Given: $\overleftrightarrow{AB} \perp \overleftrightarrow{DC}$

$\overleftrightarrow{DE} \perp \overleftrightarrow{AC}$

$\overline{BC} \cong \overline{CE}$

Concl.: $\overline{DC} \cong \overline{AC}$

Figure 5-25.

The very first thing to consider is "What triangles contain the line segments DC and AC as sides?" It is these triangles that will have to be shown to be congruent. $\triangle DCE$ has the segment DC as one of its sides, while $\overline{AC}$ is a side of $\triangle ACB$. Should it be possible to prove these triangles congruent, then $\overline{DC}$ will be congruent to $\overline{AC}$.

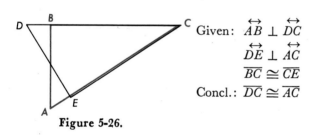

Given: $\overleftrightarrow{AB} \perp \overleftrightarrow{DC}$

$\overleftrightarrow{DE} \perp \overleftrightarrow{AC}$

$\overline{BC} \cong \overline{CE}$

Concl.: $\overline{DC} \cong \overline{AC}$

Figure 5-26.

PROOF STATEMENTS	REASONS
1. $\overleftrightarrow{AB} \perp \overleftrightarrow{DC}$	1. Given
2. $\angle ABC$ is a right angle.	2. Def. of perpendicular lines
3. $\overleftrightarrow{DE} \perp \overleftrightarrow{AC}$	3. Given
4. $\angle DEC$ is a right angle.	4. Same as 2
5. $\angle ABC \cong \angle DEC$ (a)	5. If two angles are right angles, then they are congruent. (Theorem)
6. $\overline{BC} \cong \overline{CE}$ (s)	6. Given
7. $\angle C \cong \angle C$	7. Reflexive property of congruence
8. $\triangle DCE \cong \triangle ACB$	8. A.S.A. (Postulate)
9. $\overline{DC} \cong \overline{AC}$	9. Def. of congruent polygons

With experience you will have little difficulty in keeping your attention on those triangles in which you are interested, although they may overlap. At present, however, it is advisable to use two differently colored lead pencils to distinguish one triangle from the other.

EXERCISES

1. Given: $\overline{DB} \cong \overline{DA}$
$\qquad \overline{DC} \cong \overline{DE}$
Concl.: $\angle B \cong \angle A$

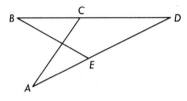

Given: $\overline{AC} \cong \overline{AE}$ **2.**
$\qquad \overline{AB} \cong \overline{AD}$
$\qquad \angle 1 \cong \angle 2$
Concl.: $\overline{BC} \cong \overline{DE}$

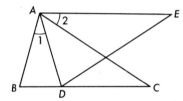

3. Given: $\overleftrightarrow{AB} \perp \overleftrightarrow{BC}$
$\qquad \overleftrightarrow{AD} \perp \overleftrightarrow{DE}$
$\qquad \angle 1 \cong \angle 2$
$\qquad \overline{AB} \cong \overline{AD}$
Concl.: $\angle C \cong \angle E$

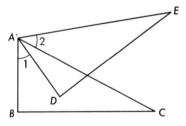

Given: $\overline{AB} \cong \overline{AC}$ **4.**
$\qquad$ E is the midpoint
$\qquad$ of $\overline{AC}$.
$\qquad$ D is the midpoint
$\qquad$ of $\overline{AB}$.
Concl.: $\angle 1 \cong \angle 2$

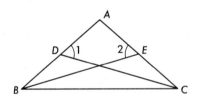

5. Given: $\overline{BE} \cong \overline{AD}$
$\qquad \angle 1 \cong \angle 2$
Concl.: $\overline{BD} \cong \overline{AE}$

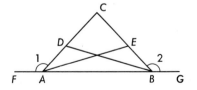

Given: $\angle 1 \cong \angle 2$ **6.**
$\qquad \overline{BC} \perp \overleftrightarrow{AB}$ and $\overleftrightarrow{CD}$
Concl.: $\overline{DB} \cong \overline{AC}$

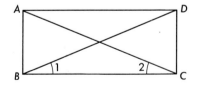

7. Given: $\overset{\leftrightarrow}{AB} \perp \overset{\leftrightarrow}{BC}$
$\overset{\leftrightarrow}{DC} \perp \overset{\leftrightarrow}{BC}$
$\angle 1 \cong \angle 2$
Concl.: $\overline{AB} \cong \overline{DC}$

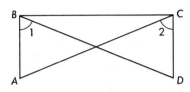

Given: $\angle 3 \cong \angle 4$ **8.**
$\angle 1 \cong \angle 2$
Concl.: $\angle 5 \cong \angle 6$

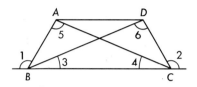

9. Given: $\angle 1 \cong \angle 2$
$\angle 3 \cong \angle 4$
Concl.: $\angle A \cong \angle B$

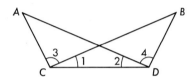

Given: $\angle ABE \cong \angle AEB$ **10.**
$\overline{BC} \cong \overline{ED}$
Concl.: $\overline{BD} \cong \overline{EC}$

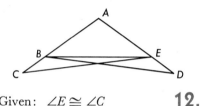

11. Given: $\overline{AE} \cong \overline{DE}$
$\overline{BE} \cong \overline{CE}$
$\overset{\leftrightarrow}{AE} \perp \overset{\leftrightarrow}{BE}$
$\overset{\leftrightarrow}{DE} \perp \overset{\leftrightarrow}{EC}$
Concl.: $\angle A \cong \angle D$

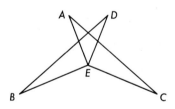

Given: $\angle E \cong \angle C$ **12.**
$\angle 1 \cong \angle 2$
B is the midpoint
of $\overline{EC}$.
Concl.: $\overline{AB} \cong \overline{DB}$

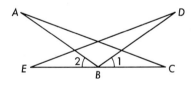

■ The Isosceles Triangle

Thus far we have examined triangles in which there existed no special features about the triangles. There are, however, certain triangles that contain elements that make them distinguishable from the general run of triangles. These peculiarities revolve about the relations that might exist between the sides of a triangle or perhaps the angles of the triangle. Thus, a triangle with three congruent sides is called an *equilateral triangle*, while one with three congruent angles is an *equiangular triangle*. A complete list of these special triangles is given below.

Distinguishing Features of Special Triangles

Sides	Name	Angles	Name
3 Congruent Sides	Equilateral Triangle	3 Congruent Angles	Equiangular Triangle
2 Congruent Sides	Isosceles Triangle	1 Right Angle	Right Triangle
No Congruent Sides	Scalene Triangle	1 Obtuse Angle	Obtuse Triangle
		3 Acute Angles	Acute Triangle

The definitions for these triangles are very similar.

DEFINITION 28: An equiangular triangle is a triangle having three congruent angles.

DEFINITION 29: A right triangle is a triangle having a right angle.

DEFINITION 30: An equilateral triangle is a triangle having three congruent sides.

DEFINITION 31: An isosceles triangle is a triangle having two congruent sides.

It is the isosceles triangle to which we will turn our attention at this time. The two congruent sides of the isosceles triangle are called the *legs*

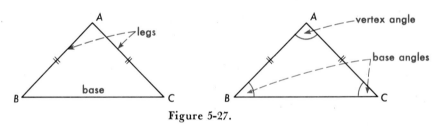

Figure 5-27.

($\overline{AB}$ and $\overline{AC}$), while the third side is called the *base* ($\overline{BC}$). The two angles whose common side is the base ($\angle B$ and $\angle C$) are called the *base angles*, while the angle formed by the congruent sides is the *vertex angle*. In terms of the words given in this paragraph, what property about an isosceles triangle is given in its definition? Examine the base angles of an isosceles triangle. What do you believe we will be able to prove about these angles? What property of the equilateral triangle is given to it by its definition?

Although our ultimate objective is to prove that the base angles of an isosceles triangle are congruent, we will have to make a slight detour to pick up certain properties that are needed to do this.

DEFINITION 32-A: The interior of an angle is a set of points such that if a ray whose endpoint is the vertex of the angle is drawn through any one of the points in the set, the ray will be between the sides of the angle.

Now we would like to go further and define the *interior of a triangle*. Almost intuitively we get the feeling that points P, Q, and R of Figure 5-28 belong

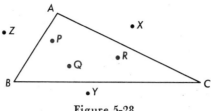

Figure 5-28.

to the interior of $\triangle ABC$, while X, Y, and Z do not. Notice, furthermore, that from the definition of the interior of an angle the points P, Q, and R are in the interior of both $\angle A$ and $\angle B$. The same can not be said for point X, for although it is in the interior of $\angle B$, it is not in the interior of $\angle A$. How is point Y related to the interiors of angles A and B? How is point Z related to the interiors of angles A and B? With this property in mind the following definition was made.

DEFINITION 32-B: The interior of a triangle is the set of points that are common to the interiors of any two angles of the triangle.

In reference to the isosceles triangle, if we are to prove that the base angles are congruent, we are immediately confronted with a difficulty.

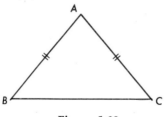

Figure 5-29.

Our principal method for proving angles to be congruent is through congruent triangles, yet in Figure 5-29 there is only one triangle! We are in need of two triangles, one that will contain $\angle B$ and the other $\angle C$. Perhaps the best way of obtaining two such triangles would be by drawing a ray through point A. Any ray, however, as seen in Figure 5-30, would not give us triangles that are congruent.

Since $\overline{AB}$ is already congruent to $\overline{AC}$, and $\overline{AD}$ is congruent to itself by the reflexive property of congruence, then, obviously, it seems advisable that the ray we draw should be the bisector of $\angle BAC$, thus making the included angles congruent. "So," you say, "draw the bisector and be on with the proof!" This would be nice, and this is exactly what was done for many hundreds of years. Mathematicians were disturbed by this, too, for

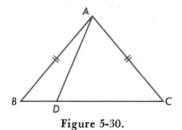

Figure 5-30.

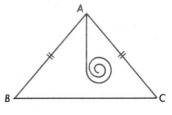

Figure 5-31.

equally as long a period. "How do we know," they wondered (see Figure 5-31), "that when we draw the bisector of $\angle A$, this ray might not get lost within the interior of the triangle and never emerge? Or, should it intersect a second side of the triangle, why must it be $\overline{BC}$ and not either $\overline{AB}$ or $\overline{AC}$?" Overcoming the first question was their greater problem and they did this by postulating that

POSTULATE 15: A line that intersects one side of a triangle and enters the interior of the triangle must intersect a second side of the triangle.

This postulate is known as Pasch's Axiom† after the man who first stated it. Now the proof of the second question that was raised follows rather readily. Restating it, it becomes, "Must the bisector of $\angle A$ intersect side BC, or can it intersect $\overline{AB}$ or $\overline{AC}$ and therefore bypass $\overline{BC}$?" If the bisector were to intersect $\overline{AC}$ as shown in Figure 5-32, it would have to do it

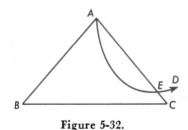

Figure 5-32.

at some point E. This would imply that there exists two lines through points A and E, *the side AC and the bisector AD*. This, however, is in contradiction to Postulate 4 which states that "There exists one and *only* one line through two points." Hence, the bisector AD can not intersect side AC. By the same reasoning, it can not intersect side AB. But by Pasch's Axiom, it *must* intersect some side of the triangle! This will have to be side BC since it is the only remaining side.

A proof such as the one just presented is called an *indirect proof*. We will examine this type of proof much more carefully at a later point in our work. Now, however, there is still one further question that has to be clarified

† Recall that on page 54 it was stated that the terms "axiom" and "postulate" are used interchangeably.

and that is, "How do we know that the bisector of an angle even exists?" This we will have to assume.

POSTULATE 16: Every angle has a bisector.

Now we have the tools necessary to prove the theorem about the isosceles triangle.

THEOREM 9: **If two sides of a triangle are congruent, then the angles opposite those sides are congruent.**

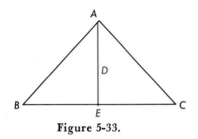

Given: $\overline{AB} \cong \overline{AC}$
Concl.: $\angle B \cong \angle C$

Figure 5-33.

PROOF STATEMENTS	REASONS
1. $\overline{AB} \cong \overline{AC}$ (s)	1. Given
2. Let $\overrightarrow{AD}$ be the bisector of $\angle BAC$.	2. Every angle has a bisector. (Postulate)
3. $\overrightarrow{AD}$ must intersect $\overline{BC}$ at some point E.	3. Pasch's Axiom
4. $\angle BAE \cong \angle CAE$ (a)	4. Def. of the bisector of an angle
5. $\overline{AE} \cong \overline{AE}$	5. Reflexive property of congruence
6. $\triangle ABE \cong \triangle ACE$	6. S.A.S. (Postulate)
7. $\angle B \cong \angle C$	7. Def. of congruent polygons

Now is a convenient time to prove the reverse of Theorem 9, for we can show the applications of both to the proofs of problems.

THEOREM 10: **If two angles of a triangle are congruent, then the sides opposite those angles are congruent.**

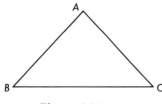

Given: $\angle B \cong \angle C$
Concl.: $\overline{AB} \cong \overline{AC}$

Figure 5-34.

ANALYSIS: As before, we will need the assumption on the bisector of an angle of a triangle. This time, however, it will be the base angles that are

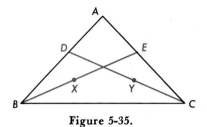

Figure 5-35.

bisected rather than the vertex angle. To prove $\overline{AB} \cong \overline{AC}$, it is necessary to show that $\triangle ABE \cong \triangle ACD$. Examination of these two triangles brings to light the fact that there are only two pairs of elements that are congruent: $\angle A \cong \angle A$, and $\angle ACD \cong \angle ABE$ (why?). The included sides between these angles are $\overline{AB}$ and $\overline{AC}$. But this is just the conclusion we are trying to draw on the basis of the fact that the triangles are congruent! Hence, another method of attack will be needed to prove $\triangle ABE \cong \triangle ACD$.

By proving $\triangle DBC \cong \triangle ECB$ we can obtain enough information to prove $\triangle ABE \cong \triangle ACD$. On the basis of the analysis, try to prove this theorem yourself before reading the proof below.

PROOF STATEMENTS	REASONS
1. $\angle B \cong \angle C$ (a)	1. Given
2. Let $\overrightarrow{BX}$ be the bisector of $\angle ABC$ and $\overrightarrow{CY}$ be the bisector of $\angle ACB$.	2. Every angle has a bisector. (Postulate)
3. $\overrightarrow{BX}$ must intersect $\overline{AC}$ at some point E, while $\overrightarrow{CY}$ must intersect $\overline{AB}$ at some point D.	3. Pasch's Axiom
4. $\angle EBC \cong \angle DCB$ (a)	4. Halves of congruent angles are congruent. (Postulate)
5. $\overline{BC} \cong \overline{BC}$ (s)	5. Reflexive property of congruence
6. $\triangle DBC \cong \triangle ECB$	6. A.S.A. (Postulate)
7. $\overline{BE} \cong \overline{CD}$ (s)	7. Def. of congruent polygons
8. $\angle BDC \cong \angle CEB$	8. Same as 7
9. $\angle ADC$ is supp. to $\angle BDC$.	9. Reverse of def. of supp. angles
10. $\angle AEB$ is supp. to $\angle CEB$.	10. Same as 9

11. $\angle ADC \cong \angle AEB$ (a)	11. If two angles are supplementary to two congruent angles, then they are congruent. (Theorem)
12. $\angle ABE \cong \angle ACD$ (a)	12. Same as 4
13. $\triangle ABE \cong \triangle ACD$	13. *A.S.A.* (Postulate)
14. $\overline{AB} \cong \overline{AC}$	14. Same as 7

It is interesting to note that although we seem to have come a long way from our original definitions and postulates, all but one of the reasons used in the preceding proof is either a definition or a postulate. We must never lose sight of the fact that every one of our proofs can always be traced back to the postulates and definitions upon which we previously agreed.

In the proof of Theorem 10 we did not use nor did we need the fact that the bisectors *BE* and *CD* intersected. Can you apply Pasch's Axiom to prove that these rays intersect?

Before we proceed further, there are three line segments whose definitions we need. These are

DEFINITION 33: An altitude of a triangle is a line segment drawn from any vertex perpendicular to the opposite side (extended, if necessary) of the triangle.

DEFINITION 34: A median of a triangle is a line segment drawn from any vertex to the midpoint of the opposite side of the triangle.

DEFINITION 35: An angle bisector of a triangle is a line segment that bisects any angle of a triangle and terminates in the opposite side.

In Figure 5-36 an altitude was drawn from vertex *A* to side *BC*. In Figure 5-37 the median was drawn from *B* to $\overline{AC}$, while in Figure 5-38 the

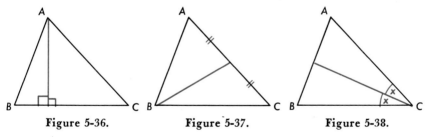

| Figure 5-36. | Figure 5-37. | Figure 5-38. |

angle bisector of $\angle ACB$ was drawn. How many altitudes will a triangle have? How many medians? How many angle bisectors? Draw an obtuse triangle and draw in the three altitudes. Do all three of them lie within the interior of the triangle? Draw a right triangle with its three altitudes. What did two of the altitudes turn out to be? What is true about all three altitudes of the right triangle? If in the obtuse triangle that you drew you extend the altitudes far enough, will the altitudes also meet at a common point?

Draw two of the medians of a triangle. Can you prove on the basis of Pasch's Axiom that they must meet in the interior of the triangle? Can you prove that two angle bisectors of a triangle must also intersect in the interior of a triangle? Must two altitudes of a triangle meet in the interior of the triangle? Give an illustration to justify your answer.

Illustration 1 of the Theorems on the Isosceles Triangle:

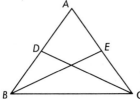

Figure 5-39.

Given: $\triangle ABC$ is isosceles with
$\overline{AB} \cong \overline{AC}$.
$\overline{CD}$ is the median to $\overline{AB}$.
$\overline{BE}$ is the median to $\overline{AC}$.
Concl.: $\overline{CD} \cong \overline{BE}$

ANALYSIS: By proving $\triangle DBC \cong \triangle ECB$, $\overline{CD}$ can be shown to be congruent to $\overline{BE}$.

PROOF	STATEMENTS	REASONS
1. $\triangle ABC$ is isosceles with $\overline{AB} \cong \overline{AC}$.		1. Given
2. $\angle ABC \cong \angle ACB$ (a)		2. If two sides of a triangle are congruent, the angles opposite those sides are congruent. (Theorem)
3. $\overline{CD}$ is the median to $\overline{AB}$.		3. Given
4. D is the midpoint of $\overline{AB}$.		4. Def. of a median
5. $\overline{BE}$ is median to $\overline{AC}$.		5. Given
6. E is the midpoint of $\overline{AC}$.		6. Same as 4
7. $\overline{BD} \cong \overline{CE}$ (s)		7. Halves of congruent line segments are congruent. (Postulate)
8. $\overline{BC} \cong \overline{BC}$ (s)		8. Reflexive property of congruence
9. $\triangle DBC \cong \triangle ECB$		9. S.A.S. (Postulate)
10. $\overline{BE} \cong \overline{CD}$		10. Def. of congruent polygons

Illustration 2:

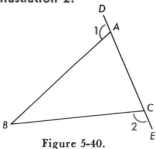

Figure 5-40.

Given: $\angle 1 \cong \angle 2$
Concl.: $\triangle ABC$ is an isosceles triangle.

ANALYSIS: $\triangle ABC$ will be isosceles if we can show two sides to be congruent. Two sides will be congruent if two angles are congruent. Since $\angle 1 \cong \angle 2$, it is possible to prove that $\angle BAC \cong \angle BCA$. Hence, two angles of the triangle are congruent and the proof can be completed.

PROOF	STATEMENTS	REASONS
1. $\angle 1 \cong \angle 2$		1. Given
2. $\angle BAC$ is supp. to $\angle 1$.		2. Reverse of def. of supp. angles
3. $\angle BCA$ is supp. to $\angle 2$.		3. Same as 2
4. $\angle BCA \cong \angle BAC$		4. If two angles are supplementary to two congruent angles, then they are congruent. (Theorem)
5. $\overline{BA} \cong \overline{BC}$		5. If two angles of a triangle are congruent, then the sides opposite those angles are congruent. (Theorem)
6. $\triangle ABC$ is isosceles.		6. Rev. of def. of an isosceles triangle

EXERCISES

1. Given: $\triangle ABC$ is isosceles with $\overline{AB} \cong \overline{AC}$.
$\overline{AD}$ is the median to $\overline{BC}$.
Concl.: $\overrightarrow{AD}$ bisects $\angle BAC$.

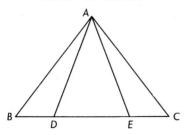

Given: $\triangle ABC$ is isosceles with $\overline{AB} \cong \overline{AC}$.   **2.**
Concl.: $\angle 1 \cong \angle 2$

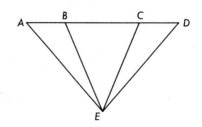

3. Given: $\overline{AB} \cong \overline{AC}$
$\overline{BE} \cong \overline{CD}$
Concl.: $\overline{AD} \cong \overline{AE}$

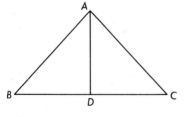

Given: $\overline{EB} \cong \overline{EC}$ **4.**
$\angle AEC \cong \angle DEB$
Concl.: $\overline{AB} \cong \overline{CD}$

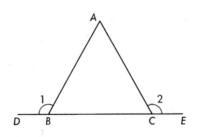

5. Given: $\overline{AC} \cong \overline{AD}$
$\overline{EC} \cong \overline{BD}$
Concl.: $\angle EAD \cong \angle BAC$

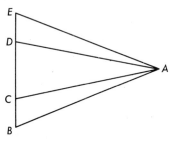

Given: $\overline{EB} \cong \overline{EC}$ **6.**
$\angle DEB \cong \angle AEC$
Concl.: $\triangle EAD$ is isosceles.

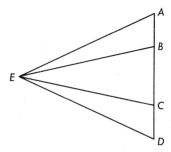

7. Given: $\overline{AB} \cong \overline{AE}$
$\overrightarrow{AC}$ and $\overrightarrow{AD}$ trisect
$\angle BAE$.
Concl.: $\triangle ACD$ is isosceles.

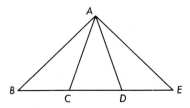

Given: $\overline{AC} \cong \overline{AD}$ **8.**
C and D are trisection
points of $\overline{BE}$.
Concl.: $\triangle ABE$ is isosceles.

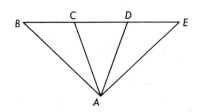

9. Given: D is the midpoint
of $\overline{BC}$.
$\overline{ED} \cong \overline{FD}$
$\angle EDC \cong \angle FDB$
Concl.: $\triangle ABC$ is isosceles.

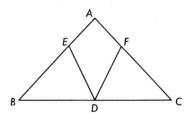

Given: $\overline{AB} \cong \overline{AC}$ **10.**
$\overrightarrow{AD}$ bisects $\angle BAC$.
Concl.: $\overline{AD}$ is the median
to $\overline{BC}$.

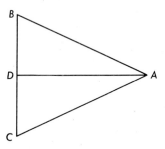

11. Given: $\overline{AD}$ is the median to $\overline{BC}$.
$\overline{AD}$ is the altitude to $\overline{BC}$.
Concl.: $\triangle ABC$ is isosceles.

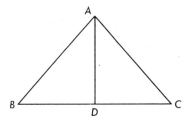

Given: $\overline{BA} \cong \overline{BC}$
D, E, and F are the midpoints of $\overline{BA}$, $\overline{AC}$, and $\overline{CB}$ respectively.
Concl.: $\overline{DE} \cong \overline{FE}$ **12.**

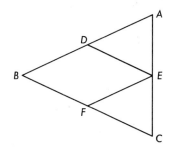

13. Given: $\overleftrightarrow{DE}$ and $\overleftrightarrow{FG} \perp \overleftrightarrow{BC}$
$\angle 1 \cong \angle 2$
$\overline{DE} \cong \overline{FG}$
Concl.: $\triangle ABC$ is isosceles.

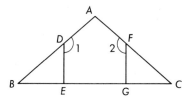

Given: $\overleftrightarrow{AD}$ and $\overleftrightarrow{FC}$ trisect $\overline{BE}$.
$\angle B \cong \angle E$
$\overline{AB} \cong \overline{FE}$
Concl.: $\triangle GCD$ is isosceles. **14.**

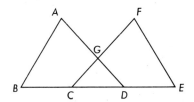

15. Given: $\overline{AB} \cong \overline{DC}$
$\angle BAD \cong \angle CDA$
Concl.: $\triangle EAD$ is isosceles.

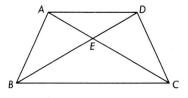

Given: $\overleftrightarrow{AB}$ and $\overleftrightarrow{DC} \perp \overleftrightarrow{BC}$
$\overline{AB} \cong \overline{DC}$
Concl.: $\triangle EBC$ is isosceles. **16.**

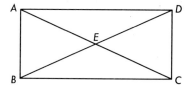

17. Given: $\overline{AB} \cong \overline{AC}$

   $\overrightarrow{CD}$ bisects $\angle ACB$.

   $\overrightarrow{BE}$ bisects $\angle ABC$.

  Concl.: $\overline{DC} \cong \overline{EB}$

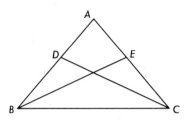

Given: $\overline{AB} \cong \overline{AC}$ **18.**

   $\overrightarrow{CD}$ bisects $\angle ACB$.

   $\overrightarrow{BD}$ bisects $\angle ABC$.

Concl.: $\triangle DBC$ is isosceles.

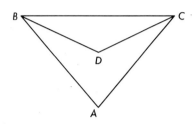

19. Given: $\angle B \cong \angle C$

    $\angle 1 \cong \angle 2$

    $\overline{BE} \cong \overline{FC}$

  Concl.: $\overline{AD} \cong \overline{AG}$

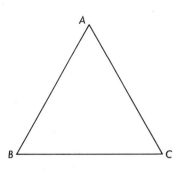

Given: $\overline{AB} \cong \overline{AC} \cong \overline{BC}$ **20.†**
Concl.: $\angle A \cong \angle B \cong \angle C$

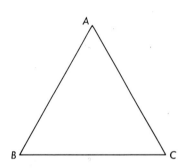

21.† Given: $\angle A \cong \angle B \cong \angle C$
   Concl.: $\overline{AB} \cong \overline{AC} \cong \overline{BC}$

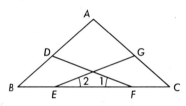

Given: Isosceles triangles **22.**
   ABC and DBC on
   the same base $\overline{BC}$

Concl.: $\angle ABD \cong \angle ACD$

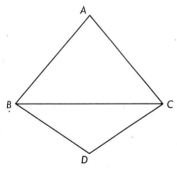

† This problem is often considered as a theorem. What would the statement of this theorem be?

■ The S.S.S. Theorem

There are four general methods for proving triangles to be congruent. Prior to now we have examined and assumed two of these methods. The third we shall prove in this section, while the proof of the fourth will have to be delayed until more information has been established that will make that proof possible.

In order to develop this third statement of congruence, we shall need yet another theorem and another postulate.

THEOREM 11: If two triangles are congruent to the same triangle, then they are congruent to each other.

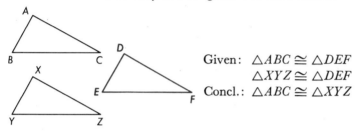

Given: $\triangle ABC \cong \triangle DEF$
$\triangle XYZ \cong \triangle DEF$
Concl.: $\triangle ABC \cong \triangle XYZ$

Figure 5-41.

ANALYSIS: Triangles ABC and XYZ can readily be shown to be congruent by the *S.A.S.* postulate. From the congruency correspondence $ABC \leftrightarrow DEF$ we can conclude that $\overline{AB} \cong \overline{DE}$. Similarly, $\overline{XY} \cong \overline{DE}$ and, therefore, $\overline{AB} \cong \overline{XY}$. In the same way, $\overline{BC}$ can be shown congruent to $\overline{YZ}$, and $\angle B$ congruent to $\angle Y$.

PROOF	STATEMENTS	REASONS
1. $\triangle ABC \cong \triangle DEF$		1. Given
2. $\overline{AB} \cong \overline{DE}$, $\angle B \cong \angle E$, $\overline{BC} \cong \overline{EF}$		2. Def. of congruent polygons
3. $\triangle XYZ \cong \triangle DEF$		3. Given
4. $\overline{XY} \cong \overline{DE}$, $\angle Y \cong \angle E$, $\overline{YZ} \cong \overline{EF}$		4. Same as 2
5. $\overline{AB} \cong \overline{XY}$ (s) $\angle B \cong \angle Y$ (a) $\overline{BC} \cong \overline{YZ}$ (s)		5. Transitive property of congruence (Postulate)
6. $\triangle ABC \cong \triangle XYZ$		6. *S.A.S.* (Postulate)

The postulate we need deals with angles and is comparable to one already established for line segments. The very first postulate made was

that a line can be extended as far as desired in either direction. One interpretation of this statement is

> If we start with a given line and a point P of that line, it is possible to
> find a second point Q of this line such that $\overline{PQ}$ will be congruent to any
> line segment that is given to us.

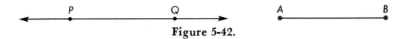

Figure 5-42.

Thus, by starting with the point P it was possible to find Q such that
$\overline{PQ} \cong \overline{AB}$.

Now, we want to establish a comparable postulate for angles:

POSTULATE 17: At a given point of a given line there exists an angle whose
vertex is the given point and one of whose sides is a ray of the given line
such that this angle is congruent to any given angle.

To illustrate, this postulate implies that by starting with some point P
of the line PQ it is possible to find an angle such as $\angle RPQ$ that will be
congruent to the given $\angle ABC$.

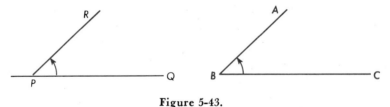

Figure 5-43.

We now have the weapons necessary to prove the following theorem.

**THEOREM 12: Two triangles are congruent if there exists a corre-
spondence between the vertices in which three sides
of one are congruent to those corresponding sides of
the other. (The symbols for this statement are *S.S.S.*)**

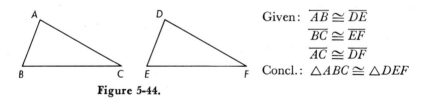

Figure 5-44.

Given: $\overline{AB} \cong \overline{DE}$
        $\overline{BC} \cong \overline{EF}$
        $\overline{AC} \cong \overline{DF}$
Concl.: $\triangle ABC \cong \triangle DEF$

ANALYSIS: Our method of attack will be to set up a third triangle. $\triangle ABC$
and $\triangle DEF$ will both be proved congruent to this third triangle. Hence,
by the theorem just established, it will follow that $\triangle ABC \cong \triangle DEF$.

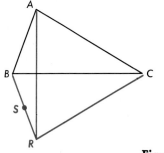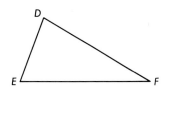

Figure 5-45.

PROOF STATEMENTS	REASONS
1. At point B of line BC there exists an angle congruent to $\angle DEF$. Let this angle be $\angle SBC$. (a)	1. Postulate 17
2. Extend $\overleftrightarrow{BS}$ so that $\overline{RB} \cong \overline{DE}$ (s)	2. A line can be extended as far as desired. (Postulate)
3. Let $\overleftrightarrow{RC}$ be the line through points R and C.	3. There exists one and only one line through two points. (Postulate)
4. Let $\overleftrightarrow{RA}$ be the line through points R and A.	4. Same as 3
5. $\overline{BC} \cong \overline{EF}$ (s)	5. Given
6. $\triangle DEF \cong \triangle RBC$	6. S.A.S. (Assumption)
Now, it is necessary to show that $\triangle ABC \cong \triangle RBC$.	
7. $\overline{RC} \cong \overline{DF}$	7. Def. of congruent polygons
8. $\overline{AC} \cong \overline{DF}$	8. Given
9. $\therefore \overline{AC} \cong \overline{RC}$ (s)	9. Transitive property of congruence
10. $\angle CAR \cong \angle CRA$	10. If two sides of a triangle ($\triangle CAR$) are congruent, the angles opposite those sides are congruent. (Theorem)
11. $\overline{AB} \cong \overline{DE}$	11. Given
12. $\overline{RB} \cong \overline{DE}$	12. Statement 2 recopied
13. $\therefore \overline{AB} \cong \overline{RB}$ (s)	13. Same as 9
14. $\angle BAR \cong \angle BRA$	14. Same as 10
15. $\angle BAC \cong \angle BRC$ (a)	15. Addition postulate of congruence
16. $\triangle ABC \cong \triangle RBC$	16. S.A.S. (Postulate)
17. $\triangle ABC \cong \triangle DEF$	17. Theorem 11

Frequent application of Theorem 12 is made to figures that involve circles. Hence, it would be well to establish some of the properties of a circle.

DEFINITION 36: A circle is a set of points such that line segments drawn from each of these points to a fixed point are congruent.

The fixed point is called the *center*. Although in Figure 5-46 there are a great many line segments that are congruent, such as $\overline{AB}$, $\overline{AC}$, and $\overline{AD}$,

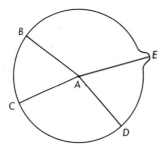

Figure 5-46.

all are *not* congruent, for $\overline{AE}$ is not congruent to the others. Hence, this curve would not be a circle.

DEFINITION 37: A radius of a circle is a line segment drawn from any point of the circle to the center.

As an immediate consequence of the definitions of a circle and of the radius of the circle, we have the following theorem:

THEOREM 13: All radii of a circle are congruent.

The symbol for the word circle is a small circle, ⊙, and to name a circle, we use the letter at its center. Thus, to name the circle in Figure 5-47, we would call it ⊙O; in addition, from the theorem that all radii of a circle are congruent, it would follow that $\overline{OA} \cong \overline{OB}$.

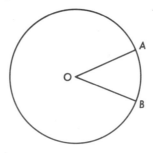

Figure 5-47.

Illustration:

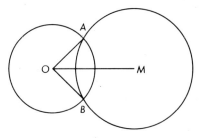

Given: $\odot O$ and $\odot M$ intersect at A and B.

Concl.: $\overrightarrow{OM}$ bisects $\angle AOB$.

Figure 5-48.

ANALYSIS: In order to prove that $\overrightarrow{OM}$ bisects $\angle AOB$, it will be necessary to prove that $\angle AOM \cong \angle BOM$. These angles can be shown to be congruent by proving them to be corresponding angles of congruent triangles. There are, however, no triangles in the drawing. What lines would you suggest drawing to obtain the triangles needed?

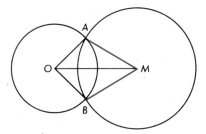

Figure 5-49.

PROOF STATEMENTS	REASONS
1. $\odot O$ and $\odot M$ intersect at A and B.	1. Given
2. Let $\overleftrightarrow{MA}$ be the line through points M and A.	2. There exists one and only one line through two points. (Postulate)
3. Let $\overleftrightarrow{MB}$ be the line through points M and B.	3. Same as 2
4. $\overline{MA} \cong \overline{MB}$ (s)	4. All radii of a circle are congruent. (Theorem)
5. $\overline{OA} \cong \overline{OB}$ (s)	5. Same as 4
6. $\overline{OM} \cong \overline{OM}$ (s)	6. Reflexive property of congruence
7. $\triangle AOM \cong \triangle BOM$	7. S.S.S. (Theorem)
8. $\angle AOM \cong \angle BOM$	8. Def. of congruent polygons
9. $\overrightarrow{OM}$ bisects $\angle AOB$.	9. Reverse of def. of bisector of an angle

EXERCISES

1. Given: $\overline{AB} \cong \overline{DC}$
$\overline{AD} \cong \overline{BC}$
Concl.: $\angle A \cong \angle C$

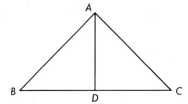

Given: $\overline{AB} \cong \overline{AC}$ **2.**
$\overline{DB} \cong \overline{DC}$
Concl.: $\overrightarrow{DA}$ bisects $\angle BDC$.

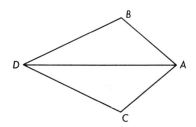

3. Given: $\overline{AB} \cong \overline{AC}$
$\overline{AD}$ is the median
to $\overline{BC}$.
Concl.: $\overrightarrow{AD}$ bisects $\angle BAC$.

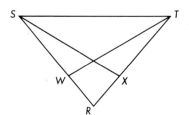

Given: $\overline{DB} \cong \overline{EC}$ **4.**
$\overline{DC} \cong \overline{EB}$
Concl.: $\angle BDC \cong \angle CEB$

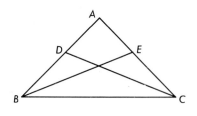

5. Given: $\overline{WS} \cong \overline{XT}$
$\overline{WT} \cong \overline{XS}$
Concl.: $\triangle RST$ is isosceles.

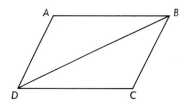

Given: Point O is center   **6.**
of $\odot O$.
$\overline{OC}$ is median to $\overline{AB}$.
Concl.: $\overrightarrow{OC}$ bisects $\angle AOB$.

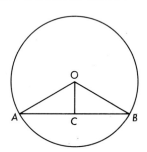

7. Given: $\odot O, \overline{AB} \cong \overline{CD}$
Concl.: $\angle 1 \cong \angle 2$

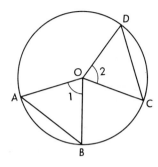

Given: $\odot A$ and B intersect **8.**
at C and D.
Concl.: $\angle CBA \cong \angle DBA$

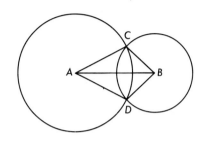

9. Given: $\odot A$ and B intersect
at C and D
Concl.: $\angle ACB \cong \angle ADB$

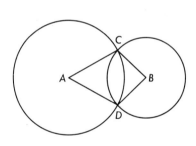

Given: $\overline{AB} \cong \overline{AC}$ **10.**
$\overline{DB} \cong \overline{DC}$.
Concl.: $\angle B \cong \angle C$

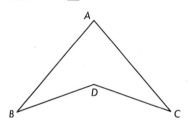

11. Given: $\odot O, \overline{AB} \cong \overline{CB}$
Concl.: $\overrightarrow{BO}$ bisects $\angle ABC$.

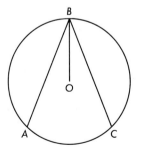

Given: $\overline{AB} \cong \overline{AC}$ **12.**
$\angle 1 \cong \angle 2$
Concl.: $\overrightarrow{AD}$ bisects $\angle BAC$.

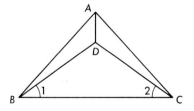

◼ The Hypotenuse-Leg Method of Congruence

You may have wondered why the "side, side, angle" method of congruence was not introduced. A glance at the diagrams below might help clarify this. Notice that whereas Figure 5-51 is congruent to Figure 5-50, Figure 5-52 was so drawn that it is not congruent to Figure 5-50.

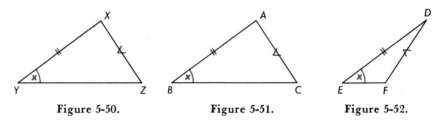

Figure 5-50.   Figure 5-51.   Figure 5-52.

And yet, the same corresponding parts in the three triangles are congruent. Thus, although triangles are *sometimes* congruent when two sides and an angle opposite one of them in one triangle are congruent to those corresponding parts in the other, they are *not always* congruent. The "side, side, angle" statement can not be a theorem. There is, however, a special situation under which they are congruent with these conditions. That case is when the triangles are right triangles.

Before developing the theorem on the congruence of right triangles, names will be given to the sides of a right triangle.

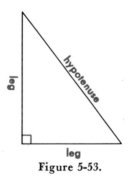

Figure 5-53.

The sides that form the right angle are called the *legs*—or occasionally, the *arms*—while the side opposite the right angle is called the *hypotenuse*.

THEOREM 14: Two right triangles are congruent if there exists a correspondence between the vertices in which the hypotenuse and leg of one are congruent to those corresponding parts in the other. (The symbols for this statement are *H.L.*)

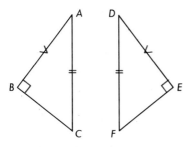

Given: $\angle B$ and $\angle E$ are right angles.

$$\overline{AC} \cong \overline{DF}$$
$$\overline{AB} \cong \overline{DE}$$

Concl.: $\triangle ABC \cong \triangle DEF$

Figure 5-54.

ANALYSIS: The proof of this theorem follows identically the same pattern as that used for the proof of the *S.S.S.* theorem.

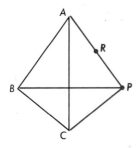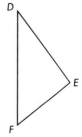

Figure 5-55.

| **PROOF** | (The reason for each statement will be left for you to supply.) |

1. At point A of line AC there exists an angle congruent to $\angle FDE$. Let this angle be $\angle CAR$. (a)

2. Extend $\overleftrightarrow{AR}$ so that $\overline{AP} \cong \overline{DE}$. (s)

3. Let $\overleftrightarrow{PC}$ be the line through P and C.

4. Let $\overleftrightarrow{PB}$ be the line through P and B.

5. $\overline{AC} \cong \overline{DF}$ (s)

6. $\therefore \triangle DEF \cong \triangle APC$

Hence, now it is necessary to show that $\triangle ABC \cong \triangle APC$.

7. $\angle APC \cong \angle E$

8. $\angle B$ and $\angle E$ are right angles.

9. $\angle B \cong \angle E$

10. $\therefore \angle APC \cong \angle B$ (a)

11. $\overline{AB} \cong \overline{DE}$

12. $\overline{AP} \cong \overline{DE}$ (See step 2.)

13. $\therefore \overline{AB} \cong \overline{AP}$

14. $\angle ABP \cong \angle APB$

15. $\angle CBP \cong \angle CPB$

16. $\overline{CB} \cong \overline{CP}$ (s)

17. $\triangle ABC \cong \triangle APC$

18. $\therefore \triangle ABC \cong \triangle DEF$

Illustration:

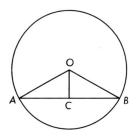

Given: $\odot O$ with $\overleftrightarrow{OC} \perp \overleftrightarrow{AB}$

Concl.: $\overrightarrow{OC}$ bisects $\angle AOB$.

Figure 5-56.

PROOF	STATEMENTS	REASONS
1. $\odot O$		1. Given
2. $\overline{OA} \cong \overline{OB}$		2. All radii of a circle are congruent. (Theorem)
3. $\overleftrightarrow{OC} \perp \overleftrightarrow{AB}$		3. Given
4. $\angle OCA$ and $\angle OCB$ are right angles.		4. Def. of perpendicular lines
5. $\overline{OC} \cong \overline{OC}$		5. Reflexive property of congruence
6. $\triangle OCA \cong \triangle OCB$		6. *H.L.* (Theorem)
7. $\angle AOC \cong \angle BOC$		7. Def. of congruent polygons
8. $\overrightarrow{OC}$ bisects $\angle AOB$.		8. Reverse of def. of the bisector of an angle

EXERCISES

1. Given: $\overleftrightarrow{AB} \perp \overleftrightarrow{AD}$
$\overleftrightarrow{CD} \perp \overleftrightarrow{AD}$
$\overline{BF} \cong \overline{CE}$
$\overline{AE} \cong \overline{DF}$
Concl.: $\angle ABF \cong \angle DCE$

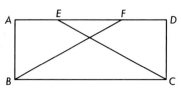

Given: $\overline{BD} \cong \overline{BC}$
$\overleftrightarrow{BD} \perp \overleftrightarrow{AD}$
$\overleftrightarrow{BC} \perp \overleftrightarrow{AC}$
Concl.: $\overrightarrow{AB}$ bisects $\angle DAC.$

2.

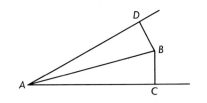

3. Given: $\odot O$

$\overset{\leftrightarrow}{OA} \perp \overset{\leftrightarrow}{AP}$

$\overset{\leftrightarrow}{OB} \perp \overset{\leftrightarrow}{BP}$

Concl.: $\overline{PA} \cong \overline{PB}$

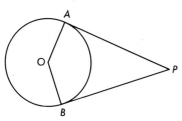

Given: $\odot O$ with $\overset{\leftrightarrow}{OD} \perp \overset{\leftrightarrow}{AB}$ **4.**

Concl.: D is the midpoint of $\overline{AB}$.

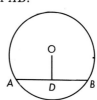

5. Given: $\overset{\leftrightarrow}{AE}$ and $\overset{\leftrightarrow}{CF} \perp \overset{\leftrightarrow}{BD}$

$\overline{BF} \cong \overline{DE}$

$\overline{AB} \cong \overline{CD}$

Concl.: $\angle 1 \cong \angle 2$

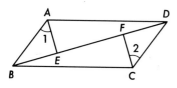

Given: $\odot O$ **6.**

$\overline{BC} \cong \overline{FD}$

$\overset{\leftrightarrow}{AB}$ and $\overset{\leftrightarrow}{EF} \perp \overset{\leftrightarrow}{CD}$

Concl.: $\overline{AB} \cong \overline{EF}$

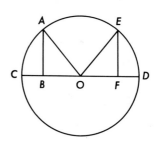

7. Given: E is the midpoint of $\overline{BD}$.

$\overline{AE} \cong \overline{CE}$

$\overset{\leftrightarrow}{AB}$ and $\overset{\leftrightarrow}{CD} \perp \overset{\leftrightarrow}{BD}$

Concl.: $\angle AED \cong \angle CEB$

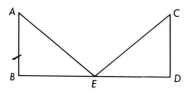

Given: $\triangle ABC$ is isosceles   **8.**
with $\overline{AB} \cong \overline{AC}$.

$\overline{AD}$ is altitude to $\overline{BC}$.

Concl.: $\overline{AD}$ is median to $\overline{BC}$.

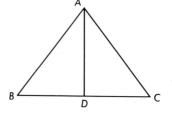

9. Given: D is the midpoint
of $\overline{BC}$.

$\overline{DE} \cong \overline{DF}$

$\overleftrightarrow{DE} \perp \overleftrightarrow{AC}$

$\overleftrightarrow{DF} \perp \overleftrightarrow{AB}$

Concl.: $\overline{AB} \cong \overline{AC}$

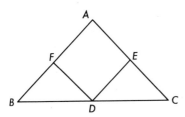

Given: $\overline{DB} \cong \overline{FC}$ **10.**

$\overline{BG} \cong \overline{CE}$

$\overleftrightarrow{DE} \perp \overleftrightarrow{BC}$

$\overleftrightarrow{FG} \perp \overleftrightarrow{BC}$

Concl.: $\triangle ABC$ is isosceles.

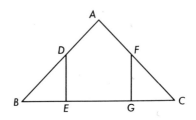

11. Given: $\overline{CD}$ is the altitude
to $\overline{AB}$.

$\overline{BE}$ is the altitude
to $\overline{AC}$.

$\overline{CD} \cong \overline{BE}$

Concl.: $\triangle ABC$ is isosceles.

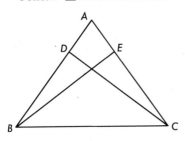

Given: $\overleftrightarrow{DG} \perp \overleftrightarrow{AC}$ **12.**

$\overleftrightarrow{EF} \perp \overleftrightarrow{AB}$

$\overline{EF} \cong \overline{DG}$

$\overline{DB} \cong \overline{EC}$

Concl.: $\triangle ABC$ is isosceles.

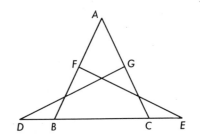

■ Problems Involving the Congruence of More Than One Pair of Triangles

In the proofs of three theorems—10, 12, and 14—it was necessary to prove two sets of triangles congruent in order to reach the conclusion we sought. In this section you will be given an opportunity to apply methods similar to those employed to prove these three theorems.

The method of approach for all the problems in this set of exercises is outlined below.

(1) Determine the pair of triangles that contain the sides or angles that you are trying to prove congruent.

(2) Attempt to prove this pair of triangles congruent.

(3) In trying to prove this pair of triangles congruent you will eventually discover that a pair of sides or a pair of angles is lacking.
(4) Find a second pair of triangles containing the parts that are lacking.
(5) Prove this second pair of triangles congruent.
(6) The rest of the proof will follow in the usual manner.

Illustration:

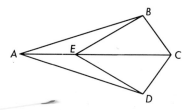

Given: $\overline{AB} \cong \overline{AD}$
$\overline{CB} \cong \overline{CD}$

Concl.: $\overrightarrow{EC}$ bisects $\angle BED$.

Figure 5-57.

ANALYSIS: $\overrightarrow{EC}$ will be the bisector of $\angle BED$ if $\angle BEC \cong \angle DEC$. Hence, for step 1, the parts that we are trying to prove congruent are $\angle\!\!\!\!\angle$ BEC and DEC, while the triangles that contain them are $\triangle BEC$ and $\triangle DEC$. In attempting to prove them congruent, following step 2, we find that $\overline{CB} \cong \overline{CD}$ and $\overline{CE} \cong \overline{CE}$ but that information is lacking concerning the included $\angle\!\!\!\!\angle$ BCE and DCE. Following the suggestion in step 4, we note that these angles may be corresponding angles of $\angle\!\!\!\!\angle$ ABC and ADC. These last two triangles can readily be shown congruent by *S.S.S.* From this it follows that $\angle\!\!\!\!\angle$ BCE and DCE are congruent. This, in turn, will make the $\angle\!\!\!\!\angle$ BEC and DEC congruent, from which the conclusion that $\overrightarrow{EC}$ bisects $\angle BED$ is apparent.

PROOF STATEMENTS	REASONS
1. $\overline{CB} \cong \overline{CD}$ (*s*)	1. Given
2. $\overline{CE} \cong \overline{CE}$ (*s*)	2. Reflexive property of congruence

At this point we discover that there are parts lacking and proceed to prove another pair of triangles congruent.

3. $\overline{AB} \cong \overline{AD}$ (*s*)	3. Given
4. $\overline{AC} \cong \overline{AC}$ (*s*)	4. Same as 2
5. $\triangle ABC \cong \triangle ADC$	5. *S.S.S.* (Theorem)
6. $\angle BCE \cong \angle DCE$ (*a*)	6. Def. of congruent polygons
7. $\triangle BEC \cong \triangle DEC$	7. *S.A.S.* (Postulate)
8. $\angle BEC \cong \angle DEC$	8. Same as 6.
9. $\overrightarrow{EC}$ bisects $\angle BED$.	9. Reverse of def. of the bisector of an angle

EXERCISES

1. Given: $\overline{AB} \cong \overline{CB}$
$\qquad\qquad \overline{AD} \cong \overline{CD}$
Concl.: $\angle AED \cong \angle CED$

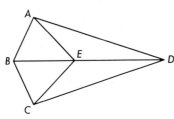

Given: $\overline{AB} \cong \overline{DC}$ **2.**
$\qquad\quad \overline{AD} \cong \overline{BC}$
$\qquad\quad G$ is the midpoint
$\qquad\quad$ of $\overline{AC}$.
Concl.: G is the midpoint
$\qquad\quad$ of $\overline{EF}$.

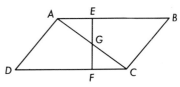

3. Given: $\overline{AB} \cong \overline{CD}$
$\qquad\qquad \overline{AD} \cong \overline{BC}$
$\qquad\qquad \angle 1 \cong \angle 2$
Concl.: $\overline{AF} \cong \overline{CE}$

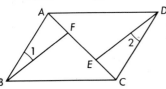

Given: $\overline{AB} \cong \overline{DC}$ **4.**
$\qquad\quad \overline{AD} \cong \overline{BC}$
Concl.: $\overline{AE} \cong \overline{EC}$

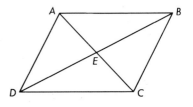

5. Given: $\overline{AB} \cong \overline{AC}$
$\qquad\qquad \overline{DB} \cong \overline{DC}$
Concl.: $\overleftrightarrow{AD}$ bisects $\overline{BC}$.

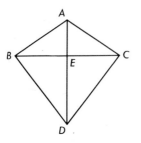

Given: $\overline{AC}$ and $\overline{BD}$ bisect   **6.**
$\qquad\quad$ each other at E.
Concl.: E is the midpoint
$\qquad\quad$ of $\overline{RS}$.

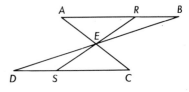

7. Given: $\overline{AB} \cong \overline{DC}$

$\overline{AD} \cong \overline{BC}$

$\overrightarrow{AE}$ bisects $\angle BAD$.

$\overrightarrow{CF}$ bisects $\angle BCD$.

Concl.: $\overline{BE} \cong \overline{FD}$

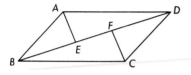

Given: $\overline{AB} \cong \overline{AC}$ **8.**

$\overline{BD} \cong \overline{CE}$

$\overline{DF} \cong \overline{EF}$

Concl.: $\angle 1 \cong \angle 2$

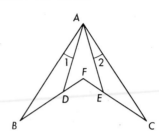

9. Given: ⊚A and B intersect at C and D.

Concl.: $\overleftrightarrow{AB}$ bisects $\overline{CD}$.

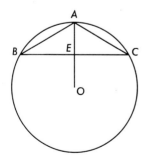

Given: $\overline{AB} \cong \overline{AC}$ **10.**

$\overline{EB} \cong \overline{EC}$

Concl.: $\overleftrightarrow{AD}$ bisects $\overline{BC}$.

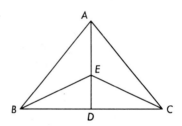

11. Given: ⊙O with $\overline{AB} \cong \overline{AC}$

Concl.: $\overleftrightarrow{OA}$ bisects $\overline{BC}$.

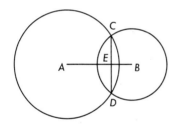

Given: $\overleftrightarrow{AB} \perp \overleftrightarrow{BC}$ **12.**

$\overleftrightarrow{DC} \perp \overleftrightarrow{BC}$

$\angle 1 \cong \angle 2$

E is the midpoint of $\overline{BC}$.

$\overline{BF} \cong \overline{CG}$

Concl.: $\angle A \cong \angle D$

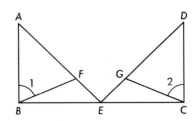

13.* Given: △*ABC* is isosceles
with $\overline{AB} \cong \overline{AC}$.
△*ADE* is isosceles
with $\overline{AD} \cong \overline{AE}$.
Concl.: △*FBC* is isosceles.

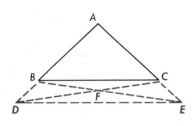

The diagram below has been **14.***
used to prove the theorem
that if two angles of a triangle are congruent, the
sides opposite them are congruent. See if you can prove
the theorem by using this
diagram.

Given: $\angle 1 \cong \angle 2$
$\overline{BD} \cong \overline{CE}$
Concl.: $\overline{AB} \cong \overline{AC}$

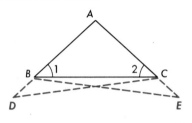

15.* Given: $\overline{AB} \cong \overline{AC}$
$\overline{AD} \cong \overline{AE}$
Concl.: $\overline{BF} \cong \overline{CF}$

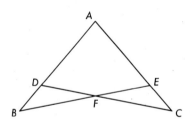

Given: $\overline{AB} \cong \overline{AC}$ **16.***
$\overline{AD} \cong \overline{AE}$
Concl.: $\overrightarrow{AF}$ bisects $\angle BAC$.

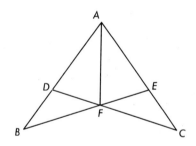

■ **Test and Review**

1. (a) Express the following matchings as a single correspondence:

Mary ↔ 1   Bill ↔ 2   Fred ↔ 3

(b) List the matchings that exist in the correspondence

1   2   3   4 ↔ 1   10   11   100

2. The correspondence *ABCD* ↔ *RST W* is a congruence correspondence between the vertices of the polygon *ABCD* and the polygon *RSTW*. What does this statement imply?

3. (a) Write a correspondence between the vertices of the two polygons below so that the corresponding parts will be congruent.

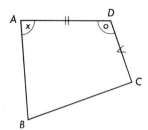 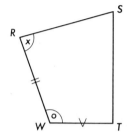

(b) What further information would be needed before it can be said that these two polygons are congruent?

4. What conditions would have to exist before it would be possible to have two triangles congruent under two different congruence correspondences?

5. The theorem on the base angles of an isosceles triangle is sometimes proved by the following method. Justify each of the steps in this proof.

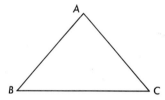

Given: △*ABC* is isosceles with
$\overline{AB} \cong \overline{AC}$.
Concl.: ∠*B* ≅ ∠*C*

PROOF	STATEMENTS	REASONS
1. $\overline{AB} \cong \overline{AC}$	1.	
2. $\overline{AC} \cong \overline{AB}$	2.	
3. ∠*A* ≅ ∠*A*	3.	
4. △*BAC* ≅ △*CAB*	4.	
5. ∠*B* ≅ ∠*C*	5.	

6. If there exists a correspondence between the vertices of two right triangles such that a leg and an acute angle whose vertex is an endpoint of this leg in one right triangle are congruent to those corresponding parts in the second right triangle, will the triangles be congruent? Justify your answer.

7. If the definition of congruent polygons was applied to prove two triangles to be congruent, what would have to be shown to be true?

8. What conclusion can be drawn if the median and the altitude to a side of a triangle were shown to be the same line segment?

9. If $\triangle ABC \cong \triangle EFG$, then $\angle A \cong \angle E$. Does this imply that if $\triangle ABC$ is not congruent to $\triangle EFG$, $\angle A$ is not congruent to $\angle E$?

10. Using a method similar to the one given in Problem 5, prove the theorem that if two angles of a triangle are congruent, then the sides opposite these angles are congruent.

Prove each of the following:

1. Given: $\overline{AC} \cong \overline{BD}$

$\overline{CE} \cong \overline{DF}$

$\overleftrightarrow{CE} \perp \overleftrightarrow{BE}$

$\overleftrightarrow{DF} \perp \overleftrightarrow{AF}$

Concl.: $\angle A \cong \angle B$

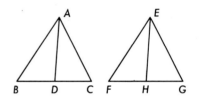

Given: $\triangle ABC \cong \triangle EFG$ **2.**

$\overrightarrow{AD}$ bisects $\angle BAC$.

$\overrightarrow{EH}$ bisects $\angle FEG$.

Concl.: $\overline{BD} \cong \overline{FH}$

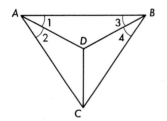

3. Given: $\angle 1 \cong \angle 3$

$\angle 2 \cong \angle 4$

Concl.: $\overrightarrow{CD}$ bisects $\angle ACB$.

Given: M is the midpoint   **4.**

of $\overline{AB}$ in $\odot O$.

D is the midpoint

of $\overline{OB}$.

C is the midpoint

of $\overline{OA}$.

Concl.: $\overline{MC} \cong \overline{MD}$

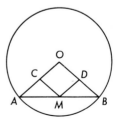

5. Given: $\overline{AB} \cong \overline{AC}$
$\qquad\qquad \overline{AD} \cong \overline{AE}$
Concl.: $\triangle FBC$ is isosceles.

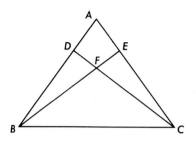

Given: $\overline{AB} \cong \overline{ED}$ **6.**
$\qquad\qquad \overline{BC} \cong \overline{DC}$
$\qquad\qquad \overline{AC} \cong \overline{EC}$
Concl.: $\overline{AD} \cong \overline{EB}$

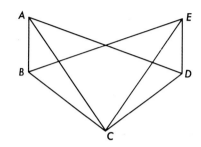

■ Try This for Fun

During the Middle Ages the theorem on the base angles of an isosceles triangle was referred to as "Pons Asinorum," or the "Bridge of Asses." He who passed over could proceed safely and enjoy the vistas that lay exposed before him. He who could not was lost forever in a mire of Greek and Euclid, a castoff on the road to "success."

It seems likely that some Medieval wit fell upon the name for this theorem after examining the diagram that was used at that time in the proof of this theorem. Notice below that it appears to resemble the cross section of the structure of a bridge.

Can you prove that in $\triangle ABC$ with $\overline{AB} \cong \overline{AC}$ that $\angle ABC \cong \angle ACB$?

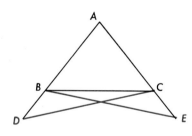

Given: Isosceles $\triangle ABC$ with
$\qquad\qquad \overline{AB} \cong \overline{AC}$
$\qquad\qquad \overline{BD} \cong \overline{CE}$
Concl.: $\angle ABC \cong \angle ACB$

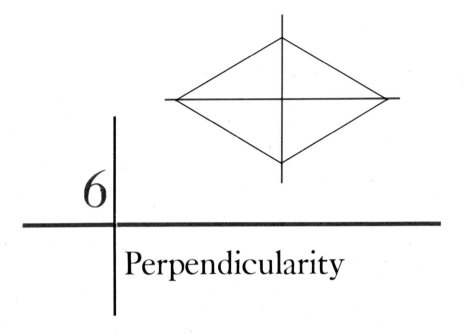

6

Perpendicularity

AN IMPORTANT SEGMENT OF THE STUDY OF geometry concerns itself with the properties of lines that are perpendicular to each other. Such questions as "Under what conditions are lines perpendicular?" and "What conclusions can be drawn if lines are perpendicular?" will be the subject of our work in this chapter.

The definition of perpendicular lines informs us that should lines be perpendicular, then right angles will be formed at their point of intersection. Using the reverse of the definition, however, to prove that lines are perpendicular is quite a cumbersome process, for it is not a simple task to show angles to be *right angles*. Proving angles to be *congruent* is another matter. We have many ways of doing this, the most important of which is through the congruence of triangles. Hence, we are led inevitably to the need for proving that lines can be shown to be perpendicular through the congruence of angles. The proof, though, depends upon a postulate and a definition that have not been established as yet.

The postulate was used many times by you in your study of algebra. If you were asked to determine the value of $a^2 + 2a$ when $a = 3$, you would replace the a by 3, square 3, and add it to the double of 3, giving you a sum of 15. Should you be pressed to give cause as to why it is possible to replace a with 3, you would very likely say, "a and 3 are equal, therefore I can

172

remove *a* and put 3 in its place." In fact, you may have expressed yourself more precisely by saying that since *a* and 3 are equal, a substitution of one for the other is permissible. Although you may not have considered this as a postulate in your study of algebra, we must do so now.

POSTULATE 18: If two numbers are equal, a substitution of one for the other is permissible. (Substitution, or Replacement, Property)

The definition we need is based on one developed earlier in our work concerning the concept of a ray being between two rays. This, as you recall, was given as,

DEFINITION 38: The ray *PB* being between two rays *PA* and *PC* means that,

$$m \angle APB + m \angle BPC = m \angle APC \text{ (See Definition 19)}.$$

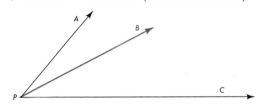

Figure 6-1.

will enable us to define a pair of angles known as *adjacent angles*. And that definition, in turn, will lead us to a relatively simple way for proving lines to be perpendicular.

DEFINITION 39: Adjacent angles, $\angle ABC$ and $\angle DBC$, are two angles such that they have a common vertex, *B*, and a common side, $\overrightarrow{BC}$, between $\overrightarrow{BA}$ and $\overrightarrow{BD}$.

In Figures 6-2 and 6-3 the angles *ABC* and *DBC* have a common vertex

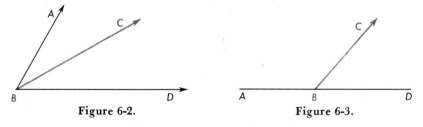

Figure 6-2.   **Figure 6-3.**

B and a common side $\overrightarrow{BC}$ that is between $\overrightarrow{BA}$ and $\overrightarrow{BD}$. Notice that in Figure 6-2 the angles *ABC* and *DBC* are both acute while in Figure 6-3, one angle is acute while the other is obtuse. Could two angles be adjacent if they both were right angles? If both had been obtuse angles, could they have been adjacent? Before answering, refer to Figure 3-10 on page 60. What condition must necessarily exist concerning the sum of the measures of the two angles in order that they be adjacent? Similarly, in Figure 6-4, $\angle ABC$ and $\angle DBC$ are not adjacent for although they have a common

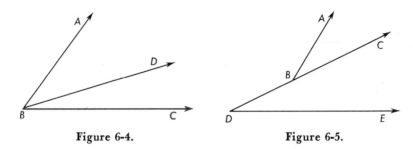

Figure 6-4.   **Figure 6-5.**

vertex B, their common side, $\overrightarrow{BC}$, is not between the other two rays, $\overrightarrow{BA}$ and $\overrightarrow{BD}$. The two angles in Figure 6-5 are not adjacent for they neither have a common vertex—in one it is B, in the other it is D—nor do they have a common side—the side of one is $\overrightarrow{BC}$ while in the other it is $\overrightarrow{DC}$.

Returning to the problem of proving lines perpendicular, we know that

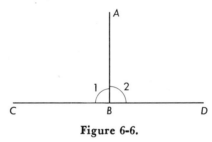

Figure 6-6.

if $\overleftrightarrow{AB} \perp \overleftrightarrow{CD}$, then $\angle 1$ and $\angle 2$ must be right angles and, in turn, we can conclude that they are congruent. What we are searching for is the reverse of this; that is, if $\angle 1 \cong \angle 2$, we would like to say that $\overleftrightarrow{AB} \perp \overleftrightarrow{CD}$. Notice that the angles 1 and 2 are adjacent angles. Hence, what we would like to prove is

THEOREM 15: If two lines intersect to form congruent adjacent angles, then the lines are perpendicular.

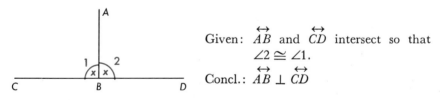

Given: $\overleftrightarrow{AB}$ and $\overleftrightarrow{CD}$ intersect so that $\angle 2 \cong \angle 1$.

Concl.: $\overleftrightarrow{AB} \perp \overleftrightarrow{CD}$

Figure 6-7.

ANALYSIS: Since we have only one way of proving lines to be perpendicular, through the reverse of the definition of perpendicular lines, we have no recourse but to show that $\angle 1$ (or $\angle 2$) is a right angle. This we can do by proving that $m \angle 1 = 90$ (or $m \angle 2 = 90$).

PROOF STATEMENTS	REASONS
1. CD is a line.	1. Given
2. $\angle CBD$ is a straight angle.	2. Rev. of def. of a straight angle
3. $\angle 1$ is supp. to $\angle 2$.	3. Rev. of def. of supp. angles
4. $m \angle 1 + m \angle 2 = 180$	4. Def. of supp. angles
5. $\angle 2 \cong \angle 1$	5. Given
6. $\therefore m \angle 1 + m \angle 1 = 180$ or $2m \angle 1 = 180$	6. Substitution postulate
7. $m \angle 1 = 90$	7. Halves of equals are equal. (Postulate)
8. Hence, $\angle 1$ is a right angle.	8. Rev. of def. of a right angle
9. $\overleftrightarrow{AB} \perp \overleftrightarrow{CD}$	9. Rev. of def. of perpendicular lines

Illustration:

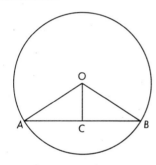

Given: $\odot O$ with $\overrightarrow{OC}$ the bisector of $\angle AOB$

Concl.: $\overleftrightarrow{OC} \perp \overleftrightarrow{AB}$

Figure 6-8.

ANALYSIS: Applying Theorem 15 to show that $\overleftrightarrow{OC} \perp \overleftrightarrow{AB}$ simply involves the need to show that $\angle OCA \cong \angle OCB$. This can be done by proving $\triangle AOC \cong \triangle BOC$.

PROOF STATEMENTS	REASONS
1. $\overrightarrow{OC}$ bisects $\angle AOB$.	1. Why?
2. $\angle AOC \cong \angle BOC$ (a)	2. Why?
3. O is the center of the $\odot$.	3. Why?
4. $\overline{OA} \cong \overline{OB}$ (s)	4. Why?
5. $\overline{OC} \cong \overline{OC}$ (s)	5. Why?
6. $\triangle AOC \cong \triangle BOC$	6. Why?
7. $\angle OCA \cong \angle OCB$	7. Why?
8. $\overleftrightarrow{OC} \perp \overleftrightarrow{AB}$	8. If two lines intersect to form congruent adjacent angles, then the lines are perpendicular.

Thus, through the use of Theorem 15 it is possible to show that lines are perpendicular by proving that they intersect to form congruent adjacent angles. As it was noted earlier, justifying that angles are congruent is far easier to do than justifying that they are right angles. The illustration just presented points up the fact that, to a large extent, the proof leading to perpendicular lines is but a repetition of the earlier proofs on congruence of triangles with the added step inferring the perpendicularity of lines based on Theorem 15.

EXERCISES

$$\boxed{\text{A}}$$

1. Given: $\overline{AB} \cong \overline{AC}$

D is the midpoint of $\overline{BC}$.

Concl.: $\overleftrightarrow{AD} \perp \overleftrightarrow{BC}$

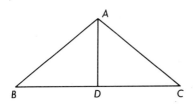

Given: $\odot O$ with C the mid- **2.** point of $\overline{AB}$

Concl.: $\overleftrightarrow{OC} \perp \overleftrightarrow{AB}$

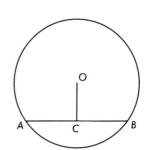

3. Given: $\overline{CA} \cong \overline{CB}$

$\overline{CD}$ is median to $\overline{AB}$.

Concl.: $\overleftrightarrow{CD} \perp \overleftrightarrow{AB}$

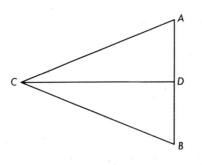

Given: $\overline{CA} \cong \overline{CB}$ **4.**

$\overline{DA} \cong \overline{DB}$

Concl.: $\overleftrightarrow{CD} \perp \overleftrightarrow{AB}$

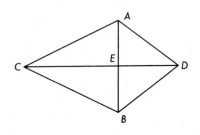

5. Given: $\overline{AB} \cong \overline{AC}$
$\overline{DB} \cong \overline{DC}$
Concl.: $\overleftrightarrow{AE} \perp \overleftrightarrow{BC}$

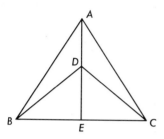

Given: $\overleftrightarrow{AC}$† bisects ∠s BAD **6.**
and BCD.
Concl.: $\overleftrightarrow{AC} \perp \overleftrightarrow{BD}$

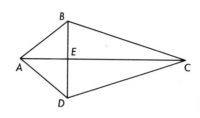

7. Given: $\overleftrightarrow{BE}$† bisects ∠s AEC
and ADC.
Concl.: $\overleftrightarrow{BE} \perp \overleftrightarrow{AC}$

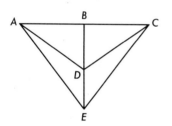

Given: $\overline{PA} \cong \overline{PB}$ **8.**
O is the center of
the ⊙.
Concl.: $\overleftrightarrow{OP} \perp \overleftrightarrow{AB}$

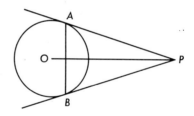

9. Given: ⊙O with $\overline{AC} \cong \overline{BC}$
Concl.: $\overleftrightarrow{OC} \perp \overleftrightarrow{AB}$

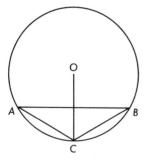

Given: ⊙O with $\overline{AB} \cong \overline{AC}$ **10.**
Concl.: $\overleftrightarrow{AD} \perp \overleftrightarrow{BC}$

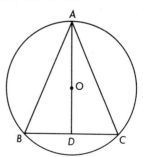

† The way this piece of Given Data is written is not mathematically sound. How should it be written?

11. Given: ⓢ *A* and *B*

Concl.: $\overleftrightarrow{AB} \perp \overleftrightarrow{CD}$

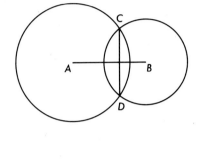

Given: $\overleftrightarrow{DB} \perp \overleftrightarrow{BA}$ **12.**

$\overleftrightarrow{DC} \perp \overleftrightarrow{CA}$

$\overline{DB} \cong \overline{DC}$

Concl.: $\overleftrightarrow{AD} \perp \overleftrightarrow{BC}$

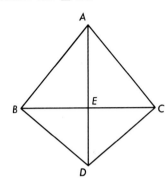

B

In each of the following problems you are to draw your own diagram, then write the Given Data and the Conclusion in terms of the letters of your diagram. Complete the proof.

1. Given: An isosceles triangle with the angle bisector of the vertex angle.
   Concl.: The angle bisector of the vertex angle is perpendicular to the base.
2. Given: A triangle with two congruent angles and a median to the side that these two angles have in common.
   Concl.: This median will be perpendicular to the side.
3. Given: A four-sided polygon in which all the sides are congruent.
   Concl.: The lines joining opposite vertices are perpendicular to each other.
4. Given: An isosceles triangle with the bisectors of each of the base angles.
   Concl.: The line drawn from the vertex of the vertex angle to the point of intersection of the two bisectors will be perpendicular to the base.
5.* Given: An isosceles triangle with the two medians to the legs.
   Concl.: The line drawn from the vertex of the vertex angle to the point of intersection of the two medians will be perpendicular to the base.

▪ Meaning of Distance and Its Relation to Perpendicular Lines

If you were asked to find the distance from point A to point B, you would very likely place the edge of your ruler along the two

A•

•B

points and read off the number of inches between them. But, why didn't you measure this distance along either of the paths shown in Figure 6-9?

Figure 6-9.

Before answering this, let us examine another question that might help clarify matters. How would you measure the distance from New York to Los Angeles? That is, would you follow a route that passed through Dallas, Texas; or the South Pole; or perhaps one that went through London, England? "No," you say, "not any of these! I'd try to find the shortest route between New York and Los Angeles." And this is precisely what we mean by *distance*; it is the *measure of the shortest path* between the objects involved.

DEFINITION 40: The distance between two geometric figures is the measure of the shortest path between them.

The shortest path between New York and Los Angeles, assuming we stay on the earth's surface, would be a section of a curve. At this point we are not prepared to say which curve it will be.

Mathematicians frequently use the term *geodesic* when referring to the shortest path. The question of determining the distance from point P to circle O resolves itself to knowing what the geodesic, or shortest path, is from

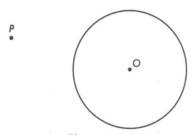

Figure 6-10.

a point to a circle. For it is the measure of the geodesic that will be the distance from P to circle O.

Let us return to the original question: "What is the distance from point

A to point B?" The answer, apparently, is "The measure of the shortest path." We will assume that the path taken along the edge of your ruler happens to be the shortest path. What is the name for the path along the edge of your ruler? What is the name for that part of the path between points A and B?

POSTULATE 19: The shortest path between two points is the line segment joining the two points.

Thus, since distance means the measure of the shortest path, this postulate implies that the distance between two points is the measure of the line segment joining the two points. Therefore, $m\ \overline{AB}$, in addition to being the measure of the line segment between A and B, can now be considered as the

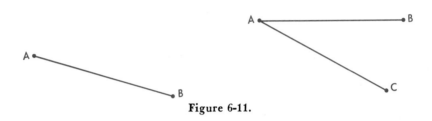

Figure 6-11.

distance between A and B. To say that $\overline{AB} \cong \overline{AC}$ implies not only that the line segments AB and AC are congruent but also that the distance from A to B is equal to the distance from A to C. Similarly, the statement that A is the same distance from B as it is from C will be interpreted as $\overline{AB} \cong \overline{AC}$.

The sentence that A *is the same distance from* B *as it is from* C is far too long. It is usually reworded as, A *is equidistant from* B *and* C, or, A *is equally distant from* B *and* C. Either of these is interpreted as before, $\overline{AB} \cong \overline{AC}$.

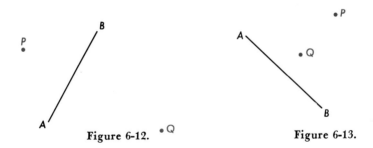

Figure 6-12.   **Figure 6-13.**

In both Figure 6-12 and Figure 6-13 how do you interpret the statement that P is equidistant from A and B? That Q is equidistant from A and B? Draw figures similar to those above. Draw the line through the points P and Q and extend it, if necessary, to intersect $\overleftrightarrow{AB}$. In what manner does $\overleftrightarrow{PQ}$

appear to be related to $\overline{AB}$? In statement form, what theorem seems to be implied by the conclusions you have just noted?

THEOREM 16: **If two points are each equidistant from the endpoints of a line segment, then the line joining them will be the perpendicular bisector of the line segment.**

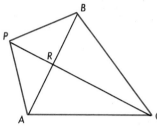

Given: $\overline{PA} \cong \overline{PB}$

$\qquad\ \ \overline{QA} \cong \overline{QB}$

Concl.: $\overset{\leftrightarrow}{PQ}$ bisects $\overline{AB}$.

$\qquad\ \ \overset{\leftrightarrow}{PQ} \perp \overset{\leftrightarrow}{AB}$

Figure 6-14.

ANALYSIS: Notice that rather than deal with the expression that P is equidistant from A and B, we have interpreted this as $\overline{PA} \cong \overline{PB}$. Similarly, Q being equidistant from A and B was restated as $\overline{QA} \cong \overline{QB}$. The congruencies are much preferred, for these are the forms with which we have dealt in the past. The problem thus becomes one of showing that $\overline{AR} \cong \overline{BR}$ and $\angle QRB \cong \angle QRA$, both of which can be done by proving $\triangle QRB \cong \triangle QRA$. Try to do this before reading the proof below.

| **PROOF** | (The reason for each statement will be left for you to supply.) |

1. $\overline{QA} \cong \overline{QB}$ (s)   7. $\triangle QRB \cong \triangle QRA$

2. $\overline{QR} \cong \overline{QR}$ (s)   8. $\overline{AR} \cong \overline{BR}$

3. $\overline{PA} \cong \overline{PB}$ 9. R is the midpoint of $\overline{AB}$.

4. $\overline{PQ} \cong \overline{PQ}$ 10. $\overset{\leftrightarrow}{PQ}$ bisects $\overline{AB}$.

5. $\therefore \triangle QPA \cong \triangle QPB$ 11. $\angle QRA \cong \angle QRB$

6. $\angle PQB \cong \angle PQA$ (a)   12. $\overset{\leftrightarrow}{PQ} \perp \overset{\leftrightarrow}{AB}$

Illustration:

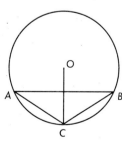

Given: $\overline{CA} \cong \overline{CB}$

$\qquad\ \ O$ is the center of the $\odot$.

Concl.: $\overset{\leftrightarrow}{OC}$ is the $\perp$ bisector of $\overline{AB}$.

Figure 6-15.

ANALYSIS: Applying Theorem 16 to this problem makes it necessary to find two points somewhere on† the line OC such that each of these points is equidistant from points A and B. Apparently, the points to select are those about which we might know something. To illustrate, one of the points to investigate would be O, since it is the center of the circle. Similarly, another point that bears investigation is C, for the Given Data contains information about C. And, lastly, it often pays to examine the point of intersection of the two lines.

In this problem, O is equidistant from A and B by the theorem on the radii of a circle, while C is equidistant from A and B from the information in the Given Data that $\overline{CA} \cong \overline{CB}$. Therefore, the conclusion follows.

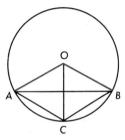

Figure 6-16.

PROOF	STATEMENTS	REASONS
1. $\overline{CA} \cong \overline{CB}$ (This statement implies that C is equidistant from points A and B.)		1. Given
2. Let $\overleftrightarrow{OA}$ and $\overleftrightarrow{OB}$ be the lines through points O and A and points O and B.		2. One and only one line exists through two points.
3. $\overline{OA} \cong \overline{OB}$ (This statement implies that O is equidistant from points A and B.)		3. All radii of a circle are congruent.
4. $\overleftrightarrow{OC}$ is the $\perp$ bisector of $\overline{AB}$.		4. If two points (O and C) are each equidistant from the endpoints (A and B) of a line segment ($\overline{AB}$), then the line joining these two points (O and C) is the perpendicular bisector of the line segment.

† Whenever we speak of a point as being "on a line," it will imply that that point is an element of the set of points of which that line consists.

Theorem 16 enables us to prove a line to be the perpendicular bisector of a line segment. Now we would like to investigate those conclusions that can be drawn if a line is known to be the perpendicular bisector of a line segment. To illustrate, let us say that $\overleftrightarrow{PQ}$ is the perpendicular bisector of $\overline{AB}$,

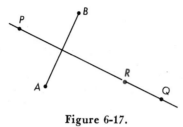

Figure 6-17.

while R is any point of $\overleftrightarrow{PQ}$ selected at random. What represents the distance from R to A? From R to B? What appears to be true about these line segments RA and RB? By expressing yourself in statement form, what theorem do you believe will be true in terms of the conclusion you have just drawn?

THEOREM 17: If a point is on the perpendicular bisector of a line segment, then it is equidistant from the endpoints of the line segment.

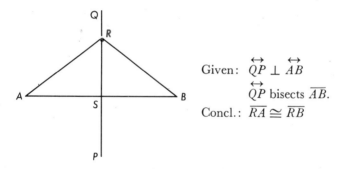

Given: $\overleftrightarrow{QP} \perp \overleftrightarrow{AB}$

$\overleftrightarrow{QP}$ bisects $\overline{AB}$.

Concl.: $\overline{RA} \cong \overline{RB}$

Figure 6-18.

ANALYSIS: You will notice that, again, we have chosen to write $\overline{RA} \cong \overline{RB}$ rather than R is equidistant from A and B. By doing this, it is immediately evident that to prove these line segments congruent, we need merely show that the two triangles are congruent. The proof will be left for you to complete.

There are a few interesting features about this proof that should be called to your attention. What did R represent on line PQ? Hence, considering what has been proved for R, what can be said about all other points on $\overleftrightarrow{PQ}$? Might R be the point S? If so, what would happen to triangles RAS

and *RBS*? Since there are no triangles if *R* coincides with *S*, does this imply that *S* can not be shown to be equidistant from *A* and *B*?

   The reverse of Theorem 17 is also a true statement. Its proof, however, involves a difficulty similar to the one encountered when proving that two angles of a triangle will be congruent if two sides are congruent. There was a need at that time for the assumption that every angle has a bisector. Now, we are faced with the need for a comparable assumption with reference to a line segment.

POSTULATE 20: Every line segment has a midpoint.

   With this postulate, we can prove that

THEOREM 18: If a point is equidistant from the endpoints of a line segment, then it lies on the perpendicular bisector of the line segment.

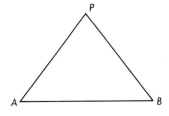

Given: $\overline{PA} \cong \overline{PB}$
Concl.: *P* lies on the ⊥ bisector of $\overline{AB}$.

Figure 6-19.

ANALYSIS: Perhaps the fastest way to show that a line is the perpendicular bisector of a line segment is to apply Theorem 16. From the Given Data, *P* is already equidistant from *A* and *B*. Hence we need but find another point that is also equidistant from points *A* and *B*. Several suggestions were made in the analysis of the proof of Theorem 16 that will help us find this second point. By selecting *M*, the midpoint of $\overline{AB}$, as the second point, the line through *P* and *M* will be the perpendicular bisector of $\overline{AB}$. This condition, in turn, implies that *P* lies on the perpendicular bisector of $\overline{AB}$; and this, of course, is what we had set out to prove.

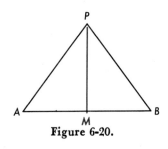

Figure 6-20.

1. Given: An isosceles triangle with a median to the base.
   Concl.: The median to the base is the perpendicular bisector of the base.
2. Given: Two isosceles triangles with the vertices of their vertex angles lying on the same side of their common base.
   Concl.: The line joining the two vertices of their vertex angles is the perpendicular bisector of their common base.
3. Given: Two isosceles triangles on the same base and the bisector of the vertex angle of one of them.
   Concl.: The line of this bisector passes through the vertex of the vertex angle of the other.
4. Given: Two intersecting circles, a line segment joining their points of intersection, and a line drawn from the center of one to the midpoint of this line segment.
   Concl.: This line passes through the center of the other circle.
5.* Given: The altitudes to two sides of an equilateral triangle.
   Concl.: The line joining the third vertex to the point of intersection of the two altitudes is the perpendicular bisector of the third side.

◼ Conditional and Categorical Statements

Mathematical statements, or propositions, fall into one of two forms. They are either

(1) Conditional Statements, or, as they are frequently called, Hypothetical Statements

or

(2) Categorical Statements

The first of these, the conditional statement, we investigated at great length earlier in this course.† Now, however, we would like not only to review that discussion but also to take a fresh look at this statement from another point of view.

(1) The *conditional proposition* is a statement containing two clauses, one beginning with the word "if," while the other begins with the word "then." We are asked to accept the truth of the antecedent, which, we learned, is the information contained in the clause beginning with the word "if." Then with the aid of our prior knowledge—that is, our definitions, our postulates, and our theorems—we are required to show in some manner *why* the consequent must follow. And, as you recall, the consequent is that part of the conditional statement that follows the word "then."

We can express this concept somewhat differently: the Given Data is contained in the antecedent, or "if-clause," while the Conclusion we are asked to justify is contained in the consequent, or "then-clause." Hence,

† See pages 85 to 88.

when we are presented with a conditional statement whose consequent we are asked to verify, our method of attack will be as follows:

(a) Draw the diagram containing all the necessary parts.

(b) Express the Given Data and the Conclusion in terms of the letters that appear in the diagram.

(c) And, finally, prove that the Conclusion follows from the Given Data.

To illustrate, consider the proposition

"If a ray is the bisector of the vertex angle of an
isosceles triangle, then it will bisect the base."

We know that the diagram should contain an isosceles triangle and the bisector of the vertex angle. This we now draw.

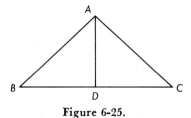

Given: $\triangle ABC$ is isosceles with
$\overline{AB} \cong \overline{AC}$.

$\overrightarrow{AD}$ bisects $\angle BAC$.

Concl.: $\overrightarrow{AD}$ bisects $\overline{BC}$.

Figure 6-25.

Having labeled the diagram, we proceed not only to indicate that the triangle is isosceles but also to point out which sides are the congruent legs. In addition, the "if-clause" contained information that a ray was the bisector of the vertex angle; this relationship we have shown by stating that $\overrightarrow{AD}$ bisects $\angle BAC$. It is not necessary to include in the Given Data that $\angle BAC$ is the vertex angle, for the fact that $\overline{AB}$ is given as congruent to $\overline{AC}$ will imply this. Referring now to the "then-clause," we note that the ray that is the bisector of the vertex angle will have to be proved to be the bisector of the base. Since $\overrightarrow{AD}$ was given as the bisector of the vertex angle, $\overrightarrow{AD}$ will have to be shown to be the bisector of the base.

There are times when the position of the "if-clause" and the "then-clause" are interchanged in a proposition. That is, the "if-clause" may appear as the second clause, while the "then-clause" appears as the first clause. The proposition analyzed in the preceding paragraph could have been written as:

"A ray will bisect the base if it bisects the
vertex angle of an isosceles triangle."

This statement was made to appear even more obscure by the omission of the word "then." It would still, however, be recognized as a conditional proposition by the fact that it contains two clauses, one of which begins with the word "if." Should you prefer, it is always possible to interchange the two clauses to have them appear in type form: "if-clause" first followed by the "then-clause." Or as it is frequently called, an "if-then" proposition.

(2) A *categorical proposition* is a statement whose verb is some form of the verb "to be." That is, the verb may be any of the words *is, was, are, were, will be*, etc. To illustrate, the conditional proposition just analyzed might have been written in the categorical form:

> "The bisector of the vertex angle of an isosceles triangle is the bisector of the base."

What form of the verb "to be" was used in this statement? In the conditional form what represented the "Given Data"? Relative to the position of the verb, where does the "Given Data" appear in the categorical form? In the conditional form what represented the "Conclusion"? Relative to the position of the verb, where does this same "Conclusion" appear in the categorical form? Thus, it can be said that in a categorical statement

(a) That part of the sentence that is prior to the verb is the "Given Data."
(b) That part of the sentence that follows the verb is the "Conclusion."

There are occasions when categorical statements are disguised through the use of verbs other than the verb "to be." Thus, the statement that

> "The bisector of the vertex angle of an isosceles triangle bisects the base"

is the same as the one given earlier. Now, however, the verb is *bisects* rather · than *is*. Be this as it may, the method for determining the "Given Data" and the "Conclusion" remain the same. With a little effort every statement of this form can be rewritten to contain the verb "to be."

EXERCISES

For each of the following propositions draw the diagram, write the "Given Data" and the "Conclusion," but do *not* write the "Proof." You are not prepared to prove most of these propositions.

1. If a line segment joins the midpoints of two sides of a triangle, then its measure is equal to one-half the measure of the third side.
2. Two isosceles triangles are congruent if a leg and a base angle of one are congruent to those corresponding parts of the other.
3. If the bisectors of two angles of a triangle are congruent, the triangle is isosceles.
4. If the medians to two sides of a triangle are congruent, then the triangle is isosceles.
5. The line segments joining the midpoints of the sides of an equilateral triangle form another equilateral triangle.

6. The opposite sides of a four-sided polygon are congruent if the opposite angles are congruent.

7. If perpendiculars are drawn from any point of the bisector of an angle to the sides of the angle, then these perpendiculars are congruent.

8. If perpendiculars are drawn from the midpoints of the legs of an isosceles triangle to the base, then these perpendiculars are congruent.

9. The line segments drawn from the midpoint of the base of an isosceles triangle perpendicular to the legs are congruent.

10. The acute angles of a right triangle are complementary.

11. A triangle is equilateral if its altitudes are congruent.

For each of the following propositions, draw the diagram and write the "Given Data," the "Conclusion," and the "Proof."

1. If a line bisects the vertex angle of an isosceles triangle, then it will be perpendicular to the base.

2. The median to the base of an isosceles triangle bisects the vertex angle.

3. The line segments joining the vertex of the vertex angle of an isosceles triangle to the trisection points of the base are congruent.

4. If the opposite sides of a four-sided polygon are congruent, then the line joining a pair of opposite vertices divides the polygon into two congruent triangles.

5. Line segments drawn from the midpoint of the base of an isosceles triangle to the midpoints of the legs are congruent.

6. If perpendicular segments drawn from the midpoint of one side of a triangle to the other two are congruent, then the triangle is isosceles.

7. If two altitudes of a triangle are congruent, then the triangle is isosceles.

8. If two triangles are congruent, the angle bisectors of a pair of corresponding angles are congruent.

9. If two triangles are congruent, the medians to a pair of corresponding sides are congruent.

10. If the line joining a pair of opposite vertices of a four-sided polygon bisects these angles, then the remaining two angles are congruent.

11. The median to the base of an isosceles triangle is perpendicular to the base.

12. If there exists a correspondence between the vertices of two isosceles triangles in which a leg and a vertex angle of one are congruent to those corresponding parts in the second, then the two triangles are congruent.

13. The angle bisectors of the base angles of an isosceles triangle form another isosceles triangle with the base.

14. The medians to the legs of an isosceles triangle are congruent.

15. A line perpendicular to the bisector of an angle forms with the sides of the angle an isosceles triangle.

16. If the perpendicular bisector of a side of a triangle passes through the opposite vertex, then the triangle is isosceles.

17. If the opposite sides of a four-sided polygon are congruent, then the opposite angles are congruent.

18. If the line segments joining the two pairs of opposite vertices of a four-sided polygon bisect each other, then the opposite sides of the polygon are congruent.

19. If the line segment joining a pair of opposite vertices of a four-sided polygon bisects these angles, then this line is the perpendicular bisector of the line segment joining the other two vertices.

20. If two line segments are drawn as the perpendicular bisectors of the legs of an isosceles triangle and they terminate in the base, then these line segments are congruent.

21. If a radius is drawn bisecting the line segment that joins two points of a circle, then the radius is perpendicular to the line segment.

22. The perpendicular bisector of a line segment whose endpoints lie on a circle passes through the center of the circle.

23. If two circles intersect, then the line joining their centers is the perpendicular bisector of the line segment joining their points of intersection.

24. If the median to the side of a triangle is also the altitude to the side, then the triangle is isosceles.

25. If two isosceles triangles have the same base, then the line joining the vertices of their vertex angles is the perpendicular bisector of the base.

26. The perpendicular bisector of the base of an isosceles triangle passes through the point of intersection of the bisectors of the base angles.

27. If a point on the base of an isosceles triangle is equidistant from the midpoints of the legs, then that point is the midpoint of the base.

28. The perpendicular bisector of the base of an isosceles triangle passes through the point of intersection of the medians to the legs of the triangle.

29. If all four sides of a four-sided polygon are congruent, then the two line segments joining pairs of opposite vertices are the perpendicular bisectors of each other.

30.* If a point is equidistant from the vertices of the base angles of an isosceles triangle, then it will lie on the bisector of the vertex angle of the triangle. (Hint: Show that this line is the perpendicular bisector of the base.)

31.* The bisector of the vertex angle of an isosceles triangle passes through the point of intersection of the bisectors of the base angles.

32.* The bisector of the vertex angle of an isosceles triangle passes through the point of intersection of the medians to the legs.

■ Test and Review

Prove each of the following:

1. Given: Circle O with $\overrightarrow{OC}$ the
bisector of $\angle AOB$

Concl.: $\overleftrightarrow{OC} \perp \overleftrightarrow{AB}$

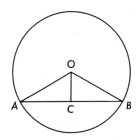

2. Given: Circle O with
$\angle CAB \cong \angle CBA$

Concl.: $\overleftrightarrow{OC} \perp \overleftrightarrow{AB}$

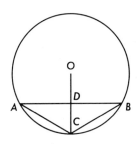

3. Given: $\overline{AB} \cong \overline{BC} \cong \overline{CD} \cong$
$\overline{DE} \cong \overline{AE}$
$\angle A \cong \angle B \cong \angle C \cong$
$\angle D \cong \angle E$
F is the midpoint
of $\overline{AE}$.

Concl.: $\overleftrightarrow{CF}$ is the $\perp$ bisector of
$\overline{BD}$. (Hint: Prove F
equidistant from B
and D.)

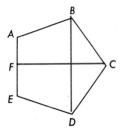

4. Given: $\angle C \cong \angle B$
$\overline{CE} \cong \overline{BD}$
$\overleftrightarrow{ME} \perp \overleftrightarrow{AC}$
$\overleftrightarrow{MD} \perp \overleftrightarrow{AB}$

Concl.: $\overleftrightarrow{AM} \perp \overleftrightarrow{BC}$

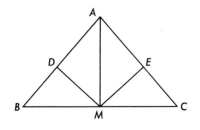

5. Given: $\overrightarrow{AD}$ bisects $\angle BAC$.
$\overline{AB} \cong \overline{AC}$
$\angle 1 \cong \angle 2$

Concl.: E lies on $\overleftrightarrow{AD}$.

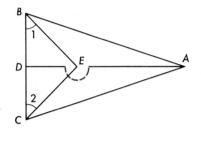

Given: Circle O with   **6.**
$\angle CAD \cong \angle CBD$
$\angle 1 \cong \angle 2$

Concl.: $\overleftrightarrow{CD}$ passes through O.

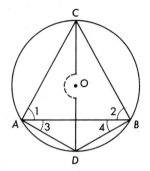

B

Prove each of the following statements:

1. The altitude to the base of an isosceles triangle is the median to the base.

2. The angle bisectors of the base angles of an isosceles triangle are congruent.

3. If two triangles are congruent, then the line segment joining the midpoints of two sides of one triangle is congruent to the line segment joining the midpoints of the pair of corresponding sides in the other triangle.

4. If the bisector of an angle whose vertex lies on a circle passes through the center of the circle, then it will be the perpendicular bisector of the line segment joining the points of intersection of the sides of the angle and the circle.

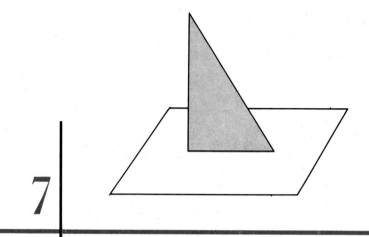

7

Perpendicularity in Space Geometry

UNTIL NOW WE HAVE ONLY CONSIDERED those figures that can be drawn on a "flat surface" but have made no attempt to either name or define this surface. We have reached the point where we would like to extend some of our concepts to the geometry of "space" rather than keeping them confined to a "flat surface." This particular time has been selected since there is a great deal of similarity between the ideas about perpendicularity that we have just established and those that we can now establish in "space" geometry.

Space and Surface

But how can we define these terms, *space* and *surface*? As with several of the terms we encountered earlier, it is not possible to define these words. Although they can be classified, we are unable to distinguish them from the other members of their class.

Both space and surface can be classified as a set of points.

In fact, *surface* is a subset of those points that are members of the set of points called *space*. Can you illustrate this by pointing to objects in your classroom? Unfortunately, it is not possible to show how the points in each of these

198

sets differs from other sets of points. Hence, *space* and *surface* must be considered the first of our undefined terms in space geometry.

The word *plane*, though, presents a different picture; this we can define. Surfaces such as the blackboard at school, the desk on which you write, the floor on which you stand, the ceiling overhead —these are all called *planes*. All of the surfaces selected have certain common properties. Select any two points on the blackboard and draw the line that exists through them. Are all the points of the line also points of the plane? Select any other two points and draw the line through them. Are there any points of this line that are not points of the plane? Can you find any two points on the blackboard through which a line can be drawn so that there are some points of the line that do not lie on the blackboard?

Now let us take a look at this same situation when the surface is either a ball or a tin can having no top or bottom. If the line is drawn that exists through the points *A* and *B*, how many points of this line would also be

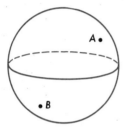
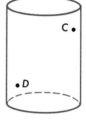

Figure 7-1.

points of the ball? Are there any points of the line that are not points of the ball? Where are these points? If a line were drawn through points *C* and *D* on the tin can, how many of the points of this line would also be points of the tin surface? Are there any points of the line that are not points of the tin surface? Where are these points? Can you find two points on the ball such that all the points of the line through them are also points of the ball? Can you find two points of the tin can such that all points of the line through them are also points of the tin surface?

These illustrations should have helped to make clear the properties of a plane as given by its definition.

DEFINITION 41: A plane is a surface such that if a line is drawn through any two points of this surface, then the points of the line will also be points of the surface.

In the case of the ball the only points of the line that were also points of the ball were *A* and *B*. If, in the case of the tin can, the point *C* was "directly above" the point *D* on the tin surface, then all points of the line *CD* would also be points of the tin surface. This, however, was true *only* if one point was "above the other" on this surface. The definition of the plane insists that the points of the line be points of the plane no matter where the two points be located on the surface.

Naming a Plane

████████████   To give the appearance of a table top, a plane is often drawn as shown in Figure 7-2. You are to picture this plane as lying horizontally

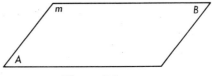

Figure 7-2.

before you, not vertically. Although there are numerous ways of naming a plane, the two most common are using either *one small letter* or *two capital letters placed at opposite vertices*. This plane can be called either plane *AB* or plane *m*.

■ The Meaning of *Determine*

Before examining any of the other properties of a plane, we will have to backtrack to take a close look at the mathematical interpretation of the word *determine*. Early in the study of geometry we assumed that

"There exists one and only one line through two points."

Rather than use the words "one and only one," it is felt that equally as expressive as this phrase is the use of the word *determine*. Thus, whenever the term *determine* is used in the mathematical sense, it implies that "one and only one" of these creatures exists under the conditions described. Based on this, the assumption just stated might have been worded as

"Two points determine a line."

How would you interpret the statement "A fixed point as center and a given line segment as a radius determine a circle"?

We would like, now, to examine those conditions under which a plane is determined. Boys will recall from their shop work that they constantly had trouble matching the four legs of a table to keep it from wobbling. Yet, tables with three legs seemed always to be firmly planted on the ground no matter how careless we were in cutting the lengths of the legs. The principle behind this is the fact that *three points will always lie in the same plane*. Should we have four points, however, any combination of three of them will lie in one plane, but it's only through chance that the fourth will lie in the same plane with the remaining three. Points that do lie in the same plane are called *coplanar points*; similarly, points that lie in the same line are *collinear*.

DEFINITION 42: Coplanar points are points that lie in the same plane.
DEFINITION 43: Collinear points are points that lie in the same line.

The surveyor uses the principle stated above when he places his transit on a tripod, for he knows that the three legs of the tripod must rest firmly on the ground. The photographer uses a tripod, also, each time he takes a "time" exposure. This principle is stated as:

POSTULATE 21: Three noncollinear points determine a plane.

Why was it necessary to say that the three points had to be noncollinear? If the three points were on the same line, then there would be many planes that would contain them, as pictured in Figure 7-3. These planes would

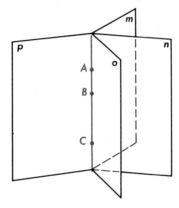

Figure 7-3.

resemble the pages of a book where the line of which the points A, B, and C are members is the binding of the book.

EXERCISES

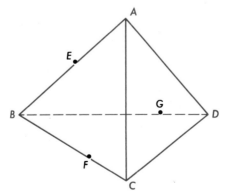

1. The diagram above resembles an Egyptian pyramid and in fact is called a *pyramid*. The questions below are to be answered in terms of this figure.
   (a) How many planes are there in this figure?

(b) How many planes contain the line AB? Using three letters, two on $\overleftrightarrow{AB}$ and the third at some other point in the plane, name the planes that contain $\overleftrightarrow{AB}$.

(c) Name two sets of three collinear points.

(d) Name two sets of five coplanar points.

(e) Name three noncollinear points.

(f) Name four noncoplanar points.

(g) How many planes contain all three points, A, C, D? Is this plane in the diagram? How many planes contain the points E, F, G? Is this plane in the diagram?

2. The diagram below is to be used for the questions that follow it.

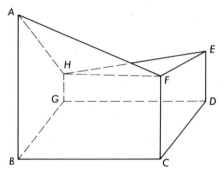

(a) Why were some of the lines drawn as dotted lines in this diagram?

(b) How many planes are there in this diagram? Using either two or three letters, where necessary, name these planes.

(c) How many of the planes contain four coplanar points that are named in the diagram?

(d) Name a plane that contains the points G and D. Will all the points of the line GD lie in this plane?

(e) Name a second plane that contains the points G and D. Will all the points of the line GD lie in this second plane? What conclusion can you draw concerning the points of line GD with reference to these two planes? Do you think there are any points other than those of line GD that are common to these two planes? $\overleftrightarrow{GD}$ is called the intersection of planes HD and BD.

(f) Name the intersection of planes HB and CA. Of planes HAF and FEH.

(g) Name the intersection of planes AG, GC, and AC.

3. (a) How many lines exist through one fixed point?

(b) How many planes exist through a fixed point?

(c) How many lines exist through two fixed points?

(d) How many planes exist through two fixed points?

(e) How many lines exist through three fixed points?

(f) How many planes exist through three fixed points?

4. (a) Given three noncollinear points, how many lines can be drawn such that each line will contain at least two of the points? Can any of these lines contain more than two of the points?

(b) Given three noncollinear points, how many planes can be drawn such that each plane will contain all three points?

5. Given four noncoplanar points, how many planes can be drawn such that each plane will contain at least three points?

6. Given points A, B, and C. Under what conditions will these points determine a plane?

7. In terms of your answer to Problem 6, are the sides and the vertices of a triangle always coplanar?

8. In terms of your answer to Problem 6, will it always be possible to balance a book that has been placed on the points of three thumb tacks? Assume that the thumb tacks are lying on a table pointing upward.

Further Conditions Under Which a Plane Is Determined

Consider a bicycle positioned so that it is resting on its handlebar and seat. Can you explain why it should be balanced in this position? Now spin the front wheel about its axle and fix your attention on a single spoke as it revolves. Should we want to stop the wheel in any position, we would place a small stick between the spokes to force the wheel to come

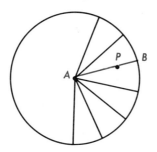

Figure 7-4.

to rest at that spot. In some ways this can be considered an application of the assumption that there exists one and only one line through two points. In this situation, the spoke passed through the point A (the axle), and as it revolved it took on many, many, different positions. However, as soon as we insisted that the spoke pass also through point P, then it was stopped dead in its tracks. There could be but one such line, or spoke, passing through A and P.

The revolving door of a department store can be examined in very much the same way. The door can take on many, many different positions as it revolves about its inner edge. But let someone place his foot in the path

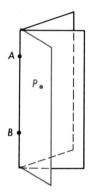

Figure 7-5.

of the door and its movement will be stopped immediately. So, too, there are infinitely many positions that a plane can take as it revolves about line *AB*. Insist, however, that this plane also contain the point *P*, and there is only one position for which this will be true. This is what we shall now prove.

THEOREM 19: A line and a point not on that line determine a plane.

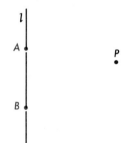

Given: Point *P* and line *l*

Concl.: Point *P* and line *l* determine a plane.

Figure 7-6.

ANALYSIS: Thus far there is only one method available to us for proving that a plane is determined: three noncollinear points determine a plane. Hence, there is no alternative but to attack this proof by using this postulate. Select points *A* and *B* as any two points on line *l*.† Since *P*, *A*, and *B* are three noncollinear points, they determine a plane. Since from the definition of a plane two points of *l*, *A* and *B*, lie on this plane, then all points of *l* lie on this plane. Hence, the conclusion follows.

In the same way, it is possible for us to prove a second theorem for determining a plane.

† A single letter is often used to name a line.

THEOREM 20: Two intersecting lines determine a plane.

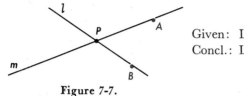

Figure 7-7.

Given: Lines l and m intersect at P.
Concl.: Lines l and m determine a plane.

ANALYSIS: The analysis is much the same as in the preceding theorem. Now, however, we must be careful about the selection of one of the three points that determine the plane. Let one of these points be P, the point of intersection of l and m. The other two points, A and B, must lie on each of the respective lines. Why should all points of line l be on the plane determined by B, P, and A? Why should all points of line m lie on this plane?

▪ Methods of Determining a Plane

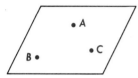

Three noncollinear points

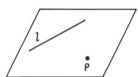

A line and a point not on the line

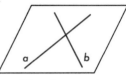

Two intersecting lines

Figure 7-8.

EXERCISES

1. If three lines pass through a common point, will the three lines lie in the same plane?

2. If three lines that are not coplanar intersect at a common point, how many planes are determined that contain at least two of these lines?

3. If AB and AC are two lines, what can be said about the points of line BC?

4. If P is a point that *is not* on line l and Q is a point that *is* on line l, then what can be said about line PQ?

5. Points R, S, and T are in plane m. Points R, S, and T are also in plane p. Under what conditions will plane m be different from plane p?

6. Lines l and m intersect. P is a point on neither l nor m.
   (a) How many planes will contain at least two of these elements?

(b) If P fell on l, how many planes would contain at least two of the elements?

(c) If P was the intersection of l and m, how many planes would contain at least two of the elements?

7. If points A, B, C, D all lie in the same plane, prove that the lines AB, AC, and AD are coplanar.

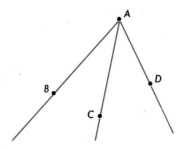

8. Points A, B, and C are the points of intersection of the three lines. Prove that the three lines lie in the same plane.

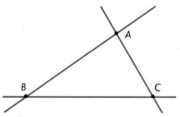

9. $\overleftrightarrow{AB}$ and $\overleftrightarrow{CD}$ intersect at E. Prove that all points of $ACBD$ lie in the same plane.

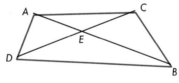

10. If D lies on $\overleftrightarrow{AB}$ and E lies on $\overleftrightarrow{AC}$, prove that the five lines of this diagram are coplanar.

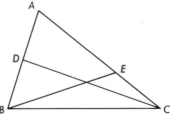

11. The drawing below is a "space" polygon. A, B, C, and D are noncoplanar points. In any manner whatsoever, justify that $\overleftrightarrow{AC}$ and $\overleftrightarrow{BD}$ do not intersect.

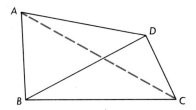

Perpendicularity Between a Line and a Plane

You may at some time have observed a man trying to drive a stake "vertically" into the ground, perhaps in the process of setting up a post for his mailbox. After having driven the post several feet into the ground, he will stand off a few yards to observe if it appears "straight." Having satisfied himself that all is well from that position, he then moves to the right and again examines the position of the post relative to the ground. Although he may again be pleased with what he observes, he may still have doubts as to whether the post is actually "vertical." Hence, he repeats the process several times more by moving to the right around the post. By doing this, he is applying the definition of a line perpendicular to a plane.

DEFINITION 44: A line perpendicular to a plane is a line that is perpendicular to every line in the plane that passes through its foot.

And, of course, it should be pointed out that the point of intersection of a line and a plane is called the *foot of the line*.

Just as the definition of perpendicular lines was a cumbersome tool to use to prove two lines to be perpendicular, so, too, is the above definition a bit unwieldy. Proving a line perpendicular to *every* line passing through its foot may become somewhat wearisome. Hence, effort is made to cut the number down. From our analysis of the man and his post, we know that a line will not be perpendicular to a plane if it is perpendicular to only one line in the plane. If we can show, however, that it is perpendicular to at least two lines in the plane, then it will be perpendicular to the plane.

THEOREM 21: **A line is perpendicular to a plane if it is perpendicular to at least two lines in the plane that pass through its foot.**

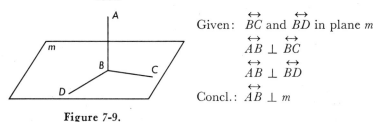

Given: $\overleftrightarrow{BC}$ and $\overleftrightarrow{BD}$ in plane m
$\overleftrightarrow{AB} \perp \overleftrightarrow{BC}$
$\overleftrightarrow{AB} \perp \overleftrightarrow{BD}$

Concl.: $\overleftrightarrow{AB} \perp m$

Figure 7-9.

ANALYSIS: In order to prove that $\overset{\leftrightarrow}{AB}$ is perpendicular to plane m, it will be necessary to prove that it is perpendicular to every line in m passing through B. This would not be possible. We get around this difficulty by selecting any line at random that lies in m and passes through B. What we can prove to be true for this line must then be true for all lines in m passing through B.

The additional lines are drawn in the figure so as to enable us to apply the theorem concerning two points each equidistant from the endpoints of a line segment. By extending $\overset{\leftrightarrow}{AB}$ so that $\overline{RB} \cong \overline{VB}$, we immediately obtain one point of $\overset{\leftrightarrow}{BY}$ equidistant from R and V. Point P will be the other point of $\overset{\leftrightarrow}{BY}$ that will be proved equidistant from R and V.

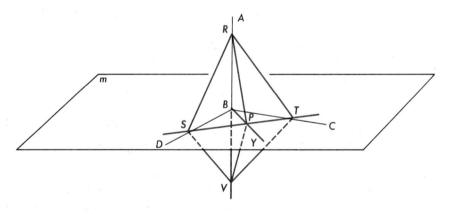

Figure 7-10.

PROOF STATEMENTS	REASONS
1. Let R be any point of AB and extend $\overset{\leftrightarrow}{AB}$ so that $\overline{BR} \cong \overline{BV}$.	1. A line can be extended as far as desired in either direction.
2. Let S be any point on $\overset{\leftrightarrow}{BD}$ and T be any point on $\overset{\leftrightarrow}{BC}$; then draw line ST.	2. There exists one and only one line through two points.
3. Within the interior of $\angle SBT$ draw $\overset{\leftrightarrow}{BY}$. It will intersect $\overline{ST}$ in some point P.	3. Pasch's Axiom
4. $\overset{\leftrightarrow}{AB} \perp \overset{\leftrightarrow}{BC}$	4. Given

5. $\therefore \overline{TR} \cong \overline{TV}$ (s)

5. If a point is on the perpendicular bisector of a line segment, then it is equidistant from the endpoints of the line segment. ($\overleftrightarrow{TB}$ is the $\perp$ bisector of $\overline{RV}$.) See Statement 1.

6. $\overleftrightarrow{AB} \perp \overleftrightarrow{BD}$

6. Given

7. $\overline{SR} \cong \overline{SV}$ (s)

7. Same as 5. ($\overleftrightarrow{SB}$ is $\perp$ bisector of $\overline{RV}$.)

8. $\overline{ST} \cong \overline{ST}$ (s)

8. Reflexive property of congruence

9. $\triangle RST \cong \triangle VST$

9. Why?

10. $\angle RTP \cong \angle VTP$ (a)

10. Why?

11. $\overline{PT} \cong \overline{PT}$

11. Why?

12. $\triangle RTP \cong \triangle VTP$

12. Why?

13. $\overline{PR} \cong \overline{PV}$

13. Why?

14. $\overleftrightarrow{PB} \perp \overleftrightarrow{RV}$

14. If two points are each equidistant from the endpoints of a line segment, then the line joining them is the perpendicular bisector of the line segment. (What are the two points and what is the line segment?)

15. $\overleftrightarrow{AB} \perp m$

15. Reverse of the definition of a line perpendicular to a plane.

Illustration:

If a line is perpendicular to a plane of a circle at its center, then any point on the line is equidistant from all points of the circle.

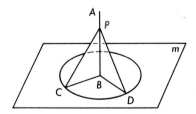

Figure 7-11.

Given: $\overleftrightarrow{AB} \perp m$

B is center of circle lying in m.

Concl.: $\overline{PC} \cong \overline{PD}$

ANALYSIS: Let P be any point on $\overleftrightarrow{AB}$. If it can be shown that P is equidistant from two points selected at random on circle B, then it will be equidistant from all points on circle B. The two points selected on circle B are C and D.

Hence, the problem simplifies to one where it is merely necessary to prove that $\overline{PC} \cong \overline{PD}$.

PROOF	STATEMENTS	REASONS
1. $\overleftrightarrow{AB} \perp m$		1. Given
2. $\overleftrightarrow{AB} \perp \overleftrightarrow{BC}$, $\overleftrightarrow{AB} \perp \overleftrightarrow{BD}$		2. Def. of a line perpendicular to a plane.
3. $\angle PBC$ and $\angle PBD$ are right angles.		3. Def. of perpendicular lines
4. $\angle PBC \cong \angle PBD$ (a)		4. If two angles are right angles, then they are congruent.
5. B is the center of the circle.		5. Given
6. $\overline{BC} \cong \overline{BD}$ (s)		6. Why?
7. $\overline{PB} \cong \overline{PB}$ (s)		7. Why?
8. $\triangle PBC \cong \triangle PBD$		8. Why?
9. $\overline{PC} \cong \overline{PD}$		9. Why?

Some of the problems in the exercises that follow depend upon an understanding of the meaning of *an oblique line to a plane.*

DEFINITION 45: An oblique line to a plane is any line that is not perpendicular to the plane but has one and only one point in common with the plane.

In the illustration above, $\overleftrightarrow{PC}$ and $\overleftrightarrow{PD}$ are oblique lines to plane m.

EXERCISES

1. If a line is perpendicular to a line in a plane, will it be perpendicular to the plane also? Explain.
2. How many lines can be drawn perpendicular to a given line at a given point of the line? What do you believe will be true about all the lines that are perpendicular to a given line at a given point of that line?
3. Lines a, b, and c are such that $a \perp b$, $a \perp c$, and $b \perp c$. Explain why each line is perpendicular to the plane determined by the other two lines.
4. In the diagram for the proof of Theorem 21, page 208, can you show that the points R, S, P, and T must be coplaner?
5. If a line passes through a vertex of a triangle and is perpendicular to

two sides at this vertex, is it perpendicular to the plane of the triangle? Justify your answer.

$$\boxed{B}$$

1. Given: $\overleftrightarrow{BC}$, $\overleftrightarrow{BD}$, and $\overleftrightarrow{BE}$
in plane m
$\overleftrightarrow{AB} \perp \overleftrightarrow{BC}$
$\overleftrightarrow{AB} \perp \overleftrightarrow{BD}$
Concl.: $\overleftrightarrow{AB} \perp \overleftrightarrow{BE}$

Given: $\overleftrightarrow{AB} \perp m$ **2.**
$\overleftrightarrow{CB}$ and $\overleftrightarrow{DB}$ in plane m
$\angle CAB \cong \angle DAB$
Concl.: $\angle ACB \cong \angle ADB$

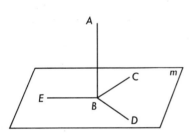

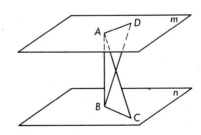

3. Given: $\overleftrightarrow{AC} \perp m$
m bisects $\overline{AC}$ at B.
Concl.: $\overrightarrow{PB}$ bisects $\angle APC$.

Given: $\overleftrightarrow{AB} \perp m$ **4.**
$\overleftrightarrow{AB} \perp n$
$\overline{AD} \cong \overline{BC}$
Concl.: $\overline{AC} \cong \overline{BD}$

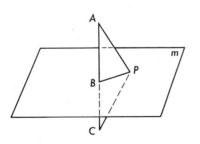

5. Given: AB and CD are two line segments in m that bisect each other at E.

$\overline{PA} \cong \overline{PB}$

$\overline{PC} \cong \overline{PD}$

Concl.: $\overleftrightarrow{PE} \perp m$

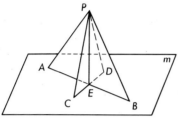

Given: $\odot O$ lies in plane m.

$\overline{AC}$ and $\overline{BD}$ intersect at O.

P is equidistant from A, B, C, and D

Concl.: $\overleftrightarrow{PO} \perp m$ **6.**

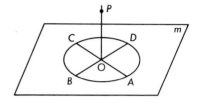

7. Given: $\overleftrightarrow{AB} \perp m$

$\overline{BC} \cong \overline{BD}$

Concl.: $\angle ACD \cong \angle ADC$

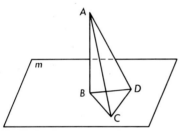

Given: $\overleftrightarrow{AD} \perp m$

$\overline{EA} \cong \overline{ED}$

Concl.: $\triangle ABC \cong \triangle DBC$ **8.**

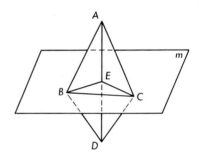

9. Given: $\overleftrightarrow{AB} \perp m$

$\overleftrightarrow{CD} \perp m$

E is the midpoint of $\overline{AD}$.

$\overline{AB} \cong \overline{DC}$

Concl.: E is equidistant from B and C.

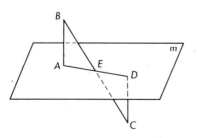

Given: $\overleftrightarrow{AC} \perp m$

$\overleftrightarrow{BD} \perp m$

$\overline{AC} \cong \overline{BD}$

P is the midpoint of $\overline{CD}$.

Concl.: P is equidistant from A and B.   **10.**

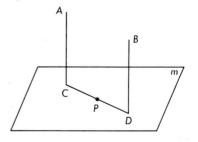

11. Given: $\overleftrightarrow{AR} \perp m$
$\overleftrightarrow{AR} \perp n$
$\overline{BD} \cong \overline{BE}$
Concl.: $\overline{CF} \cong \overline{CG}$

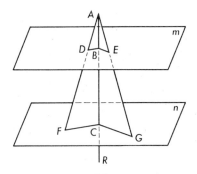

12. Given: $\overleftrightarrow{AB} \perp m$
$\overleftrightarrow{BE}$ is the $\perp$ bisector
of $\overline{DC}$.
Concl.: $\overline{AD} \cong \overline{AC}$

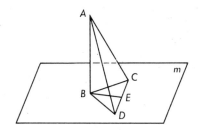

13. Given: $\overleftrightarrow{AB} \perp m$
$\overleftrightarrow{BE}$ is the $\perp$ bisector
of $\overline{DC}$.
Concl.: $\overleftrightarrow{AE} \perp \overleftrightarrow{DC}$ (Hint:
Use information
from Problem 12.)

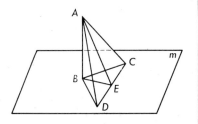

14. Given: $\overline{EA} \cong \overline{EC}$
$\overline{BA} \cong \overline{BC}$
$\angle AED \cong \angle CED$
Concl.: $\overleftrightarrow{DB} \perp \overleftrightarrow{AC}$

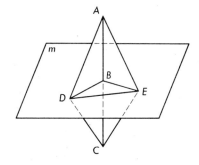

15. * Given: $\triangle ABC$ is in plane m.
P is not in plane m.
$\triangle PBC \cong \triangle ABC$
Concl.: $\angle APD \cong \angle PAD$
(Hint: Prove $\triangle DPA$
to be isosceles.)

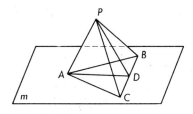

1. If from a given point not on a plane two oblique line segments and a perpendicular are drawn to a plane such that the foot of the perpendicular is equidistant from the feet of the oblique line segments, then the oblique line segments are congruent.
2. If a plane is the perpendicular bisector of a line segment, then any point on the plane is equidistant from the endpoints of the line segment.
3. If from a point on a line perpendicular to a plane congruent oblique line segments are drawn to the plane, then the foot of the perpendicular will be equidistant from the feet of the oblique line segments.
4. If from any point on a line perpendicular to a plane oblique lines are drawn to the plane so that they form congruent angles with the perpendicular, then the foot of the perpendicular is equidistant from the feet of the oblique lines.
5. If a line is perpendicular to the plane of a circle at its center, then all oblique lines drawn from any point on the perpendicular to points of the circle make congruent angles with the perpendicular.
6. Two planes are perpendicular to the same line segment at its endpoints. Oblique line segments are drawn through the midpoint of this segment terminating in the two planes. Prove that this point is also the midpoint of the oblique line segments.
7. If the foot of a perpendicular to a plane of a triangle is equidistant from the vertices of the triangle, then every point on the perpendicular is equidistant from the vertices of the triangle.

■ Test and Review

1. The diagram below is to be used in answering the questions that follow it.

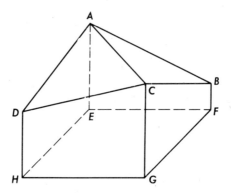

(a) Name three sets of four coplanar points.

(b) How many planes are there in this figure?

(c) Name two points that are common to planes *HF* and *BG*.

(d) Name the planes that have as two of its elements the points *A* and *E*.

(e) Name all the planes that have the point *H* in common.

(f) If $\overleftrightarrow{CG}$ is perpendicular to plane *HF*, what conclusion can be drawn?

(g) What plane is determined by the point *E* and the line *AB*?

(h) What plane is determined by the points *E*, *G*, and *H*?

(i) What plane is determined by $\overleftrightarrow{DA}$ and $\overleftrightarrow{HD}$?

2. If the four vertices of a four-sided polygon are coplanar, will the lines joining the pairs of opposite vertices also lie in that plane? Justify your answer.

3. Will the median of a triangle lie in the plane of that triangle? Justify your answer.

4. If a line is not perpendicular to a plane, what is the maximum number of lines in the plane to which it can be perpendicular?

5. If a line is perpendicular to each of two intersecting lines at their point of intersection, what can be said of the plane determined by these two intersecting lines?

6. Of four points, three are collinear. Are the four coplanar? Justify your answer.

7. If the lines *AB* and *CD* have the point *P* in common, then what can be said of the five points *A*, *B*, *C*, *D*, and *P*?

8. In the diagram at the right, point *D* is not in the plane *ABC*. Can you justify in any way why point *A* is the only point that $\overleftrightarrow{DA}$ has in common with plane *ABC*?

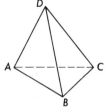

B

Prove each of the following:

1. Given: Plane m and $\odot O$
　　　　$\overleftrightarrow{PO} \perp m$
　Concl.: $\angle APO \cong \angle BPO$

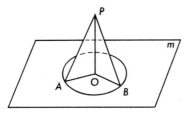

Given: Plane m bisects $\overline{AB}$. **2.**
　　　　$\overleftrightarrow{AB} \perp m$
Concl.: $\triangle PAB$ is isosceles.

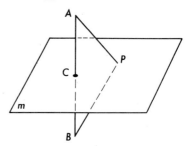

3. Given: $\overleftrightarrow{PA} \perp m$
　　　　$\angle ABC \cong \angle ACB$
　Concl.: $\angle PBC \cong \angle PCB$

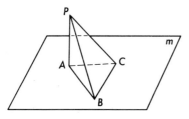

Given: $\overleftrightarrow{AB} \perp m$ **4.**
　　　　$\overline{AD} \cong \overline{AC}$
　　　　E is the midpoint
　　　　of $\overline{DC}$.
Concl.: $\overleftrightarrow{BE} \perp \overleftrightarrow{CD}$

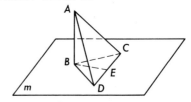

5. Given: Plane m with Q the
　　　　midpoint of $\overline{AB}$ and
　　　　$\overline{CD}$
　　　　P is equidistant from
　　　　A, B, C, and D.
　Concl.: $\overleftrightarrow{PQ} \perp m$

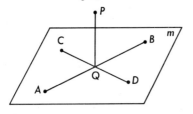

Given: Circles A and B in **6.**
　　　　plane m
　　　　$\overleftrightarrow{PQ} \perp m$
Concl.: $\triangle PRS$ is isosceles.

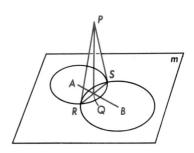

Prove each of the following statements:

1. If a line is perpendicular to the plane of a circle at its center, then all oblique lines drawn from any point on the perpendicular to points of the circle will make congruent angles with the radii drawn to these points.

2. A line is perpendicular to the plane of an isosceles triangle at the point of intersection of the angle bisectors of the base angles. If from any point on this perpendicular line segments are drawn to the vertices of the base angles, an isosceles triangle will be formed.

3. If from any point on the perpendicular bisector of a line segment a line is drawn perpendicular to the plane determined by the line segment and the perpendicular bisector, then any point of the perpendicular will be equidistant from the endpoints of the line segment.

4. Two planes are perpendicular to a line segment at its endpoints. Two oblique line segments are drawn, one from each foot and terminating in the other plane. If the oblique segments make congruent angles with the perpendicular segment, then the oblique segments are congruent.

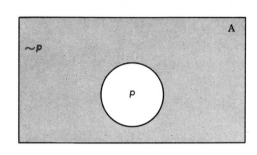

8

The Indirect Proof
and Parallelism

A PRINCIPLE THAT HAS GREAT IMPORTANCE in geometry concerns itself with the relationships that exist between various angles of a triangle. No matter what the triangle may be—whether it be acute as in Figure 8-1, obtuse as in Figure 8-2, or even right—∠1 will always bear the same relation to each of the other angles of the triangle.

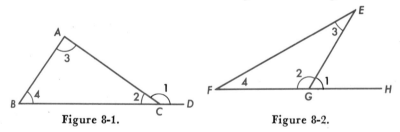

Figure 8-1.   Figure 8-2.

The apparent relation, and one with which we are familiar, is the fact that ∠1 is both supplementary and adjacent to ∠2. In addition, moreover, we will prove that its measure is greater than the measures of either ∠3 or ∠4. The mere reference to the words *greater than* implies that we will have to create new assumptions, for nowhere, thus far, have we established the tools for showing when the measure of one angle will be larger than another or when the measure of one line segment will be larger than another.

In the event that you may have forgotten some of your work in algebra, the symbol $>$ is used to replace the words "is greater than," while the symbol $<$ replaces the words "is less than." Thus, the expression

$$"5 > 2"$$

is read as

$$"5 \text{ is greater than } 2"$$

while the expression

$$"4 < 7"$$

is read as

$$"4 \text{ is less than } 7"$$

Each of these relations, or *inequalities*, can be read in either direction; that is, either from left to right, as

$$"5 \text{ is greater than } 2"$$

or from right to left, as

$$"2 \text{ is less than } 5"$$

Students who are just learning these symbols frequently confuse one with the other. A simple device for keeping them clear in your mind is to remember that *the arrowhead always points to the smaller number.*

With these symbols at our disposal, we are prepared to create a postulate establishing when one number will be larger than another.

POSTULATE 22: If a, b, and c are positive numbers

where $a = b + c$
then $a > b$ and $a > c$

Actually, this postulate points out no more than to say that

if   5 is equal to 2 plus 3
then   5 must be greater than 2
and   5 must be greater than 3

From our point of view, also, there was no need to state that a, b, and c were *positive* numbers, for we deal with no others in our work.

When, though, have we encountered a situation in geometry wherein a single number represented the sum of two other numbers? Actually, this has occurred but twice in our work. The first time was when we defined the sum of two line segments and the second when we defined the sum of two angles. Thus, in Figure 8-3 the $m \overline{AC}$ was defined as the sum of the $m \overline{AB}$

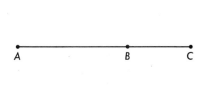

Figure 8-3.

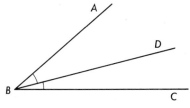

Figure 8-4.

and the m $\overline{BC}$, while in Figure 8-4 m $\angle ABC$ was defined as the sum of the measures of $\angle ABD$ and $\angle DBC$. By using symbols these relations can be expressed as

   (1) m $\overline{AC} = m$ $\overline{AB} + m$ $\overline{BC}$
   (2) m $\angle ABC = m$ $\angle ABD + m$ $\angle DBC$

Thus, by using Postulate 22, it immediately follows that

   (1) m $\overline{AC} > m$ $\overline{AB}$ and m $\overline{AC} > m$ $\overline{BC}$
   (2) m $\angle ABC > m$ $\angle ABD$ and m $\angle ABC > m$ $\angle DBC$

Quite often $\overline{AB}$ and $\overline{BC}$ are referred to as the *parts* of $\overline{AC}$, while $\angle ABD$ and $\angle DBC$ are the *parts* of $\angle ABC$. In view of this and the relations shown above, it is apparent why Postulate 22 is frequently quoted as

POSTULATE 22A: The whole is greater than any of its parts.

Let us return to the figures on page 218. An angle such as $\angle 1$ is called an *exterior* angle of a polygon. In this case, of course, it would be an exterior angle of a triangle.

DEFINITION 46: An exterior angle of a polygon is an angle that is adjacent to and·supplementary to an angle of the polygon.

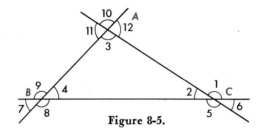

Figure 8-5.

How many exterior angles does the triangle have at vertex C? From the definition of an exterior angle, why is $\angle 6$ not an exterior angle? How is $\angle 6$ related to $\angle 2$? How many exterior angles will a triangle have? How are the two exterior angles at any vertex related?

Occasionally, for emphasis, the *angles of a triangle*—$\angle\!\!\!\angle$ 2, 3, and 4 in the diagram above—are called *interior angles of the triangle*. With reference to either exterior $\angle 1$ or $\angle 5$, the $\angle\!\!\!\angle$ 3 and 4 are spoken of as the *remote interior angles*. They are the interior angles that do not have a vertex in common with the exterior angle being considered. What are the remote interior angles with reference to exterior $\angle 11$? With reference to exterior $\angle 8$? To which exterior angles are $\angle 3$ and $\angle 4$ the remote interior angles?

THEOREM 22: The measure of an exterior angle of a triangle is greater than the measure of either of the remote interior angles.

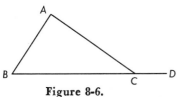

Figure 8-6.

Given: $\triangle ABC$ with exterior $\angle ACD$
Concl.: $m \angle ACD > m \angle A$
              $m \angle ACD > m \angle B$

ANALYSIS: By creating an angle that is part of $\angle ACD$, its measure will be less than the measure of $\angle ACD$. Furthermore, we will show that this angle is congruent to $\angle A$. From this it will follow that the measure of $\angle ACD$ is greater than the measure of $\angle A$. Which angle in Figure 8-7 is part of $\angle ACD$? What else will have to be shown to be true about this angle?

The proof that $m \angle ACD > m \angle B$ will be given as an exercise for you to do.

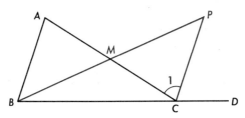

Figure 8-7.

PROOF STATEMENTS	REASONS
1. Let M be the midpoint of $\overline{AC}$.	1. Every line segment has a midpoint.
2. Let $\overleftrightarrow{BM}$ be the line through points B and M.	2. Why?
3. Extend $\overleftrightarrow{BM}$ to point P such that $\overline{MP} \cong \overline{BM}$. (s)	3. A line can be extended as far as desired in either direction.
4. Let $\overleftrightarrow{PC}$ be the line through P and C.	4. Why?
5. $\overline{AM} \cong \overline{CM}$ (s)	5. Def. of a midpoint
6. $\angle AMB \cong \angle CMP$ (a)	6. Why?
7. $\triangle AMB \cong \triangle CMP$	7. Why?
8. $\angle A \cong \angle 1$	8. Why?
9. $m \angle A = m \angle 1$	9. Def. of congruent angles
10. But, $m \angle ACD > m \angle 1$	10. The whole is greater than any of its parts.
11. $\therefore\ m \angle ACD > m \angle A$	11. Substitution postulate

EXERCISES

1. By using the diagram at the right, justify the drawing of each of the red lines and prove that $m \angle ACD > m \angle B$ by following the pattern of proof for Theorem 22.

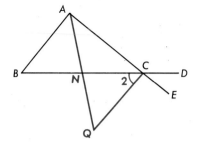

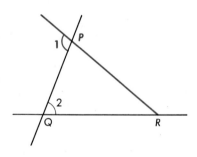

2. (a) In the drawing at the right, angles D and C are the remote interior angles with reference to which exterior angles?

(b) How is $\angle ABD$ related to $\angle D$?

(c) How is $\angle EBC$ related to $\angle D$?

(d) How is $\angle ABE$ related to $\angle DBC$?

3. (a) How does the measure of $\angle 1$ compare with that of $\angle 2$?

(b) If the $m \angle 2 = 80$, what can be said of $\angle 1$?

(c) If $\overleftrightarrow{PR}$ is made to rotate about P in a counterclockwise direction, what will happen to the measure of $\angle 1$? To the measure of $\angle 2$? Hence, eventually, how should the measure of $\angle 1$ compare with the measure of $\angle 2$?

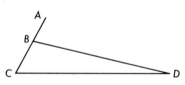

4. (a) What is the measure of $\angle ABD$?

(b) What can be said of the measure of $\angle C$?

(c) What can be said of the measure of $\angle D$?

Given: $m \angle DBC = 110$

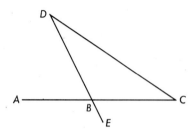

5. (a) What is the measure of $\angle ACB$?

(b) What is the measure of $\angle ACD$?

(c) Can you give any justification for the fact that $m \angle ABC$ coult *not* be 110 as noted in the Given Data?

Given: $m \angle ABC = 110$
$\overline{AB} \cong \overline{AC}$

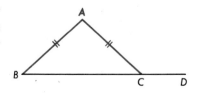

6. Can you justify the statement that one of the base angles of an isosceles triangle can not be an obtuse angle?

7. Can you justify the statement that one of the base angles of an isosceles triangle can not be a right angle?

8. (a) Can you justify why $m \angle ACD$ can not be 40 as stated in the Given Data?

   (b) Is it possible for the $m \angle ACD$ to be 90? Why or why not?

   (c) What is the least value that the measure of $\angle ACD$ may have? Why?

   Given: $m \angle ACD = 40$
   $\overline{AB} \cong \overline{AC}$

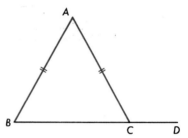

9. (a) What is the value of $m \angle 1 + m \angle 2$?

   (b) How is $m \angle C$ related to $m \angle 1$?

   (c) By using the information from (a) and (b), what can be said of $m \angle C + m \angle 2$?

   (d) What can be said of the value of $m \angle D + m \angle 2$?

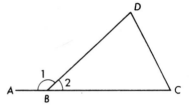

10. (a) What is the $m \angle BDC$?

    (b) What is the $m \angle BCD$?

    (c) What is the $m \angle BCA$?

    (d) What is the $m \angle ACD$?

    (e) How does $m \angle BDE$ compare with $m \angle ACD$?

    (f) $ABDC$ is a four-sided polygon. Will the measure of an exterior angle of any polygon be greater than the measure of any of the remote interior angles? Justify your answer in terms of polygon $ABDC$.

    Given: $\triangle ABC$ and $\triangle CBD$ are congruent isosceles triangles as marked in the diagram.
    $m \angle BDE = 100$

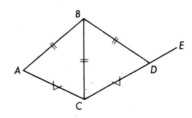

11. In isosceles $\triangle ABC$, $\overline{AB} \cong \overline{AC}$. Base BC is extended to point D. The bisectors of $\angle ABC$ and ACD intersect at E. Can you justify in any manner whatsoever that $\angle ECD$ can not be an angle of 30°?

■ Nonintersecting Lines and the Indirect Proof

We would like to pursue further the analysis begun in Problem 3 of the preceding exercises. When we examine Figure 8-8, we note

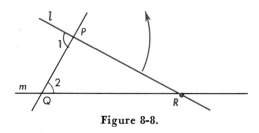

Figure 8-8.

that $m \angle 1 > m \angle 2$ on the basis of the exterior angle theorem. Now, should we allow l to rotate counterclockwise about point P, although nothing happens to the measure of $\angle 2$, the measure of $\angle 1$ grows smaller and smaller. Eventually, of course, l will coincide with line PQ, and when this occurs, the measure of $\angle 1$ will be zero. However, at some position between its present measure and that of zero, the measure of $\angle 1$ will approach and be equal to the measure of $\angle 2$. But, what happens to other points in the diagram as l rotates about P? Points P and Q will remain fixed, but point R will move off to the right.

Notice, in Figure 8-9, that although the amount of rotation from position $\overleftrightarrow{RP}$ to $\overleftrightarrow{R_2P}$ is approximately the same as from $\overleftrightarrow{R_2P}$ to $\overleftrightarrow{R_3P}$, the line segment

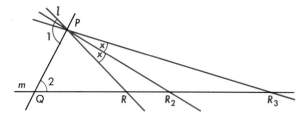

Figure 8-9.

R_2R_3 is far greater than $\overline{RR_2}$. And should l continue to be rotated to a fourth position so that another angle is formed whose measure is again the same as $m \angle RPR_2$, the point of intersection of l with m will be thrown far, far to the right. Thus, as the measure of $\angle 1$ approaches the measure of $\angle 2$, the point of intersection of l with m appears to recede so rapidly to the right that it seems to disappear completely. Were this situation expressed formally as a problem, it would be

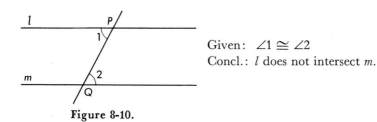

Given: $\angle 1 \cong \angle 2$

Concl.: l does not intersect m.

Figure 8-10.

ANALYSIS: This problem, obviously, involves a difficulty that we have not encountered before. Until now we have examined situations in which angles or line segments had to be proved congruent, lines had to be proved perpendicular, triangles had to be proved congruent, and the like. But at no time had it been necessary to justify that lines *do not intersect*, as we are confronted with in this problem. To show how to overcome this difficulty, we will have to take a rather lengthy detour.

Let us assume that you and your family are sitting at the dinner table one evening when the lights suddenly go out. The group of you decide to seek the cause of this event without having to leave the table. And so you make a list of possible causes:

(1) The electric power in this section of the city is out.
(2) The light bulb has become defective.
(3) The fuse for this room has blown out.
(4) The switch has become defective.
(5) The wires leading to the light have separated.
(6) The electric power on this street is out.
(7) The main fuse for the entire house has blown out.

You then proceed to examine ways of eliminating some of these possible causes. By looking through the window you discover that the lights in the house behind you are still on. This would eliminate cause number 1. The fact that the lamp in the livingroom is still on does away with causes 6 and 7. The sound of the refrigerator motor, which operates on the same fuse as the light overhead, makes short work of cause 3.

$$\cancel{1} \quad 2 \quad \cancel{3} \quad 4 \quad 5 \quad \cancel{6} \quad \cancel{7}$$

And so you move from possibility to possibility, hoping to eliminate all but one of these possible causes. If this can be done, then what conclusion can be drawn concerning the possibility that remains? We are overlooking an important factor though. Who set up these possibilities? Could there, perhaps, have been some causes that you may not have considered? If this was so, then were you to eliminate all but cause #5, would it then follow that this cause led to the event? What is the major weakness in using the method of elimination to justify a conclusion?

The mechanic who examines your father's car to determine why it is

that this statement leads but to a logical inconsistency. Experience has shown that it is far easier to write the indirect proof in *paragraph form* than resort to the *two-column form* that has been used until now. Several examples will be given to illustrate this method of proof.

Illustration 1:

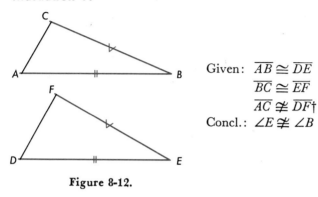

Given: $\overline{AB} \cong \overline{DE}$
$\overline{BC} \cong \overline{EF}$
$\overline{AC} \ncong \overline{DF}$†
Concl.: $\angle E \ncong \angle B$

Figure 8-12.

PROOF

By the law of the excluded middle one of these statements must be true and no other possibilities exist:

$$\angle E \ncong \angle B \quad \text{or} \quad \angle E \cong \angle B$$

Let us accept the possibility that $\angle E \cong \angle B$. From the Given Data we note that $\overline{AB} \cong \overline{DE}$ and $\overline{BC} \cong \overline{EF}$; hence, if $\angle E \cong \angle B$, it follows that $\triangle CAB \cong \triangle FDE$. If this is so, then $\overline{AC} \cong \overline{DF}$, according to the definition of congruent polygons. The Given Data, however, indicates that $\overline{AC} \ncong \overline{DF}$. Therefore, accepting the possibility that $\angle E \cong \angle B$ led to the logical inconsistency of $\overline{AC} \cong \overline{DF}$ and $\overline{AC} \ncong \overline{DF}$. According to the law of contradiction, both can not be true at the same time. Since $\overline{AC} \ncong \overline{DF}$ must be true, for it is part of the Given Data, then $\overline{AC} \cong \overline{DF}$ must be false and, so too, must $\angle E \cong \angle B$ be false. Hence, $\angle E \ncong \angle B$ must be true, for it is the only remaining possibility.

Illustration 2:

A triangle cannot have more than one obtuse angle.

---

† Whenever a slash is drawn through a symbol, it signifies that the word "not" should precede the symbol. In this case it implies "not congruent."

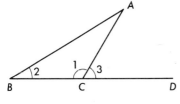

Given: $\triangle ABC$

Concl.: $\angle 1$ and $\angle 2$ are not both obtuse angles.

Figure 8-13.

PROOF

By the law of the excluded middle one of these statements must be true and no other possibilities exist:

$\angle 1$ and $\angle 2$ are not both obtuse angles.

or

$\angle 1$ and $\angle 2$ are both obtuse angles.

Let us accept the possibility that $\angle 1$ and $\angle 2$ are both obtuse angles. $\angle 1$ and $\angle 3$ are supplementary angles since their sum is a straight angle. However, from the fact that $\angle 1$ is obtuse, $\angle 3$ must be acute, for the sum of their measures is 180—the measure of one being greater than 90, the measure of the other must be less than 90. This would make the $m \angle 3$ not greater than the $m \angle 2$, since $\angle 3$ is acute but $\angle 2$ is obtuse. But this is contradictory to the theorem that the measure of the exterior angle of a triangle is greater than the measure of either of the remote interior angles.

Therefore, accepting the possibility that $\angle 1$ and $\angle 2$ are both obtuse led to the logical inconsistency of the truth of both $m \angle 3 \not> m \angle 2$ and $m \angle 3 > m \angle 2$. By the law of contradiction both can not be true at the same time. Since $m \angle 3 > m \angle 2$ must be true, for it is the result of a theorem, then $m \angle 3 \not> m \angle 2$ must be false. Therefore, the statement that $\angle 1$ and $\angle 2$ are both obtuse angles is also false. Hence, the statement that $\angle 1$ and $\angle 2$ are not both obtuse must be true, for it is the only remaining possibility.

EXERCISES

1. Write two contradictory statements that might occur in everyday experience.
2. Write two contradictory statements that might occur in geometry.
3. Write up a situation in everyday experience wherein the proof by elimination is used.

In each of the following problems you are to do three things:

(a) Decide what the extraordinary occurrence is for which a causal explanation has been formulated.

(b) State the cause that has been given that led to that event.

(c) Give at least one other possible cause that might have led to that event.

1. During a debate a child psychologist made the following statement: "The amazing increase in the sale of comic books with their sordid interpretation of crime has been accompanied by the equally amazing increase in the rate of crime committed by teenagers."

2. "Because we did not live up to our opportunity of joining the League of Nations after World War I, the League failed to prevent the most tragic war in history—the Second World War."

3. "Another advantage of establishing standards is that, inevitably, a rise in teaching standards must follow as the night the day. We are graduating only 40,000 scientists annually. Every day we postpone improving and upgrading education is a day lost in our scientific advancement."

4. "Since achieving independence, the gross volume of business in Centralia has increased by 65 percent, employment has risen, and exports have grown from 25 million to 125 million dollars annually."

Use the indirect proof in the proof of each of the following problems:

1. Given: $\overline{AC} \cong \overline{DF}$

$\overline{BC} \cong \overline{EF}$

$\angle C \not\cong \angle F$

Concl.: $\overline{AB} \not\cong \overline{DE}$

Given: $\overline{AB} \cong \overline{AC}$ **2.**

D is not the midpoint of $\overline{BC}$.

Concl.: $\overrightarrow{AD}$ does not bisect $\angle BAC$.

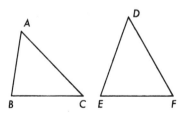

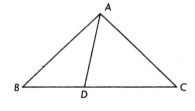

3. Given: $\overline{AB} \cong \overline{AC}$
$\overset{\leftrightarrow}{AD} \not\perp \overset{\leftrightarrow}{BC}$

Concl.: D is not the midpoint of $\overline{BC}$.

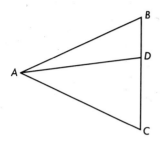

Given: B is the midpoint of $\overline{AC}$.
$\overline{DA} \not\cong \overline{DC}$

Concl.: $\overset{\leftrightarrow}{DB} \not\perp \overset{\leftrightarrow}{AC}$ **4.**

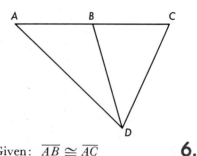

5. Given: $\odot O$ where $\overrightarrow{OD}$ does not bisect $\angle AOB$.

Concl.: $\overline{OD}$ is not the median to $\overline{AB}$.

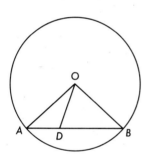

Given: $\overline{AB} \cong \overline{AC}$
$\overline{DB} \not\cong \overline{DC}$

Concl.: $\overrightarrow{AD}$ does not bisect $\angle BAC$. **6.**

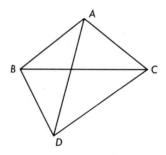

7. Given: $\overline{BA} \cong \overline{BD}$
$\overline{CD} \not\cong \overline{CA}$

Concl.: $\overset{\leftrightarrow}{BC}$ does not bisect $\overline{AD}$.

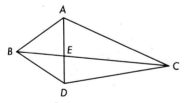

Given: $\odot O$ with $\overline{AB} \not\cong \overline{AC}$

Concl.: $\overset{\leftrightarrow}{AO}$ does not bisect $\overline{BC}$. **8.**

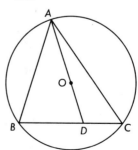

9. Given: $\triangle ABC$

Concl.: $\angle 2$ and $\angle 3$ are not both right angles. (See Illustration 2.)

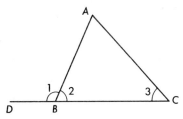

10. Given: $\overset{\leftrightarrow}{AC} \perp m$

$\overline{AB} \not\cong \overline{AD}$

Concl.: $\overline{BC} \not\cong \overline{DC}$

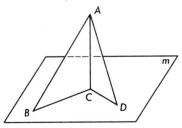

11. Given: $\overset{\leftrightarrow}{AB} \perp m$

$\overset{\leftrightarrow}{DC} \perp m$

$\overline{AB} \cong \overline{DC}$

E is not equidistant from A and D.

Concl.: E is not the midpoint of $\overline{BC}$.

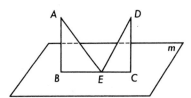

12. Given: $\odot B$ in plane m

$\overline{AC} \not\cong \overline{AD}$

Concl.: $\overset{\leftrightarrow}{AB} \not\perp m$

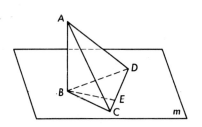

13. Given: m is the $\perp$ bisector of $\overline{AC}$.

$\overline{DA} \not\cong \overline{DC}$

Concl.: D does not lie in m.

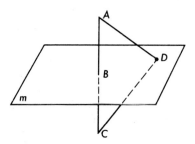

14. Given: $\overset{\leftrightarrow}{AB} \perp m$

$\overset{\leftrightarrow}{BE} \perp \overset{\leftrightarrow}{CD}$

$\overline{AC} \not\cong \overline{AD}$

Concl.: $\overline{CE} \not\cong \overline{DE}$

1. If two angles of a triangle are not congruent, then the sides opposite them are not congruent.

2. If two sides of a triangle are not congruent, then the angles opposite them are not congruent.

3. If a triangle has no two sides congruent, then the perpendicular bisector of one of the sides does not pass through the opposite vertex.

4. Two lines perpendicular to the same line do not intersect. (Hint: See Problem 9, Group C.)

5. A base angle of an isosceles triangle can not be an obtuse angle.

6. A base angle of an isosceles triangle can not be a right angle.

7. In a right triangle neither of the two angles that are not the right angle can be obtuse.

8. Any point that is not equidistant from the endpoints of a line segment is not on the perpendicular bisector of the line segment.

9. A line segment can have only one midpoint. (Hint: Use the postulate that the whole is greater than any of its parts.)

10. An angle can have only one bisector.

11. At a given point on a given line there can be only one line perpendicular to the given line.

12. From a given point not on a given line there can be only one line perpendicular to the given line.

13. Two lines perpendicular to the same plane can not intersect.

14. If from any point on a perpendicular to a plane line segments of unequal measures are drawn to the plane, they will make angles of unequal measures with the perpendicular.

15. From a given point not on a given line there can be only one plane that is perpendicular to the given line.

16. From a given point in the interior of an angle perpendicular segments are drawn to the sides of the angle. If the ray whose endpoint is the vertex of this angle and which passes through the given point is not the bisector of the angle, then the perpendicular segments are not congruent.

■ Parallelism—Section I

We have detoured so far from our original path that you may have forgotten why the need for the indirect proof arose. We were trying to prove the problem below when we realized that we had no way to prove that two lines cannot intersect. A new and different approach was necessary in order to draw our conclusion. Now we are ready to take a fresh look at this problem.

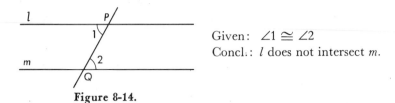

Given: $\angle 1 \cong \angle 2$
Concl.: l does not intersect m.

Figure 8-14.

ANALYSIS: By using the indirect proof, the solution to this problem is very much the same as that used in the preceding exercises.

PROOF

By the law of the excluded middle one of the following statements must be true and no other possibilities exist:

l does not intersect m or l does intersect m

Let us accept the possibility that l intersects m. This implies that l will meet

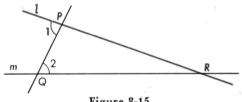

Figure 8-15.

m in some point R. The lines l, m, and PQ will form the triangle PQR. Hence, the measure of $\angle 1$ will be greater than the measure of $\angle 2$. The Given Data, however, states that $m \angle 1 = m \angle 2$. Therefore, accepting the possibility that l intersects m leads to the logical inconsistency of the truth of both $m \angle 1 = m \angle 2$ and $m \angle 1 \neq m \angle 2$. By the law of contradiction both can not be true at the same time. Since "$m \angle 1 = m \angle 2$" must be true, for it is part of the Given Data, then "$m \angle 1 \neq m \angle 2$" must be false and, therefore, the statement that "l intersects m" is also false. Hence, "l does not intersect m" must be true for it is the only remaining possibility.

In the same manner it can be shown that l cannot intersect m to the left of Q.

Two coplanar lines, such as l and m, that do not intersect are called *parallel lines*.

DEFINITION 47: Parallel lines are two coplanar lines that do not intersect.

Before it is possible to express the statement of the theorem that has just been proved, it will be necessary to define a number of other terms.

In the diagram above $\overleftrightarrow{PQ}$ is called a transversal with reference to l and m.

DEFINITION 48: A transversal is a line that intersects two other lines in two
distinct points.

In Figure 8-16, n is a transversal with reference to l and m, for it inter-

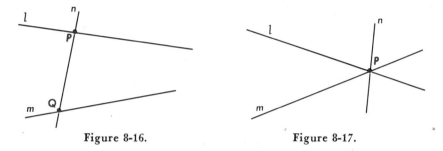

Figure 8-16.   Figure 8-17.

sects these lines in the two distinct points P and Q. In Figure 8-17 it is not a
transversal, for it intersects the two lines in but one point, P.

A point A may be selected on the transversal, and the three points Q,
P, and A can be read in the order in which they appear on that transversal.
If this order is either QPA or AQP (see Figures 8-18 and 8-19), then point A

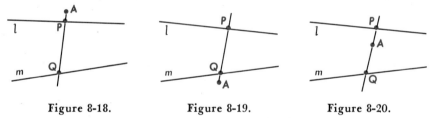

Figure 8-18.   Figure 8-19.   Figure 8-20.

is said to be in the *exterior region* with reference to the lines l and m. In either
event, A is not between P and Q. Should A be between P and Q, then the
point A falls in the *interior region* with reference to l and m. This occurs in
Figure 8-20.

For simplicity the regions are pictured in Figure 8-21.

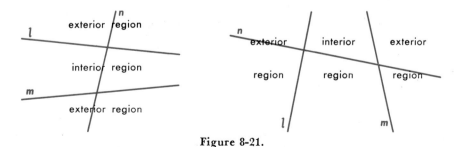

Figure 8-21.

When a transversal intersects two lines, eight angles are formed. Every pair of angles is given a special name. Several of these names are familiar to you. Thus, what is the name for the pair of angles 6 and 8? Angles 1 and 3? Angles 5 and 6? Angles 1 and 4?

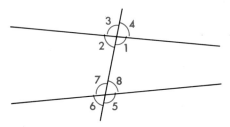

Figure 8-22.

The pairs of angles such as 2 and 8 or 1 and 7 that are in the interior region but on opposite sides of the transversal are called *alternate interior angles*. These angles can be recognized by the fact that they form the letter Z, either

in normal form   or backwards   or sideways

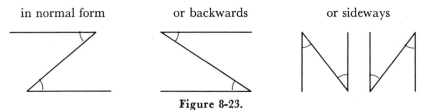

Figure 8-23.

DEFINITION 49: Alternate interior angles are two angles formed by a transversal intersecting two lines, both angles being in the interior region, on opposite sides of the transversal, and at different vertices.

In Figure 8-22 the pairs of angles such as 4 and 8, 3 and 7, 5 and 1, or 2 and 6 that are on the same side of the transversal so as one is interior and the other is exterior are called *corresponding angles*. These angles can be recognized by the fact that they form the letter F in many ways.

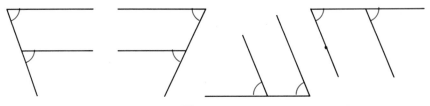

Figure 8-24.

The pairs of angles 3 and 5, or 4 and 6, of Figure 8-22, being on opposite sides of the transversal, are known also as *alternate* angles. Now, however, since they are in the exterior region, they bear the full name of *alternate exterior angles*.

DEFINITION 50: Alternate exterior angles are two angles formed by a transversal intersecting two lines, both angles being in the exterior region,
on opposite sides of the transversal, and at different vertices.

DEFINITION 51: Corresponding angles are two angles formed by a transversal intersecting two lines; the angles are at different vertices, one being
interior and the other exterior, but they are on the same side of the
transversal.

EXERCISES

1. (a) Name two pairs of alternate interior angles.
   (b) Name two pairs of alternate exterior angles.
   (c) Name four pairs of corresponding angles.
   (d) Name a pair of interior angles on the same side of the transversal.
   (e) Name a pair of exterior angles on the same side of the transversal.

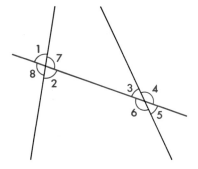

2. (a) Using l as a transversal with reference to m and n, name two pairs of
       alternate interior angles. Name a pair of alternate exterior angles.
   (b) By using m as a transversal, what name does the pair of angles 3 and
       8 have? What name does the pair of angles 2 and 5 have?
   (c) Using n as a transversal, name a pair of interior angles on the same
       side of the transversal. Name a pair of corresponding angles.

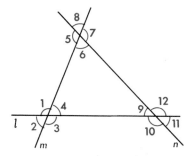

3. (a) By using $\overleftrightarrow{BD}$ as a transversal with reference to $\overleftrightarrow{AD}$ and $\overleftrightarrow{BC}$, what is
       the name of the pair of angles ADB and DBC?

(b) List a pair of angles formed by the transversal $\overleftrightarrow{BD}$ and the lines AB and DC. What is the name of this pair of angles?

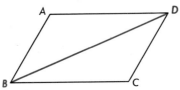

4. (a) What is the only line in the diagram that, without being extended, can act as a transversal with reference to $\overleftrightarrow{AB}$ and $\overleftrightarrow{EF}$?

(b) What is the name of the pair of angles that this line forms with $\overleftrightarrow{AB}$ and $\overleftrightarrow{EF}$?

(c) By using $\overleftrightarrow{BE}$ as a transversal with reference to the lines AC and DF, what is the name of the pair of angles ACB and FDE? Of the pair of angles ACD and FDC?

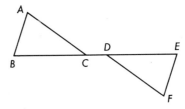

5. $\overleftrightarrow{EF}$ is used as a transversal for the questions that follow.

(a) What name can be given to the pair of angles ENH and EMK? Angles CNM and BMN?

(b) Name a pair of alternate exterior angles with reference to the lines JK and GH.

(c) Is there any special name for the pair of angles BMK and DNH? Justify your answer.

(d) Name a pair of angles in the diagram where the transversal is not a side of either angle. Does this pair of angles have a special name? Justify your answer.

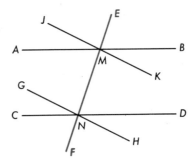

Parallelism—Section II

In terms of the words that we have recently defined, the problem that was proved on page 234 can now be stated as

THEOREM 23: If two lines are cut by a transversal such that the alternate interior angles are congruent, then the lines are parallel. †

As an exercise, without referring to the proof on page 234, see if you can prove the above theorem.

Theorem 23 is the principal method we have for proving lines parallel. The next two theorems that we are about to present are developed on the basis of Theorem 23. There is no necessity to apply the indirect proof when we attempt to justify these theorems, for now we need but show that the alternate interior angles are congruent to prove lines parallel. The symbol ‖ represents the word *parallel*.

THEOREM 24: If two lines are cut by a transversal such that the corresponding angles are congruent, then the lines are parallel.

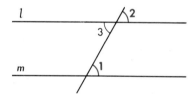

Given: $\angle 1 \cong \angle 2$
Concl.: $l \parallel m$

Figure 8-25.

ANALYSIS: Simply show that $\angle 1 \cong \angle 3$, then by the theorem on the alternate interior angles the lines will be parallel.

PROOF	STATEMENTS	REASONS
1. $\angle 1 \cong \angle 2$		1. Given
2. $\angle 3 \cong \angle 2$		2. Why?
3. $\angle 1 \cong \angle 3$		3. Why?
4. $\therefore l \parallel m$		4. If two lines are cut by a transversal such that the alternate interior angles are congruent, then the lines are parallel.

† Henceforth, unless otherwise stated, all points and lines in the statement of any theorem or problem should be considered to be coplanar.

THEOREM 25: If two lines are cut by a transversal such that the alternate exterior angles are congruent, then the lines are parallel.

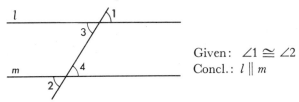

Given: $\angle 1 \cong \angle 2$

Concl.: $l \parallel m$

Figure 8-26.

ANALYSIS: By showing that $\angle 3 \cong \angle 4$ it will follow that $l \parallel m$ from the theorem on the alternate interior angles.

PROOF

The proof will be left for you to do.

THEOREM 26: If two lines are perpendicular to the same line, then they are parallel.

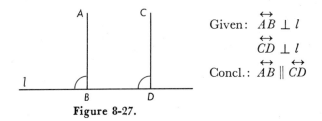

Given: $\overleftrightarrow{AB} \perp l$

$\overleftrightarrow{CD} \perp l$

Concl.: $\overleftrightarrow{AB} \parallel \overleftrightarrow{CD}$

Figure 8-27.

ANALYSIS: By showing that a pair of corresponding angles are congruent it will follow that $\overleftrightarrow{AB} \parallel \overleftrightarrow{CD}$.

Although there are a number of other methods for proving lines parallel, the three given in theorems 23, 24, and 25 have the widest application. Should you be required to prove that lines are parallel, try to prove that one of the following relations is true:

(1) The alternate interior angles formed by the lines and a transversal are congruent.

(2) The alternate exterior angles formed by the lines and a transversal are congruent.

(3) The corresponding angles formed by the lines and a transversal are congruent.

Illustration:

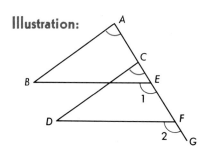

Given: $\overline{AC} \cong \overline{EF}$
$\overline{BE} \cong \overline{DF}$
$\angle 1 \cong \angle 2$
Concl.: $\overset{\leftrightarrow}{AB} \parallel \overset{\leftrightarrow}{CD}$

Figure 8-28.

ANALYSIS: By using $\overset{\leftrightarrow}{AG}$ as a transversal with reference to $\overset{\leftrightarrow}{AB}$ and $\overset{\leftrightarrow}{CD}$, we note that a pair of corresponding angles is formed. These are $\angle A$ and DCF. By proving $\triangle ABE \cong \triangle CDF$ these angles will be congruent, and hence, $\overset{\leftrightarrow}{AB}$ will be parallel to $\overset{\leftrightarrow}{CD}$.

PROOF	(The reasons will be left for you to supply.)

1. $\overline{AC} \cong \overline{EF}$
2. $\overline{CE} \cong \overline{CE}$
3. $\overline{AE} \cong \overline{CF}$ (s)
4. $\overline{BE} \cong \overline{DF}$ (s)
5. $\angle AEB$ is supp. to $\angle 1$.
6. $\angle CFD$ is supp. to $\angle 2$.

7. But, $\angle 1 \cong \angle 2$
8. $\therefore \angle AEB \cong \angle CFD$ (a)
9. $\triangle ABE \cong \triangle CDF$
10. $\angle A \cong \angle DCF$
11. $\therefore \overset{\leftrightarrow}{AB} \parallel \overset{\leftrightarrow}{CD}$

EXERCISES

$$\boxed{A}$$

1. Given: $\angle 1 \cong \angle 2$
$\overline{AB} \cong \overline{DC}$
Concl.: $\overset{\leftrightarrow}{AD} \parallel \overset{\leftrightarrow}{BC}$

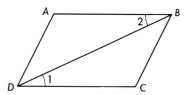

Given: $\overline{AB}$ and $\overline{CD}$ bisect   **2.**
each other at E.
Concl.: $\overset{\leftrightarrow}{AD} \parallel \overset{\leftrightarrow}{CB}$

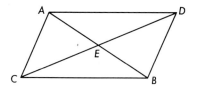

3. Given: $\angle 1 \cong \angle 2$
$\overline{BD} \cong \overline{CE}$
$\overline{AC} \cong \overline{DF}$
Concl.: $\overset{\leftrightarrow}{AB} \parallel \overset{\leftrightarrow}{EF}$

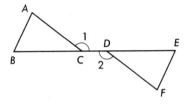

Given: $\overline{AB} \cong \overline{EF}$ **4.**
$\overline{BD} \cong \overline{CE}$
$\overline{AC} \cong \overline{DF}$
Concl.: $\overset{\leftrightarrow}{AC} \parallel \overset{\leftrightarrow}{DF}$

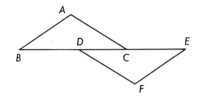

5. Given: $\overline{CE} \cong \overline{BF}$
$\overline{AE} \cong \overline{DF}$
$\angle AEC \cong \angle DFB$
Concl.: $\overset{\leftrightarrow}{AB} \parallel \overset{\leftrightarrow}{CD}$

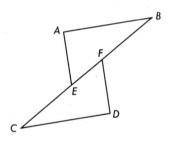

Given: $\overline{AB} \cong \overline{FC}$ **6.**
$\overline{BC} \cong \overline{DE}$
$\overset{\leftrightarrow}{AB} \perp \overset{\leftrightarrow}{BE}$
$\overset{\leftrightarrow}{FC} \perp \overset{\leftrightarrow}{BE}$
Concl.: $\overset{\leftrightarrow}{AD} \parallel \overset{\leftrightarrow}{EF}$

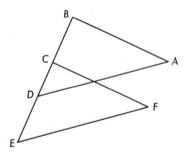

7. Given: $\odot O$ with O the
midpoint of $\overline{EF}$
Concl.: $\overset{\leftrightarrow}{AB} \parallel \overset{\leftrightarrow}{CD}$

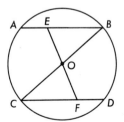

By using the diagram below **8.**
prove Theorem 24 again.
Do *not* label any other angles in the diagram.

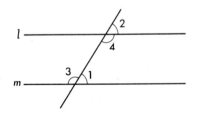

9. By using the diagram below prove Theorem 25 again. Do *not* label any other angles in the diagram.

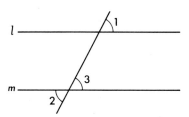

10. Given: ∠1 is supp. to ∠2.

Concl.: $\overleftrightarrow{AB} \parallel \overleftrightarrow{CD}$

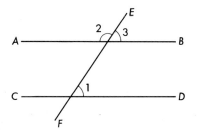

11. Given: ∠1 is supp. to ∠2.
Concl.: $l \parallel m$

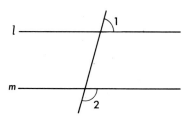

12. Given: ∠1 ≅ ∠2
∠2 is supp. to ∠3.

Concl.: $c \parallel d$

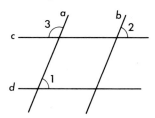

13. Given: ∠1 ≅ ∠4
∠2 ≅ ∠3
Concl.: $\overleftrightarrow{AB} \parallel \overleftrightarrow{FE}$

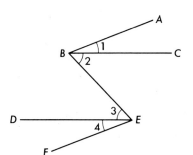

14. Given: $\overleftrightarrow{CD} \perp \overleftrightarrow{FD}$
$\overleftrightarrow{EF} \perp \overleftrightarrow{FD}$
∠CDA ≅ ∠EFB

Concl.: $\overleftrightarrow{AD} \parallel \overleftrightarrow{FB}$

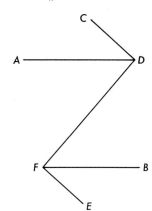

15. Given: $\angle AGE \cong \angle DEG$

$\overrightarrow{GH}$ bisects $\angle AGE$.

$\overrightarrow{EF}$ bisects $\angle DEG$.

Concl.: $\overleftrightarrow{GH} \parallel \overleftrightarrow{EF}$

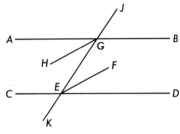

16. Given: $\angle JEB \cong \angle EGD$

$\overrightarrow{EF}$ bisects $\angle JEB$.

$\overrightarrow{GH}$ bisects $\angle EGD$.

Concl.: $\overleftrightarrow{EF} \parallel \overleftrightarrow{GH}$

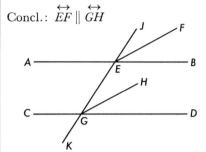

17. Given: $\triangle ABC$ is isosceles with $\overline{AB} \cong \overline{AC}$.

$\angle 1 \cong \angle C$

Concl.: $\overleftrightarrow{AD} \parallel \overleftrightarrow{BC}$

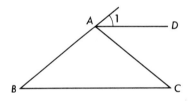

18. Given: $\triangle ABC$ is isosceles with $\overline{AB} \cong \overline{AC}$.

$\overrightarrow{CB}$ bisects $\angle ACD$.

Concl.: $\overleftrightarrow{AB} \parallel \overleftrightarrow{CD}$

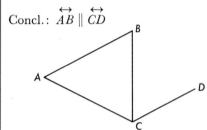

19.* Given: $\overline{AB} \cong \overline{AC}$

$\overline{AD} \cong \overline{AG}$

$\overrightarrow{AF}$ bisects $\angle DAG$.

Concl.: $\overleftrightarrow{BC} \parallel \overleftrightarrow{DG}$ (Hint: Prove that $\measuredangle AEC$ and AFG are right angles.)

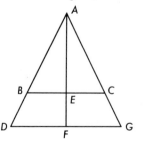

20.* Given: $\odot O$ with $\overleftrightarrow{EF}$ bisecting $\overline{AB}$ and $\overline{CD}$

Concl.: $\overleftrightarrow{AB} \parallel \overleftrightarrow{CD}$

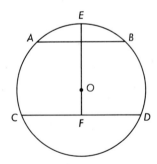

B

1. If two lines are cut by a transversal such that the interior angles on the same side of the transversal are supplementary, then the lines are parallel.
2. If the opposite sides of a four-sided polygon are congruent, then they are also parallel.
3. If a pair of corresponding sides of two congruent triangles fall on the same line but do not coincide, then either the other pairs of corresponding sides will be parallel or they will intersect to form isosceles triangles when extended.
4. Use the indirect proof to prove the theorem that if two lines are cut by a transversal such that the corresponding angles are congruent, then the lines are parallel.

■ Parallelism—Section III

When developing the theorem that two lines will be parallel when the alternate interior angles are congruent, we examined the relative positions of the lines l and m as the line l rotated about the point P. In its original position we knew that the measure of $\angle 1$ had to be greater than that of $\angle 2$. But as l was rotated about the point P, although the measure of

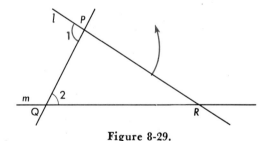

Figure 8-29.

$\angle 2$ did not change, $m \angle 1$ decreased toward zero. By using the indirect proof it was possible for us to show that when $m \angle 1$ reached the $m \angle 2$, the lines l and m could not intersect. What we did not investigate, however, was the possibility that l might not intersect m for some value of $m \angle 1$ where $m \angle 1$ was not equal to $m \angle 2$!

We did note in passing (see page 224) that as $m \angle 1$ approached $m \angle 2$ in size, a small amount of rotation threw the point of intersection of l and m a great distance to the right. Assume that in rotating l counterclockwise the position was eventually reached wherein the point of intersection between l and m could not be found. What would that imply concerning these two lines? Let us say also that when this position is reached, the $m \angle 1$ is still

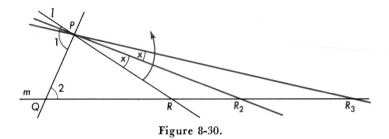

Figure 8-30.

larger than $m \angle 2$. Since we already know that l does not intersect m when $m \angle 1$ equals $m \angle 2$, we are faced with the situation that there must be at least two lines through P that do not intersect m. In fact, had we rotated line l about point P in a clockwise direction, we might again come to a first position of l on the left where l does not intersect m. By virtue of this pos-

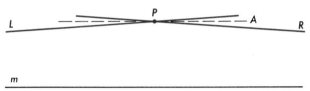

Figure 8-31.

sibility, it would seem that we have a first parallel on the right, $\overleftrightarrow{PR}$; a first parallel on the left, $\overleftrightarrow{PL}$; and a whole mass of lines, such as $\overleftrightarrow{PA}$, within the angle formed by their intersection that also do not intersect line m. Can you show by the indirect proof that if $\overleftrightarrow{PR}$ does not intersect m, $\overleftrightarrow{PA}$ can not intersect m?

For over 2,000 years mathematicians were disturbed by this analysis. It was their feeling that the drawing above was merely an optical illusion and that the two parallels through P were in reality but a single line. And so, they, like we, were faced with two roads down which we might travel: either

(1) Through P there exists one and only one line that does not intersect m.

or

(2) Through P there exist many lines that do not intersect m.

Which of these possibilities do you believe to be the more plausible?

The collector and organizer of the subject of geometry, Euclid, lived approximately 330 B.C. In the process of logically arranging the definitions, postulates, and theorems, he, too, encountered the difficulty described above. After trying unsuccessfully to prove that through P there can be only one line that does not intersect m,† he finally resorted to listing this as his fifth

† The form of Euclid's statement was not the same as this, but equivalent to this. This particular statement is attributed to Playfair, a mathematician who lived during the eighteenth century.

postulate. Mathematicians that followed him, however, were not satisfied that this statement could not be proved in terms of Euclid's preceding four postulates. Hence, for over 2,000 years, "proofs" containing subtle errors in reasoning were presented for the fifth postulate.

Around the year 1815 A.D., two men, living thousands of miles apart, came out with separate studies showing what would happen to the subject matter of geometry were the second road followed rather than the first. These men were Johann Bolyai and Nicolai Lobachevsky.

This, though, was not the end. About the year 1855 a third mathematician, Bernhard Riemann, set forth the possibility that:

(3) Through *P* there exists no line that can be drawn that does not intersect *m*.

Your immediate reaction will be to say, "This is foolish. Have not we proved that when the alternate interior angles are congruent, the lines can not intersect!" Yes, but if you examine the proof of this statement, you will see that it depends on the theorem about the exterior angle of a triangle. If the proof of that theorem was carefully analyzed, it would turn up the fact that that proof depends upon the postulate that one and only one line exists through two points. Hence, in developing his geometry, Riemann had to discard this postulate also.

Well, where does this lead us? Can we ask the question, "Which of the three is the 'correct' postulate?" No, for this would indicate that we have forgotten the foundation laid in the early weeks of this course. At that time it was pointed out that it mattered not what our definitions and postulates were just so long as we agreed upon them and that they did not contradict one another. Each mathematician has the right to start with his own postulates and pursue them as he will.

A more interesting question might have been "Which postulate leads to results that are in keeping with the world we observe about us?" This, too, has to be answered by hedging. Riemannian geometry gives most accurate results when dealing with astronomical distances; Lobachevsky's geometry leads to greatest accuracy when dealing with the movement of atoms within a molecule; all three geometries give comparable results when dealing with measurements on a small area of the earth's surface. Euclidean geometry, however, is far easier to apply and far easier to learn. In view of the latter reason, this is the path we will pursue. At some later date we will take a short detour to browse about the fields we might have observed had we followed the roads taken by Lobachevsky and Riemann.

POSTULATE 25: Through a given point not on a given line there exists one and only one line that is parallel to the given line. (The Parallel Postulate, or Euclid's Fifth Postulate)

With the aid of this postulate we are prepared to prove the converses of the earlier theorems on parallel lines. This is the first time the term *converse* has been used, although there were earlier occasions when, perhaps, we should have used it.† If two statements are so related wherein the given data of the first is the conclusion of the second and also the conclusion of the first is the given data of the second, then the second statement is said to be the converse of the first.

First Statement:

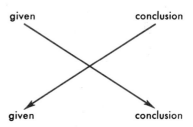

Second Statement,
   or Converse:

You may have noticed that were these related statements *definitions*, then the second would be the "Reverse" of the first. All such related statements other than definitions, however, are called the converses of each other. Later in our work we will examine converse statements much more thoroughly.

THEOREM 27: If two parallel lines are cut by a transversal, then the alternate interior angles are congruent.

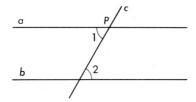

Given: $a \parallel b$
Concl.: $\angle 1 \cong \angle 2$

Figure 8-32.

ANALYSIS: There is nothing we know that relates parallel lines to congruent angles. Thus, as with the first theorem on proving lines parallel, we will have to resort again to the indirect proof. Assuming that $\angle 1 \not\cong \angle 2$ will enable us to draw a second line through P to make an angle with c that is congruent to $\angle 2$. Hence, this second line through P will also be parallel to b. Why?

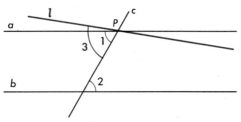

Figure 8-33.

† See theorems 9 and 10, page 145.

This will lead to a statement contradictory to Postulate 25. What is this postulate?

PROOF

By the law of the excluded middle one of the following statements must be true and no other possibilities exist:

$$\angle 1 \cong \angle 2 \quad \text{or} \quad \angle 1 \ncong \angle 2$$

Let us accept the possibility that $\angle 1 \ncong \angle 2$. Then by Postulate 17 concerning the existence of an angle at a particular point on a line, we can say that there exists an $\angle 3$ at point P that is congruent to $\angle 2$. From this it follows that $l \parallel b$, for if the alternate interior angles are congruent, the lines are parallel. But the Given Data states that a is already parallel to b. Therefore, there are two lines through P parallel to b. Postulate 25, however, limits to only one the number of lines that can exist through P parallel to b. Therefore, accepting the possibility that $\angle 1 \ncong \angle 2$ led to a logical inconsistency of the truth of both statements. By the law of contradiction both cannot be true at the same time. Since we have accepted Postulate 25 as true, the statement that both l and a are parallel to b must be false, and, therefore, the statement that $\angle 1 \ncong \angle 2$ is also false. Hence, $\angle 1 \cong \angle 2$, for it is the only remaining possibility.

THEOREM 28: If two parallel lines are cut by a transversal, then the corresponding angles are congruent.

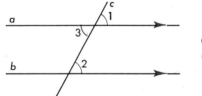

Given: $a \parallel b$
Concl.: $\angle 1 \cong \angle 2$

Figure 8-34.

ANALYSIS: Since the lines are parallel, Theorem 27 enables us to say that $\angle 2 \cong \angle 3$. But $\angle 1$ is also congruent to $\angle 3$, hence $\angle 1$ and $\angle 2$ are congruent.

PROOF	STATEMENTS	REASONS
1. $a \parallel b$		1. Given
2. $\angle 2 \cong \angle 3$		2. If two parallel lines are cut by a transversal, then the alternate interior angles are congruent.
3. $\angle 1 \cong \angle 3$		3. Why?
4. $\angle 1 \cong \angle 2$		4. Transitive property of congruence

THEOREM 29: If two parallel lines are cut by a transversal, then the alternate exterior angles are congruent.

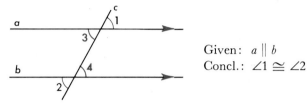

Given: $a \parallel b$
Concl.: $\angle 1 \cong \angle 2$

Figure 8-35.

ANALYSIS: From the fact that the lines are parallel $\angle 3 \cong \angle 4$. Since $\angle 1$ and $\angle 2$ are congruent respectively to these two angles, they will be congruent to each other.

PROOF

The proof will be left for you to do.

The next two theorems can very easily be proved on the basis of the previous three theorems on parallel lines. Their proofs will be left for you to do.

THEOREM 30: If two lines are parallel to the same line, then they are parallel to each other.
THEOREM 31: If a line is perpendicular to one of two parallel lines, then it is also perpendicular to the other.

Illustration:

If a line intersects the legs of an isosceles triangle and is parallel to the base, it cuts off another isosceles triangle.

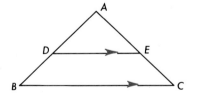

Given: $\triangle ABC$ is isosceles with
$\overline{AB} \cong \overline{AC}$.
$\overleftrightarrow{DE} \parallel \overleftrightarrow{BC}$
Concl.: $\triangle ADE$ is isosceles.

Figure 8-36.

ANALYSIS: Since $\angle B \cong \angle C$, it will be possible to show that $\angle ADE$ is congruent to $\angle AED$. Hence, it follows that $\overline{AD} \cong \overline{AE}$ and, therefore, that $\triangle ADE$ is isosceles.

PROOF	STATEMENTS	REASONS
1. $\overline{AB} \cong \overline{AC}$		1. Why?
2. $\angle B \cong \angle C$		2. Why?
3. $\overleftrightarrow{DE} \parallel \overleftrightarrow{BC}$		3. Why?
4. $\angle ADE \cong \angle B$		4. If two parallel lines are cut by a transversal, then the corresponding angles are congruent.
5. $\angle AED \cong \angle C$		5. Why?
6. $\angle ADE \cong \angle AED$		6. Why?
7. $\therefore \overline{AD} \cong \overline{AE}$		7. If two angles of a triangle are congruent, then the sides opposite these angles are congruent.
8. $\triangle ADE$ is isosceles.		8. Reverse of def. of an isosceles triangle.

$$\boxed{A}$$

1. Given: $\overline{BE} \cong \overline{CF}$
$\overleftrightarrow{AB} \parallel \overleftrightarrow{DE}$
$\overleftrightarrow{AC} \parallel \overleftrightarrow{DF}$
Concl.: $\overline{AC} \cong \overline{DF}$

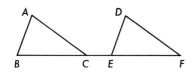

Given: $\overline{AB} \cong \overline{CD}$
$\overline{FC} \cong \overline{BE}$
$\overleftrightarrow{AB} \parallel \overleftrightarrow{CD}$
Concl.: $\overline{AF} \cong \overline{DE}$ **2.**

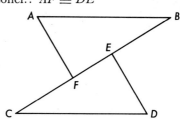

3. Given: $\overline{AB} \cong \overline{CD}$
$\overleftrightarrow{AF} \parallel \overleftrightarrow{ED}$
$\overleftrightarrow{BE} \parallel \overleftrightarrow{FC}$
Concl.: $\overline{BE} \cong \overline{FC}$

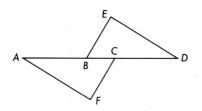

Given: $\angle 1 \cong \angle 2$
$\overline{AB} \cong \overline{FE}$
$\overleftrightarrow{AB} \parallel \overleftrightarrow{EF}$
Concl.: $\overleftrightarrow{AC} \parallel \overleftrightarrow{DF}$ **4.**

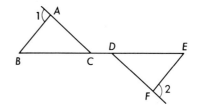

5.   Given: $\odot O$ with $\overleftrightarrow{AB}$ and $\overleftrightarrow{CD}$
               intersecting at O
               $\overleftrightarrow{AD} \parallel \overleftrightarrow{CB}$

     Concl.: $\overline{OD} \cong \overline{OC}$

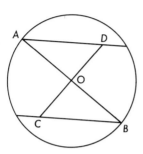

Given: $a \parallel b$ **6.**
          $c \parallel d$

Concl.: $\angle 1 \cong \angle 2$

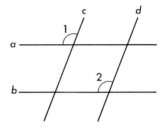

7.   Given: $a \parallel b$
              $c \parallel d$

     Concl.: $\angle 1 \cong \angle 2$

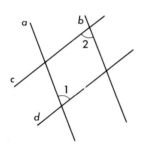

Given: $\angle 1 \cong \angle 2$ **8.**

Concl.: $\angle 3 \cong \angle 4$

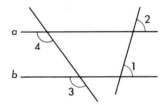

9.   Given: $\overleftrightarrow{AB} \parallel \overleftrightarrow{DC}$
               $\overleftrightarrow{AD} \parallel \overleftrightarrow{BC}$

     Concl.: $\overline{AB} \cong \overline{DC}$

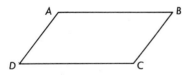

Given: AD and BC inter-   **10.**
          secting lines
          $\overleftrightarrow{AB} \parallel \overleftrightarrow{CD}$
          $\overline{EC} \cong \overline{ED}$

Concl.: $\triangle EAB$ is isosceles.

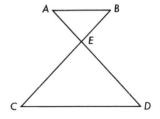

11. Given: $\odot O$ with $\overleftrightarrow{AB} \parallel \overleftrightarrow{CD}$
      Concl.: $\triangle OCD$ is isosceles.

Given: $\overleftrightarrow{AB} \parallel \overleftrightarrow{CD}$ **12.**
      $\angle D \cong \angle B$
Concl.: $\overleftrightarrow{BC} \parallel \overleftrightarrow{DE}$

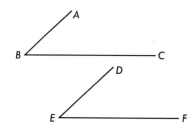

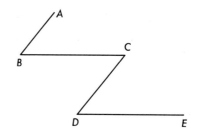

13. Given: $\overleftrightarrow{AB} \parallel \overleftrightarrow{DE}$
      $\overleftrightarrow{BC} \parallel \overleftrightarrow{EF}$
      Concl.: $\angle B \cong \angle E$ (Hint:
      Extend $\overleftrightarrow{DE}$ until it
      intersects $\overleftrightarrow{BC}$.)

Given: $\overleftrightarrow{AB} \parallel \overleftrightarrow{DC}$ **14.**
      $\overleftrightarrow{AD} \parallel \overleftrightarrow{BC}$
      $\overline{BF} \cong \overline{DE}$
Concl.: $\overleftrightarrow{AE} \parallel \overleftrightarrow{FC}$

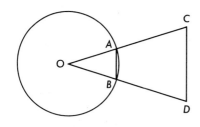

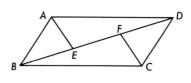

15. Given: $\overleftrightarrow{AB} \parallel \overleftrightarrow{DC}$
      $\overline{AB} \cong \overline{DC}$
      $\overline{BF} \cong \overline{ED}$
      $\overleftrightarrow{AE} \perp \overleftrightarrow{BD}$
      Concl.: $\overleftrightarrow{CF} \perp \overleftrightarrow{BD}$

Given: $\overleftrightarrow{AB} \parallel \overleftrightarrow{DC}$ **16.**
      $\overline{AB} \cong \overline{DC}$
      $\overleftrightarrow{EF}$ bisects $\overline{AC}$.
Concl.: $\overleftrightarrow{AC}$ bisects $\overline{EF}$.

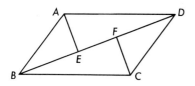

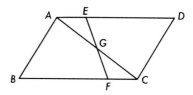

17. Given: $\overrightarrow{EC}$ bisects $\angle AED$.

$\overleftrightarrow{AB} \parallel \overleftrightarrow{CD}$

Concl.: $\triangle DEC$ is isosceles.

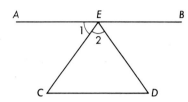

Given: $\overrightarrow{AD}$ bisects $\angle CAE$.   **18.**

$\overleftrightarrow{AD} \parallel \overleftrightarrow{BC}$

Concl.: $\triangle ABC$ is isosceles.

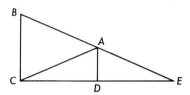

19. Given: $\odot O$ with $\overleftrightarrow{AD} \parallel \overleftrightarrow{BC}$

Concl.: $\overline{AB} \cong \overline{DC}$ (Hint: Draw lines AO and DO.)

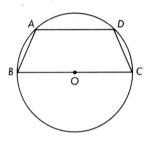

Using the diagram below and   **20.**
the indirect proof, prove the theorem that if two parallel lines are cut by a transversal, then the corresponding angles are congruent.

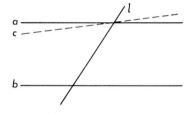

B

1. If two sides of a four-sided polygon are congruent and parallel, then the other two sides are congruent.
2. If two sides of a four-sided polygon are congruent and parallel, then the other two sides are parallel.
3. If both pairs of opposite sides of a four-sided polygon are parallel, then the opposite angles are congruent.
4. If both pairs of opposite sides of a four-sided polygon are parallel, then the line segments joining opposite vertices bisect each other.
5. If two parallel lines are cut by a transversal, the interior angles on the same side of the transversal are supplementary.
6. If a line is drawn parallel to a leg of an isosceles triangle and intersects the other two sides, then it cuts off another isosceles triangle.
7. If through any point on the bisector of an angle a line is drawn parallel

to one of the sides of the angle, then an isosceles triangle is formed.

8. The bisectors of a pair of corresponding angles of parallel lines are parallel.

9. The bisectors of a pair of alternate exterior angles of parallel lines are parallel.

10. State and prove the converse of example 4.

11. If the bisector of an exterior angle of a triangle is parallel to one of the sides of the triangle, then the triangle is isosceles.

12. If a triangle is isosceles, then the line through the vertex of the vertex angle parallel to the base bisects the exterior angle at that vertex.

13. If both pairs of opposite sides of a four-sided polygon are parallel, then a line joining opposite vertices that bisects one of the angles will bisect the other also.

14. If two lines are parallel, then perpendicular segments drawn from two points of the first to the second are congruent.

15. If the sides of one angle are parallel to the sides of another angle, then the angles are either supplementary or congruent.

16. By using the indirect proof, prove the theorem that if two lines are parallel to the same line, then they are parallel to each other.

17. If a line intersects one of two parallel lines, then it intersects the other also. (Use the indirect method of proof.)

18. If a line intersects one side of a triangle and is parallel to the second side, then it must intersect the third side of the triangle. (Use the indirect method of proof.)

19.* If two lines are parallel respectively to two intersecting lines, then the first two lines must intersect each other. (Use the indirect method of proof.)

20.* By using the indirect proof and Pasch's Axiom prove that a line that is parallel to one side of a triangle and passes through the vertex formed by the other two, can not pass into the interior of the triangle.

■ Uniqueness and Existence

The Parallel Postulate and several of the problems in the set of exercises on page 233 afford us an excellent opportunity to call attention to an important concept in mathematics. Thus, Problem 11 stated, "At a given point on a given line there can be only one line perpendicular to the given line." By proving this statement you have emphasized the fact that *no more than one* line can be drawn perpendicular to a line at a particular point on that line. What you have confirmed, from a mathematical standpoint, is the *uniqueness* of this perpendicular. You, as an individual, stand out, for there is *only one* such as you in the entire world; that is, you are *unique.* Uniqueness, from a mathematical standpoint, implies, too, that there is *only one* of these creatures under the conditions stated.

Thus, through the proof of Problem 11 you have confirmed the uniqueness of a perpendicular at a given point on a given line. Yet, is this enough? No, for we would also like to know if such a line *does* exist? To show *existence* we must verify that such a creature is possible in terms of prior definitions and assumptions that we have made. To illustrate this procedure we will show that there must exist a perpendicular at a given point on a given line.

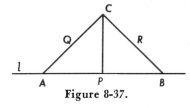

Figure 8-37.

Given: Line *l* and point *P*

Concl.: At point *P* there exists a perpendicular to line *l*.

PROOF STATEMENTS	REASONS
1. Let *A* be a point of line *l* other than point *P*.	1. A property given to a line was that it was a set of points.
2. Extend *l* through point *P* so that $\overline{AP} \cong \overline{BP}$.	2. A line can be extended as far as desired.
3. At *A* let $\angle QAB$ be any acute angle.	3. Postulate on the existence of an angle. (Postulate 17)
4. At *B* let $\angle RBA$ be the angle that is congruent to $\angle QAB$.	4. Same as 3
5. $\overleftrightarrow{QA}$ and $\overleftrightarrow{RB}$ must intersect at some point *C*.	5. See if you can prove by the indirect method that $\overleftrightarrow{QA}$ and $\overleftrightarrow{RB}$ can not be parallel.
6. Let *CP* be the line through points *C* and *P*.	6. Why?
7. $\overline{CA} \cong \overline{CB}$	7. If two angles of a triangle are congruent, the sides opposite these angles are congruent.
8. ∴ $\overleftrightarrow{CP} \perp l$	8. If two points (*C* and *P*) are each equidistant from the endpoints of a line segment ($\overline{AB}$), then the line ($\overleftrightarrow{CP}$) joining them is the perpendicular bisector of the line segment.

The proof above and your proof to Problem 11 on page 233 establishes the theorem that

THEOREM 32: **At a given point on a given line there exists one and only one line that is perpendicular to the given line.**

The word "one" in the above statement implies the existence of this perpendicular. Its existence we established by the proof above. The words "only one" imply the uniqueness of this perpendicular. This uniqueness you established in the proof of Problem 11 on page 233. From a similar point of view, the Parallel Postulate establishes the *uniqueness* of a line through a given point parallel to a given line, while the theorem that if the alternate interior angles are congruent, the lines are parallel establishes the *existence* of such a line.

There are several other statements on existence and uniqueness that you have examined as problems in the past that will be re-examined now. One of these is Problem 12 on page 233. Through this problem you proved the uniqueness of a perpendicular from a given point not on a given line to the given line. Now, we shall establish the existence of this perpendicular.

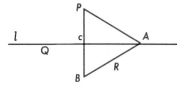

Given: Line *l* and point *P*

Concl.: Through *P* there exists a perpendicular to *l*.

Figure 8-38.

| **PROOF** | (The reasons will be left for you to supply.) |

1. Let point A be any point of line l.

2. Let $\overleftrightarrow{PA}$ be the line through P and A.

3. Let $\angle RAQ$ be the angle at A that is congruent to $\angle PAQ$.

4. Extend $\overleftrightarrow{AR}$ so that $\overline{BA} \cong \overline{PA}$.

5. Let $\overleftrightarrow{PB}$ be the line through P and B.

6. $\overline{CA} \cong \overline{CA}$

7. $\triangle PAC \cong \triangle BAC$

8. $\angle PCA \cong \angle BCA$

9. $\overleftrightarrow{PB} \perp l$

The proof above and Problem 12, page 233, establish the theorem that

THEOREM 33: **From a given point not on a given line there exists one and only one line that is perpendicular to the given line.**

By your proof of Problem 9, page 233, you confirmed the uniqueness of the midpoint of a line segment, while Postulate 20 informed us of the existence of this point. Can you combine these two principles into a single statement? Similarly, proving problem 10, page 233, implies the uniqueness of a bisector of an angle, while Postulate 16 brings to our attention the existence of this ray. Can you combine the two principles into a single statement?

EXERCISES

1. Is Problem 15, page 233, a "uniqueness" statement or an "existence" statement? How would the statement have been worded had it been both?

2. Prove: At the endpoint of a given ray there is only one angle on one side of this ray that is congruent to a given angle.

(a) Is this a "uniqueness" statement or an "existence" statement?

(b) When have we encountered the other of these two statements?

3. Prove: There exists a point that is equidistant from two given points. (Hint: See the diagram for the proof of Theorem 32.)

Is this point unique? If not, how many such points are there and where do they lie?

4. Prove: There exists a point on a circle that is equidistant from two other points on the circle.

Is this point unique? If not, where does the other, or others, lie?

5. Prove: There exists an isosceles triangle whose vertex angle is a given angle.

Is this triangle unique? If not, what relation do you believe will exist between the bases of these triangles?

6. Prove: A line segment has one and only one perpendicular bisector. (Hint: First show how to get one perpendicular bisector and then use the indirect method of proof to prove that this is the only perpendicular bisector of this line segment.)

■ The Parallelogram—Part I

Referring to a four-sided polygon as we have been until now is both unnecessary and a bit awkward. Not only are we going to name this polygon but also we will devote this section to a discussion of the properties of special four-sided polygons.

DEFINITION 52: A quadrilateral is a polygon that has four sides.

In order to obtain an over-all picture of the words that are about to be brought into this language, a family tree of the quadrilateral and its off-springs are pictured in Figure 8-39.

From the diagram in Figure 8-39 we note that there are two special types of quadrilaterals: the parallelogram and the trapezoid. In turn, the general variety of parallelograms has two special varieties: the rectangle and the rhombus. We will work our way down one side of the tree at a time.

DEFINITION 53: A parallelogram is a quadrilateral in which the opposite sides are parallel.

It is quite simple to recall the property of a parallelogram given to it by its definition: the word *parallel*ogram contains the term *parallel* as part

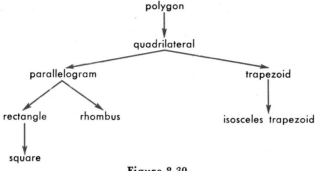

Figure 8-39.

of its spelling, while the property given to this quadrilateral by its definition is that the opposite sides are *parallel*. The symbol representing the word parallelogram is the drawing of a small parallelogram, ▱. What property about the sides of a parallelogram do you believe you will be able to prove?

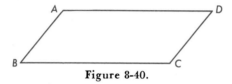

Figure 8-40.

What property about the angles? Draw a parallelogram; then draw the line segments joining the two pairs of opposite vertices. These line segments are called the *diagonals* of a parallelogram. What do you believe will be true about the diagonals of a parallelogram?

DEFINITION 54: A rectangle is a parallelogram with one right angle.

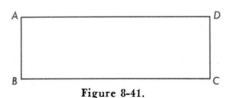

Figure 8-41.

You may have wondered why the rectangle is not defined as a parallelogram with four right angles. The reasoning behind this is very much the same as the reason for not defining an isosceles triangle as a triangle

(1) with two congruent sides,
(2) with two congruent angles,
(3) whose bisector of the vertex angle is perpendicular to the base,
(4) whose bisector of the exterior angle at the vertex is parallel to the base.

Certainly what we have said of the isosceles triangle is true, for we have proved all but one of these at some time in our work. In formulating a definition, however, we try to list as *few* properties as possible that will distinguish that term from all other words in its class. All other properties of the figure we prove. Thus, if we say that a rectangle is a parallelogram that simply has one right angle, this will suffice to distinguish it from all other parallelograms. Furthermore, on the basis of this definition we can prove that a rectangle has four right angles.

DEFINITION 55: A square is a rectangle with two adjacent sides congruent.

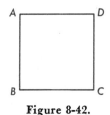

Figure 8-42.

In view of the discussion about the rectangle, can you justify why the square was not defined as a rectangle with four congruent sides? If we had defined the square by placing it in the category of *polygons* rather than in its *nearest* class, the rectangle, then what properties should we have included in its definition to distinguish the square from the other polygons?

DEFINITION 56: A rhombus is a parallelogram with two adjacent sides congruent.

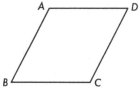

Figure 8-43.

What property do you believe, from observation, that a rhombus has that is not given to it by its definition? What property does the square have that the rhombus does not have?

Now we will move down the other branch of the quadrilateral tree to examine the second set of terms.

DEFINITION 57: A trapezoid is a quadrilateral that has one and only one pair of sides parallel.

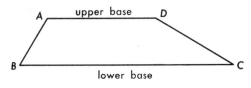

Figure 8-44.

The parallel sides of a trapezoid are called the bases. In what way does a trapezoid differ from a parallelogram?

DEFINITION 58: An isosceles trapezoid is a trapezoid in which the nonparallel sides are congruent.

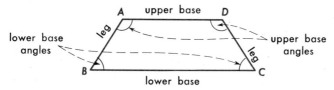

Figure 8-45.

Notice that there is a similarity between naming the parts of an isosceles trapezoid and the parts of an isosceles triangle. What property does the isosceles trapezoid have that is not given to it by its definition?

THEOREM 34: The opposite sides of a parallelogram are congruent.

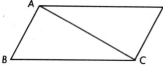

Given: $ABCD$ is a $\square$.
Concl.: $\overline{AD} \cong \overline{BC}$
$\overline{AB} \cong \overline{DC}$

Figure 8-46.

ANALYSIS: By drawing a diagonal we can prove that the two triangles that are formed will be congruent and, hence, our conclusion will follow.

PROOF STATEMENTS	REASONS
1. $ABCD$ is a parallelogram.	1. Given
2. $\overleftrightarrow{AD} \parallel \overleftrightarrow{BC}$, $\overleftrightarrow{AB} \parallel \overleftrightarrow{DC}$	2. Def. of a parallelogram
3. Let $\overleftrightarrow{AC}$ be the line through points A and C.	3. Why?
4. $\angle DAC \cong \angle BCA$ (a)	4. Why?
5. $\angle DCA \cong \angle BAC$ (a)	5. Why?
6. $\overline{AC} \cong \overline{AC}$ (s)	6. Why?
7. $\triangle BAC \cong \triangle DCA$	7. Why?
8. $\overline{AD} \cong \overline{BC}$, $\overline{AB} \cong \overline{DC}$	8. Why?

THEOREM 35: The opposite angles of a parallelogram are congruent.

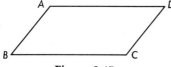

Given: $ABCD$ is a $\square$.
Concl.: $\angle A \cong \angle C$
$\angle B \cong \angle D$

Figure 8-47.

ANALYSIS: As in the preceding proof, drawing a diagonal will give us a pair of congruent triangles, and, hence, ∠B can be shown congruent to ∠D. By drawing the other diagonal the other pair of angles can be shown to be congruent.

PROOF

The proof of Theorem 35 will be left for you to do.

THEOREM 36: The diagonals of a parallelogram bisect each other.

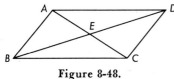

Given: $ABCD$ is a $\square$.

Concl.: $\overset{\leftrightarrow}{AC}$ bisects $\overline{BD}$.

$\overset{\leftrightarrow}{BD}$ bisects $\overline{AC}$.

Figure 8-48.

ANALYSIS: By proving $\triangle AED \cong \triangle CEB$, both conclusions will follow.

| PROOF | (The reasons will be left for you to supply.) |

1. $ABCD$ is a $\square$.
2. $\overset{\leftrightarrow}{AD} \parallel \overset{\leftrightarrow}{BC}$
3. $\angle ADB \cong \angle CBD$
4. $\angle CAD \cong \angle BCA$
5. $\overline{AD} \cong \overline{BC}$
6. $\triangle AED \cong \triangle CEB$

7. $\overline{BE} \cong \overline{DE}$
8. E is the midpoint of $\overline{BD}$.
9. $\overset{\leftrightarrow}{AC}$ bisects $\overline{BD}$.
10. $\overline{AE} \cong \overline{CE}$
11. E is the midpoint of $\overline{AC}$.
12. $\overset{\leftrightarrow}{BD}$ bisects $\overline{AC}$.

In summary we can say that should a quadrilateral be a parallelogram, there are immediately four conclusions that can be drawn:

(1) The opposite sides are parallel.
(2) The opposite sides are congruent.
(3) The opposite angles are congruent.
(4) The diagonals bisect each other.

It should be borne in mind that these properties are true not only of the general parallelogram but also of each of the quadrilaterals that were classified as parallelograms. These are the rectangle, the square, and the rhombus.

THEOREM 37: All four sides of a square are congruent.

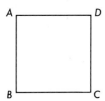

Given: $ABCD$ is a square with $\overline{AB} \cong \overline{DA}$.

Concl.: $\overline{AB} \cong \overline{BC} \cong \overline{CD} \cong \overline{DA}$

Figure 8-49.

PROOF	STATEMENTS	REASONS
1. $ABCD$ is a square with $\overline{AB} \cong \overline{DA}$.	1. Given
2. $\overline{BC} \cong \overline{DA}$	2. The opposite sides of a parallelogram are congruent.
3. $\overline{CD} \cong \overline{AB}$	3. Same as 2
4. $\overline{AB} \cong \overline{BC} \cong \overline{CD} \cong \overline{DA}$	4. Transitive property of congruence

THEOREM 38: All four sides of a rhombus are congruent.

The proof of Theorem 38 is left for you to do.

THEOREM 39: The lower base angles of an isosceles trapezoid are congruent.

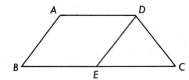

Given: $ABCD$ is a trapezoid with $\overline{DC} \cong \overline{AB}$.
Concl.: $\angle B \cong \angle C$

Figure 8-50.

PROOF	STATEMENTS	REASONS
1. $ABCD$ is a trapezoid.	1. Given
2. Let $\overleftrightarrow{DE}$ be the line through D that is parallel to $\overleftrightarrow{AB}$.	2. The Parallel Postulate
3. $\overleftrightarrow{AD} \parallel \overleftrightarrow{BC}$	3. Def. of a trapezoid
4. $ABED$ is a parallelogram.	4. Reverse of def. of a parallelogram.
5. $\overline{DE} \cong \overline{AB}$	5. Why?
6. $\overline{DC} \cong \overline{AB}$	6. Given
7. $\overline{DE} \cong \overline{DC}$	7. Why?
8. $\angle C \cong \angle DEC$	8. Why?
9. $\angle B \cong \angle DEC$	9. If two lines are parallel, then the corresponding angles are congruent.
10. $\therefore \angle B \cong \angle C$	10. Why?

EXERCISES

A

1. Given: *ABCD* is a □.
   E is the midpoint
   of $\overline{FG}$.
   Concl.: *E* is the midpoint
   of $\overline{AC}$.

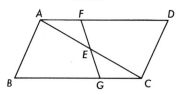

Given: *ABCD* is a □.   **2.**
   $\overline{BE} \cong \overline{DF}$
Concl.: $\overline{AF} \cong \overline{CE}$

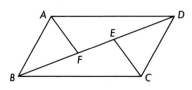

3. Given: *ABCD* is a □.
   $\overline{BE} \cong \overline{DF}$
   Concl.: $\overleftrightarrow{EF}$ bisects $\overline{AC}$.

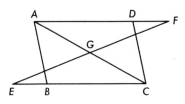

Given: *ABCD* is a □.   **4.**
   F is the midpoint
   of $\overline{AB}$.
   G is the midpoint
   of $\overline{CD}$.
Concl.: *E* is the midpoint
   of $\overline{AC}$.

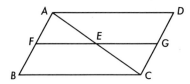

5. Given: *ABCD* is a □.
   $\overline{BF} \cong \overline{DE}$
   Concl.: $\angle 1 \cong \angle 2$

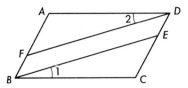

Given: *ABCD* is a □ with   **6.**
   $\overleftrightarrow{EF}$ passing through *G*.
   $\overleftrightarrow{EF}$ bisects $\overline{AD}$.
Concl.: $\overleftrightarrow{EF}$ bisects $\overline{BC}$.

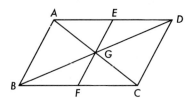

7. Given: $ABCD$ is a $\square$.
        E is the midpoint
        of $\overline{AD}$.
        F is the midpoint
        of $\overline{BC}$.
Concl.: $\overline{AG} \cong \overline{HC}$

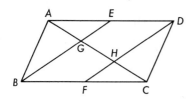

Given: $ABCD$ is an isosceles   **8.**
        trapezoid with
        $\overleftrightarrow{AD} \parallel \overleftrightarrow{BC}$.
Concl.: $\triangle EBC$ is an isos-
        celes $\triangle$.

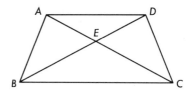

9. Given: $ABCD$ is a trapezoid
        with $\overleftrightarrow{AD} \parallel \overleftrightarrow{BC}$.
        $\overrightarrow{CA}$ bisects $\angle BCD$.
        $\overrightarrow{BD}$ bisects $\angle CBA$.
Concl.: $ABCD$ is an isosceles
        trapezoid (Hint:
        Prove $\triangle$ ADC and
        DAB are isosceles.)

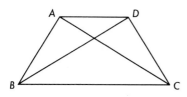

Given: $ABCD$ is a rectangle.   **10.**
        $P, Q, R,$ and S are the
        midpoints of their
        respective sides.
Concl.: $\overline{PQ} \cong \overline{QR} \cong \overline{RS} \cong \overline{SP}$
        (Hint: Prove that all
        the angles of a
        rectangle are right
        angles.)

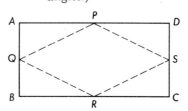

11. Given: $ABCD$ is an isos. trap.
        with $\overleftrightarrow{AD} \parallel \overleftrightarrow{BC}$.
        $\overleftrightarrow{RS} \perp$ bi. $\overline{BC}$
Concl.: $\overleftrightarrow{RS}$ passes thru E.

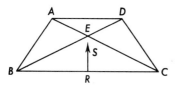

Given: $ABCD$ is an isos. trap.   **12.**
        with $\overleftrightarrow{AD} \parallel \overleftrightarrow{BC}$.
        $\overleftrightarrow{RS} \perp$ bi. $\overline{BC}$
Concl.: $\overleftrightarrow{RS}$ passes thru E.

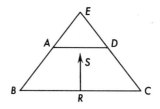

13. Given: $ABCD$ is an isosceles trapezoid with $\overleftrightarrow{AD} \parallel \overleftrightarrow{BC}$.

E is the midpoint of $\overline{AD}$.

F is the midpoint of $\overline{BC}$.

Concl.: $\overleftrightarrow{EF} \perp \overleftrightarrow{AD}$ (Hint: Draw $\overline{AF}$ and $\overline{DF}$, then prove them congruent.)

Given: $\triangle ABC$ is isosceles with $\overline{AB} \cong \overline{AC}$. **14.***

$\overleftrightarrow{PQ} \parallel \overleftrightarrow{AC}$

$\overleftrightarrow{PR} \parallel \overleftrightarrow{AB}$

Concl.: $m\,\overline{AB} + m\,\overline{AC} =$ perimeter of $AQPR$ (Hint: How would you define the perimeter of a polygon?)

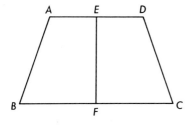

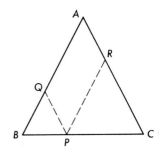

1. The diagonals of an isosceles trapezoid are congruent.

2. The diagonals of a rectangle are congruent.

3. The line joining the midpoints of two opposite sides of a parallelogram bisects either diagonal of the parallelogram.

4. A pair of consecutive angles of a parallelogram are supplementary.

5. The upper base angles of an isosceles trapezoid are congruent.

6. If the nonparallel sides of an isosceles trapezoid are extended until they intersect, two isosceles triangles will be formed.

7. The diagonals of a rhombus are perpendicular to each other.

8. If a diagonal of a parallelogram bisects one of the two angles whose vertices it connects, then the parallelogram is a rhombus.

9. If the diagonals of a parallelogram are perpendicular to each other, then the parallelogram is a rhombus.

10.* If the bisectors of the upper base angles of an isosceles trapezoid intersect at the midpoint of the lower base, then two of the three triangles formed will be congruent isosceles triangles.

11.* If the diagonals of a parallelogram are congruent, then the parallelogram is a rectangle. (Hint: Extend the base through one of its vertices and prove that the adjacent angles at that vertex are congruent.)

12.* If the lines joining consecutive midpoints of the sides of a parallelogram form a rhombus, then the parallelogram is a rectangle. (Hint: See the suggestion for Problem 11.)

13.* The perpendicular bisector of the lower base of an isosceles trapezoid passes through the midpoint of the upper base. (Hint: Use the information from Problem 5.)

14.* The perpendicular bisector of the lower base of an isosceles trapezoid passes through the point of intersection of the bisectors of the lower base angles.

■ The Parallelogram—Part II

The theorems on the parallelogram in Part I enabled us to draw conclusions in the event the quadrilateral was a parallelogram. In this unit we are going to investigate those properties that will make a quadrilateral a parallelogram. Primarily, of course, we have at our disposal the reverse of the definition of a parallelogram. That is, by showing that the opposite sides of a quadrilateral are parallel, the quadrilateral will be a parallelogram. Hence, the first theorem developed to show that a quadrilateral is a parallelogram will, of necessity, be based on the reverse of the definition of a parallelogram.

THEOREM 40: **If the opposite sides of a quadrilateral are congruent, then the quadrilateral is a parallelogram.**

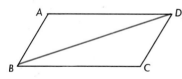

Given: $\overline{AD} \cong \overline{BC}$
$\overline{AB} \cong \overline{DC}$
Concl.: $ABCD$ is a $\square$.

Figure 8-51.

PROOF	(The reasons will be left for you to supply.)
1. $\overline{AD} \cong \overline{BC}$ (s)	6. $\angle ABD \cong \angle CDB$
2. $\overline{AB} \cong \overline{DC}$ (s)	7. $\overleftrightarrow{AB} \parallel \overleftrightarrow{CD}$
3. Let $\overleftrightarrow{BD}$ be the line through points B and D.	8. $\angle ADB \cong \angle CBD$
4. $\overline{BD} \cong \overline{BD}$ (s)	9. $\overleftrightarrow{AD} \parallel \overleftrightarrow{BC}$
5. $\triangle ABD \cong \triangle CDB$	10. $ABCD$ is a $\square$. (Rev. of the def. of a parallelogram.)

THEOREM 41: **If the diagonals of a quadrilateral bisect each other, then the quadrilateral is a parallelogram.**

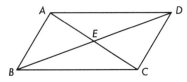

Given: $\overleftrightarrow{AC}$ bisects $\overline{BD}$.

$\overleftrightarrow{BD}$ bisects $\overline{AC}$.

Concl.: $ABCD$ is a $\square$.

Figure 8-52.

ANALYSIS: By proving two pairs of triangles congruent it is possible to show that $\overline{AD} \cong \overline{BC}$ and $\overline{AB} \cong \overline{CD}$. Then by Theorem 40, $ABCD$ will have to be a parallelogram.

PROOF

The proof of Theorem 41 is left for you to do.

You may have noticed that Theorems 40 and 41 are the converses of theorems that we had proved earlier. What were those theorems? The last of the basic methods for showing a quadrilateral to be a parallelogram is not the converse of a prior theorem. It does have wide application, though.

In each of the methods examined thus far, it has been necessary to show something to be true about *both* pairs of opposite sides of the quadrilateral before being able to conclude that it was a parallelogram. If, however, our information concerned itself with only one pair of sides, what properties would have to hold before we might conclude that the quadrilateral was a parallelogram? Would it be sufficient to know that this pair of sides was congruent? Can you draw a quadrilateral with one pair of sides congruent and yet with the quadrilateral not being a parallelogram? Would it be sufficient to know that one pair of sides was parallel before concluding that the quadrilateral was a parallelogram? Can you draw a quadrilateral with one pair of sides parallel and yet the quadrilateral is not a parallelogram?

THEOREM 42: **If a quadrilateral has one pair of sides congruent and parallel, then the quadrilateral is a parallelogram.**

Given: $\overleftrightarrow{AD} \parallel \overleftrightarrow{BC}$

$\overline{AD} \cong \overline{BC}$

Concl.: $ABCD$ is a $\square$.

Figure 8-53.

ANALYSIS: By drawing in the diagonal, $\overline{BD}$, it is possible to prove that the two triangles formed are congruent. From this it will follow that $\overline{AB} \cong \overline{CD}$, and hence, by Theorem 40, $ABCD$ will be a parallelogram.

PROOF

The proof of Theorem 42 is left for you to do.

Summarized below is all the information we know about a parallelogram.

Ways to Prove That a Quadrilateral Is a Parallelogram		Conclusions That Can Be Drawn If a Quadrilateral Is a Parallelogram
(1) If the opposite sides are parallel.	reverse →	**(1)** The opposite sides are parallel.
(2) If the opposite sides are congruent.	converse →	**(2)** The opposite sides are congruent.
(3) If the diagonals bisect each other.	converse →	**(3)** The diagonals bisect each other.
(4) If two sides are congruent and parallel.		**(4)** The opposite angles are congruent.

Illustration:

If the bisectors of a pair of opposite angles of a parallelogram do not coincide, then they form another parallelogram.

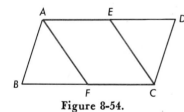

Figure 8-54.

Given: $ABCD$ is a $\square$.

$\overrightarrow{AF}$ bisects $\angle BAD$.

$\overrightarrow{CE}$ bisects $\angle BCD$.

Concl.: $AFCE$ is a $\square$.

ANALYSIS: By proving $\triangle ABF$ to be congruent to $\triangle CDE$ it will follow that $\overline{BF} \cong \overline{DE}$. Since $ABCD$ is a parallelogram, $\overline{AD} \cong \overline{BC}$ and, therefore, $\overline{AE} \cong \overline{FC}$. But $\overline{AE}$ and $\overline{FC}$ are also parallel by virtue of the fact that $ABCD$ is a parallelogram. Hence, $AFCE$ is a parallelogram, for one pair of sides are congruent and parallel.

Stating that $\overleftrightarrow{AE} \parallel \overleftrightarrow{FC}$ implies the very same meaning as $\overleftrightarrow{AD} \parallel \overleftrightarrow{BC}$, since a line can be named by the letters of any two points of that line. It is usually considered best to name the parallel lines in terms of the letters that appear at the vertices of the quadrilateral *that is being shown to be a parallelogram*. In this problem, this would imply saying that $\overleftrightarrow{AE} \parallel \overleftrightarrow{FC}$ rather than $\overleftrightarrow{AD} \parallel \overleftrightarrow{BC}$.

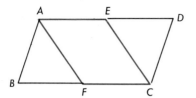

Figure 8-54.

| **PROOF** | (The reasons will be left for you to supply.) |

1. $ABCD$ is a parallelogram.
2. $\overline{AB} \cong \overline{CD}$ (s)
3. $\angle B \cong \angle D$ (a)
4. $\angle BAD \cong \angle BCD$
5. $\overrightarrow{AF}$ bisects $\angle BAD$.
6. $\overrightarrow{CE}$ bisects $\angle BCD$.
7. $\angle BAF \cong \angle DCE$ (a)
8. $\triangle ABF \cong \triangle CDE$

9. $\overline{BF} \cong \overline{DE}$
10. But, $\overline{BC} \cong \overline{AD}$
11. $\therefore \overline{FC} \cong \overline{AE}$
12. However, $\overleftrightarrow{AE} \parallel \overleftrightarrow{FC}$ (Def. of a parallelogram)
13. $\therefore AFCE$ is a parallelogram. (Theorem 42)

EXERCISES

1. Given: $ABCD$ is a $\square$.
$\overline{BE} \cong \overline{DF}$
Concl.: $AECF$ is a $\square$.

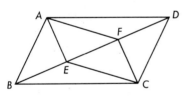

Given: $ABCD$ is an isosceles **2.**
trapezoid with
$\overline{AB} \cong \overline{DC}$.
$\angle 1 \cong \angle 2$
Concl.: $ABED$ is a $\square$.

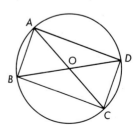

3. Given: $\overleftrightarrow{AC} \parallel \overleftrightarrow{DF}$
$\angle 1 \cong \angle 2$
Concl.: $\overline{BD} \cong \overline{CE}$

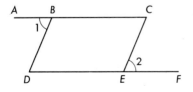

Given: $\odot O$ with $\overleftrightarrow{AC}$ and $\overleftrightarrow{BD}$ **4.**
intersecting at O
Concl.: $ABCD$ is a $\square$.

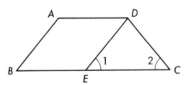

5. Given: $ABCD$ is a $\square$.
$\overleftrightarrow{AE}$ and $\overleftrightarrow{DF} \perp \overleftrightarrow{BF}$
Concl.: $AEFD$ is a rectangle.

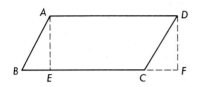

Given: $ABCD$ is a $\square$.   **6.**
$\overline{BQ} \cong \overline{DS}$
$\overline{PA} \cong \overline{RC}$
Concl.: $PQRS$ is a $\square$.

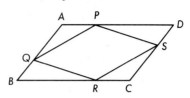

7. Given: $\overline{AC}$ and $\overline{EF}$ bisect
each other at G.
E is the midpoint
of $\overline{AD}$.
F is the midpoint
of $\overline{BC}$.
Concl.: $ABCD$ is a $\square$.

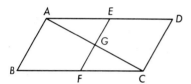

Given: $ABCD$ is a $\square$.   **8.**
$\overline{AP} \cong \overline{CQ}$
Concl.: $PBQD$ is a $\square$.

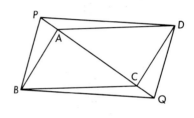

9. Given: $ABCD$ is a $\square$.
$\overline{AP} \cong \overline{BQ} \cong \overline{CR} \cong$
$\overline{DS}$
Concl.: $PQRS$ is a $\square$.

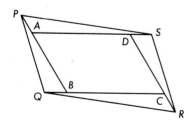

Given: M is the midpoint   **10.**
of $\overline{BD}$.
P is the midpoint
of $\overline{AD}$.
Q is the midpoint
of $\overline{BC}$.
$\angle 1 \cong \angle 2$
Concl.: $ABCD$ is a $\square$.

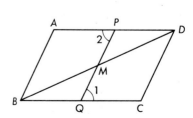

11. Given: $\overline{BE}$ is the median in $\triangle ABC$.
    $\angle DAC \cong \angle FCA$
Concl.: $ADCF$ is a ▱.

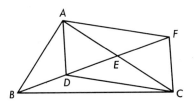

12. Given: $ABCD$ is a ▱.
    R, S, T, W are the midpoints of $\overline{AM}$, $\overline{BM}, \overline{CM}, \overline{DM}$ respectively.
Concl.: $RSTW$ is a ▱.

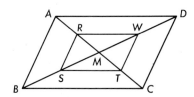

13. Given: All lines in this figure are coplaner.
    $ABDE$ is a ▱.
    $AEFC$ is a ▱.
Concl.: $BDFC$ is a ▱.

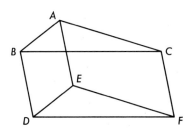

14. Given: $ABCD$ is a ▱.
    E is the midpoint of $\overline{AD}$.
    F is the midpoint of $\overline{BC}$.
Concl.: $AFCE$ is a ▱.

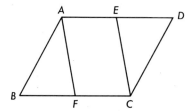

15. Given: $ABCD$ is a ▱.
    $\overline{BE} \cong \overline{DF}$
Concl.: $\overleftrightarrow{AC}$ bisects $\overline{EF}$. (Hint: Prove that $AECF$ is a ▱.)

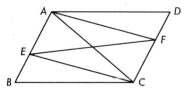

16. Given: D is the midpoint of $\overline{AB}$.
    E is the midpoint of $\overline{AC}$.
    E is the midpoint of $\overline{DF}$.
Concl.: $DBCF$ is a ▱.

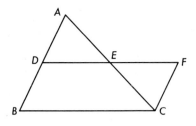

17. Given: $ABCD$ is not a $\square$.
P is the midpoint
of $\overline{AD}$.
Q is the midpoint
of $\overline{BC}$.
Concl.: $AQCP$ is not a $\square$.
(Hint: Use indirect
proof.)

Given: $\overline{DM} \cong \overline{MB}$ **18.**
$ABCD$ is not a $\square$.
Concl.: $\overline{AM} \ncong \overline{MC}$

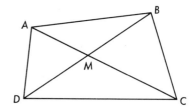

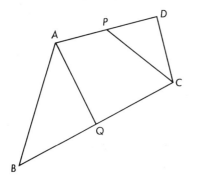

B

1. If two parallel lines are cut by a transversal, then the bisectors of all the interior angles will form a parallelogram.
2. If a pair of opposite exterior angles of a parallelogram are bisected, then another parallelogram will be formed.
3. If the median to one side of a triangle is drawn and then extended its own length, the line segments joining this endpoint with the endpoints of the side will form a parallelogram.
4. If consecutive midpoints of the sides of a parallelogram are joined in order, then another parallelogram will be formed.
5. If consecutive pairs of angles of a quadrilateral are supplementary, then the quadrilateral is a parallelogram.
6. If the diagonal $\overline{AC}$ of parallelogram $ABCD$ is trisected at points P and Q where the order of the points on diagonal $\overline{AC}$ is A, P, Q, C, then $PBQD$ is a parallelogram.
7. If each diagonal of a parallelogram is extended congruent segments in both directions and these new endpoints are joined in order, then the quadrilateral formed will be a parallelogram.
8. The line segment joining the midpoints of a pair of opposite sides of a parallelogram will be congruent to either of the other two sides.

9. The bisectors of all four angles of a parallelogram form another parallelogram. (Hint: Use information proved in the illustrative problem on page 269.)

10.* The median to the hypotenuse of a right triangle is congruent to either of the segments of the hypotenuse. (Hint: Extend the median its own length; then draw line segments from this endpoint to the endpoints of the hypotenuse.)

11.* If a line bisects one side of a triangle and is parallel to the second side, then it bisects the third side. (Hint: See the diagram of Problem 16, Group A.)

■ Test and Review

$$\boxed{A}$$

Prove each of the following:

1. Given: $\overleftrightarrow{AB} \parallel \overleftrightarrow{CD}$
$\overleftrightarrow{GH} \parallel \overleftrightarrow{EF}$
Concl.: $\angle 1 \cong \angle 2$

Given: $\overleftrightarrow{AB}$ and $\overleftrightarrow{CD}$ intersect   **2.**
at center of $\odot O$.
Concl.: $\overleftrightarrow{AC} \parallel \overleftrightarrow{DB}$

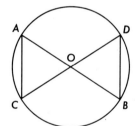

3. Given: $\overleftrightarrow{AB} \parallel \overleftrightarrow{DC}$
$\overleftrightarrow{AD} \parallel \overleftrightarrow{BC}$
$\overline{AF} \cong \overline{EC}$
Concl.: $\overleftrightarrow{BE} \parallel \overleftrightarrow{DF}$

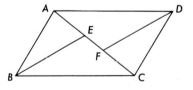

Given: $ABCD$ is a $\square$.   **4.**
$AFED$ is a $\square$.
Concl.: $\overline{BC} \cong \overline{FE}$

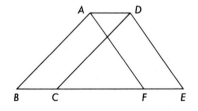

5. Given: $\overrightarrow{AF}$ bisects exterior
angle DAB of $\triangle ABC$.
$\overleftrightarrow{GB} \parallel \overleftrightarrow{AF}$

Concl.: $\triangle ABG$ is isosceles.

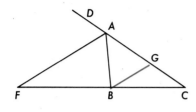

Given: $ABCD$ is an isosceles   **6.**
trapezoid with
$\overleftrightarrow{AD} \parallel \overleftrightarrow{BC}$.
R is the midpoint
of $\overline{PB}$.
S is the midpoint
of $\overline{PC}$.

Concl.: $\triangle PRS$ is isosceles.
(Hint: Prove $\triangle PBC$
isosceles.)

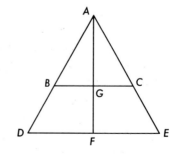

7. Given: $ABCD$ is a quadrilateral.
E is the midpoint
of $\overline{AD}$.
F is the midpoint
of $\overline{BC}$.
$\overline{AC}$ and $\overline{EF}$ bisect each
other.

Concl.: $ABCD$ is a $\square$.

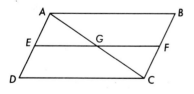

Given: $\overline{AB} \cong \overline{AC}$ **8.**
$\overline{BD} \cong \overline{CE}$
$\overleftrightarrow{AF} \perp \overleftrightarrow{DE}$

Concl.: $\overleftrightarrow{BC} \parallel \overleftrightarrow{DE}$ (Hint:
Prove $\overleftrightarrow{AF} \perp \overleftrightarrow{BC}$.)

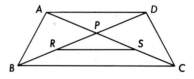

9. Given: $\overline{AB} \not\cong \overline{AC}$
$\overleftrightarrow{AD} \perp \overleftrightarrow{BC}$

Concl.: D is not the midpoint of $\overline{BC}$.

Given: $\overline{AB} \cong \overline{AC}$
$\overleftrightarrow{AD}$ does not bisect $\overline{BC}$.

Concl.: $\overline{DB} \not\cong \overline{DC}$

10.

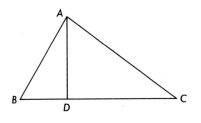

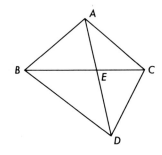

B

Prove each of the following statements:

1. A diagonal of a rhombus bisects two of the angles of the rhombus.

2. If the bisectors of the lower base angles of an isosceles trapezoid are extended until they intersect, they will form an isosceles triangle with the lower base of the trapezoid.

3. If a pair of opposite angles of a trapezoid are supplementary, then the trapezoid is isosceles.

4. If a pair of opposite angles of a quadrilateral are congruent while a pair of opposite sides are paraliel, then the quadrilateral is a parallelogram.

5. The line joining the midpoints of a pair of opposite sides of a parallelogram is parallel to the remaining two sides of the parallelogram.

6. If the diagonals of a parallelogram are perpendicular, then the parallelogram is a rhombus.

7. If the lower base angles of a trapezoid are congruent, then the trapezoid is isosceles.

8. If a median is drawn to a side of a triangle and perpendicular segments are drawn from the endpoints of this side to the median (extended if necessary), then the perpendicular segments are congruent.

9. If the perpendicular bisector of the lower base of a trapezoid passes through the midpoint of the upper base, then the trapezoid is isosceles.

10. If a line is drawn through the endpoints of the medians to the legs of an isosceles triangle, it will be parallel to the base of the triangle.

Using the indirect proof, prove each of the following statements.

1. If the lower base angles of a trapezoid are not congruent, then the trapezoid is not isosceles.
2. If two line segments do not bisect each other, then the line segments joining their endpoints do not form a parallelogram.
3. If a line is perpendicular to one side of an angle, then it is not perpendicular to the other side also.
4. If the diagonals of a parallelogram are not congruent, then the parallelogram is not a rectangle.
5. If a line is not perpendicular to the bisector of an angle, it will not form congruent angles with the sides of the angle.
6. If the diagonals of a parallelogram are not perpendicular, then the parallelogram is not a rhombus.
7. If the perpendicular bisector of one side of a triangle does not pass through the intersection of the other two sides, then these two sides are not congruent.
8. If the bisectors of two angles of a given triangle do not form an isosceles triangle with a side of the given triangle, then this triangle is not isosceles.

Try This For Fun

If the three medians of a triangle are drawn, they will intersect at a point that is one of the trisection points of each of the medians. Were we to draw the triangle on a piece of cardboard, then cut the triangle away from the rest of the cardboard, it would be possible to balance this figure on the point of a pin that had been placed at the intersection of the medians. For this reason, this point of intersection is called the center of gravity of the triangle.

Although we are not prepared to prove all that we have just stated, we can show that the point of intersection of two of the medians is a trisection point of both of them.

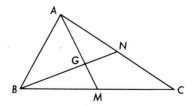

Given: Any $\triangle ABC$ with $\overline{AM}$ and $\overline{BN}$ two of the medians

Concl.: $m\,\overline{GM} = \frac{1}{2}m\,\overline{AG}$

Suggestion: Extend $\overleftrightarrow{AM}$ so that $\overline{GM} \cong \overline{MP}$. Also extend $\overleftrightarrow{BN}$ so that $\overline{GN} \cong \overline{NQ}$. Draw $\overleftrightarrow{BP}$, $\overleftrightarrow{CP}$, $\overleftrightarrow{AQ}$, $\overleftrightarrow{CQ}$, and $\overleftrightarrow{GC}$.

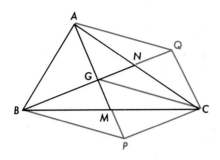

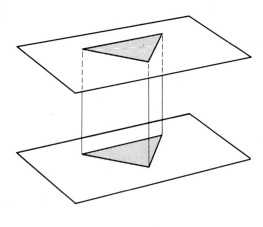

9

Parallelism in Space

AS YOU MIGHT SUSPECT, THERE ARE MANY principles in space geometry that will be similar to those on parallelism that we encountered in the geometry of the plane. In this unit we plan to call your attention to a few of these. It would be best, of course, to start with the definition of parallel planes.

DEFINITION 59: Parallel planes are two planes that do not have a point in common.

Now that we made this definition, another look at an earlier definition is needed. *Parallel lines* were defined as "two lines in the same plane that do not intersect." The point can be raised as to why we insisted that the two lines lie in the same plane. This was done so as to eliminate certain lines in space that do not intersect but that we prefer not to think of as being parallel. Consider the ceiling and floor of your room; any line drawn in the ceiling would never intersect a line that you had drawn on the floor. Yet, only some of these would you consider to be parallel to the line that was drawn on the floor. To illustrate, we would probably consider lines *a*, *b*, and *c*, but not *x*, to be parallel to *y*. What is there peculiar about the relation that exists between *a* and *y*, or *b* and *y*, or *c* and *y* that does not exist between *x* and *y*? Notice that it appears as if a single plane could be drawn

279

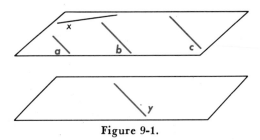

Figure 9-1.

that might contain both *a* and *y*; the same can be said of *b* and *y* and of *c* and *y*. The pair of lines *x* and *y*, however, do not lie in any common plane. Thus, to have the definition of parallel lines agree with our idea of what we would like parallel lines to be, we insist that they must lie in the same plane. Hence, the existence of parallel lines implies the existence of a plane that will contain them. This is made even a bit more emphatic by the agreement that this be the *only* plane that will contain them. Thus, we have created a fourth method for determining a plane.

POSTULATE 26: Two parallel lines determine a plane.

Lines such as *x* and *y* in the diagram above are called *skew lines*. Since two intersecting lines determine a plane and so do two parallel lines, it would seem almost natural that the definition of skew lines be

DEFINITION 60: Skew lines are two lines that are not coplanar.

In terms of the intersection of two lines how might you have defined skew lines? Look around your classroom and find several pairs of skew lines.

In our earlier contact with space geometry there was no need to consider the nature of the intersection of two planes. Henceforth, however, many of the properties we develop will have their origin in knowing the set of points in which two planes intersect. The drawing below is that of a room very much like your classroom.

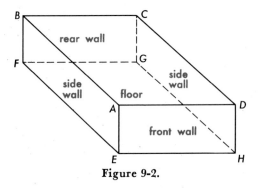

Figure 9-2.

Notice that the front wall and floor of the room have in common the points of the line *EH*. Similarly, the intersection of the rear wall and the floor are those points of the line *FG* for they are points of both the rear wall and the floor. Where will the points lie that represent the intersection of the side wall *AF* and the rear wall? Where will the points lie that represent the intersection of the side wall *CH* and the front wall?

POSTULATE 27: The intersection of two planes is a line.

What name would you give to the pair of planes that are the ceiling and floor of your classroom? In Figure 9-2 these are the parallel planes *BD* and *FH*. Notice that the ceiling intersects the front wall in the line *AD*, while the floor intersects the front wall in the line *EH*. It would appear as if these two lines of intersection, $\overleftrightarrow{AD}$ and $\overleftrightarrow{EH}$, are parallel. Similarly, the ceiling and floor intersect the side wall *AF* in the lines *AB* and *EF*, which also appear to be parallel. In what way are the two side walls related to each other? In what lines does the rear wall intersect the two side walls? What appears to be true about these lines? In view of this analysis, what proposition do you think can be proved?

THEOREM 43: **If a plane intersects two parallel planes, the lines of intersection will be parallel.**

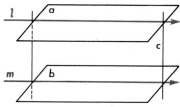

Given: *a* ∥ *b*

Plane *c* intersects *a* and *b* in *l* and *m*.

Concl.: *l* ∥ *m*

Figure 9-3.

ANALYSIS: Many, many of the theorems in space geometry—and particularly those on parallelism—are developed on the basis of the indirect proof. At this stage of the work this method of approach will probably lead to success more often than not.

PROOF

By the law of the excluded middle one of the following statements must be true and no other possibility exists:

$$l \parallel m \quad \text{or} \quad l \nparallel m$$

Let us accept the possibility that *l* ∦ *m*. Since the two lines lie in the same plane, *c*, then being "not parallel" implies that they intersect at some point, *P*. Since *P* lies in *l*, *P* must lie in *a* by definition of a plane. Similarly, since *P* lies in *m*, it must lie in *b*. This means that *a* and *b* are not parallel, for they have the point *P* in common. The Given Data, however, states that *a* ∥ *b*. Therefore, accepting the possibility that *l* ∦ *m* led to the logical inconsistency of the truth of both *a* ∥ *b* and *a* ∦ *b*. By the law of contradic-

tion both cannot be true at the same time. Since $a \parallel b$ must be true, for
it is part of the Given Data, then $a \not\parallel b$ must be false and, therefore, $l \not\parallel m$
is also false. Hence, $l \parallel m$ must be true for it is the only remaining possibility.

**THEOREM 44: If two planes are perpendicular to the same line, then
they are parallel.**

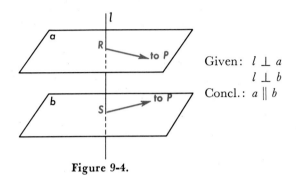

Given: $l \perp a$
          $l \perp b$

Concl.: $a \parallel b$

Figure 9-4.

PROOF

By the law of the excluded middle one of the following
statements must be true and no other possibility exists:

$$a \parallel b \quad \text{or} \quad a \not\parallel b$$

If we accept the possibility that $a \not\parallel b$, it will imply that a and b have some
point, P, in common. The line l and the point P will determine a plane that

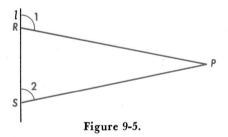

Figure 9-5.

intersects plane a in the line PR and the plane b in the line PS. $\overleftrightarrow{PR}$ must
be perpendicular to line l, for, by definition, if a line is perpendicular to a
plane, it is perpendicular to every line in the plane that passes through its
foot. This will make $\angle 1$ a right angle. In the same way, $\overleftrightarrow{PS}$ is perpendicular
to line l, and therefore $\angle 2$ is also a right angle. Thus, $m \angle 1 = m \angle 2$.

However, the theorem on the exterior angle of a triangle enables us to say that $m \angle 1 > m \angle 2$. Therefore, accepting the possibility that $a \not\parallel b$ led to the logical inconsistency of the truth of both $m \angle 1 > m \angle 2$ and $m \angle 1 \not> m \angle 2$. By the law of contradiction both cannot be true at the same time. Since $m \angle 1 > m \angle 2$ must be true, for it is a theorem, then $m \angle 1 \not> m \angle 2$ must be false and, therefore, the statement $a \not\parallel b$ is also false. Hence, $a \parallel b$ must be true, for it is the only remaining possibility.

Notice the similarity between the statement of Theorem 44 and that of Theorem 26.

THEOREM 45: If two planes are parallel to the same plane, then they are parallel to each other.

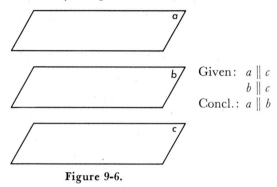

Given: $a \parallel c$
         $b \parallel c$
Concl.: $a \parallel b$

Figure 9-6.

PROOF

By the law of the excluded middle one of the following statements must be true and no other possibility exists:

$$a \parallel b \quad \text{or} \quad a \not\parallel b$$

If we accept the possibility that $a \not\parallel b$, it will imply that they have some point, P, in common. Let this point and any line, l, in plane c determine a plane. This plane will intersect plane a in line PR, which will be parallel

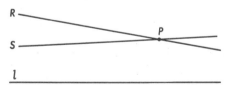

Figure 9-7.

to line l, for if a plane intersects two parallel planes, the lines of intersection are parallel. In the same way, this plane will intersect plane b in line PS, which will also be parallel to line l. This means that there are two lines through P parallel to l. This, however, contradicts the Parallel Postulate, which states that through P there can be only one line parallel to l. Therefore, accepting the possibility that $a \not\parallel b$ led to the logical inconsistency of the truth of both statements. By the law of contradiction both cannot be true at the same time. Since we have accepted the truth of the Parallel Postulate, the statement that both $\overleftrightarrow{PR}$ and $\overleftrightarrow{PS}$ are parallel to l must be false and, therefore, the statement that $a \not\parallel b$ is also false. Hence, $a \parallel b$ must be true, for it is the only remaining possibility.

Notice the similarity between the statement of Theorem 45 and that of Theorem 30. If, however, the statement of Theorem 30 were applied to space geometry, its proof would be quite difficult. We will assume, though, that it is true.

POSTULATE 28: If two lines in space are parallel to the same line, they are parallel to each other.

THEOREM 46: If a line is perpendicular to one of two parallel planes, it is perpendicular to the other also.

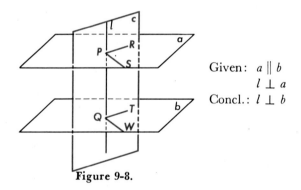

Given: $a \parallel b$
$\qquad$ $l \perp a$
Concl.: $l \perp b$

Figure 9-8.

ANALYSIS: In order that l be perpendicular to b, it is necessary to prove that it is perpendicular to two lines passing through its foot; these will be $\overleftrightarrow{QT}$ and $\overleftrightarrow{QW}$.

PROOF	STATEMENTS	REASONS
1. In plane a select any point R and let $\overleftrightarrow{PR}$ be the line passing through these two points.	1. There exists one and only one line through two points.
2. l and $\overleftrightarrow{PR}$ determine plane c.	2. Two intersecting lines determine a plane.

3. c intersects b in $\overleftrightarrow{QT}$.	3. The intersection of two planes is a line.
4. $a \parallel b$	4. Given
5. $\overleftrightarrow{PR} \parallel \overleftrightarrow{QT}$	5. If a plane intersects two parallel planes, the lines of intersection are parallel.
6. $l \perp a$	6. Given
7. $l \perp \overleftrightarrow{PR}$	7. Def. of a line perpendicular to a plane
8. $l \perp \overleftrightarrow{QT}$	8. If a line is perpendicular to one of two parallel lines, it is also perpendicular to the other.

In the same way, by drawing $\overleftrightarrow{PS}$ in plane a it is possible to show that l is perpendicular to $\overleftrightarrow{QW}$.

9. $l \perp b$	9. A line is perpendicular to a plane if it is perpendicular to at least two lines in the plane passing through its foot.

EXERCISES

1. Given: $a \parallel b$

$\qquad \overleftrightarrow{AB} \parallel \overleftrightarrow{CD}$

Concl.: $\overline{AB} \cong \overline{CD}$

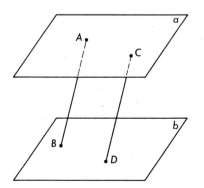

Given: $\overleftrightarrow{PQ} \parallel \overleftrightarrow{RS}$

$\qquad \overleftrightarrow{PQ} \parallel \overleftrightarrow{VT}$

$\qquad a \parallel b$

Concl.: $\triangle RPV \cong \triangle SQT$

2.

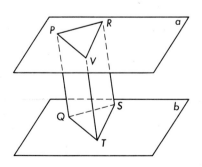

3. Given: $a \parallel b$
$\overline{PR} \parallel \overline{SQ}$

Concl.: $\overline{PQ}$ and $\overline{SR}$ bisect each other.

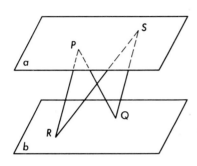

Given: $a \parallel b$ **4.**
$\overline{PQ} \cong \overline{PR}$

Concl.: $\overline{QS} \cong \overline{RT}$

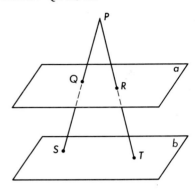

5. Given: $a \perp l$
$b \perp l$
$\overline{PQ} \cong \overline{RS}$
c contains $\overline{PQ}$ and $\overline{RS}$.

Concl.: $\overline{PR} \cong \overline{QS}$

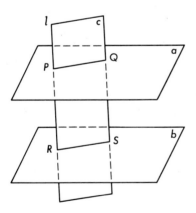

Given: $a \perp l$ **6.**
$b \perp l$
$\overline{PQ} \cong \overline{RS}$
c contains $\overline{PQ}$ and $\overline{RS}$.

Concl.: $\overline{PS} \cong \overline{RQ}$

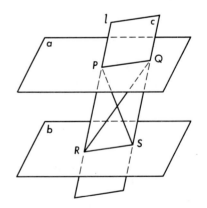

7. Given: $a \perp l$
$\quad\quad\quad$ $b \perp l$
$\quad\quad\quad$ c and d contain l.
$\quad$ Concl.: $\angle PQR \cong \angle STW$
$\quad\quad\quad$ (Hint: Make $\overline{PQ} \cong \overline{ST}$
$\quad\quad\quad$ and $\overline{RQ} \cong \overline{TW}$, then
$\quad\quad\quad$ prove $\triangle PQR \cong$
$\quad\quad\quad$ $\triangle STW$.)

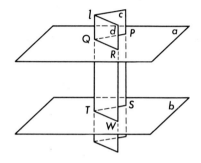

Given: plane $BD \parallel$ plane FH $\quad$ **8.**
$\quad\quad\quad$ plane $BE \parallel$ plane CH
$\quad\quad\quad$ plane $AH \parallel$ plane BG
Concl.: $\overline{AC} \cong \overline{EG}$
(The figure in this problem
$\quad\quad$ is called a paral-
$\quad\quad$ lelepiped.)

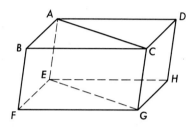

9. By using the diagram and Given Data in Problem 8, prove that $\square ABCD \cong \square EFGH$. (Hint: See the definition of congruent polygons on page 118.)

Given: Each of the pairs of $\quad$ **10.**
$\quad\quad\quad$ opposite planes are
$\quad\quad\quad$ parallel.
$\quad\quad\quad$ Lines FG, EH, AD,
$\quad\quad\quad$ and BC are perpen-
$\quad\quad\quad$ dicular to planes AF
$\quad\quad\quad$ and DG.
Concl.: $\overline{AG} \cong \overline{FD}$ (Assume that $\overline{AG}$
$\quad\quad\quad$ and $\overline{FD}$ intersect.)

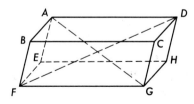

11. Given: $a \parallel b$

$c \parallel b$

$\overleftrightarrow{WS}$ bisects $\overline{PR}$ at Q.

Concl.: $\overleftrightarrow{PR}$ bisects $\overline{WS}$.

Given: $a \parallel b$ **12.** *

$c \parallel b$

$\overline{ST} \cong \overline{TW}$

Concl.: $\overline{PQ} \cong \overline{QR}$

(Hint: Let $\overleftrightarrow{UV}$ be the line through T that is parallel to $\overleftrightarrow{PR}$.)

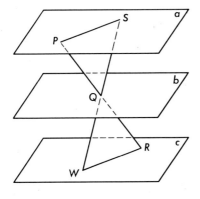

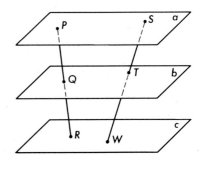

B

Use the indirect proof for each of the problems in this group.

1. Two lines can not be perpendicular to the same plane at the same point on the plane.†
2. From a given point not on a given plane there can be no more than one line perpendicular to the given plane.†
3. Two lines that are both perpendicular to the same plane can not intersect.
4. Through a given point not on a given plane two planes can not exist that are both parallel to the given plane.
5. At a given point on a given line two planes can not exist that are both perpendicular to the given line.
6. Through a given point not on a given line two planes can not exist that are both perpendicular to the given line.
7. If a given line is perpendicular to a given plane, then any line that is perpendicular to the given line at its foot lies in the given plane.

† These statements are often considered as theorems.

8.* If a given line is parallel to a given plane, then the intersection of any plane containing this line with the given plane must be parallel to the given line.†

9.* If each of two intersecting lines is parallel to a given plane, then the plane determined by these lines is parallel to the given plane.†

■ Dihedral Angles

At this time we want to examine the figure in space geometry that is comparable to the angle in plane geometry. This figure is called a *dihedral angle*. To define it, however, will require a number of terms that we have not encountered as yet. The first of these is the *half-plane*. Consider in Figure 9-9 the points in plane m with reference to the line AB. If the line

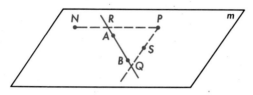

Figure 9-9.

$\overrightarrow{PS}$ is drawn, it will intersect $\overleftrightarrow{AB}$ in Q. When this point of intersection, Q, is *not* between the two points P and S, then these two points are said to be on the *same side* of $\overleftrightarrow{AB}$. On the other hand, the line PN intersects $\overleftrightarrow{AB}$ at some point R such that R is between P and N. In this event, P and N are said to be on *opposite sides* of $\overleftrightarrow{AB}$. Those points that are on the same side of $\overleftrightarrow{AB}$ are said to be in the half-plane with reference to $\overleftrightarrow{AB}$ where $\overleftrightarrow{AB}$ is the *edge* of that half-plane.

DEFINITION 61: Points on the same side of a given line in a given plane are the set of points not containing the line such that if a line is drawn through any two points of the set, it will intersect the given line at a point that is not between these two points.

DEFINITION 62: A half-plane is the set of points on the same side of a given line in a given plane.

The given line may act as an edge for many half-planes. To illustrate, the bound edge of your book can be considered as the edge of those half-planes consisting of the pages of the book.

† These statements are often considered as theorems.

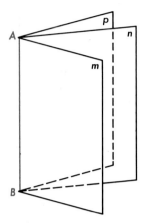

Figure 9-10.

$\overleftrightarrow{AB}$ is the edge of half-planes m, n, and p.

DEFINITION 63: A dihedral angle is a set of points consisting of the union of two half-planes and the edge common to them.

From this definition it is quite apparent that unless two half-planes have a common edge, there will be no dihedral angle. The edge of a dihedral angle is comparable to the vertex of an angle, while the half-planes AF and AG are similar to the sides of an angle. The half-planes AF and AG are called the *faces* of the dihedral angle.

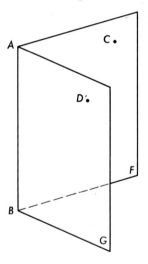

Figure 9-11.

A dihedral angle is named by using a point in each half-plane and two points along the edge. If there is no possibility for confusion, a dihedral angle can also be named by the two points along its edge. In the figure above, the dihedral angle can be named as either $\angle G$–AB–F or $\angle AB$.

Our next concern is with the measure of a dihedral angle. This problem is overcome rather easily by relating an angle whose measure we know to that of the dihedral angle. To do this, we create the angle called the *plane angle*.

DEFINITION 64: A plane angle of a dihedral angle is an angle whose vertex lies on the edge of the dihedral angle and whose sides are perpendicular to the edge, each side lying in a different face of the dihedral angle.

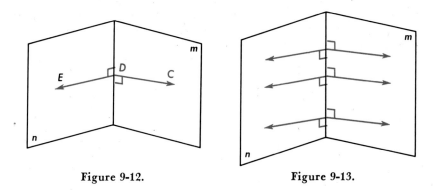

Figure 9-12.   Figure 9-13.

With this definition at our disposal, the measure of a dihedral angle becomes

DEFINITION 65: The measure of a dihedral angle is the measure of its plane angle.

It might appear that by this definition we may have neatly entrapped ourselves, for a dihedral angle has many plane angles as seen in Figure 9-13. If the measures of all these plane angles are not the same, then it is evident that Definition 65 is poorly designed. Quite fortunately this is not so, for it can be proved that

THEOREM 47: The plane angles of a dihedral angle are congruent.

PROOF

The proof of this theorem is identically the same as that of Problem 7, page 287. It will be left for you to do.

It seems almost needless to point out the next definition.

DEFINITION 66: Congruent dihedral angles are dihedral angles that have the same measure.

A number of problems we would like to present at this time are dependent upon a principle that seems obvious enough, yet would require several additional theorems before it can be proved. Rather than become involved in the proofs of these theorems that have little value for us in our work, we will postulate the principle we need.

POSTULATE 29: If one of two parallel lines is perpendicular to a plane, the other is also.

Illustration:

If two parallel planes are cut by a third one, then the alternate interior dihedral angles are congruent.

ANALYSIS: We will try to introduce a plane into this figure that will give us plane angles at both P and Q. It will then be merely a matter of proving plane angles to be congruent to show that the alternate interior dihedral angles are congruent.

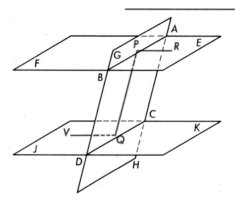

Given: $EF \parallel KJ$
Concl.: $\angle E-AB-H \cong$
            $\angle J-DC-G$

Figure 9-14.

PROOF STATEMENTS	REASONS
1. $\overleftrightarrow{EF} \parallel \overleftrightarrow{KJ}$	1. Given
2. $\overleftrightarrow{AB} \parallel \overleftrightarrow{CD}$	2. If a plane intersects two parallel planes, then their lines of intersection are parallel.
3. Let plane a be perpendicular to $\overleftrightarrow{AB}$ at point P.	3. See Problem 5, page 288.
4. $\therefore a \perp \overleftrightarrow{CD}$	4. If one of two parallel lines is perpendicular to a plane, the other is also.
5. a intersects planes EF, KJ, and GH in lines PR, PQ, and VQ respectively.	5. The intersection of two planes is a line.
6. $\overleftrightarrow{AB} \perp \overleftrightarrow{PR}$, $\overleftrightarrow{AB} \perp \overleftrightarrow{PQ}$	6. Def. of a line perpendicular to a plane

7. ∴ ∠RPQ is the plane angle of ∠E–AB–H.	7. Def. of a plane angle
8. $\overset{\leftrightarrow}{CD} \perp \overset{\leftrightarrow}{QV}$, $\overset{\leftrightarrow}{CD} \perp \overset{\leftrightarrow}{PQ}$	8. Same as 6
9. ∴ ∠PQV is a plane angle of ∠J–DC–G.	9. Same as 7
10. But, $\overset{\leftrightarrow}{PR} \parallel \overset{\leftrightarrow}{VQ}$	10. Same as 2
11. ∴ m ∠RPQ = m ∠PQV	11. If two parallel lines are cut by a transversal, then the alternate interior angles are congruent.
12. m ∠E–AB–H = m ∠RPQ	12. Def. of the measure of a dihedral angle
13. m ∠J–DC–G = m ∠PQV	13. Same as 12
14. m ∠E–AB–H = m ∠J–DC–G	14. If two numbers are equal to two equal numbers, they are equal to each other.
15. ∠E–AB–H ≅ ∠J–DC–G	15. Def. of congruent dihedral angles

Having defined a dihedral angle, we are now in a position to define perpendicular planes. By considering the definition of perpendicular lines, what do you believe the definition of perpendicular planes will be?

DEFINITION 67: Perpendicular planes are two planes that intersect to form right dihedral angles.

By virtue of this definition it will be possible to prove planes to be perpendicular if we can show that they intersect to form right dihedral angles. To show that a dihedral angle is a right dihedral angle will necessitate showing that the plane angle of that dihedral angle is a right angle. However, you may recall that proving an angle to be a right angle was no simple task. To avoid the difficulty of proving lines to be perpendicular by resorting to the reverse of the definition of perpendicular lines, we developed the theorem that if two lines meet to form congruent adjacent angles, the lines would be perpendicular. Similarly, in space geometry we will try to prove planes perpendicular not by referring to the reverse of Definition 67, but rather by proving that the planes intersect to form congruent adjacent dihedral angles.

First, though, it will be necessary for us to prove this property.

THEOREM 48: If two planes intersect to form congruent adjacent dihedral angles, then the planes are perpendicular.

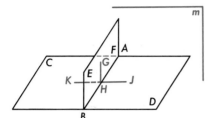

Given: $\angle E\text{-}AB\text{-}D \cong$
$\quad\quad\;\; \angle E\text{-}AB\text{-}C$

Concl.: plane $EF \perp$ plane CD

Figure 9-15.

ANALYSIS: By showing plane angles GHK and GHJ to be congruent it will follow that $\overleftrightarrow{GH} \perp \overleftrightarrow{KJ}$. Therefore, $\angle GHJ$ is a right angle. This, in turn, will make $\angle E\text{-}AB\text{-}D$ a right dihedral angle. Hence, plane EF will be perpendicular to plane CD by the reverse of the definition of perpendicular planes.

PROOF STATEMENTS	REASONS
1. Let plane m be perpendicular to $\overleftrightarrow{AB}$ at point H.	1. See Problem 5, page 288.
2. m intersects EF in line GH and CD in line KJ.	2. The intersection of two planes is a line.
3. $\overleftrightarrow{AB} \perp \overleftrightarrow{GH}$, $\overleftrightarrow{AB} \perp \overleftrightarrow{KJ}$	3. Def. of a line perpendicular to a plane
4. $\angle GHJ$ is the plane angle of $\angle E\text{-}AB\text{-}D$.	4. Def. of a plane angle
5. $\angle GHK$ is the plane angle of $\angle E\text{-}AB\text{-}C$.	5. Same as 4
6. $m\,\angle E\text{-}AB\text{-}D =$ $m\,\angle E\text{-}AB\text{-}C$	6. Given
7. $m\,\angle GHJ =$ $m\,\angle E\text{-}AB\text{-}D$	7. Def. of the measure of a dihedral angle
8. $m\,\angle GHK =$ $m\,\angle E\text{-}AB\text{-}C$	8. Same as 7
9. $\therefore m\,\angle GHJ = m\,\angle GHK$	9. If two numbers are equal to two equal numbers, then they are equal to each other.
10. $\overleftrightarrow{GH} \perp \overleftrightarrow{KJ}$	10. If two lines intersect to form congruent adjacent angles, the lines are perpendicular.
11. $\angle GHJ$ is a right angle.	11. Def. of perpendicular lines
12. $\angle E\text{-}AB\text{-}D$ is a right dihedral angle.	12. Why?
13. Plane $EF \perp$ plane CD	13. Why?

EXERCISES

1. If two dihedral angles are right dihedral angles, then they are congruent.

2. If two dihedral angles are vertical dihedral angles, then they are congruent.

3. Using the problem proved on page 292 and Problem 2 above, prove that if two parallel planes are cut by a third plane, the alternate exterior dihedral angles will be congruent.

4. If two dihedral angles are congruent, the supplements of these two dihedral angles will be congruent.

5. By using the problem proved on page 292 and Problem 4 above, prove that if two parallel planes are cut by a third plane, the corresponding dihedral angles will be congruent.

   By using the information from Problems 3 and 5 prove Problems 6 and 7.

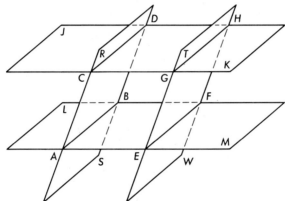

6. Given: $JK \parallel LM$, $RS \parallel TW$.
   Concl.: $\angle T\text{-}GH\text{-}K \cong \angle R\text{-}AB\text{-}M$

7. Given: $JK \parallel LM$, $RS \parallel TW$.
   Concl.: $\angle S\text{-}CD\text{-}K \cong \angle L\text{-}EF\text{-}T$

8. Use Problem 5 to prove that if a plane is perpendicular to one of two parallel planes, then it is also perpendicular to the other.

9. Prove that the edge of a dihedral angle is perpendicular to the plane determined by one of its plane angles.

10. Use Problem 9 to prove that the planes determined by the plane angles of a dihedral angle are parallel.

11.* If a line is perpendicular to a given plane, then any plane containing that line is perpendicular to the given plane. †

† This statement is often considered as a theorem.

◼ Test and Review

Justify your answer to all questions except 4, 10, and 12.

1. How would you account for the fact that the intersections of the side wall with the ceiling and floor of your classroom are parallel lines?

2. If each of two lines is parallel to a plane, will the plane determined by these lines necessarily be parallel to the plane?

3. Four lines in space are parallel to each other. Will the plane determined by any two of these lines necessarily be parallel to the plane determined by the other two?

4. If two lines are parallel and one of them is perpendicular to a plane, must the other also be perpendicular to the plane?

5. (a) Does a half-plane include its edge?
   (b) How does a half-line differ from a ray?
   (c) Is there any figure in space geometry that is comparable to the ray in plane geometry?

6. What is the maximum measure that a dihedral angle can have?

7. If a line is parallel to each of two planes, are the planes necessarily parallel?

8. If a line is perpendicular to each of two planes, are the planes necessarily parallel?

9. (a) If a line is parallel to a plane, is it parallel to all lines in the plane?
   (b) If a line is parallel to a plane, will it intersect any line in the plane?

10. If two lines are perpendicular to the same plane, will the lines necessarily be parallel?

11. If two lines are parallel to the same plane, are they necessarily parallel to each other?

12. There are six dihedral angles in the diagram below. Name them.

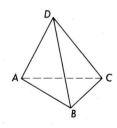

B

Prove each of the following:

1. Given: $m \parallel n$

         p intersects m and n in

         $\overset{\leftrightarrow}{AB}$ and $\overset{\leftrightarrow}{CD}$.

         $\overline{AB} \cong \overline{CD}$

Concl.: $\overline{AC} \cong \overline{BD}$

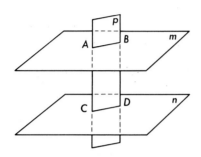

Given: $m \parallel n$

         $\overline{BC} \cong \overline{DE}$

Concl.: $\overline{AD} \cong \overline{AB}$ **2.**

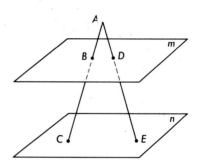

3. Given: $m \parallel n$

         p intersects m and n in

         $\overset{\leftrightarrow}{AB}$ and $\overset{\leftrightarrow}{CD}$.

         $\overline{AB} \cong \overline{CD}$

Concl.: $\overline{AD}$ and $\overline{BC}$ bisect

        each other.

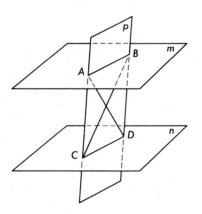

Given: $\overset{\leftrightarrow}{PQ} \perp a$

         $\overset{\leftrightarrow}{PQ} \perp b$

         M is the midpoint

         of $\overline{PQ}$.

         $\overline{RS}$ is any line segment

         through M with end-

         points in a and b.

Concl.: M is the midpoint   **4.**

        of $\overline{RS}$.

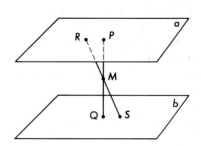

5. Given: $\overleftrightarrow{AB} \parallel m$

p and q contain $\overleftrightarrow{AB}$.

p and q intersect m

in $\overleftrightarrow{CD}$ and $\overleftrightarrow{EF}$.

Concl.: $\overleftrightarrow{CD} \parallel \overleftrightarrow{EF}$

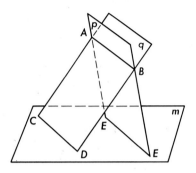

Given: $a \parallel b$ **6.**

$\overleftrightarrow{AD} \parallel \overleftrightarrow{CF}$

$\overleftrightarrow{BE} \parallel \overleftrightarrow{CF}$

Concl.: $\angle A \cong \angle D$

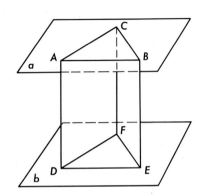

Prove each of the following statements:

1. If two dihedral angles are straight dihedral angles, then they are congruent.

2. If two dihedral angles are complementary to the same dihedral angle, then they are congruent.

3. A line intersects two parallel planes. Any plane containing this line will intersect these planes in two lines that form congruent angles with the given line.

■ Try This For Fun

For years mathematicians have been formulating problems in geometry wherein the reasoning that leads to the conclusion is perfectly valid, yet the conclusion is in contradiction to the postulates that have been established. In each, of course, there is some obscure error that the person who designed the problem has tried to hide. This error usually occurs in the manner in which the diagram is drawn. One of the more interesting of these problems that has intrigued mathematics students for years appears here.

PROBLEM: To prove that the measure of a right angle is equal to the measure of an obtuse angle.

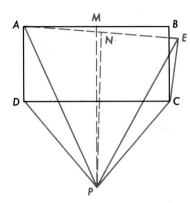

Given: $ABCD$ is a rectangle.

$\overleftrightarrow{PM}$ is the $\perp$ bisector of $\overline{AB}$.

$\overleftrightarrow{PN}$ is the $\perp$ bisector of $\overline{AE}$.

$\overline{EC} \cong \overline{AD}$

Concl.: $\angle ECD \cong \angle ADC$ (Hence, the measure of the obtuse angle ECD is equal to the measure of the right angle ADC.)

(1) Can you show this conclusion to be valid? (Suggestion: Prove $\triangle ADP \cong \triangle ECP$.)

(2) Can you point out where the error was made in the drawing of the diagram?

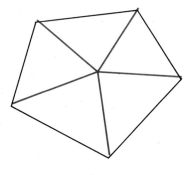

10

The Angles of a Polygon

THE ACCEPTANCE OF THE PARALLEL POSTU-late has made possible the proof of one of the most widely used theorems in plane geometry.

THEOREM 49: **The sum of the measures of the angles of a triangle is equal to 180.**

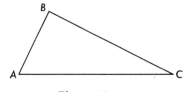

Given: $\triangle ABC$

Concl.: $m \angle A + m \angle B + m \angle C = 180$

Figure 10-1.

ANALYSIS: There is only one major condition that we are aware of under which we would encounter 180; this occurs in the measure of a straight angle. Hence, an obvious move is to relate angles A, B, and C to a straight angle. In addition, since the proof of this theorem is based on the parallel postulate, the need for parallel lines is apparent. To bring this condition and the previous one into the picture, it would seem best to have one of the parallel lines pass through a vertex of the triangle.

300

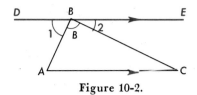

Figure 10-2.

PROOF STATEMENTS	REASONS
1. Let $\overleftrightarrow{DE}$ be the line through B that is parallel to $\overleftrightarrow{AC}$.	1. Parallel postulate
2. $m \angle DBE = 180$	2. Def. of a straight angle
3. $m \angle DBE = m \angle 1 + m \angle B + m \angle 2$	3. Def. of the sum of angles
4. $\therefore m \angle 1 + m \angle B + m \angle 2 = 180$	4. Transitive property of equality
5. But, $\angle A \cong \angle 1$ and $\angle C \cong \angle 2$	5. Why?
6. $\therefore m \angle A + m \angle B + m \angle C = 180$	6. Substitution postulate

This theorem paves the way for two very important theorems, one of which is another and final method for proving triangles congruent.

THEOREM 50: **If two angles of one triangle are congruent to two angles of a second triangle, then the third angles are congruent.**

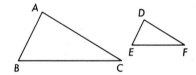

Given: $\angle A \cong \angle D$
$\angle B \cong \angle E$
Concl.: $\angle C \cong \angle F$

Figure 10-3.

PROOF STATEMENTS	REASONS
1. $\angle A \cong \angle D$ and $\angle B \cong \angle E$	1. Why?
2. $m \angle A + m \angle B = m \angle D + m \angle E$	2. Why?
3. $m \angle A + m \angle B + m \angle C = 180$	3. The sum of the measures of the angles of a triangle equals 180.
4. $m \angle C = 180 - (m \angle A + m \angle B)$	4. Subtraction postulate
5. $m \angle D + m \angle E + m \angle F = 180$	5. Why?
6. $m \angle F = 180 - (m \angle D + m \angle E)$	6. Why?
7. $m \angle F = 180 - (m \angle A + m \angle B)$	7. Substitution postulate
8. $m \angle C = m \angle F$	8. Transitive property of equality
9. $\angle C \cong \angle F$	9. Why?

THEOREM 51: **Two triangles are congruent if there exists a correspondence between the vertices in which two angles and a side opposite one of them in one triangle are congruent to those corresponding parts in the second triangle.** (The symbols for this statement are *A.A.S.*)

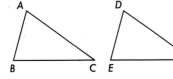

Given: $\angle A \cong \angle D$
$\angle B \cong \angle E$
$\overline{AC} \cong \overline{DF}$
Concl.: $\triangle ABC \cong \triangle DEF$

Figure 10-4.

PROOF	(The reasons will be left for you to supply.)
1. $\angle A \cong \angle D$ (*a*)	4. $\overline{AC} \cong \overline{DF}$ (*s*)
2. $\angle B \cong \angle E$	5. $\triangle ABC \cong \triangle DEF$
3. $\angle C \cong \angle F$ (*a*)	

Illustration 1:

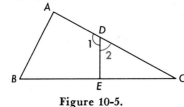

Given: $\overleftrightarrow{DE} \perp \overleftrightarrow{BC}$
$\overleftrightarrow{BA} \perp \overleftrightarrow{AC}$
Concl.: $\angle 1$ is supp. to $\angle B$.

Figure 10-5.

ANALYSIS: $\angle 1$ is already supplementary to $\angle 2$, hence if $\angle 2 \cong \angle B$, the conclusion will follow. Notice that it will not be necessary to prove triangles to be congruent in order to show that $\angle 2 \cong \angle B$.

PROOF	(The reasons will be left for you to supply.)
1. $\overleftrightarrow{DE} \perp \overleftrightarrow{BC}$	6. $\angle C \cong \angle C$
2. $\angle DEC$ is a right angle.	7. $\angle B \cong \angle 2$ (Theorem 50)
3. $\overleftrightarrow{BA} \perp \overleftrightarrow{AC}$.	8. But, $\angle 1$ is supp. to $\angle 2$.
4. $\angle BAC$ is a right angle.	9. $\therefore$ $\angle 1$ is supp. to $\angle B$.
5. $\angle DEC \cong \angle BAC$	

Illustration 2:

The perpendicular line segments from the midpoints of the legs of an isosceles triangle to the base are congruent.

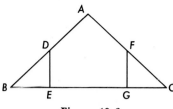

Figure 10-6.

Given: $\overline{AB} \cong \overline{AC}$

D is the midpoint of $\overline{AB}$.

F is the midpoint of $\overline{AC}$.

$\overleftrightarrow{DE}$ and $\overleftrightarrow{FG} \perp \overleftrightarrow{BC}$

Concl.: $\overline{DE} \cong \overline{FG}$

| PROOF | (The reasons will be left for you to supply.) |

1. $\overline{AB} \cong \overline{AC}$

2. $\angle B \cong \angle C$ (a)

3. D is the midpoint of $\overline{AB}$.

4. F is the midpoint of $\overline{AC}$.

5. $\overline{DB} \cong \overline{FC}$ (s)

6. $\overleftrightarrow{DE} \perp \overleftrightarrow{BC}$

7. $\angle DEB$ is a right angle.

8. $\overleftrightarrow{FG} \perp \overleftrightarrow{BC}$

9. $\angle FGC$ is a right angle.

10. $\angle DEB \cong \angle FGC$ (a)

11. $\triangle DBE \cong \triangle FCG$

12. $\therefore \overline{DE} \cong \overline{FG}$

The following two theorems are an immediate consequence of the theorem on the sum of the angles of a triangle. Their proofs will be left for you to do.

THEOREM 52: The measure of an exterior angle of a triangle is equal to the sum of the measures of the remote interior angles.

THEOREM 53: The acute angles of a right triangle are complementary.

EXERCISES

$\boxed{\text{A}}$

1. In the diagram at the right, find the measure of
   (a) $\angle 3$, if $m \angle 1 = 80$, $m \angle 2 = 60$
   (b) $\angle 4$, if $m \angle 1 = 85$, $m \angle 3 = 35$
   (c) $\angle 1$, if $m \angle 2 = x$, $m \angle 3 = y$
   (d) $\angle 7$, if $m \angle 5 = 140$, $m \angle 2 = 50$
   (e) $\angle 5$, if $m \angle 7 = 70$, $m \angle 2 = 60$
   (f) $\angle 6$, if $m \angle 5 = 150$, $m \angle 4 = 120$
   (g) $\angle 3$, if $m \angle 1 + m \angle 2 = x$

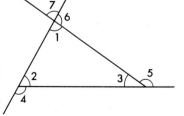

2. In $\triangle XYZ$, $\overline{XY} \cong \overline{XZ}$.

(a) If $m \angle X = 80$, $\angle Y$ is an angle of how many degrees?

(b) If $m \angle Y = 40$, how many degrees are there in $\angle X$?

3. How many degrees are there in each angle of an isosceles right triangle?

4. How many degrees are there in each angle of an equilateral triangle?

5. If the measures of two angles of a triangle are 80 and 60 respectively, how many degrees are there in the angle formed by the bisectors of these angles?

6. In the diagram at the right, $m \angle A = 80$ and $m \angle C = 30$. How many degrees are there in $\angle BDC$ if $\overrightarrow{BD}$ bisects $\angle ABC$?

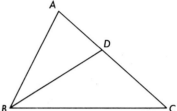

7. In $\triangle ABC$, $\overline{AC} \cong \overline{BC}$, $\angle A$ and $\angle B$ are bisected, and the bisectors intersect at D. If $m \angle C = 40$, how many degrees are there in $\angle D$?

8. The side BC of $\triangle ABC$ is extended to D. $\angle ABC$ and $\angle ACD$ are bisected and the bisectors meet at E. If $m \angle ABC = 80$ and $m \angle ACB = 60$, how many degrees are there in $\angle E$?

9. Sides BA and BC of $\triangle BAC$ are extended through A and C to points E and D respectively. The bisectors of the exterior angles EAC and DCA meet at P. If $m \angle BAC = 60$ and $m \angle BCA = 40$, how many degrees are there in $\angle APC$?

10. In the diagram at the right, $\overleftrightarrow{AB} \parallel \overleftrightarrow{CD}$, $m \angle 2 = 70$, and $m \angle 4 = 120$. How many degrees are there in each of the other angles?

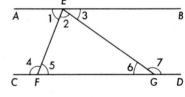

11. In the diagram at the right, $\overline{BE}$ and $\overline{CD}$ are altitudes, while $m \angle ABC = 70$ and $m \angle ACB = 40$. How many degrees are there in $\angle BFC$?

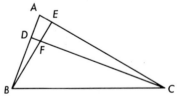

12. If, in $\triangle ABC$, $m \angle A = m \angle B + m \angle C$, then $\angle A$ is an angle of how many degrees?

13.* In the triangle at the right, $\overrightarrow{BD}$ and $\overrightarrow{CD}$ are the bisectors of angles ABC and ACB. Can you show in any way that $m \angle D = 90 + \frac{1}{2} m \angle A$?

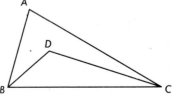

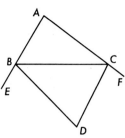

14.* In the diagram at the right, $\overrightarrow{BD}$ and $\overrightarrow{CD}$ are the bisectors of the exterior angles *EBC* and *FCB*. Can you show in any way that $m \angle D = 90 - \frac{1}{2}m \angle A$?

15.* The altitudes to sides *AB* and *AC* in acute $\triangle ABC$ intersect at point *E*. Can you show in any way that $m \angle BEC = m \angle B + m \angle C$?

16.* Angle *B* is an obtuse angle in $\triangle ABC$. The altitudes to sides *AB* and *AC* intersect at point *E* when they are extended. Can you show in any way that $m \angle BEC = 180 - (m \angle B + m \angle C)$?

17.* Base *BC* of $\triangle ABC$ is extended to point *D*. The bisectors of $\angle B$ and $\angle ACD$ intersect at point *E*. Can you show in any way that $m \angle E = \frac{1}{2}m \angle A$?

B

1. Given: $\overleftrightarrow{AB} \perp \overleftrightarrow{DF}$
$\overleftrightarrow{AC} \perp \overleftrightarrow{DG}$
Concl.: $\angle D \cong \angle A$

Given: $\angle 1 \cong \angle A$
Concl.: $\angle B \cong \angle CED$ **2.**

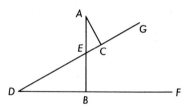

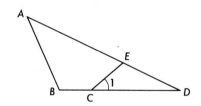

3. Given: $\overleftrightarrow{DC} \perp \overleftrightarrow{AB}$
$\overleftrightarrow{BE} \perp \overleftrightarrow{AD}$
Concl.: $\angle D \cong \angle B$

Given: $\overleftrightarrow{DE} \parallel \overleftrightarrow{AB}$ **4.**
$\overleftrightarrow{DF} \parallel \overleftrightarrow{CB}$
$\angle 1 \cong \angle 2$
Concl.: $\angle A \cong \angle C$

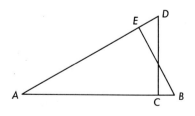

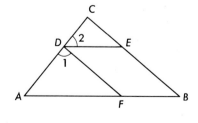

5. Given: $\overline{AB} \cong \overline{AC}$

$\overleftrightarrow{ED} \perp \overleftrightarrow{AB}$

$\overleftrightarrow{EF} \perp \overleftrightarrow{AC}$

Concl.: $\angle CEF \cong \angle DEB$

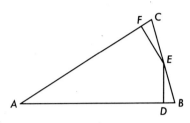

6. Given: $\overline{AD}$ and $\overline{CE}$ are altitudes.

Concl.: $\angle BCE \cong \angle BAD$

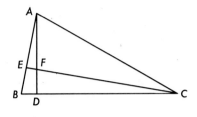

7. Given: $\angle ACB$ is a right angle.

$\overleftrightarrow{CD} \perp \overleftrightarrow{AB}$

Concl.: $\angle ACD \cong \angle B$

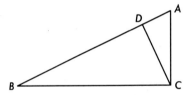

8. Using the diagram below with the suggested line CE, prove the theorem that the sum of the measures of the angles of a triangle is equal to 180.

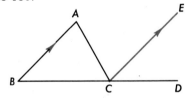

9. Using the diagram below with the suggested lines PQ and PR, prove the theorem that the sum of the measures of the angles of a triangle is equal to 180.

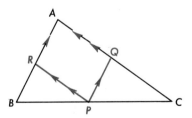

10. Given: $\overline{AB} \cong \overline{AC}$

$\angle 1 \cong \angle 2$

M is the midpoint of $\overline{BC}$.

Concl.: $\overline{DM} \cong \overline{EM}$

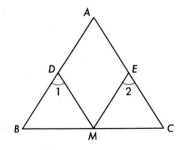

11. Given: $ABCD$ is a $\square$.
$$\overleftrightarrow{AF} \perp \overleftrightarrow{CD}$$
$$\overleftrightarrow{AE} \perp \overleftrightarrow{BC}$$
$$\overline{AF} \cong \overline{AE}$$
Concl.: $ABCD$ is a rhombus.

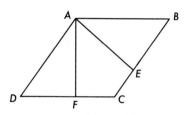

Given: $ABCD$ is a $\square$. **12.**
$$\overleftrightarrow{AE} \perp \overleftrightarrow{BC}$$
$$\overleftrightarrow{CF} \perp \overleftrightarrow{AD}$$
Concl.: $\overline{AE} \cong \overline{CF}$

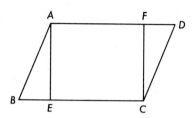

13. Given: $\overleftrightarrow{BD} \perp \overleftrightarrow{DC}$
$$\overleftrightarrow{CA} \perp \overleftrightarrow{AB}$$
$$\angle 1 \cong \angle 2$$
Concl.: $\overline{AB} \cong \overline{CD}$

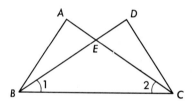

Given: $\overline{BQ}$ is the median **14.**
to $\overline{AC}$.
$$\overleftrightarrow{CR} \perp \overleftrightarrow{BR}$$
$$\overleftrightarrow{AP} \perp \overleftrightarrow{BR}$$
Concl.: $APCR$ is a $\square$.

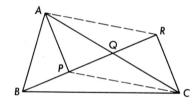

15. Given: $\overline{AC} \cong \overline{AB}$
$$\overline{BE} \cong \overline{CH}$$
$$\overleftrightarrow{EF} \perp \overleftrightarrow{BG}$$
$$\overleftrightarrow{GH} \perp \overleftrightarrow{BG}$$
Concl.: D is the midpoint
of $\overline{EH}$.

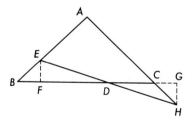

Given: $\triangle DAC$ is isos. with **16.***
$\overline{DA} \cong \overline{DC}$.
$$\overline{DB} \cong \overline{DC}$$
Concl.: $\angle BAC$ is a right angle. (Hint: Prove
$m \angle BAC = m \angle B$
$+ m \angle C$ and see
Problem 12,
group A.)

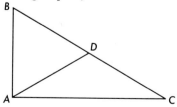

17. * Given: △*ABC* is isosceles
with $\overline{AB} \cong \overline{AC}$.
(Diagram at right.)
$\overleftrightarrow{FG} \parallel \overleftrightarrow{HJ}$
$\overrightarrow{BF}$ bisects ∠*ABH*.
$\overrightarrow{CG}$ bisects ∠*ACJ*.
Concl.: $\overline{BF} \cong \overline{CG}$

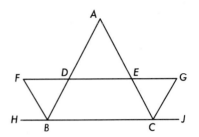

1. The altitude to the base of an isosceles triangle bisects the vertex angle.
2. The perpendicular line segments from any point on the bisector of an angle to the sides of the angle are congruent.
3. The altitudes to the legs of an isosceles triangle are congruent.
4. Corresponding altitudes of congruent triangles are congruent.
5. If perpendicular line segments are drawn from the vertices of the upper base to the lower base of an isosceles trapezoid, then these segments are congruent.
6. If perpendicular line segments are drawn from a pair of opposite vertices of a parallelogram to the diagonal joining the remaining vertices, then these segments are congruent.
7. If perpendicular line segments are drawn from the midpoint of the base of an isosceles triangle to the legs of the triangle, then these perpendiculars are congruent.
8. If line segments are drawn from any point on the base of an isosceles triangle to make congruent angles with the base, they will make congruent angles with the legs of the triangle.
9. If from the point of intersection of the altitudes to the legs of an isosceles triangle a line is drawn to the vertex of the vertex angle, then this line bisects the vertex angle.
10. If a point is not on the bisector of an angle, then the perpendicular line segments drawn from this point to the sides of the angle will not be congruent. (Hint: Use the indirect proof.)
11. From the midpoint of a side of a triangle perpendicular line segments are drawn to the other two sides. If the perpendicular segments are not congruent, then the sides to which they are drawn are not congruent. (Hint: Use the indirect proof.)
12. In an isosceles right triangle one of the congruent sides can not be the hypotenuse.

The Angles of a Polygon

It is just a short jump from finding the sum of the measures of the angles of a triangle to finding the sum of the measures of the angles of any polygon. Perhaps our statement should not have been so broad, for we do not intend to determine the sum of the measures of the angles of the polygon in Figure 10-7.

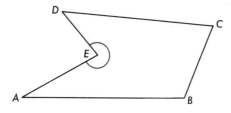

Figure 10-7.

Recall that early in our work it was agreed not to concern ourselves with angles that were greater than a straight angle. In this polygon, $\angle E$ is greater than a straight angle; hence, polygons where this occurs will be excluded from our work. In reality, we have limited ourselves to an investigation of *convex polygons* only.

DEFINITION 68: A convex polygon is a polygon in which each of the angles is less than a straight angle.

Henceforth, whenever the term polygon is used, it will be understood to imply only the *convex* polygon and no other.

THEOREM 54: **The sum of the measures of the angles of a polygon of n sides is $180(n - 2)$.**

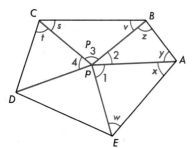

Figure 10-8.

Given: Polygon $ABCDE$ . . . containing n sides

Concl.: $m \angle A + m \angle B + m \angle C + \dots$
$= 180(n - 2)$

ANALYSIS: We resort to dividing the polygon into triangles so as to enable us to use the theorem on the sum of the measures of the angles of a triangle. This is done by selecting a point P in the interior of the polygon and drawing lines from this point to each of the vertices. There will then exist a one-to-one correspondence between each of the triangles and each of the sides of the polygon.

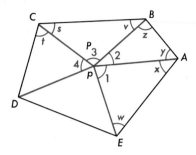

Figure 10-8.

PROOF	STATEMENTS	REASONS
1. Let P be a point in the interior of $ABCDE\ldots$ and let $\overleftrightarrow{PA}$ be the line through P and A.		1. There exists one and only one line through two points.
2. The same is true of $\overleftrightarrow{PB}$, $\overleftrightarrow{PC}$, etc.		2. Same as 1
3. $m\angle 1 + m\angle w + m\angle x = 180$ $m\angle 2 + m\angle y + m\angle z = 180$ etc.		3. Why?
4. $m\angle 1 + m\angle 2 + \ldots + (m\angle x + m\angle y) + (m\angle z + m\angle v) + \ldots = 180n$		4. Addition postulate
5. But $\angle x + \angle y = \angle A$ $\angle z + \angle v = \angle B$ etc.		5. Def. of the sum of two angles
6. $\therefore (m\angle x + m\angle y) + (m\angle z + m\angle v) + \ldots = m\angle A + m\angle B + m\angle C + \ldots$		6. Addition postulate
7. Also, $m\angle 1 + m\angle 2 + m\angle 3 + \ldots = 360$, or 2 straight angles		7. Why?
8. $360 + (m\angle A + m\angle B + m\angle C + \ldots) = 180n$		8. Substitution postulate (See step 4.)
9. $\therefore m\angle A + m\angle B + m\angle C + \ldots = 180n - 360$ or $m\angle A + m\angle B + m\angle C + \ldots = 180(n - 2)$		9. Subtraction postulate

This theorem paves the way for the proof of a theorem that seems to be unreasonable at first glance. No matter how many sides a polygon may have, be it 3 or 3,000, the sum of the measures of the exterior angles formed by extending these sides in the same order is always 360!

THEOREM 55: The sum of the measures of the exterior angles of a polygon formed by extending the sides in the same order is equal to 360.

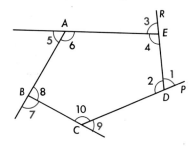

Given: Polygon $ABCDE$ . . . containing n sides

Concl.: Sum of the measure of the exterior angles shown = 360.

Figure 10-11.

ANALYSIS: Notice that there exists a one-to-one correspondence between each vertex of the polygon and each pair of angles marked in the diagram. Those marked in red are the exterior angles; those in black, the interior. Thus, if we subtract the sum of the interior from the sum of all pairs, we will be left with simply the sum of the exterior angles.

PROOF STATEMENTS	REASONS
1. $m \angle 1 + m \angle 2 = 180$, or $m \angle CDP$ $m \angle 3 + m \angle 4 = 180$, or $m \angle DER$ etc.	1. Def. of the sum of two angles
2. $(m \angle 1 + m \angle 2) + (m \angle 3 + m \angle 4) +$ $(m \angle 5 + m \angle 6) + \ldots = 180n$ or $(m \angle 1 + m \angle 3 + m \angle 5 + \ldots) +$ $(m \angle 2 + m \angle 4 + m \angle 6 + \ldots) = 180n$	2. Addition postulate
3. But $m \angle 2 + m \angle 4 + m \angle 6 + \ldots =$ $180(n - 2)$	3. Why?
4. $\therefore (m \angle 1 + m \angle 3 + m \angle 5 + \ldots) +$ $180(n - 2) = 180n$	4. Substitution postulate
5. Hence $m \angle 1 + m \angle 3 + m \angle 5 + \ldots =$ $180n - 180(n - 2)$ or $m \angle 1 + m \angle 3 + m \angle 5 + \ldots =$ $180n - 180n + 360$ or $m \angle 1 + m \angle 3 + m \angle 5 + \ldots = 360$	5. Subtraction postulate

For simplicity, polygons are given names in accordance with the number of sides, or angles, they possess. Thus, a three-sided polygon is called a 3-gon; a five-sided polygon is a 5-gon; a twenty-seven–sided polygon is a 27-gon; etc. Special polygons whose sides are relatively few in number are more often referred to by the names listed below.

Number of Sides	Name		
3	*triangle*	or	3-gon
4	*quadrilateral*	or	4-gon
5	*pentagon*	or	5-gon
6	*hexagon*	or	6-gon
8	*octagon*	or	8-gon
10	*decagon*	or	10-gon
12	*duodecagon*	or	12-gon

Illustration 1:

Find the sum of the measures of the angles of a 15-gon.

METHOD:
$$S = (n - 2)180$$
$$= (15 - 2)180$$
$$= 13 \cdot 180$$
$$= 2,340$$

Illustration 2:

Find the measure of each angle of an equiangular 20-gon.

METHOD: Since the measures of the angles of the polygon are equal, then the measures of the exterior angles will also be equal. In view of the fact that the sum of the measures of the exterior angles is equal to 360, then dividing 360 by 20 will give the size of each.

Each exterior angle: $360 \div 20 = 18$
Each interior angle: $180 - 18 = 162$

EXERCISES

1. Find the sum of the measures of the angles of each of the following polygons:
   (a) 7-gon   (d) pentagon
   (b) 15-gon   (e) octagon
   (c) 100-gon   (f) decagon

2. What is the measure of each exterior angle of each of the following equiangular polygons?
   (a) 30-gon   (c) hexagon
   (b) 72-gon   (d) duodecagon

3. What is the measure of each interior angle of each of the following equiangular polygons?
   (a) 18-gon   (c) quadrilateral
   (b) 40-gon   (d) octagon

4. If the sum of the measures of the angles of a polygon is given by each of the following numbers, how many sides does the polygon have?
   (a) 900
   (b) 1,260
   (c) 9,360
   (d) 15 straight angles

5. If the measure of each exterior angle of an equiangular polygon is given by each of the following numbers, how many sides does the polygon have?
   (a) 30
   (b) 45
   (c) 72
   (d) k

6. If the measure of each angle of an equiangular polygon is given by each of the following numbers, how many sides does the polygon have?
   (a) 165
   (b) 140
   (c) 172
   (d) k

7. The measure of each angle of an equiangular polygon is five times as large as the measure of an exterior angle of the polygon. What is the name of the polygon?

8. (a) What is the largest measure an exterior angle of an equiangular polygon may have?
   (b) What is the smallest measure that an angle of an equiangular polygon may have?

9. How many sides does a polygon have if the sum of the measures of its angles is five times as large as the sum of the measures of its exterior angles?

10. Two angles of a quadrilateral are supplementary. Show that the other two angles are also supplementary.

▉ A Brief Journey into Non-Euclidean Geometry†

Earlier we discussed the possibility of the existence of postulates other than the parallel postulate:

"Through a given point there exists only one line that is parallel to a given line."

As a consequence of accepting this postulate we were able to prove that the sum of the measures of the angles of any triangle is equal to 180.

At this time we would like to explore briefly what might have happened had we not accepted the parallel postulate but instead had assumed either of the following statements:

(1) Through a given point there exist two lines parallel to a given line, one falling to the right of the given point, the other to the left. (Lobachevsky; see pages 245-247.)

† Optional topic.

(2) Through a given point there exists no lines that can be drawn parallel to a given line. That is, two lines will always have at least one point in common. (Riemann.)

Geometries that accept either of the above assumptions are called non-Euclidean geometries, for they have discarded the Euclidean postulate on parallelism. All propositions on congruency, other than the *A.A.S.* theorem, and all those on perpendicularity apply equally well in the three geometries, as the proofs of these theorems are not dependent on parallel lines. Why was the *A.A.S.* theorem excluded? All theorems, however, whose proofs are based on the concepts of parallelism will differ in the three geometries.

Our goal in this short section will be to try to determine what the sum of the measures of the angles of a triangle will be in the two non-Euclidean geometries. To simplify our work, we are going to discard the above postulates and replace them with equivalent statements. The new postulates are based on the quadrilateral in Figure 10-12, whose properties are given at the right of the diagram.

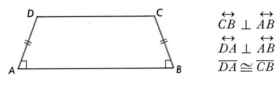

$$\overleftrightarrow{CB} \perp \overleftrightarrow{AB}$$
$$\overleftrightarrow{DA} \perp \overleftrightarrow{AB}$$
$$\overline{DA} \cong \overline{CB}$$

Figure 10-12.

This quadrilateral, having two right angles and two congruent sides, is called an isosceles birectangular quadrilateral. The properties of this figure were first investigated by a Jesuit priest named Saccheri, who lived around the middle of the eighteenth century. He had hoped to show through his analysis of this quadrilateral that the Euclidean postulate on parallel lines could be proved. Unfortunately, he made several errors in his work. Had he not, he would probably have been the first person to publish material in the field of non-Euclidean geometry.

The new postulates to which we have referred concern themselves with the *summit angles*, *C* and *D*, in the Saccheri quadrilateral.

Lobachevsky: The summit angles, *C* and *D*, are acute angles.
Euclid: The summit angles, *C* and *D*, are right angles.
Riemann: The summit angles, *C* and *D*, are obtuse angles.

With these three postulates as our tools we will now prove that

In Lobachevsky's geometry: The sum of the measures of the angles of a triangle is less than 180.
In Euclidean geometry: The sum of the measures of the angles of a triangle is equal to 180.

In Riemannian geometry: The sum of the measures of the angles of a triangle is greater than 180.

Our proof will be separated into two parts. In Part A we will show that there exists a Saccheri quadrilateral in the figure that we have drawn. In Part B we will show that the sum of the measures of the summit angles in this quadrilateral is equal to the sum of the measures of the angles of the triangle.

Let $\triangle CDE$ be any triangle.

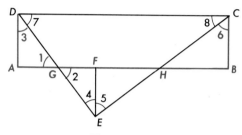

Figure 10-13.

| PROOF | PART A | (The reasons will be left for you to supply.) |

1. Let G and H be the midpoints of $\overline{DE}$ and $\overline{CE}$ respectively.

2. Let $\overleftrightarrow{GH}$ be the line through points G and H.

3. Let $\overleftrightarrow{EF}$ be the line through E that is perpendicular to $\overleftrightarrow{GH}$.

4. Extend $\overleftrightarrow{FG}$ to A so that $\overline{FG} \cong \overline{GA}$.

5. Extend $\overleftrightarrow{FH}$ to B so that $\overline{FH} \cong \overline{HB}$.

6. Let $\overleftrightarrow{DA}$ be the line through points D and A.

7. Let $\overleftrightarrow{CB}$ be the line through points C and B.

Now by proving $\overline{DA} \cong \overline{CB}$ and $\angle A$ and $\angle B$ to be right angles, we can show that $ABCD$ is a Saccheri quadrilateral.

8. $\overline{DG} \cong \overline{GE}$

9. $\overline{AG} \cong \overline{GF}$

10. $\angle 1 \cong \angle 2$

11. $\therefore \triangle DAG \cong \triangle EFG$

12. Hence, $\angle DAG \cong \angle EFG$

13. But $\overleftrightarrow{EF} \perp \overleftrightarrow{GH}$

14. Thus, $\angle EFG$ is a right angle.

15. $\therefore \angle DAG$ is a right angle.

16. Also, $\overline{DA} \cong \overline{FE}$

In a similar manner, $\triangle CBH$ can be shown to be congruent to $\triangle EFH$.

17. Hence, $\angle CBH$ is a right angle.

18. And $\overline{CB} \cong \overline{FE}$

19. $\therefore \overline{CB} \cong \overline{DA}$

20. Hence, $ABCD$ is a Saccheri quadrilateral.

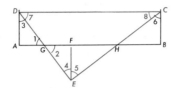

Figure 10-13.

| PROOF | PART B | (The reasons will be left for you to supply.) |

We will now show that the sum of the measures of the summit angles, $\angle ADC$ and $\angle BCD$, is equal to the sum of the measures of the angles of $\triangle CDE$.

1. Since $\triangle DAG \cong \triangle EFG$, then $\angle 3 \cong \angle 4$
2. Since $\triangle CBH \cong \triangle EFH$, then $\angle 6 \cong \angle 5$
3. But, $m \angle 7 + m \angle 8 + m \angle CED =$ the sum of the measures of the angles of $\triangle CDE$ ·
4. $\therefore m \angle 7 + m \angle 8 + m \angle 4 + m \angle 5 =$ the sum of the measures of the angles of $\triangle CDE$
5. Hence, $m \angle 7 + m \angle 8 + m \angle 3 + m \angle 6 =$ the sum of the measures of the angles of $\triangle CDE$
6. But, $\angle 3 + \angle 7 = \angle ADC$
7. And, $\angle 6 + \angle 8 = \angle BCD$
8. $\therefore m \angle ADC + m \angle BCD =$ the sum of the measures of the angles of $\triangle CDE$

Thus, we have shown that the sum of the measures of the angles of any triangle is equal to the sum of the measures of the summit angles of a Saccheri isosceles birectangular quadrilateral. However,

(1) In Lobachevsky's geometry we assumed that each of the summit angles is acute and, hence, the sum of their measures is less than 180.
(2) In Euclid's geometry we assumed that each of the summit angles is a right angle and, hence, the sum of their measures is 180.
(3) In Riemann's geometry we assumed that each of the summit angles is obtuse and, hence, the sum of their measures is greater than 180.

Therefore, it now follows that in each of the three geometries the sum of the measures of the angles of a triangle will be respectively either,

(1) less than 180
(2) equal to 180
(3) greater than 180

A great many of the theorems in the non-Euclidean geometries involve relationships between numbers that are unequal. Hence, before considering any problems, we will have to establish two postulates concerning the relative size of quantities. One of these postulates will indicate the existence and uniqueness of the order of size of two numbers, while the other will permit us to transfer the relation of size of three numbers among themselves.

POSTULATE 30: Given any two numbers a and b, one and only one of these three relationships must be true: $a < b$, $a = b$, $a > b$. (Existence and Uniqueness of Order)

POSTULATE 31: Given any three numbers a, b, and c, where $a > b$ and $b > c$, then $a > c$. (Transitivity of Order)

Illustration:

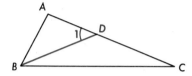

Given: $m\,\overline{AC} > m\,\overline{AB}$
Concl.: $m\,\angle ABC > m\,\angle C$

Figure 10-14.

PROOF STATEMENTS	REASONS
1. Since $m\,\overline{AC} > m\,\overline{AB}$, let $\overline{AD} \cong \overline{AB}$.	1. A line can be extended as far as desired.
2. Let $\overleftrightarrow{BD}$ be the line through points B and D.	2. There exists one and only one line through two points.
3. $m\,\angle ABD = m\,\angle 1$	3. Why?
4. $m\,\angle ABC > m\,\angle ABD$	4. The whole is greater than any of its parts.
5. $\therefore m\,\angle ABC > m\,\angle 1$	5. Substitution postulate
6. But, $m\,\angle 1 > m\,\angle C$	6. The measure of an exterior angle of a triangle is greater than the measures of either of the remote interior angles.
7. $\therefore m\,\angle ABC > m\,\angle C$	7. Postulate on transitivity of order

Can you justify that point D in the above proof must fall between A and C such that the order of points is A, D, C and not A, C, D?

EXERCISES

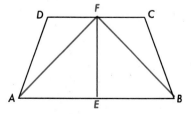

1. Prove that the summit angles of a Saccheri quadrilateral are congruent. (Hint: Draw $\overleftrightarrow{EF} \perp \overleftrightarrow{AB}$ at the midpoint E of $\overline{AB}$.)

2. Prove that the perpendicular bisector of the lower base of a Saccheri quadrilateral is also the perpendicular bisector of the upper base.

3. * Given: $\overleftrightarrow{DA} \perp \overleftrightarrow{AB}$

$\overleftrightarrow{CB} \perp \overleftrightarrow{AB}$

$m\,\overline{DA} > m\,\overline{CB}$

Concl.: $m\,\angle C > m\,\angle D$

(Hint: Find point E such that $\overline{AE} \cong \overline{BC}$. Since $ABCE$ will be a Saccheri quadrilateral, we can use information proved in Problem 1. See the method in the illustration on page 317.)

4. * Given: $\overleftrightarrow{DA} \perp \overleftrightarrow{AB}$, $\overleftrightarrow{CB} \perp \overleftrightarrow{AB}$

$m\,\angle C > m\,\angle D$

Concl.: $m\,\overline{DA} > m\,\overline{CB}$

(Hint: Use the indirect proof by setting up the possibilities in terms of the assumption on existence and uniqueness of the order of two numbers. Eliminate two of the possibilities by applying Problems 1 and 3.)

5. Given: $\overleftrightarrow{DA} \perp \overleftrightarrow{AB}$, $\overleftrightarrow{CB} \perp \overleftrightarrow{AB}$

$\angle C \cong \angle D$

Concl.: $\overline{DA} \cong \overline{CB}$

(Hint: Use the indirect proof by setting up the possibilities in terms of the assumption on existence and uniqueness of the order of two quantities. Eliminate two of the possibilities by applying Problem 3.)

6. Given: $ABCD$ is a Saccheri quadrilateral in Lobachevsky's
geometry. $\overleftrightarrow{EF}$ is the $\perp$ bisector of $\overline{AB}$.

Concl.: $m\,\overline{CB} > m\,\overline{EF}$

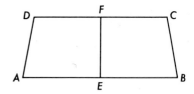

(Hint: By Problem 2, $\angle EFC$ was shown to be a right angle. Hence, how do $\angle EFC$ and $\angle C$ compare? Now apply Problem 4.)

7. Given: $ABCD$ is a Saccheri quadrilateral in Riemann's ge-
ometry. $\overleftrightarrow{EF}$ is the $\perp$ bisector of $\overline{AB}$.

Concl.: $m\,\overline{EF} > m\,\overline{CB}$.

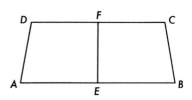

8. Given: $ABCD$ is a Saccheri quadrilateral in Euclidean ge-
ometry. $\overleftrightarrow{EF}$ is the $\perp$ bisector of $\overline{AB}$.

   Concl.: $\overline{EF} \cong \overline{CB}$

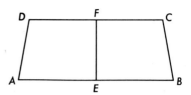

Problems 6, 7, and 8 present a rather interesting point of departure
for the three geometries:

1. If in Lobachevsky's geometry two lines have a common perpendicular,
   that perpendicular segment will be the *shortest* path between the two
   lines, for on either side of this common perpendicular the two lines will
   diverge. (See Problem 6.)
2. If in Riemann's geometry two lines have a common perpendicular,
   that perpendicular will be the *greatest* path between the two lines, for
   on either side of this common perpendicular the two lines approach each
   other. (See Problem 7.)
3. If in Euclidean geometry two lines have a common perpendicular, they
   will have many, many, common perpendiculars, all of which will be
   congruent. (See Problem 8.)

■ Test and Review

1. Using the information shown in each diagram, find the measures of
   the angles marked x and y.

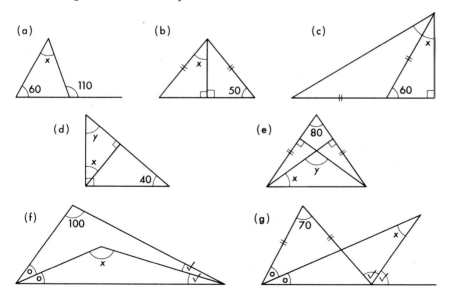

2. In $\triangle ABC$, $\overrightarrow{CR}$ bisects $\angle ACB$ and $\overline{AS}$ is the altitude to $\overline{BC}$. $\overleftrightarrow{AS}$ and $\overleftrightarrow{CR}$ intersect at T. If $m \angle CAS = 40$, then what is the measure of $\angle ATR$?

3. If the measure of one of the acute angles of a rhombus is 70, then what is the measure of an angle formed by a diagonal and one of the sides? (Give two answers.)

4. If the measure of one of the acute angles of a right triangle is five times that of the other acute angle, what is the measure of each?

5. What is the measure of the acute angle formed by two of the medians of an equilateral triangle?

6. If the measure of the vertex angle of an isosceles triangle is 66, what is the measure of the obtuse angle formed by the median to the base and the altitude to a leg?

7. If the sum of the measures of two of the angles of a triangle is equal to the measure of the third angle, then what can be said of the triangle?

8. If two angles of a triangle are congruent and one-half the sum of their measures is equal to the measure of the third angle, then what can be said of the triangle?

9. If the measure of an exterior angle at the vertex of the vertex angle of an isosceles triangle is four times as large as the measure of its adjacent interior angle, how large is each angle of the triangle?

10. Find the sum of the measures of the angles of each of the following polygons:
    (a) 20-gon   (b) hexagon

11. What is the measure of each interior angle of the following equiangular polygons?
    (a) 24-gon   (b) pentagon

12. The sum of the measures of three angles of a quadrilateral is 290. What is the measure of the fourth angle?

13. (a) If the measure of an exterior angle of an equiangular polygon is 12, how many sides does the polygon have?
    (b) If the measure of an exterior angle of an equiangular polygon is 18, what is the sum of the measures of the angles of the polygon?

14. (a) How many degrees are there in each exterior angle of an equiangular 6-gon?
    (b) How many degrees are there in each exterior angle of an equiangular 12-gon?
    (c) If the number of sides of an equiangular polygon is doubled, how will this affect the measure of each exterior angle?
    (d) If the number of sides of an equiangular polygon is quadrupled, how will this affect the measure of each exterior angle?

15. Justify why the measure of an angle of an equiangular polygon can not be 130?

16.* Can you show in any way that one of the angles formed by the altitudes to two sides of a triangle is congruent to the angle formed by these sides?

17.* In acute $\triangle ABC$ side BC is extended to point D. The altitude BF is extended to intersect the bisector of $\angle ACD$ at point E. Can you show in any way that $m \angle E = \frac{1}{2}m \angle C$?

$$\boxed{B}$$

Prove each of the following:

1. Given: $\triangle ABC$ is isosceles.
with $\overline{AB} \cong \overline{AC}$
$\overleftrightarrow{ED} \perp \overleftrightarrow{BC}$
$\overleftrightarrow{EF} \perp \overleftrightarrow{AC}$
Concl.: $\angle 1 \cong \angle 2$

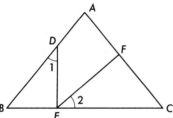

Given: $\triangle ABC$ with any line **2.**
AF intersecting $\overline{BC}$
$\overleftrightarrow{BE} \perp \overleftrightarrow{AF}$
$\overleftrightarrow{CF} \perp \overleftrightarrow{AF}$
Concl.: $\angle EBD \cong \angle FCD$

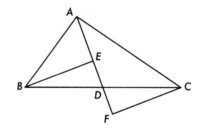

3. Given: $\triangle ABC$ is isosceles
with $\overline{AB} \cong \overline{AC}$.
$\angle C \cong \angle 1$
Concl.: $\triangle ADE$ is isosceles.

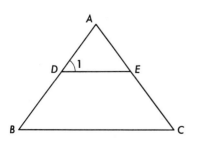

Given: $\triangle ABC$ is isosceles **4.**
with $\overline{AB} \cong \overline{AC}$.
$\overleftrightarrow{BA}$ is extended to D.
$\overleftrightarrow{DE} \perp \overleftrightarrow{BC}$
Concl.: $\triangle ADF$ is isosceles.

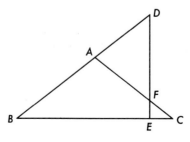

5. Given: △ABC with $\overline{AB} \cong \overline{AC}$
$\overline{BE}$ is the altitude to $\overline{AC}$.
$\overline{CD}$ is the altitude to $\overline{AB}$.
$\overleftrightarrow{FG} \perp \overleftrightarrow{BC}$
Concl.: $\overrightarrow{FG}$ bisects $\angle BFC$.

Given: $\overleftrightarrow{EF}$ and $\overleftrightarrow{AB}$ intersect at **6.**
center of $\odot O$.
$\overleftrightarrow{AD} \perp \overleftrightarrow{EF}$
$\overleftrightarrow{BC} \perp \overleftrightarrow{EF}$
Concl.: $\overline{AD} \cong \overline{BC}$

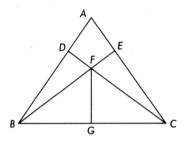

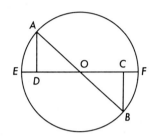

Prove each of the following statements:

1. Perpendicular line segments are drawn from any point on a given side of a triangle to the other sides of the triangle. If these segments make congruent angles with the given side, then the triangle is isosceles.
2. If perpendicular line segments are drawn from the midpoints of the legs to the base of an isosceles triangle, then the segments are congruent.
3. If perpendicular line segments are drawn from two vertices of a triangle to the median (extended) from the third vertex, then these line segments are congruent.
4. If two angles of a triangle are complementary, then the triangle is a right triangle.
5. If the sides of one angle are perpendicular respectively to the sides of a second angle, then the angles are either congruent or supplementary.
6. If an altitude of a triangle does not bisect the angle from which it is drawn, then the sides forming this angle are not congruent.

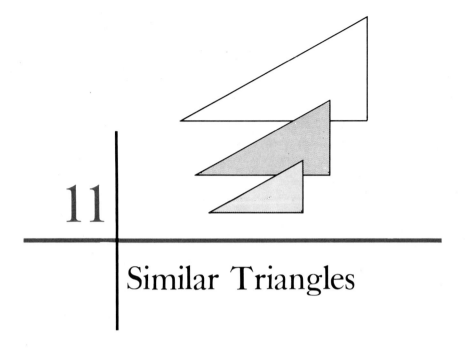

11

Similar Triangles

WE WOULD LIKE TO TURN OUR ATTENTION again to the polygon. Earlier we had devoted time to considering those conditions under which two polygons, particularly triangles, might have the same "size" and "shape"; that is, be congruent. Now, we want to investigate those properties alone that give polygons the same "shape." Specifically, they would appear like the pairs of polygons pictured in Figure 11-1.

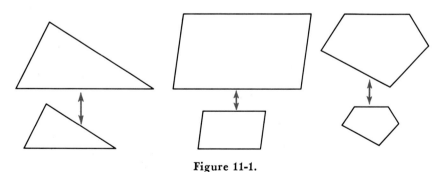

Figure 11-1.

Basic to the development of this unit is a theorem on parallel lines that must be proved.

323

THEOREM 56: **If three or more parallel lines intercept† congruent segments on one transversal, they will intercept congruent segments on every transversal.**

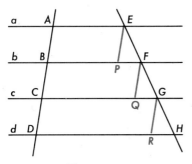

Given: $a \parallel b \parallel c \parallel d$

$\overline{AB} \cong \overline{BC} \cong \overline{CD}$

Concl.: $\overline{EF} \cong \overline{FG} \cong \overline{GH}$

Figure 11-2.

ANALYSIS: By proving triangles congruent it is possible to prove that the segments are congruent.

| **PROOF** | (The reasons will be left for you to supply.) |

1. Let $\overleftrightarrow{EP}$ be the line through E that is parallel to $\overleftrightarrow{AB}$.
2. Same for $\overleftrightarrow{FQ}$ and $\overleftrightarrow{GR}$.
3. ∴ $\overleftrightarrow{EP} \parallel \overleftrightarrow{FQ} \parallel \overleftrightarrow{GR}$
4. $a \parallel b \parallel c \parallel d$
5. $ABPE$, $BCQF$, and $CDRG$ are ⑤.

6. $\overline{EP} \cong \overline{AB}, \overline{FQ} \cong \overline{BC}, \overline{GR} \cong \overline{CD}$
7. But $\overline{AB} \cong \overline{BC} \cong \overline{CD}$
8. ∴ $\overline{EP} \cong \overline{FQ} \cong \overline{GR}$ (s)
9. $\angle PEF \cong \angle QFG \cong \angle RGH$ (a)
10. $\angle EFP \cong \angle FGQ \cong \angle GHR$ (a)
11. ∴ $\triangle EPF \cong \triangle FQG \cong \triangle GRH$
12. ∴ $\overline{EF} \cong \overline{FG} \cong \overline{GH}$

Establishing this theorem opens the way for the proof of two interesting theorems concerning a triangle.

THEOREM 57: **If a line bisects one side of a triangle and is parallel to a second side, then it bisects the third side of the triangle.**

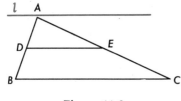

Given: $\overleftrightarrow{DE} \parallel \overleftrightarrow{BC}$

$\overleftrightarrow{DE}$ bisects $\overline{AB}$.

Concl.: $\overleftrightarrow{DE}$ bisects $\overline{AC}$.

Figure 11-3.

† "Intercept" will mean "cut off."

ANALYSIS: By allowing line l to be the line through A that is parallel to $\overleftrightarrow{BC}$, we will have three parallel lines. Since the transversal $\overline{AB}$ is cut into two congruent segments, we can immediately apply Theorem 56.

PROOF

The proof is left for you to do.

THEOREM 58: If a line bisects two sides of a triangle, then it is parallel to the third side.

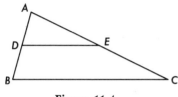

Given: $\overleftrightarrow{DE}$ bisects $\overline{AB}$.

$\overleftrightarrow{DE}$ bisects $\overline{AC}$.

Concl.: $\overleftrightarrow{DE} \parallel \overleftrightarrow{BC}$

Figure 11-4.

ANALYSIS: Since we have Theorem 57 at our disposal, it would seem that an advisable approach would be the indirect proof.

PROOF

By the law of the excluded middle one of these statements must be true and no other possibility exists:

$$\overleftrightarrow{DE} \parallel \overleftrightarrow{BC} \quad \text{or} \quad \overleftrightarrow{DE} \nparallel \overleftrightarrow{BC}$$

Let us accept the possibility that $\overleftrightarrow{DE} \nparallel \overleftrightarrow{BC}$. Then by the parallel postulate there exists only one line through D that is parallel to $\overleftrightarrow{BC}$. Let this line be

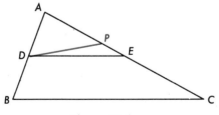

Figure 11-5.

DP. Hence, since $\overleftrightarrow{DP}$ bisects $\overline{AB}$, by Theorem 57 it must also bisect $\overline{AC}$. This implies that P is the midpoint of $\overline{AC}$ and, therefore, $m\,\overline{AP} = \frac{1}{2}m\,\overline{AC}$.

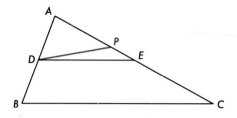

Figure 11-5.

The Given Data, however, informs us that $\overleftrightarrow{DE}$ bisects $\overline{AC}$; therefore, $m\ \overline{AE} = \frac{1}{2}m\ \overline{AC}$. Thus, $m\ \overline{AE} = m\ \overline{AP}$. But this is contradictory to the postulate that the whole is greater than any of its parts. Therefore, accepting the possibility that $\overleftrightarrow{DE} \not\parallel \overleftrightarrow{BC}$ led to the logical inconsistency of the truth of both $m\ \overline{AE} = m\ \overline{AP}$ and $m\ \overline{AE} \neq m\ \overline{AP}$. By the law of contradiction both cannot be true at the same time. Since $m\ \overline{AE} \neq m\ \overline{AP}$ must be true as the result of a postulate, $m\ \overline{AE} = m\ \overline{AP}$ must be false and, therefore, the statement $\overleftrightarrow{DE} \not\parallel \overleftrightarrow{BC}$ is also false. Hence, $\overleftrightarrow{DE} \parallel \overleftrightarrow{BC}$ is true, for it is the only remaining possibility.

EXERCISES

A

1. By using the diagram below in which $\overleftrightarrow{DE}$ is extended so that $\overline{DE} \cong \overline{EF}$, prove Theorem 58. (Hint: Show that $DBCF$ is a parallelogram.)

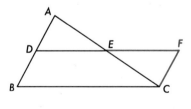

2. By using the diagram below in which $\overleftrightarrow{EF}$ is the line through E parallel to $\overleftrightarrow{AB}$, prove Theorem 57.

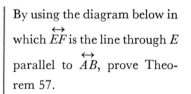
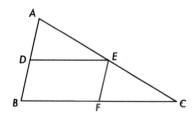

3. Given: *P* is the midpoint of $\overline{AB}$.
Q is the midpoint of $\overline{AC}$.

Concl.: $m\,\overline{PQ} = \frac{1}{2}m\,\overline{BC}$ (Hint: Let *R* be the midpoint of $\overline{BC}$ and prove *PBRQ* to be a parallelogram.) State as a proposition what you have proved in this problem.

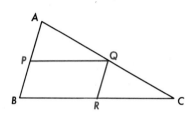

4. Given: $a \parallel b \parallel c$
$x \parallel y \parallel z$
$\overline{AB} \cong \overline{BC}$

Concl.: $\overline{PQ} \cong \overline{QR}$

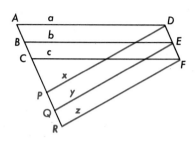

5. Given: *P* is the midpoint of $\overline{AB}$.
Q is the midpoint of $\overline{AC}$.

Concl.: $\overleftrightarrow{PQ}$ bisects $\overline{AD}$.

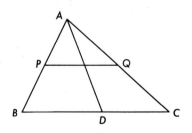

6. Given: $\overline{BM}$ is the median to $\overline{AC}$.
P is the midpoint of $\overline{AB}$.
R is the midpoint of $\overline{BC}$.
$\overleftrightarrow{PQ}$ and $\overleftrightarrow{RS} \parallel \overleftrightarrow{BM}$

Concl.: $\overline{AQ} \cong \overline{QM} \cong \overline{MS} \cong \overline{SC}$

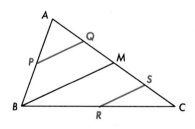

7. Given: $\overline{BM}$ is the median to $\overline{AC}$.

$\overline{CP}$ is the median to $\overline{AB}$.

R is the midpoint of $\overline{BC}$.

$\overleftrightarrow{PQ}$ and $\overleftrightarrow{RS} \parallel \overleftrightarrow{BM}$

Concl.: T and W are trisection points of $\overline{PC}$.

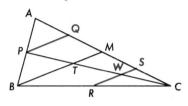

Given: $ABCD$ is a $\square$. **8.***

E is the midpoint of $\overline{AD}$.

F is the midpoint of $\overline{BC}$.

Concl.: $\overleftrightarrow{BE}$ and $\overleftrightarrow{DF}$ trisect $\overline{AC}$. (Hint: Prove $BFDE$ to be a parallelogram; then let $l \parallel \overleftrightarrow{BE}$ and $m \parallel \overleftrightarrow{FD}$.)

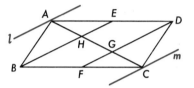

9. Given: D, G, and E are the midpoints of $\overline{AB}$, $\overline{AF}$, and $\overline{AC}$ respectively.

Concl.: Points D, G, and E are collinear.

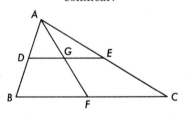

Given: $a \parallel b \parallel c$ **10.**

$\overline{AB} \cong \overline{BC}$

Concl.: $\overline{DE} \cong \overline{EF}$ (Hint: Let $\overleftrightarrow{AF}$ be the line joining points A and F.) What is the statement of the space theorem that you have proved through this problem?

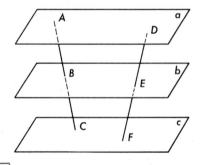

$\boxed{\text{B}}$

1. A line that bisects one of the nonparallel sides of a trapezoid and is parallel to the bases bisects the remaining side.

2. A line that bisects the nonparallel sides of a trapezoid is parallel to the bases. (Hint: Use the indirect proof; follow the method applied in Theorem 58.)

3. A line that bisects the nonparallel sides of a trapezoid will bisect either diagonal.

4. If line segments are drawn between the midpoints of consecutive sides of a quadrilateral, the quadrilateral formed will be a parallelogram.

5. If a line is drawn from the midpoint of the hypotenuse of a right triangle perpendicular to either leg, it will bisect the leg.

6. If line segments are drawn from the midpoints of the legs of an isosceles triangle to the midpoint of the base, then these line segments will form a rhombus with the legs of the triangle.

7. If lines are drawn joining the midpoints of the three sides of a triangle, then four congruent triangles will be formed.

■ Ratios and Proportion

Before going further, we would like to review briefly a unit that you studied in algebra. Necessary to an understanding of the work we plan to develop is the knowledge of a few simple algebraic principles.

Ratio

A ratio is the quotient of the measures of two quantities if the quantities are measured in the same unit.

Thus, if we wanted to compare the length of a blackboard 24 feet long to its width of 3 feet, we would merely divide 24 by 3 and express the answer by saying that the length is 8 times as long as the width. Had 3 been divided by 24, the result would have been designated by saying that the width is $\frac{1}{8}$ the size of the length. Both of these answers can be written in what is known as the ratio form:

$$8:1 \quad \text{or} \quad \frac{8}{1} \quad \text{and} \quad 1:8 \quad \text{or} \quad \frac{1}{8}$$

In the definition of a ratio we were careful to point out that the quantities have to be measured in the same unit before it is possible to compare them. Thus, suppose a blackboard is measured as 24 *feet* long and 36 *inches* wide. Before these measurements can be compared, they will have to be expressed in terms of a common unit. That is, either the 24 feet will have to be changed to inches, or the 36 inches changed to feet. On the other hand, the weight of a person, 180 pounds, can *never* be compared to his height, 6 feet, for it is not possible to express the weight and the height in terms of a common unit of measure.

Proportion

A proportion is an equation in which the left side and the right side of the equation are single ratios.

Thus, the equation $\frac{3}{4} = \frac{6}{8}$ is a proportion, for it contains a single ratio on each side of the equal sign. This proportion can also be written in the form $3:4 = 6:8$. In either form it can be read in one of two ways:

(1) 3 over 4 equals 6 over 8.

(2) 3 is to 4 as 6 is to 8.

The *general proportion* is usually written in terms of the elements a, b, c, and d, and is expressed as

$$\frac{a}{b} = \frac{c}{d} \quad \text{or} \quad a:b = c:d$$

In the proportion $\frac{3}{4} = \frac{6}{8}$, what are the values of a, b, c, and d? Each of the terms of a proportion is called a *proportional*. By examining the proportion $a:b = c:d$ it is easy to realize why the a is called the *first proportional*; the b, the *second proportional*; etc.

Special proportions arise in which the second and third terms are identical. Examples of these are

$$\frac{2}{6} = \frac{6}{18}, \quad \frac{1}{3} = \frac{3}{9}, \quad \frac{a}{b} = \frac{b}{c}$$

Proportions such as these are called *mean proportions*. In a mean proportion the c is considered as the *third proportional* to the terms a and b, while the b is referred to as the *mean proportional* to a and c.

In the general proportion $a:b = c:d$ the first and fourth terms of the proportion—that is, a and d—are called the *extremes* of the proportion, while the second and third proportionals, b and c, are known as the *means*. A very important theorem concerning the relationship between these quantities is

THEOREM 59: The product of the means of a proportion is equal to the product of the extremes.

Given: $\dfrac{a}{b} = \dfrac{c}{d}$ 　　　　　　　　　Concl.: $ad = bc$

PROOF	STATEMENTS	REASONS
1. $\dfrac{a}{b} = \dfrac{c}{d}$		1. Given
2. $bd = bd$		2. Reflexive property of equality
3. $bd \cdot \dfrac{a}{b} = bd \cdot \dfrac{c}{d}$ or $\quad ad = bc$		3. If equals are multiplied by equals, the products will be equal.

This theorem gives us a handy way of finding any one of the terms in a proportion when given the remaining three terms.

Illustration:

Find the fourth proportional to 5, 7, and 4.

SOLUTION: $$\frac{5}{7} = \frac{4}{x}$$

∴ by Theorem 59 $5x = 28$

or $x = 5\frac{3}{5}$ (The fourth proportional)

The converse of Theorem 59 is also true; that is,

THEOREM 60: If the product of two numbers is equal to the product of two other numbers, either pair may be made the means of a proportion, while the other pair is made the extremes of the proportion.

Given: $xy = wz$ Concl.: $\dfrac{x}{w} = \dfrac{z}{y}$

PROOF	STATEMENTS	REASONS
1. $xy = wz$		1. Given
2. $wy = wy$		2. Reflexive property of equality
3. $\dfrac{xy}{wy} = \dfrac{wz}{wy}$		3. If equals are divided by equals, the quotients will be equal.
or $\dfrac{x}{w} = \dfrac{z}{y}$		

Illustration:

If $2x = 3y$, then what is the ratio of x to y?

SOLUTION: In the relation $2x = 3y$ the product of the two numbers 2 and x is equal to the product of the numbers 3 and y. Hence, Theorem 60 can be applied. Since x is to be one of the extremes, the other must be 2. Similarly, since y is the second proportional, 3 will have to be the third.

Hence, $\dfrac{x}{y} = \dfrac{3}{2}$

THEOREM 61: If four numbers (a, b, c, d) are in proportion $\left(\dfrac{a}{b} = \dfrac{c}{d}\right)$, they are in proportion by addition $\left(\dfrac{a+b}{b} = \dfrac{c+d}{d}\right)$.

Given: $\dfrac{a}{b} = \dfrac{c}{d}$ Concl.: $\dfrac{a+b}{b} = \dfrac{c+d}{d}$

ANALYSIS: By adding 1 to each side of the equation $\dfrac{a}{b} = \dfrac{c}{d}$, the conclusion will follow.

PROOF

The proof will be left for you to do.

EXERCISES

6 ft. 8 in.

2 ft. 6 in.

1. Find the ratio of the following:
   (a) A quarter to a half dollar
   (b) Two feet to three inches
   (c) Ten ounces to two pounds
   (d) The length of the rectangle at the right to its width.
   (e) The measure of a right angle to the measure of a straight angle.

2. Find the value of x in each of the following proportions:

(a) $\dfrac{x}{2} = \dfrac{5}{12}$
(b) $\dfrac{3}{x} = \dfrac{12}{8}$

(c) $\dfrac{5}{7} = \dfrac{x+1}{14}$
(d) $\dfrac{3}{4} = \dfrac{2x-1}{12}$

3. Find the fourth proportional if the first three proportionals are
   (a) 2, 3, 8   (b) 5, 7, 9
   (c) a, b, c (d) $x, 2x, 3x$

4. Find the third proportional of a mean proportion if the first and second proportionals are
   (a) 2, 4   (b) 4, 12   (c) 3, 5   (d) a, b

5. Find the mean proportional of a mean proportion if the first and third proportionals are
   (a) 1, 4   (b) 3, 12   (c) $\frac{1}{2}$, 18   (d) $2a, 8a$

6. Write eight different proportions expressing a relation between 3, 4, 2, and 6 if $3 \cdot 4 = 2 \cdot 6$.

7. If $5a = 7b$, then what is the ratio of a to b?

8. Complete each of the following proportions under the conditions given:

(a) If $2x = 4y$, then $\dfrac{x}{y} = ?$

(b) If $3 \cdot 4 = 4x$, then $\dfrac{3}{4} = ?$

(c) If $5 \cdot 7 = 2y$, then $\dfrac{y}{5} = ?$

(d) If $x^2 = ab$, then $\dfrac{a}{x} = ?$

(e) If $\dfrac{x}{y} = \dfrac{3}{4}$, then $\dfrac{x+y}{y} = ?$

(f) If $\dfrac{a}{b} = \dfrac{9}{5}$, then $\dfrac{a-b}{b} = ?$

(g) If $\dfrac{a}{b} = \dfrac{3}{4}$, then $\dfrac{b}{a} = $?

(h) If $\dfrac{a + b}{b} = \dfrac{17}{10}$, then $\dfrac{a}{b} = $?

Theorems Basic to the Proofs of Similarity

The definition of a ratio insisted that the quantities being compared be measured in the same unit. Our concern is not with the nature of a unit of measure in general but, rather, with the unit that pertains specifically to line segments. In order to clarify this concept, we will have to re-examine the much earlier discussion we had on the measure of a line segment.

As you recall, the measure of a line segment is simply the co-ordinate of the right endpoint of the line segment when the left endpoint coincides with the zero point on the number line. Thus, in Figure 11-6 the measure

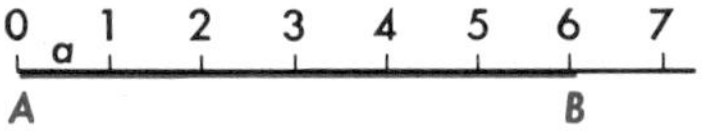

Figure 11-6. 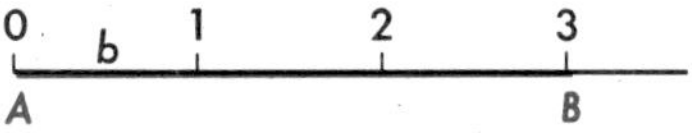   **Figure 11-7.**

of $\overline{AB}$ would be 6, for the co-ordinate of B is 6 on the number line. The name given to the segment a whose endpoints are "0" and "1" is the *unit of measure* on this number line. Thus, the unit of measure, a, is contained an *exact, or integral, number* of times, 6, in $\overline{AB}$. Had we doubled our unit of measure, as we did in Figure 11-7, then the measure of $\overline{AB}$ would now be 3 rather than 6. Again, the unit of measure, b, is contained an integral number of times in $\overline{AB}$. To avoid confusion as to whether the measure of $\overline{AB}$ is 6 or 3, or any other number depending on the selection of the unit of measure, we say that $m\,\overline{AB}$ is 6 in a units or $m\,\overline{AB}$ is 3 in b units. In reality, when we consider the definition of the sum of line segments, it is often far better to express these relations as

$$\overline{AB} = 6a \quad \text{or} \quad \overline{AB} = 3b$$

Pursuing this further, we see a *common unit* of measure to two line segments will be one that is contained in both segments an exact, or integral, number of times. Specifically, if the inch was contained in $\overline{CD}$ $9\frac{1}{2}$ times and in $\overline{EF}$ $7\frac{1}{4}$ times, then a common unit of measure for these two line segments is the $\frac{1}{4}$ inch. It will be contained 38 times in $\overline{CD}$ and 29 times in $\overline{EF}$.

Figure 11-8.

Unfortunately, all line segments do not have a common unit of measure. Line segments that do are called by the frightening name of *commensurable* segments. Those that do not have a common unit of measure are called *incommensurable* segments. There are several pairs of incommensurable segments with which you have had contact in the past. The circumference of a circle and the diameter of the same circle have no common unit of measure. The unit of measure that fits into the diameter exactly 1 time will fit into the circumference *approximately* 3.1416 times; it can not fit into the circumference exactly. Another pair of line segments that are incommensurable are the leg and hypotenuse of an isosceles right triangle.

The proof of the next theorem necessitates finding a common unit of measure to two line segments. As just explained, this does not always exist. Hence, our proof is true only under the condition that the line segments are *commensurable*. We will assume, however, that this theorem is also true when the line segments are not commensurable. This is proved in more advanced fields of mathematics.

THEOREM 62: **If a line is parallel to one side of a triangle, then the ratios of the measures of corresponding segments of the other two sides will be equal.**

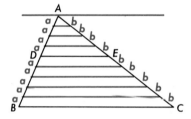

Given: $\overline{AD}$ and $\overline{DB}$ are commensurable.

$\overleftrightarrow{DE} \parallel \overleftrightarrow{BC}$

Concl.: $\dfrac{m\,\overline{AD}}{m\,\overline{DB}} = \dfrac{m\,\overline{AE}}{m\,\overline{EC}}$

Figure 11-9.

PROOF STATEMENTS	REASONS
1. $\overline{AD}$ and $\overline{DB}$ are commensurable.	1. Given
2. Let a be the common unit of measure for $\overline{AD}$ and $\overline{DB}$.	2. Def. of commensurable line segments
3. Let a fit into $\overline{AD}$ k times and into $\overline{DB}$ p times.	3. Def. of a unit of measure
4. $m\,\overline{AD} = k$	4. Def. of the measure of a line segment
5. $m\,\overline{DB} = p$	5. Same as 4
6. $\dfrac{m\,\overline{AD}}{m\,\overline{DB}} = \dfrac{k}{p}$	6. Division postulate

Now we will try to show that the ratio of the measures of $\overline{AE}$ and $\overline{EC}$ is also k over p.

7. At each point of division on $\overline{AB}$ draw a line parallel to $\overleftrightarrow{AC}$.	7. Parallel postulate
8. But $\overleftrightarrow{DE} \parallel \overleftrightarrow{BC}$	8. Given
9. Hence, each of these lines is parallel to each other and to $\overleftrightarrow{DE}$.	9. If two lines are parallel to the same line, then they are parallel to each other.
10. These parallels intersect con-congruent segments called b on $\overline{AC}$.	10. If three or more parallel lines intercept congruent segments on one transversal, they intercept congruent segments on every transversal.

Note that there exists a one-to-one correspondence between each of the "a" units and each of the "b" units.

11. Hence, $\overline{AE} = kb$	11. Def. of the sum of line segments
12. $m\,\overline{AE} = k$	12. Same as 4
13. And $\overline{EC} = pb$	13. Same as 11
14. $m\,\overline{EC} = p$	14. Same as 4
15. $\dfrac{m\,\overline{AE}}{m\,\overline{EC}} = \dfrac{k}{p}$	15. Same as 6
16. $\dfrac{m\,\overline{AD}}{m\,\overline{DB}} = \dfrac{m\,\overline{AE}}{m\,\overline{EC}}$	16. Transitive property of equality

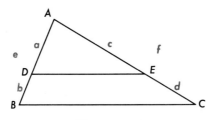

Figure 11-10.

For the sake of simplifying our symbols, we will use the following notation:

$$m\,\overline{AD} = a \qquad m\,\overline{AE} = c \qquad m\,\overline{AB} = e$$
$$m\,\overline{DB} = b \qquad m\,\overline{EC} = d \qquad m\,\overline{AC} = f$$

Now the proportion

$$\frac{m\,\overline{AD}}{m\,\overline{DB}} = \frac{m\,\overline{AE}}{m\,\overline{EC}}$$

can be rewritten in the much simpler form of

$$\frac{a}{b} = \frac{c}{d}$$

The above relation is but one of the many different proportions that will hold if $\overset{\leftrightarrow}{DE} \parallel \overset{\leftrightarrow}{BC}$ (see Figure 11-10). From the theorem on addition, Theorem 61, this proportion will lead to the truth of

$$\frac{a+b}{b} = \frac{c+d}{d} \quad \text{or} \quad \frac{e}{b} = \frac{f}{d} \quad \text{or} \quad \frac{m\,\overline{AB}}{m\,\overline{DB}} = \frac{m\,\overline{AC}}{m\,\overline{EC}}$$

From the theorem that the product of the means is equal to the product of the extremes, the middle proportion above will become

$$e \times d = b \times f \tag{1}$$

and, on the basis of Theorem 60, this product can be rewritten as eight different proportions. Similarly, the original proportion that was obtained from Theorem 62 can be written as

$$a \times d = b \times c \tag{2}$$

This product, too, will lead to eight different proportions. Finally, by transforming one of the proportions found in (2), $\frac{b}{a} = \frac{d}{c}$, by the use of the addition theorem, it follows that

$$\frac{b+a}{a} = \frac{d+c}{c} \quad \text{or} \quad \frac{e}{a} = \frac{f}{c} \quad \text{or} \quad \frac{m\,\overline{AB}}{m\,\overline{AD}} = \frac{m\,\overline{AC}}{m\,\overline{AE}}$$

From this proportion we obtain a third product:

$$e \times c = a \times f \tag{3}$$

that will also lead to eight different proportions. Theorem 62 will be quoted when applying any one of these *24 different proportions.*

At first glance it would seem almost impossible to try to recall these 24 proportions. You will find, however, that you will almost automatically sense proportions that are not true. Thus, you will *never* cross the "parallel" when setting up a ratio; that is, the ratio $a:d$ will equal no other ratio, nor will $b:c$. Similarly, the proportion starting with $e:c$ cannot be completed.

We are more fortunate with the converse of Theorem 62; it is not nearly so lengthy nor so difficult. On the other hand, its importance is not nearly so great either.

THEOREM 63: **If a line intersects two sides of a triangle so that the ratios of the measures of corresponding segments are equal, then the line is parallel to the third side:**

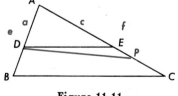

Given: $\dfrac{a}{e} = \dfrac{c}{f}$

Concl.: $\overset{\leftrightarrow}{DE} \parallel \overset{\leftrightarrow}{BC}$

Figure 11-11.

ANALYSIS: We will use the indirect proof by assuming that $\overleftrightarrow{DE} \not\parallel \overleftrightarrow{BC}$ and show that this leads to the logical inconsistency that $\overline{AE} \cong \overline{AP}$ and $\overline{AE} \not\cong \overline{AP}$.

PROOF

By the law of the excluded middle one of the following statements is true and no other possibility exists:

$$\overleftrightarrow{DE} \parallel \overleftrightarrow{BC} \quad \text{or} \quad \overleftrightarrow{DE} \not\parallel \overleftrightarrow{BC}$$

Let us accept the possibility that $\overleftrightarrow{DE} \not\parallel \overleftrightarrow{BC}$; then, through D let $\overleftrightarrow{DP}$ be the line that is parallel to $\overleftrightarrow{BC}$. By Theorem 62 $\frac{a}{e} = \frac{x}{f}$, where x is the measure of $\overline{AP}$. Hence, it follows that

$$x = \frac{a \times f}{e}$$

Similarly, from the Given Data

$$\frac{a}{e} = \frac{c}{f}$$

therefore

$$c = \frac{a \times f}{e}$$

Thus, we can say that $x = c$ by the transitive property of equality. But we have a postulate stating that the whole is greater than any of its parts. This implies that $x > c$. Therefore, accepting the possibility that $\overleftrightarrow{DE} \not\parallel \overleftrightarrow{BC}$ led to the logical inconsistency of the truth of both $x = c$ and $x \neq c$. By the law of contradiction both cannot be true at the same time. Since $x \neq c$ must be true as the result of a postulate, then $x = c$ must be false and, therefore, the statement $\overleftrightarrow{DE} \not\parallel \overleftrightarrow{BC}$ is also false. Hence, $\overleftrightarrow{DE} \parallel \overleftrightarrow{BC}$ is true, for it is the only remaining possibility.

In view of the previous few proofs it should be quite apparent that the symbolism involving the measures of line segments can become so involved as to be distracting. However, since the measures of line segments are important to the development of the work on similar polygons, it was imperative that our symbols be simplified. It was for just this occasion that we had been waiting to introduce the symbol AB without anything above it. Each time AB was written earlier in our work, it was either

(1) a line, $\overleftrightarrow{AB}$ written with the double arrow above it

or   (2) a ray, $\overrightarrow{AB}$ written with the single arrow above it

or   (3) a segment, $\overline{AB}$ written with a segment above it

Henceforth, should AB appear with no mark above it, it will signify that it represents *the measure of the line segment* AB. Thus,

$$AB = m \, \overline{AB}$$

Numerical Illustration:

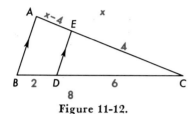

Given: $\overleftrightarrow{DE} \parallel \overleftrightarrow{AB}$
$CE = 4,\ CD = 6,\ BD = 2$
To find: AC

Figure 11-12.

ANALYSIS: It is suggested that each of the six segments be labeled as was was done in the triangle above. Always labeling the measure of the segment that you are asked to find with the symbol x will avoid one of the possibilities of error. You are now free to choose any one of the 24 different proportions that follow when a line is parallel to one side of a triangle. Two are shown here.

First Solution	Second Solution
$\dfrac{x}{4} = \dfrac{8}{6}$	$\dfrac{4}{x-4} = \dfrac{6}{2}$
$6x = 32$	$8 = 6x - 24$
$x = 5\frac{1}{3}$	$5\frac{1}{3} = x$

EXERCISES

1. Given: $\overleftrightarrow{DE} \parallel \overleftrightarrow{BC}$

For the diagram at the right complete each of the following proportions:

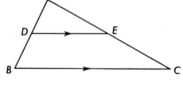

(a) $\dfrac{AE}{EC} = ?$ (b) $\dfrac{BD}{DA} = ?$ (c) $\dfrac{DB}{EC} = ?$

(d) $\dfrac{AD}{AE} = ?$ (e) $\dfrac{AC}{AE} = ?$ (f) $\dfrac{AB}{DB} = ?$

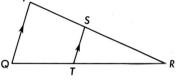

2. Given: $\overleftrightarrow{ST} \parallel \overleftrightarrow{PQ}$

For the diagram at the right complete each of the following proportions:

(a) $RP:RS = ?$ **(b)** $QT:TR = ?$ **(c)** $PS:SR = ?$
(d) $PS:QT = ?$ **(e)** $QR:PR = ?$ **(f)** $RT:RQ = ?$

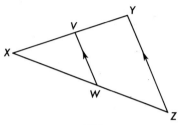

3. Given: $\overleftrightarrow{VW} \parallel \overleftrightarrow{YZ}$

For the diagram at the right complete each of the following proportions. If any of them can not be completed, indicate this by drawing a line through the equality sign.

(a) $\dfrac{YV}{WZ} = ?$ **(b)** $\dfrac{XW}{VY} = ?$ **(c)** $\dfrac{XZ}{WZ} = ?$

(d) $\dfrac{XV}{XW} = ?$ **(e)** $\dfrac{XV}{XZ} = ?$ **(f)** $\dfrac{WZ}{XZ} = ?$

(g) $\dfrac{XV}{XY} = ?$ **(h)** $\dfrac{VY}{WZ} = ?$ **(i)** $\dfrac{WZ}{XV} = ?$

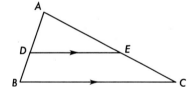

4. Given: $\overleftrightarrow{DE} \parallel \overleftrightarrow{BC}$

In terms of the diagram at the right find the measures requested.

(a) $AD = 2$, $DB = 4$, $AE = 5$, $EC = ?$
(b) $DB = 6$, $EC = 8$, $AE = 5$, $AD = ?$
(c) $AE = 5$, $AD = 4$, $EC = 7$, $AB = ?$
(d) $AB = 12$, $AD = 3$, $AE = 4$, $EC = ?$
(e) $AB = 10$, $AC = 12$, $EC = 8$, $DB = ?$
(f) $DB = 8$, $AB = 18$, $AE = 12$, $AC = ?$

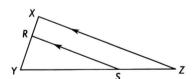

5. Given: $\overleftrightarrow{RS} \parallel \overleftrightarrow{XZ}$

In terms of the diagram at the right find the measures requested.

(a) $XR = 4$, $RY = 6$, $YS = 8$, $SZ = ?$
(b) $YX = 12$, $YZ = 16$, $SZ = 4$, $YR = ?$
(c) $XR = 5$, $YS = 10$, $SZ = 6$, $XY = ?$
(d) $YR = YS$, $RX = 7$, $SZ = ?$
(e) $YX = YZ$, $YS = 9$, $YR = ?$

6. Under which of the following condi-
tions will $\overleftrightarrow{DE}$ be parallel to $\overleftrightarrow{AB}$ in the
diagram at the right?

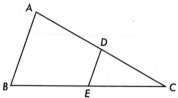

   (a) $AC = 10$, $CD = 4$, $EC = 2$, $BC = 5$
   (b) $AC = 12$, $AD = 8$, $EC = 3$, $BC = 9$
   (c) $EC = 6$, $BC = 14$, $AD = 12$, $DC = 8$
   (d) $AD = 6$, $EC = 14$, $BC = 18$, $DC = 21$
   (e) $BE = 20$, $DC = 10$, $AC = 25$, $BC = 36$

B

1. Given: $\overleftrightarrow{AD} \parallel \overleftrightarrow{EF} \parallel \overleftrightarrow{BC}$

Concl.: $\dfrac{AE}{EB} = \dfrac{DF}{FC}$

(Hint: Draw $\overleftrightarrow{AC}$.)

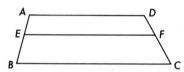

Given: $\dfrac{AD}{AE} = \dfrac{DB}{EC}$ **2.**

Concl.: $\dfrac{AD}{AB} = \dfrac{AP}{AQ}$

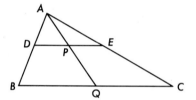

3. Given: $\overleftrightarrow{AB} \parallel \overleftrightarrow{CD}$
          $\overleftrightarrow{EB} \parallel \overleftrightarrow{FD}$

Concl.: $\dfrac{PE}{PF} = \dfrac{PA}{PC}$

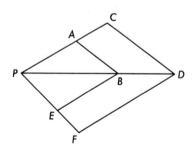

Given: $\overleftrightarrow{DE} \parallel \overleftrightarrow{AC}$ **4.**
          $\overleftrightarrow{DC} \parallel \overleftrightarrow{AP}$

Concl.: $\dfrac{BE}{EC} = \dfrac{BC}{CP}$

$\left(\text{Hint: Prove both ra-}\right.$

$\left.\text{tios equal to } \dfrac{BD}{DA}.\right)$

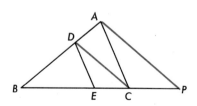

5. Given: $\overrightarrow{AD}$ bisects $\angle BAC$.
$\qquad\qquad \overleftrightarrow{BE} \parallel \overleftrightarrow{AD}$

Concl.: $\dfrac{CA}{AB} = \dfrac{CD}{DB}$

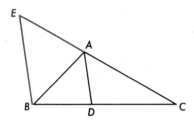

6. Given: $\overrightarrow{AR}$ bisects exterior $\angle QAB$.
$\qquad\qquad \overleftrightarrow{BP} \parallel \overleftrightarrow{RA}$

Concl.: $\dfrac{RC}{RB} = \dfrac{AC}{AB}$

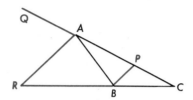

7. Given: $ABCD$ is a trapezoid with $\overleftrightarrow{AD} \parallel \overleftrightarrow{BC}$.
$\qquad\qquad DR:RC = DQ:QB$
$\qquad\qquad AP:PB = DQ:QB$

Concl.: Points P, Q, and R are collinear.

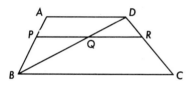

8. Given: $\overleftrightarrow{QS} \parallel \overleftrightarrow{AC}$
$\qquad\qquad \overleftrightarrow{QR} \parallel \overleftrightarrow{AB}$

Concl.: $\overleftrightarrow{RS} \parallel \overleftrightarrow{BC}$

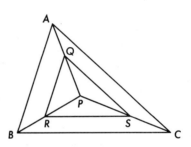

9. Given: $\overleftrightarrow{DF} \parallel \overleftrightarrow{AC}$
$\qquad\qquad \overleftrightarrow{DE} \parallel \overleftrightarrow{AB}$

Concl.: $\overleftrightarrow{EF} \parallel \overleftrightarrow{BC}$

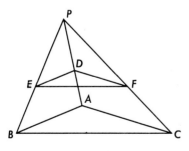

10. Given: plane $a \parallel$ plane $b \parallel$ plane c

Concl.: $\dfrac{AB}{BC} = \dfrac{AD}{DE}$

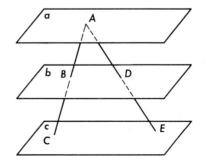

1. If a line is parallel to the bases of a trapezoid, it divides the two diagonals into two equal ratios.
2. If a line is drawn intersecting the legs of an isosceles triangle so as to form a second isosceles triangle, then it is parallel to the base.
3. If a line intersects two sides of a triangle but is not parallel to the third side, then it does not divide the first two sides into two equal ratios.
4. If a line intersects two sides of a triangle but does not divide these two sides into two equal ratios, then it is not parallel to the third side.
5. In space geometry three parallel planes will divide two segments into two equal ratios.

■ Similar Triangles

We have drifted so far from the goal that we had set for ourselves at the outset of this chapter that it would seem that we may have lost sight of where we are going. Originally our objective was to establish conditions under which polygons would have the "same shape," although not necessarily be congruent. Our detour, though seemingly lengthy, was indeed imperative for the proofs that are to follow.

The mathematical term for the words "same shape" is the word *similar*. But to show polygons similar by trying to prove that they have the "same shape" would be as difficult as trying to prove polygons congruent by somehow establishing the fact that they "fit exactly." The terms "same shape" or "fit exactly" are far too vague to lend themselves to a precise meaning. Hence, similar polygons will be defined in a manner much the same as used when defining congruent polygons.†

DEFINITION 69: Similar polygons are two polygons in which there exists a one-to-one correspondence between the vertices such that

(1) All the corresponding angles are congruent.
(2) All the ratios of the measures of the corresponding sides are equal.

How do we interpret this in the case of our most important polygon, the triangle? There are six correspondences that can be arranged between

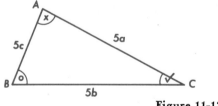
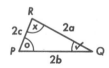

Figure 11-13.

† It might be advisable to review pages 114 through 120.

the vertices of two triangles. If any one of these leads to the corresponding angles being congruent and the ratios of the measures of the corresponding sides being equal, then these triangles will be similar. To illustrate, examine the two triangles above. The six correspondences are

1	2	3
$ABC \leftrightarrow PQR$	$ABC \leftrightarrow PRQ$	$ABC \leftrightarrow QPR$
4	5	6
$ABC \leftrightarrow QRP$	$ABC \leftrightarrow RPQ$	$ABC \leftrightarrow RQP$

Any other correspondence that can be set up for the sets of elements $\{A, B, C\}$ and $\{P, Q, R\}$ by rearranging the elements in $\{A, B, C\}$ will simply be equivalent to one of the six correspondences above. From the markings in the triangles, since $\angle A$ is not congruent to $\angle P$, it follows immediately that neither the first nor second correspondence can be a *similarity correspondence*. In the same way, we can discard the third and fourth correspondence. In both the fifth and sixth, $\angle A$ is congruent to its corresponding angle, $\angle R$; however, in the sixth, $\angle B$ is not congruent to its corresponding angle, $\angle Q$. Hence, the sixth correspondence is out also.

Although the corresponding angles are congruent in the fifth correspondence, we must investigate still further to see if the ratios of the measures of the corresponding sides are also equal.

$$ABC \leftrightarrow RPQ$$

From our understanding of a correspondence between the vertices of two polygons, the three pairs of corresponding sides will be

$$\overline{AB} \text{ and } \overline{RP} \qquad \overline{BC} \text{ and } \overline{PQ} \qquad \overline{AC} \text{ and } \overline{RQ}$$

The markings in the diagram indicate that their ratios will be

$$\frac{AB}{RP} = \frac{5}{2}, \qquad \frac{BC}{PQ} = \frac{5}{2}, \qquad \frac{AC}{RQ} = \frac{5}{2}$$

Hence

$$\frac{AB}{RP} = \frac{BC}{PQ} = \frac{AC}{RQ}$$

Now, finally, since there exists a correspondence in which both the corresponding angles are congruent and the ratios of the measures of the corresponding sides are equal, we can say that the triangles are similar. Had the fifth correspondence, too, failed to hold under these two conditions, it would follow that these triangles were not similar.

To have to prove triangles congruent by resorting to the definition would be a long and tiresome process. Hence, a number of methods were developed (*S.A.S.*, *A.S.A.*, etc.) to drastically shorten this process. So, too, is the case for similar triangles. We plan, now, to prove several theorems that will enable us to show triangles to be similar under less trying conditions than those needed for polygons in general. In fact, our theorems will show that if but one of the two requirements for similarity can be shown to hold, *triangles* will be similar. This is *not* true for any other polygons.

THEOREM 64: Two triangles are similar if there exists a correspondence between the vertices in which the corresponding angles are congruent.

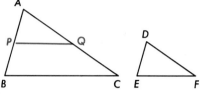

Given: $\angle A \cong \angle D$
$\angle B \cong \angle E$
$\angle C \cong \angle F$
Concl.: $\triangle ABC \sim \triangle DEF$†

Figure 11-14.

ANALYSIS: Since the corresponding angles are already congruent by the Given Data, it is merely necessary to prove that

$$\frac{AB}{DE} = \frac{AC}{DF} = \frac{BC}{EF}$$

If this is true, then by the reverse of the definition of similar polygons we can conclude that the triangles are similar.

PROOF	STATEMENTS	REASONS
1. Let P be a point on $\overleftrightarrow{AB}$, extended if necessary, such that $\overline{AP} \cong \overline{DE}$.		1. A line can be extended as far as desired.
2. Let $\angle APQ \cong \angle B$		2. At a given point on a line there exists an angle that is congruent to any given angle.
3. $\overleftrightarrow{PQ} \parallel \overleftrightarrow{BC}$		3. Why?
4. $\angle E \cong \angle B$		4. Why?
5. $\therefore \angle APQ \cong \angle E$		5. Why?
6. $\angle A \cong \angle D$		6. Why?
7. $\therefore \triangle DEF \cong \triangle APQ$		7. Why?
8. Since $\overline{AP} \cong \overline{DE}$		8. See step 1.
9. And $\overline{AQ} \cong \overline{DF}$		9. Why?
10. But $\dfrac{AB}{AP} = \dfrac{AC}{AQ}$		10. If a line is parallel to one side of a triangle, then the ratios of the measures of the corresponding segments of the other sides will be equal.
11. $\therefore \dfrac{AB}{DE} = \dfrac{AC}{DF}$		11. Substitution postulate

† The symbol for the word similar is $\sim$.

In the same way, had point R been found on $\overleftrightarrow{BC}$ so that $\overline{BR} \cong \overline{EF}$ and $\angle BRS$ was made congruent to $\angle C$, it could be shown that $\dfrac{AB}{DE} = \dfrac{BC}{EF}$.

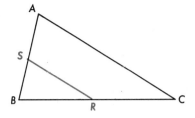

Figure 11-15.

12. Hence, $\dfrac{AB}{DE} = \dfrac{AC}{DF} = \dfrac{BC}{EF}$	12. Transitive property of equality
13. $\therefore \triangle ABC \sim \triangle DEF$	13. Reverse of the def. of similar polygons

As though this method for proving triangles to be similar was not simple enough to apply, there is yet a shorter method. By an earlier theorem we know that if two angles of one triangle are congruent respectively to two angles of a second triangle, then the third angles will be congruent. Hence, rather than prove three pairs of corresponding angles to be congruent to show that triangles are similar, we need merely prove two pairs congruent. Having proved these to be congruent, the congruence of the third pair will immediately follow by the theorem just quoted.

THEOREM 65: **Two triangles are similar if there exists a correspondence between the vertices in which two pairs of corresponding angles are congruent.** (*A.A.* Theorem on Similarity)

PROOF

The proof will be left for you to do.

There is a likeness between the statements on congruence and those on similarity. To prove triangles congruent, we need not only two pairs of corresponding angles to be congruent but also a pair of corresponding sides. If merely the two pairs of angles are congruent, the triangles will be similar, not congruent. Thus, the *A.A.* theorem on similarity is comparable to the *A.A.S.* theorem or *A.S.A.* postulate on congruency. In the same way there will be two further theorems on similarity to compare with the *S.S.S.* and *S.A.S.* method for proving triangles congruent.

THEOREM 66: **Two triangles are similar if there exists a correspondence between the vertices in which the ratios of the measures of two pairs of corresponding sides are equal and the angles included between each pair of sides are congruent.** (*S.A.S.* Theorem on Similarity)

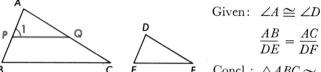

Given: $\angle A \cong \angle D$

$$\frac{AB}{DE} = \frac{AC}{DF}$$

Concl.: $\triangle ABC \sim \triangle DEF$

Figure 11-16.

ANALYSIS: Since we already know that $\angle A \cong \angle D$, by showing that $\angle B$ is congruent to $\angle E$ the two triangles will be similar upon the basis of the *A.A.* theorem on similarity.

PROOF	STATEMENTS	REASONS
1.	Let P be a point on $\overleftrightarrow{AB}$, extended if necessary, such that $\overline{AP} \cong \overline{DE}$.	1. Why?
2.	Let Q be a point on $\overleftrightarrow{AC}$, extended if necessary, such that $\overline{AQ} \cong \overline{DF}$.	2. Why?
3.	$\angle A \cong \angle D$ (a)	3. Given
4.	$\therefore \triangle APQ \cong \triangle DEF$	4. S.A.S.
5.	$\angle E \cong \angle 1$	5. Why?
6.	$\dfrac{AB}{DE} = \dfrac{AC}{DF}$	6. Given
7.	$\therefore \dfrac{AB}{AP} = \dfrac{AC}{AQ}$	7. Substitution postulate (See steps 1 and 2.)
8.	$\overleftrightarrow{PQ} \parallel \overleftrightarrow{BC}$	8. Why?
9.	$\angle B \cong \angle 1$	9. Why?
10.	$\therefore \angle B \cong \angle E$ (a)	10. Why? (See steps 5 and 9.)
11.	$\triangle ABC \sim \triangle DEF$	11. A.A. theorem on similarity

THEOREM 67: Two triangles are similar if there exists a correspondence between the vertices in which the ratios of the measures of corresponding sides are equal. (S.S.S. Theorem on Similarity)

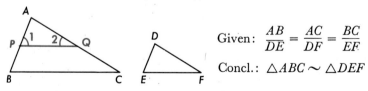

Given: $\dfrac{AB}{DE} = \dfrac{AC}{DF} = \dfrac{BC}{EF}$

Concl.: $\triangle ABC \sim \triangle DEF$

Figure 11-17.

ANALYSIS: We will try to prove the two triangles similar by showing that two pairs of angles are congruent. This can be done by showing that both $\angle B$ and $\angle E$ are congruent to $\angle 1$, and also that both $\angle C$ and $\angle F$ are congruent to $\angle 2$.

PROOF — STATEMENTS	REASONS
1. Let P be a point on $\overleftrightarrow{AB}$, extended if necessary, such that $\overline{AP} \cong \overline{DE}$.	1. Why?
2. Let Q be a point on $\overleftrightarrow{AC}$, extended if necessary, such that $\overline{AQ} \cong \overline{DF}$.	2. Why?
3. $\dfrac{AB}{DE} = \dfrac{AC}{DF}$	3. Why?
4. $\dfrac{AB}{AP} = \dfrac{AC}{AQ}$	4. Substitution postulate
5. $\overleftrightarrow{PQ} \parallel \overleftrightarrow{BC}$	5. If a line intersects two sides of a triangle such that the ratios of the measures of corresponding segments are equal, then the line is parallel to the third side.
6. $\angle B \cong \angle 1$ and $\angle C \cong \angle 2$	6. Why?
7. $\therefore \triangle ABC \sim \triangle APQ$	7. A.A. theorem on similarity
8. $\dfrac{AB}{AP} = \dfrac{BC}{PQ}$	8. Def. of similar polygons
9. $AB \cdot PQ = BC \cdot AP$	9. Why?
10. $PQ = \dfrac{BC \cdot AP}{AB}$	10. Division postulate
11. $PQ = \dfrac{BC \cdot DE}{AB}$	11. Substitution postulate (See step 1.)
12. But $\dfrac{AB}{DE} = \dfrac{BC}{EF}$	12. Given
13. Hence, $EF = \dfrac{BC \cdot DE}{AB}$	13. Same as 9 and 10
14. $\therefore PQ = EF$	14. Why?
15. Hence, $\triangle APQ \cong \triangle DEF$	15. S.S.S.
16. $\angle E \cong \angle 1$ and $\angle F \cong \angle 2$	16. Why?
17. $\therefore \angle B \cong \angle E$ and $\angle C \cong \angle F$	17. Why? (See steps 16 and 6.)
18. $\triangle ABC \sim \triangle DEF$	18. A.A. theorem on similarity

Illustration:

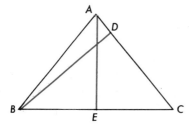

Given: $\overline{AE}$ and $\overline{BD}$ are altitudes in $\triangle ABC$.

Concl.: $\triangle AEC \sim \triangle BDC$

Figure 11-18.

ANALYSIS: You will find that in most cases the best and usually the only method to apply to prove triangles similar is the *A.A.* theorem on similarity. This is particularly true when *no* information is given concerning equal ratios as is the case in this problem.

PROOF STATEMENTS	REASONS
1. $\overline{AE}$ and $\overline{BD}$ are altitudes in $\triangle ABC$.	1. Given
2. $\overleftrightarrow{AE} \perp \overleftrightarrow{BC}$	2. Def. of an altitude
3. $\angle AEC$ is a right angle.	3. Def. of perpendicular lines
4. $\overleftrightarrow{BD} \perp \overleftrightarrow{AC}$	4. Same as 2
5. $\angle BDC$ is a right angle.	5. Same as 3
6. $\angle AEC \cong \angle BDC$ (a)	6. Why?
7. $\angle C \cong \angle C$ (a)	7. Why?
8. $\triangle AEC \sim \triangle BDC$	8. *A.A.* theorem on similarity

EXERCISES

1. The similarity correspondence between $\triangle RST$ and $\triangle XYZ$ is of the form $RST \leftrightarrow YXZ$. What three ratios will be equal?

2. The similarity correspondence between $\triangle ABC$ and $\triangle DEF$ is of the form $ABC \leftrightarrow FDE$. If $AB = 6$, $BC = 5$, $AC = 9$, and $FE = 3$, then what are the measures of $\overline{FD}$ and $\overline{DE}$?

3. What conditions would have to exist under which it would be possible to have two distinct similarity correspondences between the vertices of two triangles?

4. In △*ABC* below find the lengths of the remaining sides.

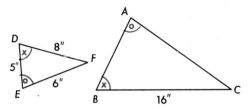

5. Find the length of side *BC* in the diagram below.

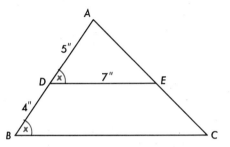

6. The stick 6 feet long casts a shadow 4 feet long. The flag pole casts a shadow 24 feet long at the same time. How high is the flag pole? Can you explain why the triangles are similar?

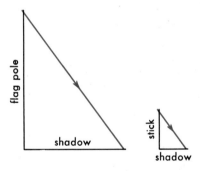

7. In the diagram below, the man is 6 feet tall, while his shadow is 9 feet long. If the lamp post is 30 feet high, how far is the man from the lamp post? Can you explain why the triangles are similar?

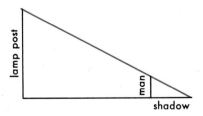

8. In the diagram below find the distance across the pond.

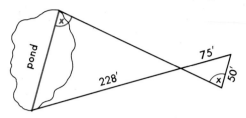

9. (a) By using the theorem that if four numbers are in proportion, they are in proportion by addition (Theorem 61), can you show that the ratio of the perimeters of two similar triangles is equal to the ratio of the measures of any two corresponding sides. (The perimeter of a triangle is the sum of the measures of its sides.)

(b) The perimeters of two similar triangles are 24 and 18 respectively. If the measure of a side of the first is 8, find the measure of the side corresponding to this one in the second triangle.

B

1. Given: $\overleftrightarrow{DE} \parallel \overleftrightarrow{AB}$
Concl.: $\triangle ABC \sim \triangle EDC$

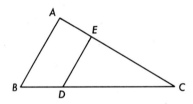

2. Given: $\overleftrightarrow{AB} \perp \overleftrightarrow{BE}$
$\overleftrightarrow{CD} \perp \overleftrightarrow{BE}$
Concl.: $\triangle ABE \sim \triangle CDE$

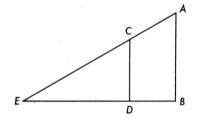

3. Given: $\overleftrightarrow{AB} \perp \overleftrightarrow{BC}$
$\overleftrightarrow{ED} \perp \overleftrightarrow{AC}$
Concl.: $\triangle AED \sim \triangle ABC$

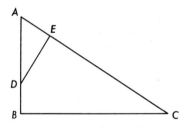

4. Given: $\overline{CD}$ and $\overline{BE}$ are altitudes of $\triangle ABC$.
Concl.: $\triangle DFB \sim \triangle EFC$.

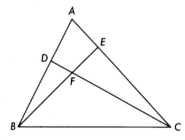

5. Given: *ABCD* is a parallelo-gram in which $\overleftrightarrow{AD}$ has been extended to *E*.

Concl.: $\triangle ABE \sim \triangle CFB$

Given: $\overleftrightarrow{AB} \parallel \overleftrightarrow{EF}$ **6.**
$\overleftrightarrow{AC} \parallel \overleftrightarrow{DF}$

Concl.: $\triangle ABC \sim \triangle FED$

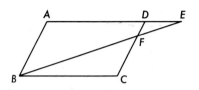

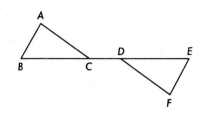

7. Given: $\triangle ABC$ is isosceles with $\overline{AB} \cong \overline{AC}$.
$\overleftrightarrow{DE} \perp \overleftrightarrow{AB}$
$\overleftrightarrow{DF} \perp \overleftrightarrow{AC}$

Concl.: $\triangle DEB \sim \triangle DFC$

Given: $\overleftrightarrow{DE} \parallel \overleftrightarrow{AB}$ **8.**
$\overleftrightarrow{DF} \parallel \overleftrightarrow{AC}$

Concl.: $\triangle DEF \sim \triangle ABC$

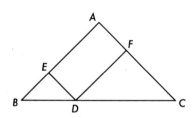

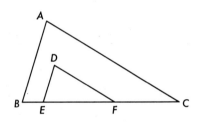

9. Given: $\overline{AB} \cong \overline{AC}$
$\overleftrightarrow{AD} \perp \overleftrightarrow{BC}$
$\overleftrightarrow{EF} \perp \overleftrightarrow{AC}$

Concl.: $\triangle ABD \sim \triangle ECF$

Given: $\dfrac{BE}{AC} = \dfrac{BC}{BD}$ **10.**
$\angle 1 \cong \angle 2$

Concl.: $\triangle ABD \sim \triangle EBC$

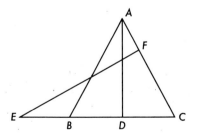

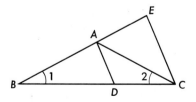

11. Given: △*ABE* ≅ △*ACD*
Concl.: △*ADE* ~ △*ABC*
(Hint: Use *S.A.S.* the-
orem on similarity.)

Given: △*DGC* ≅ △*EFB*   **12.**
∠1 ≅ ∠2
Concl.: △*AFG* ~ △*ABC*

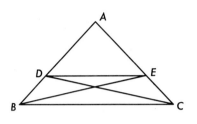

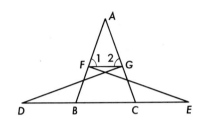

1. Two right triangles are similar if an acute angle of one is congruent to an acute angle of the other.
2. Two triangles that are similar to the same triangle are similar to each other.
3. Equilateral triangles are similar triangles.
4. If from each of two points on the bisector of an angle perpendiculars are drawn, one to each side of the angle, two similar triangles will be formed.
5. If two triangles have their sides respectively parallel, then the triangles are similar.
6. An altitude to the hypotenuse of a right triangle will divide the triangle into two triangles such that either of these triangles will be similar to the original triangle.
7. If from two points, one on each leg of an isosceles triangle, perpendiculars are dropped to the base, the two triangles formed will be similar.
8. If two parallel lines intersect two intersecting lines and form two triangles, these two triangles will be similar.
9. Two isosceles triangles are similar if a base angle of one is congruent to a base angle of the other.
10. If two similar triangles have a pair of corresponding sides congruent, then the triangles are congruent.
11. Two isosceles right triangles are similar.
12. The line segments joining the midpoints of the sides of a triangle form a triangle that is similar to the original triangle.

■ Proving Ratios Equal and Products Equal

After we had proved two triangles to be congruent, it was possible for us to conclude that the corresponding sides and corresponding angles were congruent. In the same way, once triangles have been shown to be similar, the definition of similar polygons leads us to the fact that the ratios of the measures of the corresponding sides will be equal. As an example, consider the triangles in Figure 11-19. Were it necessary to prove that $\dfrac{AB}{RS} = \dfrac{BC}{ST}$, we would show, in some manner, that $\triangle ABC \sim \triangle RST$. The

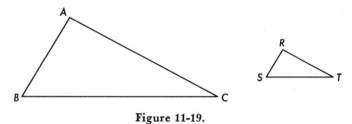

Figure 11-19.

definition of similar polygons would then enable us to conclude that the two ratios were equal.

There are times when the proportion may be written as

$$\frac{AB}{BC} = \frac{RS}{ST} \quad \text{(See Figure 11-19.)} \tag{1}$$

that is, where the terms in each ratio come from a single triangle rather than being corresponding sides in the two triangles. We know, however, that the above proportion leads to the product

$$AB \cdot ST = BC \cdot RS$$

This product, in turn, can be rewritten as any one of eight different proportions. One of these is

$$\frac{AB}{RS} = \frac{BC}{ST} \tag{2}$$

which is identical to the proportion discussed earlier and involves the ratios of the corresponding sides of the triangles. In proportion (1) the corresponding sides were the first and third proportionals; also the second and fourth. From our analysis above we see that this can be rewritten in form (2), where the corresponding sides appear as the first and second proportionals; also the third and fourth. Hence, we will consider that either form (1) or form (2) follows from the fact that triangles are similar.

Illustration:

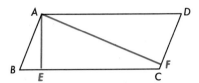

Given: $ABCD$ is a parallelogram.

$$\overleftrightarrow{AE} \perp \overleftrightarrow{BC}$$

$$\overleftrightarrow{AF} \perp \overleftrightarrow{CD}$$

Concl.: $\dfrac{AB}{AE} = \dfrac{AD}{AF}$

Figure 11-20.

PROOF	(The reasons will be left for you to supply.)

1. $ABCD$ is a parallelogram.
2. $\angle B \cong \angle D$
3. $\overleftrightarrow{AE} \perp \overleftrightarrow{BC}$
4. $\angle AEB$ is a right angle.
5. $\overleftrightarrow{AF} \perp \overleftrightarrow{CD}$

6. $\angle AFD$ is a right angle.
7. $\angle AEB \cong \angle AFD$
8. $\triangle ABE \sim \triangle ADF$
9. $\dfrac{AB}{AE} = \dfrac{AD}{AF}$

(Def. of similar polygons)

Situations also arise in which we may be asked to prove that two product relations are equal. Thus, in the illustration above consider the conclusion of:

$$AB \cdot AF = AE \cdot AD$$

Since these four numbers can be expressed as the proportion

$$\frac{AB}{AE} = \frac{AD}{AF}$$

the proof of this problem becomes identically the same as the one illustrated with one additional step:

10. $AB \cdot AF = AD \cdot AE$	10. The product of the means of a proportion is equal to the product of the extremes.

As a word of suggestion, should a conclusion call for showing that the product of the measures of two segments is equal to the product of the measures of two other segments, rewrite these four numbers in the form of a proportion. By examining the terms of the proportion, the triangles that must be shown to be similar can more readily be determined than from the product form.

Remember that, as before, in most instances the first and second proportionals will be the measures of line segments in the first triangle, while the third and fourth proportionals will be the measures of line segments in the second triangle. If this is not so, then the first and third proportionals will be the measures of line segments in the first triangle, while the remaining proportionals will be the measures of segments in the second triangle.

EXERCISES

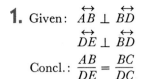

1. Given: $\overleftrightarrow{AB} \perp \overleftrightarrow{BD}$
$\overleftrightarrow{DE} \perp \overleftrightarrow{BD}$

Concl.: $\dfrac{AB}{DE} = \dfrac{BC}{DC}$

Given: $\overleftrightarrow{AD} \perp \overleftrightarrow{CD}$ **2.**
$\overleftrightarrow{CB} \perp \overleftrightarrow{AB}$

Concl.: $\dfrac{AD}{DE} = \dfrac{BC}{BE}$

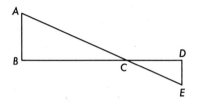

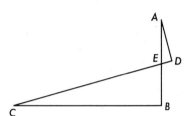

3. Given: $\angle C$ is a right angle.
$\overleftrightarrow{DE} \perp \overleftrightarrow{AB}$

Concl.: $\dfrac{AD}{AB} = \dfrac{AE}{AC}$

Given: $ABCD$ is a trape-   **4.**
zoid with $\overleftrightarrow{AD} \parallel \overleftrightarrow{BC}$.

Concl.: $\dfrac{AE}{EC} = \dfrac{AD}{BC}$

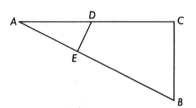

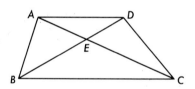

5. Given: $ABCD$ is a parallelogram.

Concl.: $\dfrac{AB}{AF} = \dfrac{DE}{FE}$

Given: $\overline{BD}$ and $\overline{CE}$ are al-   **6.**
titudes in $\triangle ABC$.

Concl.: $\dfrac{DF}{EF} = \dfrac{CF}{BF}$

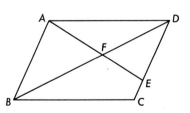

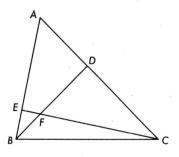

7. Given: $\overline{AE}$ and $\overline{BD}$ are altitudes in $\triangle ABC$.

Concl.: $\dfrac{CE}{CD} = \dfrac{CA}{CB}$

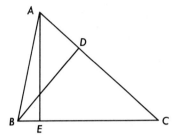

8. Given: $\triangle ABC \sim \triangle RST$

$\overrightarrow{AD}$ bisects $\angle BAC$.

$\overrightarrow{RW}$ bisects $\angle SRT$

Concl.: $\dfrac{AD}{AB} = \dfrac{RW}{RS}$

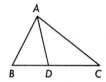

9. Given: $\triangle ABC \sim \triangle RST$

$\overline{BD}$ is an altitude to $\overline{AC}$.

$\overline{SW}$ is an altitude to $\overline{RT}$.

Concl.: $\dfrac{BD}{SW} = \dfrac{AC}{RT}$

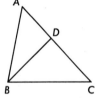

10. Given: $\overleftrightarrow{EF} \parallel \overleftrightarrow{BC}$

Concl.: $\dfrac{EG}{BD} = \dfrac{GF}{DC}$

(Hint: Prove both ratios equal to the same ratio.)

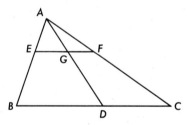

11. Given: $\overleftrightarrow{EG} \parallel \overleftrightarrow{BC}$

$\overleftrightarrow{FG} \parallel \overleftrightarrow{CD}$

Concl.: $\dfrac{EG}{BC} = \dfrac{GF}{CD}$

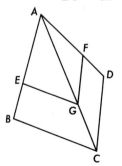

12. Given: $ABCD$ is a parallelogram.

$\overline{EF}$ and $\overline{GH}$ intersect diagonal $\overline{AC}$ at P.

Concl.: $\dfrac{EP}{PF} = \dfrac{GP}{PH}$

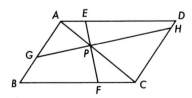

13. Given: $\overset{\leftrightarrow}{DF} \parallel \overset{\leftrightarrow}{AB}$

         $\angle 1 \cong \angle 2$

Concl.: $BC:AC = BD:AF$

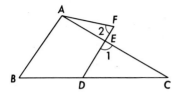

Given: $\triangle ACD$ is equilateral.   **14.**

        C and D are trisection

        points of $\overline{BE}$.

Concl.: $(AB)^2 = BC \cdot BE$

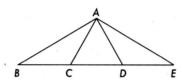

15. Given: $\overset{\leftrightarrow}{AB} \perp \overset{\leftrightarrow}{BD}$

         $\overset{\leftrightarrow}{DC} \perp \overset{\leftrightarrow}{AC}$

Concl.: $BE \cdot ED = AE \cdot EC$

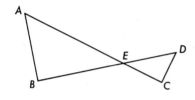

Given: $ABCD$ is a parallel-   **16.**

        ogram.

        $\overset{\leftrightarrow}{AE} \perp \overset{\leftrightarrow}{BC}$

        $\overset{\leftrightarrow}{AF} \perp \overset{\leftrightarrow}{CD}$

Concl:

     (a) $AE \cdot AD = AF \cdot AB$

     (b) $AE \cdot BC = AF \cdot CD$

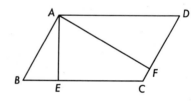

17. Given: $\angle ACB$ is a right

         angle.

         $\overline{CD}$ is an altitude

         to $\overline{AB}$.

Concl.: $(AC)^2 = AB \cdot AD$

         (Hint: Rewrite as

         $AC \cdot AC$.)

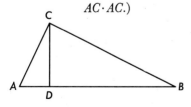

Given: $\angle ACB$ is a right   **18.**

        angle.

        $PQRS$ is a rec-

        tangle.

Concl.: $(PQ)^2 = AQ \cdot BR$

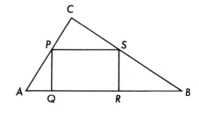

19. Given: $\overline{AB} \cong \overline{AC}$
$\overline{AD}$ and $\overline{BF}$ are
altitudes.
Concl.: $AB:BE = AD:DC$

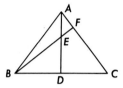

20.

Given: All points are
coplaner.
$\overleftrightarrow{BC} \parallel \overleftrightarrow{EF}$
$\overleftrightarrow{AB} \parallel \overleftrightarrow{DE}$
Concl.: $\triangle ABC \sim \triangle DEF$

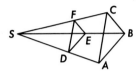

21. Given: $\overline{AB} \cong \overline{AC}$
$\overline{CB} \cong \overline{CD}$
Concl.: $AB \cdot DB = (CB)^2$

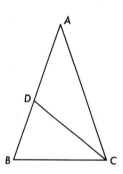

22.*

Given: $\triangle ABC$ is isosceles
with $\overline{AB} \cong \overline{AC}$.
$\overleftrightarrow{CD} \perp \overleftrightarrow{AB}$
Concl.: $(BC)^2 = 2\, AB \cdot BD$
(Hint: Let $\overleftrightarrow{AE}$ be
the perpendicular
from A to $\overleftrightarrow{BC}$.)

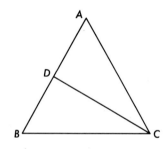

23.* Given: $\overleftrightarrow{AB} \perp \overleftrightarrow{BF}$
$\overleftrightarrow{CD} \perp \overleftrightarrow{BF}$
$\overleftrightarrow{EF} \perp \overleftrightarrow{BF}$
Concl.: $BD \cdot EF = DF \cdot AB$

Given: $\overleftrightarrow{AB} \perp \overleftrightarrow{BC}$
$\overleftrightarrow{DC} \perp \overleftrightarrow{BC}$
$\overleftrightarrow{BD} \perp \overleftrightarrow{AC}$
Concl.: $(BC)^2 = AB \cdot DC$

24.*

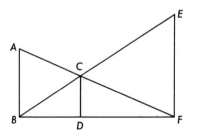

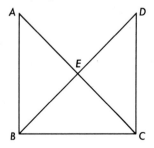

25.* Given: $\overset{\leftrightarrow}{BC} \parallel \overset{\leftrightarrow}{FE}$
$\qquad\qquad \overset{\leftrightarrow}{AC} \parallel \overset{\leftrightarrow}{FD}$

Concl.:

(a) $\triangle ABC \sim \triangle DEF$

(b) $\overset{\leftrightarrow}{AB} \parallel \overset{\leftrightarrow}{ED}$

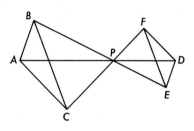

Given: M is the midpoint   **26.***
of $\overline{AB}$.

$\overset{\leftrightarrow}{CQ} \parallel \overset{\leftrightarrow}{AB}$

M, R, Q, P are collinear.

Concl.: $\dfrac{MR}{RQ} = \dfrac{PM}{PQ}$

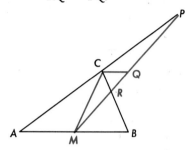

27.* Given: $\overset{\leftrightarrow}{AD} \parallel \overset{\leftrightarrow}{BC}$
$\qquad\qquad \triangle ABE \sim \triangle DCE$

Concl.: $ABCD$ is an isosceles trapezoid.

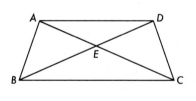

Given: plane $a \parallel$ plane b **28.**
Concl.: $\triangle ABC \sim \triangle PQR$

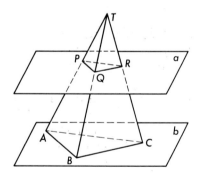

$$\boxed{B}$$

1. The diagonals of a trapezoid divide each other into two equal ratios.
2. Triangle ACB is a right triangle with angle C the right angle. If from any point P on leg BC a perpendicular is drawn to the hypotenuse AB meeting it at D, then $BP \cdot BC = BD \cdot BA$.
3. A median to a side of a triangle bisects all line segments parallel to that side and terminated by the other two sides.
4. The ratio of the measures of corresponding medians of two similar

triangles is equal to the ratio of the measures of any two corresponding sides.

5. If three lines pass through a common point and intersect two parallel lines, then the three ratios of the measures of the segments cut off by the parallel lines are equal.

6. If, in a right triangle an altitude is drawn to the hypotenuse, then the measure of the altitude is the mean proportional between the measures of the segments of the hypotenuse.

7. If two triangles are similar, the ratio of the measures of corresponding altitudes is equal to the ratio of the measures of corresponding medians drawn from the same vertex.

8. If an altitude is drawn to the hypotenuse of a right triangle, then the product of the measures of the altitude and the hypotenuse is equal to the product of the measures of the legs of the right triangle.

9.* If a line segment terminating in the nonparallel sides of a trapezoid is parallel to the bases and passes through the point of intersection of the diagonals, then it is bisected by the diagonals.

■ The Right Triangle

If an altitude is drawn to the hypotenuse of a right triangle, several theorems result that have numerical application. In addition, these theorems will enable us to prove the most widely known property in the field of geometry, the Theorem of Pythagoras.

THEOREM 68: In a right triangle with an altitude to the hypotenuse the square of the measure of either leg is equal to the product of the measures of the entire hypotenuse and the segment of the hypotenuse adjacent to that leg.

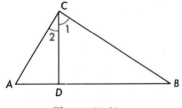

Given: $\angle ACB$ is a right angle.
$\overline{CD}$ is the altitude to $\overline{AB}$.
Concl.: **(a)** $(BC)^2 = BA \cdot BD$
(b) $(AC)^2 = AB \cdot AD$

Figure 11-21.

ANALYSIS: Part (a) of the conclusion can be proved rather easily by showing $\triangle BCD \sim \triangle BAC$. Part (b) of the conclusion is very much the same except that $\triangle CAD$ must be shown to be similar to $\triangle BAC$. You may have noticed that Part (b) is the same as Problem 15, page 357.

PROOF	(The reasons will be left for you to supply.)
1. $\angle ACB$ is a right angle.	6. $\angle B \cong \angle B$
2. $\overline{CD}$ is the altitude to $\overline{AB}$.	7. $\triangle BCD \sim \triangle BAC$
3. $\overleftrightarrow{CD} \perp \overleftrightarrow{AB}$	8. $\dfrac{BC}{BA} = \dfrac{BD}{BC}$
4. $\angle CDB$ is a right angle.	9. $(BC)^2 = BA \cdot BD$ (Part (a))
5. $\angle ACB \cong \angle CDB$	

The proof of Part (b) is left for you to do.

THEOREM 69: **In a right triangle with an altitude to the hypotenuse the square of the measure of the altitude is equal to the product of the measures of the segments of the hypotenuse.**

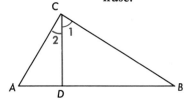

Given: $\angle ACB$ is a right angle.
$\overline{CD}$ is the altitude to $\overline{AB}$.
Concl: $(CD)^2 = AD \cdot DB$

Figure 11-22.

ANALYSIS: After rewriting the conclusion in terms of the proportion

$$\frac{CD}{AD} = \frac{DB}{CD}$$

we find that it is necessary to prove $\triangle ACD \sim \triangle CBD$. The two angles at D can readily be shown to be congruent. It is also evident that we will not show $\angle B$ to be congruent to $\angle A$, for if this were so, $\triangle ACB$ would be isosceles, which it is not. Hence, this implies that we will have to prove $\angle A$ to be congruent to $\angle 1$.

PROOF	(The reasons will be left for you to supply.)
1. $\overline{CD}$ is an altitude to $\overline{AB}$.	7. $\angle A$ is complementary to $\angle 2$.
2. $\overleftrightarrow{CD} \perp \overleftrightarrow{AB}$	(Theorem 53)
3. $\angle CDA$ and $\angle CDB$ are right angles.	8. $\angle A \cong \angle 1$
	9. $\triangle ACD \sim \triangle CBD$
4. $\angle CDA \cong \angle CDB$	10. $\dfrac{CD}{AD} = \dfrac{DB}{CD}$
5. $\angle ACB$ is a right angle.	11. $(CD)^2 = AD \cdot DB$
6. $\angle 1$ is complementary to $\angle 2$.	

As a point of interest, in the proofs of the last two theorems not only were the two small triangles proved similar to each other but they were also both proved similar to the large triangle.

Quite frequently the sides of a triangle are labeled with small letters, while the angles opposite them are labeled with the same capital letters. When the right triangle is so lettered, it becomes

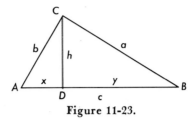

Figure 11-23.

This lettering enables us to see that Theorems 68 and 69 have given us information concerning the squares of a, h, and b. This is

$$\textbf{(1)}\ a^2 = cy \qquad \textbf{(2)}\ h^2 = xy \qquad \textbf{(3)}\ b^2 = cx$$

In trying to find the solution to numerical problems, it is best to label all six segments before deciding which of the three equations listed above is appropriate.

Illustration:

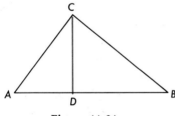

Given: $\triangle ABC$ is a right triangle with $\overline{CD}$ the altitude to the hypotenuse $\overline{AB}$.
$AC = 9$, $AD = 6$
To Find: $DB = ?$

Figure 11-24.

METHOD: As suggested, label all six segments at the outset. For this prob-

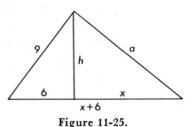

Figure 11-25.

lem the three equations listed above become

$$\textbf{(1)}\ a^2 = x\,(x + 6) \qquad \textbf{(2)}\ h^2 = 6x \qquad \textbf{(3)}\ 9^2 = 6\,(x + 6)$$

Since we are looking for the number labeled "x," we will use the equation in which x is the only placeholder that appears. In this case it is equation (3):

$$81 = 6x + 36$$
$$45 = 6x$$
$$7\tfrac{1}{2} = x$$

There may be situations in which it is necessary to find first a segment other than the one for which we are looking. This will depend on which of the three equations contains a single placeholder. Once this placeholder has been found, substitute its value in the equation containing the measure you have been asked to find.

EXERCISES

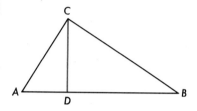

1. Given: $\triangle ABC$ is a right triangle with $\overline{CD}$ the altitude to the hypotenuse.

   (a) $AD = 4, DB = 16, CD = ?$ (b) $DB = 4, AB = 9, BC = ?$
   (c) $AB = 27, DB = 24, AC = ?$ (d) $AC = 6, AD = 3, AB = ?$
   (e) $CD = 10, AD = 5, DB = ?$ (f) $BC = 8, AB = 16, AD = ?$
   (g) $AB = 12, AD = 4, CD = ?$ (h) $AD = 6, DB = 8, BC = ?$
   (i) $BC = 4, AB = 8, CD = ?$ (j) $AB = 10, AC = 6, BC = ?$

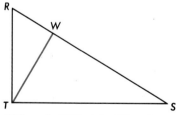

2. Given: $\triangle RST$ is a right triangle with $\overline{TW}$ the altitude to the hypotenuse. (The last three problems in this group will involve the solution of quadratic equations.)

   (a) $RT = 12, RS = 16, RW = ?$ (b) $SW = 6, RW = 8, ST = ?$
   (c) $TW = 5, RW = 6, RS = ?$ (d) $ST = 4, RW = 6, WS = ?$
   (e) $TW = 6, RS = 13, RW = ?$ (f) $RT = 9, WS = 24, RS = ?$
   (Two answers)

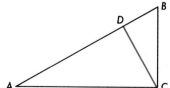

3. Given: $\triangle ACB$ is a right triangle with $\overline{CD}$ the altitude to the hypotenuse.
   $BC = 6, BD = 4$
   To Find: AB, AD, CD, AC

4. Given: $\triangle QPS$ is a right triangle with
$\overline{PR}$ the altitude to the hypotenuse.
$QR = 2$, $RS = 8$
To Find: QS, PR, PQ, PS

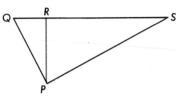

5. In an isosceles right triangle the measure of the altitude to the hypotenuse
is 4. What is the measure of each leg?

B

1. Given: $\overleftrightarrow{AC} \perp \overleftrightarrow{CB}$
$\overleftrightarrow{DE} \perp \overleftrightarrow{CB}$
$\overleftrightarrow{CD} \perp \overleftrightarrow{AB}$
Concl.: $(CD)^2 + (DE)^2 =$
$AD \cdot DB + CE \cdot EB$

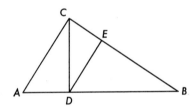

2. Given: $PQRS$ is a rectangle.
$\overleftrightarrow{RW} \perp \overleftrightarrow{QS}$
$\overleftrightarrow{RW}$ intersects $\overleftrightarrow{QP}$ at T.
Concl.: $(PS)^2 = RW \cdot RT$

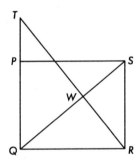

3. Given: $\overleftrightarrow{AB} \perp \overleftrightarrow{BC}$
$\overleftrightarrow{DC} \perp \overleftrightarrow{BC}$
$\overleftrightarrow{BE} \perp \overleftrightarrow{AC}$
Concl.: $BE \cdot BD = CE \cdot CA$

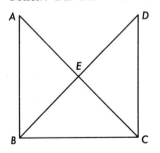

4. Given: $\angle ACB$ is a right angle.
$\overleftrightarrow{CD} \perp \overleftrightarrow{AB}$
Concl.: $\dfrac{(CB)^2}{(CA)^2} = \dfrac{BD}{AD}$

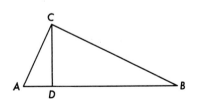

5. Given: Circle O with O on $\overline{AB}$.
$\overleftrightarrow{AC} \perp \overleftrightarrow{CB}$
$\overleftrightarrow{AB} \perp \overleftrightarrow{DC}$
Concl.: $AE \cdot EB = CE \cdot ED$

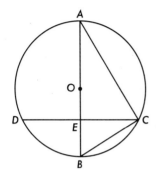

Given: $\overleftrightarrow{AD} \perp \overleftrightarrow{BC}$
$\overleftrightarrow{DE} \perp \overleftrightarrow{AC}$
$\overleftrightarrow{DF} \perp \overleftrightarrow{AB}$
Concl.: $AE \cdot AC = AF \cdot AB$

6.

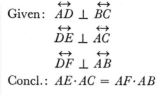

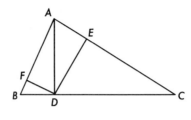

7. Given: In space geometry
$\overleftrightarrow{PA} \perp$ plane m
$\overleftrightarrow{AD} \perp \overleftrightarrow{PB}$
$\overleftrightarrow{AE} \perp \overleftrightarrow{PC}$
Concl.: $PD \cdot PB = PE \cdot PC$

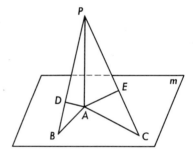

■ The Theorem of Pythagoras

The relationship between the legs and the hypotenuse of a right triangle was known for certain special right triangles long before it was proved for every right triangle. During the time of the ancient Egyptians this relationship was held in secret trust by their religious leaders. Each time a building was to be erected, these men, called "rope stretchers," had to be employed to lay out the corners of the structure so as to form a right angle.

During the sixth century B.C. a secret mathematical society was organized by the Greek mathematician Pythagoras, and for obvious reasons it was called the Pythagorean Society. Story has it that any mathematical discoveries made by a member of the group could not be told to the world at large without permission having been granted by Pythagoras. Supposedly, a Pythagorean developed a proof for the theorem on the right triangle and announced it to friends before consulting Pythagoras. For breaking faith with the organization, the man was "done away with" in true modern gangland style!

Many, many proofs have since been given for the Theorem of Pythagoras. In fact, recently someone has collected and published close to 300 of these proofs, one of which was developed by President Garfield. Those presented by the Greeks were probably based on areas of squares and are quite a bit more difficult than the one given below.

THEOREM 70: **The square of the measure of the hypotenuse of a right triangle is equal to the sum of the squares of the measures of the legs.**

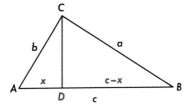

Given: $\triangle ACB$ is a right triangle with $\angle ACB$ the right angle.

Concl.: $c^2 = a^2 + b^2$

Figure 11-26.

ANALYSIS: Theorem 68 enables us to draw conclusions about both a^2 and b^2. Hence, it is merely a matter of adding these two quantities and hoping that their sum will turn out to be c^2.

PROOF STATEMENTS	REASONS
1. Let $\overleftrightarrow{CD}$ be the perpendicular from C to $\overline{AB}$.	1. There exists one and only one perpendicular from a given point to a given line.
2. $\angle ACB$ is a right angle.	2. Why?
3. $b^2 = cx$	3. Why?
4. $a^2 = c\,(c - x)$	4. Why?
5. $a^2 + b^2 = cx + c\,(c - x)$ or $\quad a^2 + b^2 = cx + c^2 - cx$ or $\quad a^2 + b^2 = c^2$	5. Addition postulate

EXERCISES

1. Given: $\triangle ABC$ is a right triangle with $\angle C$ the right angle.

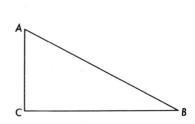

(a) $AC = 5$, $BC = 12$, $AB = ?$ (b) $AB = 20$, $BC = 16$, $AC = ?$
(c) $AC = 10$, $AB = 26$, $BC = ?$ (d) $AC = 5$, $BC = 6$, $AB = ?$

2. Determine the length of the diagonal of a rectangle whose sides are 6 inches and 8 inches respectively.

3. (a) Find the length of the diagonal of a square one of whose sides is 4 inches.

   (b) Find the length of the diagonal of a square one of whose sides is a units long.

4. Find the altitude to the base of an isosceles triangle if one of its legs is 26 feet long while the base is 48 feet.

5. (a) Determine the length of one of the sides of a square whose diagonal is 6 inches.

   (b) Determine the length of one of the sides of a square whose diagonal is $2a$ units long.

6. (a) Determine the length of a side of a rhombus whose diagonals are 18 inches and 24 inches respectively.

   (b) Determine the length of one diagonal of a rhombus if the other diagonal is 30 inches while a side is 25 inches.

7. (a) How long is an altitude of an equilateral triangle if one of its sides is 10 inches?

   (b) How long is an altitude of an equilateral triangle if one of its sides is $2a$ units long?

8. (a) One of the legs of an isosceles right triangle is 6 inches. How long is the hypotenuse?

   (b) One of the legs of an isosceles right triangle is a units long. How long is the hypotenuse?

9. (a) The hypotenuse of an isosceles right triangle is 8 inches. What is the length of each leg?

   (b) The hypotenuse of an isosceles right triangle is a units. What is the length of each leg?

10. (a) Find the side of an equilateral triangle whose altitude is 6 inches.

    (b) Find the side of an equilateral triangle whose altitude is $3a$ units long.

11. One of the nonparallel sides of a trapezoid is perpendicular to the bases. The other of these sides is 10 inches, and the upper and lower bases are 9 inches and 17 inches respectively. How long is the side whose length was not given?

12. The upper and lower bases of an isosceles trapezoid are 16 feet and 46 feet respectively. If one of the equal sides is 17 feet, how long is the altitude? (The altitude is the common perpendicular to the bases.)

13. A ladder 41 feet long leans against a building and reaches a point on the building that is 40 feet above the ground. How far from the bottom of the building is the foot of the ladder?

14. A rope 85 feet long is attached to the top of a high vertical pole. When stretched tight, the rope reaches a point on the ground that is 13 feet from the foot of the pole. How long is the pole?

15. The box at the right has dimensions as shown. How far is it from A to C? (Hint: Find AB first.)

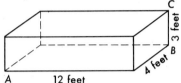

16. The dimensions of the box at the right are all equal. Using the dimension shown,
    (a) Find the distance AB.
    (b) Find the distance AC.

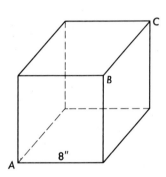

17. If, in the diagram at the right, P is the midpoint of $\overline{BC}$, find AD.

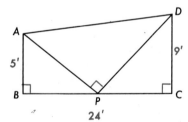

18. In the diagram at the right find the measure of $\overline{CD}$.

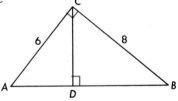

19. During a wind storm a pole 20 feet long snapped in a way such that the topmost point of the upper section leaned over and reached a point on the ground that was 10 feet from the foot of the pole, while the lowest point of this section still remained attached to the pole. How long was this upper section?

$$\boxed{B}$$

1. Given: $\overleftrightarrow{AB} \perp \overleftrightarrow{BC}$
$\overleftrightarrow{DC} \perp \overleftrightarrow{BC}$
Concl.: $(AC)^2 - (AB)^2 =$
$(DB)^2 - (DC)^2$

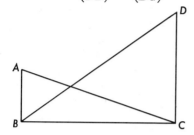

Given: $\overleftrightarrow{DB} \perp \overleftrightarrow{AC}$
Concl.: $(AD)^2 + (BC)^2 =$
$(AB)^2 + (DC)^2$ **2.**

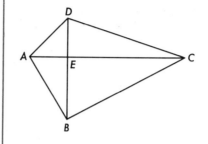

3. Given: $\angle ABC$ is a right
angle.
Concl.: $(AC)^2 + (DE)^2 =$
$(AE)^2 + (DC)^2$

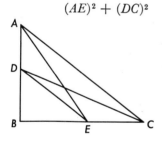

Given: $\overleftrightarrow{AC} \perp \overleftrightarrow{CB}$
$\overleftrightarrow{DE} \perp \overleftrightarrow{CB}$
$\overleftrightarrow{DF} \perp \overleftrightarrow{AC}$
$\overleftrightarrow{CD} \perp \overleftrightarrow{AB}$
Concl.: $(CD)^2 = CE \cdot EB +$
$CF \cdot FA$ **4.**

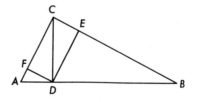

5. Given: $\overleftrightarrow{BD} \perp \overleftrightarrow{AD}$
C is the midpoint of $\overline{AD}$.
$m \angle A = 45$
Concl.: $(AB)^2 = 8(AC)^2$

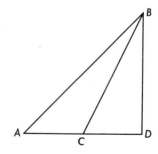

6. Using the diagram at the right, prove that $c^2 = a^2 + b^2 + 2ax$.

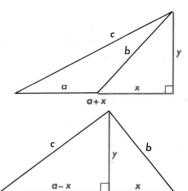

7. Using the diagram at the right, prove that $c^2 = a^2 + b^2 - 2ax$.

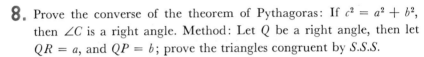
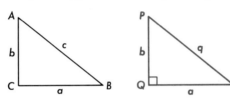

8. Prove the converse of the theorem of Pythagoras: If $c^2 = a^2 + b^2$, then $\angle C$ is a right angle. Method: Let Q be a right angle, then let $QR = a$, and $QP = b$; prove the triangles congruent by $S.S.S.$

9. (a) Referring to Problem 8, show that the numbers $2n$, $n^2 - 1$, and $n^2 + 1$ can represent the measures of the sides of a right triangle. Three numbers such that the sum of the squares of any two is equal to the square of the third are called Pythagorean Numbers.
(b) Show that the numbers $2b + 2$, $b^2 + 2b$, and $b^2 + 2b + 2$ are Pythagorean Numbers.

10. (a) Prove that in a right triangle whose acute angles are 30° and 60° the ratio of the measure of the hypotenuse to the measure of the side opposite the 30° angle is 2:1.
(b) Prove that in a right triangle whose acute angles are 30° and 60° the ratio of the measure of the side opposite the 60° angle to the measure of the side opposite the 30° angle is $\sqrt{3}$:1. (Hint: For the proof of both **(a)** and **(b)**, start with an equilateral triangle.)

11. Using the theorem of Pythagoras, prove that if in space geometry two oblique lines and a perpendicular are drawn to a plane from a point such that the foot of the perpendicular is equidistant from the feet of the oblique lines, then the oblique lines are congruent.

12. State and prove the converse of Problem 11 by applying the theorem of Pythagoras.

Test and Review

1. Find the value of x in each of the following proportions:

   (a) $\dfrac{4}{9} = \dfrac{7}{x}$

   (b) $\dfrac{6}{x-2} = \dfrac{7}{x+3}$

2. Find the fourth proportional to 3, 7, and 5.

3. Find the third proportional of a mean proportion if the first and second proportionals are $2a$ and $3b$.

4. Find the mean proportional of a mean proportion if the first and third proportionals are $2a$ and $18ab^2$.

5. Write eight different proportions expressing the relation between 2, 3, a, and b if $2a = 3b$.

6. If $a = 2b$, then what is the ratio of a to b?

7. If the measures of the angles of a triangle are in the ratio of $1:2:3$, then what is the measure of each angle?

8. If $\dfrac{AB}{BC} = \dfrac{4}{5}$, then find $\dfrac{AB + BC}{BC}$.

9. Use the diagram at the right to find the measure of each of the following segments given that $\overleftrightarrow{DE} \parallel \overleftrightarrow{BC}$.

   (a) $\overline{AC}$ (b) $\overline{DE}$

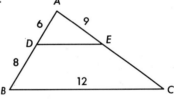

10. Use the diagram at the right to find the measure of each of the following segments given that $\overleftrightarrow{SV} \parallel \overleftrightarrow{RW}$.

    (a) $\overline{TW}$ (b) $\overline{RW}$

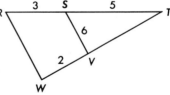

11. The similarity correspondence between the vertices of $\triangle ABC$ and $\triangle DEF$ is $ABC \leftrightarrow EFD$. Name the pairs of angles in the two triangles that are congruent.

12. If the measures of two corresponding sides of two similar triangles are 8 and 12 respectively and the measure of the median to the first side is 6, what is the measure of the median to the second side?

13. The measures of two of the altitudes of a triangle are 3 and 5 respectively. If the measure of the side to which the second is drawn is 8, what is the measure of the side to which the first is drawn?

14. Using the information given in the diagram at the right, find the measure of each of the following segments:

    (a) $\overline{WS}$ (b) $\overline{RT}$

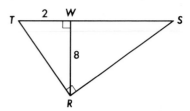

15. If the altitude to the hypotenuse of a right triangle divides the hypotenuse into segments whose measures are 2 and 8 respectively, then what is the perimeter of the triangle?

16. (a) The upper and lower bases of an isosceles trapezoid are 16 and 24 respectively. If one of the legs makes an angle of 45° with the lower base, what is the perimeter of the trapezoid?

    (b) If the angle had been 60°, what would the perimeter have been?

    (c) If the angle had been 30°, what would the perimeter have been?

$$\boxed{B}$$

Prove each of the following:

1. Given: $\triangle ACB$ with $\angle C$ the right angle.

$$\overleftrightarrow{DE} \perp \overleftrightarrow{CB}$$

Concl.: $\dfrac{BA}{BC} = \dfrac{BD}{BE}$

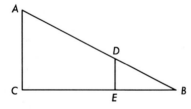

2. Given: $\dfrac{AF}{FB} = \dfrac{AG}{GC}$

Concl.: $\dfrac{AD}{AH} = \dfrac{AE}{AJ}$

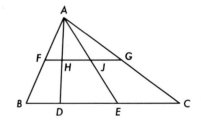

3. Given: D is the midpoint of $\overline{AC}$.

E is the midpoint of $\overline{BC}$.

Concl.: $\triangle PAB \sim \triangle PED$

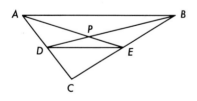

4. Given: $\overrightarrow{BE}$ bisects $\angle ABC$.

$\angle 1 \cong \angle 2$

Concl.: $\dfrac{AE}{EC} = \dfrac{AD}{DE}$

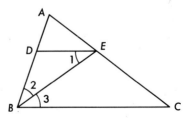

5. Given: $\angle 1 \cong \angle ACB$
Concl.: $(BC)^2 = BD \times BA$

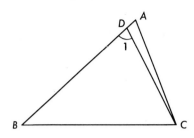

Given: $\overline{AD}$ and $\overline{BE}$ are alti- **6.**
tudes in $\triangle ABC$.
Concl.: $CA \times CE = CB \times CD$

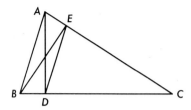

7. Given: $ABCD$ is a trapezoid
with the nonparallel
sides extended to in-
tersect at P.

Concl.: $\dfrac{PF}{PE} = \dfrac{AB}{DC}$

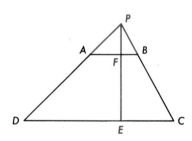

Given: Rectangle $ACBF$ **8.**

$\overleftrightarrow{CE} \perp \overleftrightarrow{AB}$

Concl.: $(BF)^2 = AE \times AF$

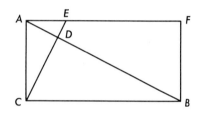

$$\boxed{\text{C}}$$

Prove each of the following statements:

1. If two triangles are congruent, then they are similar.
2. If the midpoints of the sides of an isosceles trapezoid are joined in order, the quadrilateral formed will be a rhombus.
3. If line segments are drawn joining the midpoints of the opposite sides of a quadrilateral, they will bisect each other.
4. The ratio of the measures of corresponding angle bisectors of two similar triangles is equal to the ratio of the measures of any two corresponding sides.
5. If a line joins the midpoints of two opposite sides of a parallelogram, it will bisect both diagonals.

6. If the vertex angle of one isosceles triangle is congruent to the vertex angle of a second isosceles triangle, then the ratio of the measures of their bases is equal to the ratio of the measures of their legs.

7. Two medians of a triangle intersect at a point such that the ratio of the measures of the segments of one is equal to the ratio of the measures of the segments of the other.

8. If two parallel planes intersect two intersecting lines, then the ratio of the measures of the segments of one will be equal to the ratio of the measures of the segments of the other.

■ Try This For Fun

Principles in mathematics frequently bear the name of the person who first noted them. Thus, we are already familiar with Euclid's Fifth Postulate, The Theorem of Pythagoras, Aristotle's Laws of Logic, Pasch's Axiom, and others. Among the theorems in geometry that bear their originator's name, perhaps the most intriguing is Ceva's Theorem:

> If from the vertices of a triangle concurrent lines are drawn intersecting at a point in the interior of the triangle, then of the six segments formed by the intersections of these lines with the sides of the triangle the product of the measures of three alternating segments is equal to the product of the measures of the remaining three segments.

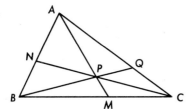

Given: $\overset{\leftrightarrow}{AM}$, $\overset{\leftrightarrow}{BQ}$, and $\overset{\leftrightarrow}{CN}$ are concurrent at P.

Concl.: $AN \times BM \times CQ = NB \times MC \times QA$

Can you prove this theorem? Suggestion: Through B and C draw lines parallel to $\overset{\leftrightarrow}{MA}$.

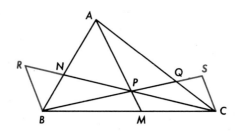

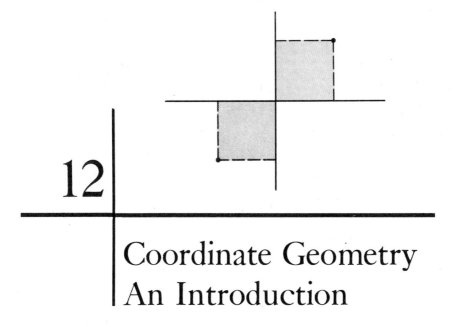

12

Coordinate Geometry
An Introduction

THE PRINCIPLES OF SIMILARITY OF TRIANGLES
and the theorem of Pythagoras have opened before us a broad new field—
the field of analytic, or coordinate, geometry. Until now we have concerned
ourselves with a rather stilted and cumbersome tool developed some 2,000
years ago by Greek mathematicians. Unfortunately, they had neither the
algebra nor the arithmetic that we currently possess and, hence, were forced
to formulate their mathematics in terms of lines, or angles, or solids that
they actually perceived.

The development of algebra led a seventeenth century mathematician
and philosopher, René Descartes, to take the first giant step in geometry
since the time of the Greeks. By showing how algebraic methods can be
applied to geometric situations, he made possible a great deal of the growth
of modern mathematics. This tool is not only very powerful but also relatively simple to understand. We shall try to develop some of its elementary
concepts and show how they can be used to prove a few of the propositions
we had proved earlier.

This is not meant to belittle the value of *synthetic geometry*, the geometry
of the ancient Greeks, for as we shall see, there are a number of situations
in which a "synthetic" proof will be far easier than an "analytic" one.
However, other than possibly for a brief course in what is called "college

375

geometry," synthetic geometry "goes nowhere," nor does it have extensive practical application. Analytic geometry, on the other hand, forms the basis of many areas of mathematics and has wide application.

◼ Plotting Points

In the study of algebra and also as part of the early work in geometry we become familiar with a line that was called either the number line, or the number scale, or, possibly, the number axis. Basically, we assumed that a one-to-one correspondence existed between the points of this line and the real numbers. The real numbers were the whole numbers, fractions, mixed numbers, decimals, irrational numbers ($\sqrt{2}$, $\sqrt[3]{7}$, π), and, incidentally, all of these might have been either positive or negative. They did not include, however, numbers such as $\sqrt{-25}$ that were called imaginary and expressed as $5i$. And so, the assumption that was made was that for each real number there exists a unique point of the number line and, conversely, for each point there exists a unique real number.

The number line was frequently drawn horizontally with an arrowhead

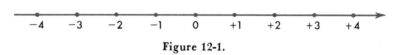

$$-4 \qquad -3 \qquad -2 \qquad -1 \qquad 0 \qquad +1 \qquad +2 \qquad +3 \qquad +4$$

Figure 12-1.

at the right to indicate the direction in which the numbers increased. There is nothing sacred about its being drawn horizontally, for equally well the number line may have been drawn as shown in Figure 12-2 (again, the

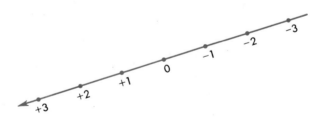

Figure 12-2.

arrowhead shows the positive direction). Through custom, however, the line *is* drawn horizontally and the direction in which the numbers increase *is* to the right.

The number from which we start counting is called zero, while the point on the number axis representing this number is referred to as the *origin*. By asking the question "How is the position of each of these numbers determined on the number line?", we bring to light a rather important feature. The position of each number is determined by its distance from the origin. Thus, the position of the point representing the number +3 is determined by the fact that this point will be 3 units to the right of the origin. Hence, we can say that the distance from the point +3 to the origin is 3 units. Notice that the name for the point is given by the number that leads to the point. This number is called the *coordinate* of the point. In this case, the coordinate of the point is +3. Thus, the coordinate of a point on the number line represents not only the name for that point but also the distance from that point to the origin. Similarly, knowing the coordinate of a point, we are really being told a direction through which the point can be located on the number line.

To illustrate, the point whose coordinate is −4 (think of this as both the name for the point as well as its distance from the origin) is found 4 units to the left of the origin.

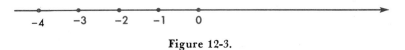

Figure 12-3.

The geometry we are learning, however, is not limited to figures that exist on a line, but rather, to figures existing in a plane. This confronts us squarely with the need to represent points of a plane in some manner similar to that used to represent points of a line. To do this, we set up two number

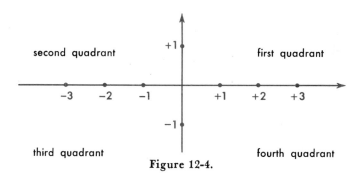

Figure 12-4.

lines that are perpendicular to each other. Each of these divides the plane into two half-planes, while the two together will divide the plane into four quarter-planes called *quadrants*. The quadrants are numbered as shown in the diagram.

Each point of the number line was represented by a real number indicating the distance from that point to the origin. In keeping with this idea, a point of the plane will be represented by a *pair of real numbers* representing the distances from that point to each of the number lines. But what represents the distance from a point to a line?

In the discussion of distance earlier in the text† it was pointed out that

† See page 179.

the distance between two objects was always measured along the shortest path, or geodesic, between the two objects. When these two objects are points, we assume that the shortest path will be the line segment joining these two points. At this time we will further assume

POSTULATE 32: The shortest path between a point and a line is the perpendicular line segment from the point to the line.

In view of this, the distance from a point to a line is the measure of the perpendicular segment between the point and the line. In each of the diagrams of Figure 12-5 the measure of the red segment is the distance from the point P to the line l.

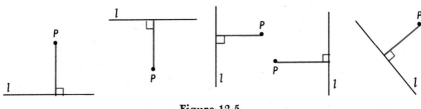

Figure 12-5.

Return now to the points in a plane and their representation by a pair of real numbers. As in the case of the number line, the pair of real numbers are called the *coordinates of the point*. They represent not only the name for the point but also the distances from that point to each of the number lines, called *axes*.

To illustrate, consider the point whose name is $(+3, +5)$. In reference to a number line, the $+3$ indicated that the point was located 3 units to the right of the origin on the number line. On a plane the direction $+3$ will indicate that the point is 3 units to the right of the vertical axis. Unfortunately, that direction is not sufficient to locate the point in the plane, for to be 3 units to the right of the vertical axis is to be anywhere along a line parallel to the vertical axis and 3 units to its right. Each of the points on the

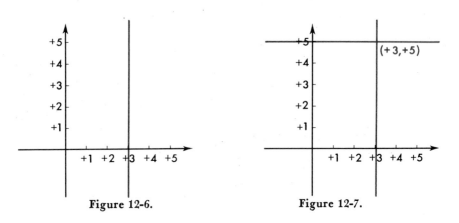

Figure 12-6.　　　　　　　　**Figure 12-7.**

red line in Figure 12-6 above fulfills the condition that it is 3 units to the right of the vertical axis. Thus, the need for the second coordinate. The +5 indicates that the point must also be 5 units above the horizontal axis. The point of intersection of the two red lines represents the point (+3, +5). Since two lines can have but one point in common, the pair of numbers (+3, +5) represents one and only one point.

A pair of numbers such as (+3, +5) is called an *ordered pair*, for the order in which the numbers are written is extremely important. The first coordinate, by agreement, will *always* represent the direction with reference to the vertical axis; in this case, it states that the point is 3 units to the right of the vertical axis. The second coordinate will *always* represent the direction with reference to the horizontal axis; in this case, it states that the point is 5 units above the horizontal axis. Were the order of these two numbers reversed—that is, (+5, +3)—to what point would these directions lead us?

As in the case of the direction of the single number axis, there is nothing but custom that insists that these lines be drawn horizontally and vertically. Frequently the horizontal axis is called the *x-axis*, while the vertical one is called the *y-axis*. The combination of the two are known as the *coordinate axes*. The representation of points in a plane by the method described is called the *Cartesian Coordinate System*.

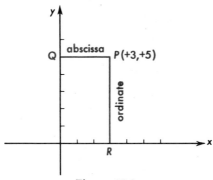

Figure 12-8.

The distance from the point to the vertical axis is called the *abscissa* of the point. In the diagram above the abscissa is the measure of line segment QP, which is given by the first coordinate, +3. The distance from the point to the horizontal axis is called the *ordinate* of the point. In this diagram the ordinate is the measure of line segment RP, which is given by the second coordinate, +5. Thus, since one of the functions of the coordinates of a point is to indicate the distances from the point to each of the axes, the coordinates are often called the abscissa and ordinate of a point.

It is *extremely important* that we realize that the pair of directions—the point is 3 units to the right of the vertical axis and 5 units above the horizontal axis—can be given in any one of three ways:

(1) the ordered pair of numbers: $(+3, +5)$

(2) the pair of equations: $\begin{cases} x = +3 \\ y = +5 \end{cases}$

(3) by its abscissa and ordinate:

The abscissa is $+3$ and the ordinate is $+5$.

Note that when the directions are given as a pair of equations, the x element represents the first coordinate in the ordered pair, or the distance from the vertical axis; the y element represents the second coordinate in the ordered pair, or the distance from the horizontal axis.

Should one and only one direction be given—such as, $x = -2$—this would uniquely establish not a point but an entire set of points all located on the line that is two units to the left of the vertical axis and parallel to it. Remember that the direction $x = -2$ is read as, "The point is two units to the left of the vertical axis." (See Figure 12-9.) Similarly, the single direction

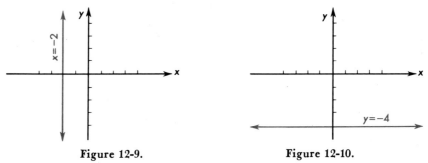

Figure 12-9.   Figure 12-10.

"The ordinate of the point is -4" will lead to a set of points all on a line parallel to the x-axis and 4 units below it. Were this direction restated, it would simply be that the point is 4 units below the horizontal axis. (See Figure 12-10.)

Before leaving this topic, it would be well to point out that we have been assuming that

POSTULATE 33: For a specific pair of axes there exists a one-to-one correspondence between the set of ordered pairs of real numbers and the set of points of a plane.

EXERCISES†

1. Draw a pair of coordinate axes and locate each of the following points:

(a) $(+5, +7)$	**(b)** $(+6, 9)$	**(c)** $(7, +4)$
(d) $(2, 10)$	**(e)** $(-3, 6)$	**(f)** $(-7, 2)$
(g) $(4, -6)$	**(h)** $(8, -3)$	**(i)** $(-4, -9)$
(j) $(-12, -3)$	**(k)** $(0, 5)$	**(l)** $(7, 0)$
(m) $(0, -14)$	**(n)** $(-15, 0)$	**(o)** $(0, 0)$‡

† Use coordinate (or squared) paper for these exercises.
‡ This point is called the origin.

2. Draw the triangle having the following vertices:
   (a) (0, 0), (6, 0), (0, 8)   (b) (2, 14), (2, 2), (7, 2)
   (c) (−4, 7), (8, 7), (8, −9)   (d) (7, 4), (3, 6), (8, 6)
   (e) (2, 5), (−4, 7), (−2, −3)   (f) (−6, −4), (0, 0), (2, −7)

3. The triangle in example 2a is a right triangle. How long is the hypotenuse?

4. The triangles in examples 2b and 2c are right triangles.
   (a) Find the length of the legs of each of these triangles.
   (b) Find the length of the hypotenuse of each of these triangles.

5. Determine the set of points located by each of the following directions:
   (a) $x = 6$ (b) $y = 8$ (c) $x = -4$ (d) $y = -2$ (e) $y = 0$

6. Determine the set of points located by each of the following directions:
   (a) The abscissa of the point is always 10.
   (b) The ordinate of the point is always −7.
   (c) The ordinate of the point is always 0.
   (d) The ordinate of the point is always equal to the abscissa of the point.

7. Represent each of the following points by a pair of equations:
   (a) (5, 9)   (b) (4, −7)   (c) (−3, 0)
   (d) The abscissa is −5, while the ordinate is −7.

8. Represent each of the following statements by an equation:
   (a) The abscissa of a point is always 4.
   (b) The ordinate of a point is always −12.
   (c) The abscissa of a point is always 0.
   (d) The abscissa of the point is always equal to the ordinate of the point.
   (e) The ordinate of the point is always five more than the abscissa of the point.
   (f) The abscissa of the point is always greater than 5.
   (g) The ordinate of the point is always greater than the abscissa of the point.

9. In each of the following problems three of the vertices of a parallelogram are given. Find the fourth vertex so that one pair of sides is parallel to either the x-axis or the y-axis. There are two possibilities in each problem. Find the coordinates of both points.
   (a) (0, 0), (2, 3), (8, 3)   (b) (0, 0), (0, −10), (6, 2)
   (c) (4, 5), (2, 3), (8, 3)   (d) (2, 10), (2, 1), (7, 3)
   (e) (−5, 4), (−7, −2), (6, 4)   (f) (0, 0), (a, 0), (c, d)

10. (a) The length of a side of a square is b. The coordinates of one of the vertices is (0, 0), while the vertex opposite this is in the first quadrant. Find the coordinates of the three vertices not given.

(b) If the vertex opposite the origin is in the second quadrant, find the coordinates of the three vertices.

(c) If the vertex opposite the origin is in the fourth quadrant, find the coordinates of the three vertices.

11. Two of the vertices of an equilateral triangle are $(0, 0)$ and $(10, 0)$. If the third vertex is in the first quadrant, find its coordinates.

12. The vertices of the base of an isosceles triangle are $(0, 0)$ and $(2a, 0)$. Through the means of an equation give a description for the abscissa of the third vertex.

13. The lower base of an isosceles trapezoid is 12 units, while the upper base is 10 units in length. The distance between the bases is 4 units. If the lower base lies on the x-axis with its midpoint at the origin, what are the coordinates of the four vertices?

14. (a) A set of points lie on a line that is parallel to the x-axis. Which of the coordinates is the same for all points?

(b) A set of points lie on a line that is perpendicular to the vertical axis. Which of the coordinates is the same for all points?

■ Distance Between Two Points and Dividing a Line Segment into Any Given Ratio

It would be rather confusing if in a problem involving many points these points were named (a, b), (c, d), (e, f), and the like. Labeling the points in this way, we would soon become bewildered as to whether the coordinate m represented the abscissa of a point or the ordinate. In addition, there is no way of knowing whether this is the abscissa or ordinate of the twelfth point in question, the fifteenth point in question, or perhaps even the first. To overcome this difficulty, points are very often labeled with the symbols x and y only; for the abscissa, of course, we always use the letter x, while the letter for the ordinate is y. In addition, to distinguish one point from another *subscripts* are used. Thus, the first point in our discussion will be written as (x_1, y_1), the second as (x_2, y_2), and the like. It then becomes immediately evident that the symbol x_{15} appearing in any problem will represent the abscissa of the fifteenth point.

Which of the coordinates of two points will be the same if these two points appear on a line that is parallel to the y-axis? If the first of these points is written as (x_1, y_1), how will you express the second of the points? If, in the

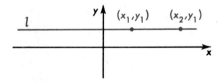

Figure 12-11.

same way, two points are on a line that is parallel to the x-axis, the *ordinates* of these points will be the same. This is so since the ordinate of a point is the distance from that point to the x-axis. But the two points are equidistant from the x-axis; hence, their ordinates must be equal. Therefore, should we label the first (x_1, y_1), the ordinate of the second will also have to be y_1. The abscissa of the second point, however, can not be x_1, for this would signify that the two points were the same distance from the y-axis, which they are not. In view of this we label the abscissa of the second point x_2.

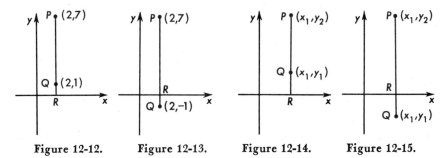

Figure 12-12.   Figure 12-13.   Figure 12-14.   Figure 12-15.

In Figure 12-12 the points P and Q are on a line parallel to the y-axis; hence, their abscissas are the same. To find the distance from Q to P, we must first realize that the ordinate 1 represents the distance RQ, while the ordinate 7 is the distance RP. Thus, by subtracting 1 from 7 we obtain the distance QP. It appears then that

> If two points are on a line parallel to the y-axis, the distance between them can be found by subtracting the ordinate of the first point from that of the second point.

Let us suppose, however, that we had selected P as our first point and Q as the second, then it would appear that the distance from P to Q would be

$$1 - 7 \quad \text{or} \quad -6$$

Thus, we seem to be faced with an inconsistency. Whereas in one case the distance between the points was 6, in the other it was -6! To overcome this difficulty, it has been agreed that,

POSTULATE 34: The distance between two points on a line parallel to the y-axis is the absolute value of the difference of their ordinates; that is, $|y_2 - y_1|$.

Thus, it would make no difference whether P or Q was selected as the first point, for

$$|7 - 1| = |6| = 6 \quad \text{and} \quad |1 - 7| = |-6| = 6$$

In the event you may have forgotten, the absolute value of a number, briefly, is that number devoid of its sign. As in the illustration above, both the absolute value of 6 (written as $|6|$) and the absolute value of -6 is 6.

Is Postulate 34 true, though, for the two points in Figure 12-13 where P is above the x-axis, while Q is below? In this case the distance RP is 7, the distance QR is 1, and, hence, the distance QP is 8. Now it appears that one ordinate is being added to the other rather than being subtracted! This is not so, however, for the ordinate of the first point is -1, and should we express the difference between the ordinate of the second point and that of the first point, it would be

$$|7 - (-1)|$$

From our knowledge of algebra, we realize that we must change the sign of the subtrahend and hence this difference becomes

$$|7 + 1|, \quad \text{or} \quad 8$$

Thus, Postulate 34 applies whether P and Q are on the same side of the x-axis or on opposite sides.

In Figure 12-14 $RQ = y_1$, $RP = y_2$, and, hence,

$$QP = |y_2 - y_1|$$

In Figure 12-15 QP will still be $|y_2 - y_1|$, for as in Figure 12-13 y_1 is a negative value. Therefore, when subtracting y_1 from y_2, its sign will be changed to a positive one and then it will be added to y_2. This is exactly what occured in Figure 12-13. Had both P and Q been placed below the x-axis, we would find that Postulate 34 still held.

The discussion concerning Postulate 34 led to the conclusion that this principle will hold equally well no matter where the points P and Q happened to fall. In general, the selection of the quadrants in which to place the points in any discussion *does not in any way affect the proof of any theorem in analytic geometry.* In view of this, when proving any theorem, we shall always place the points in the first quadrant. By so doing, we reduce the possibility of making errors in the signs of the numbers.

If two points lie on a line that is parallel to the x-axis, their ordinates will be the same. Through an analysis very much the same as that just completed, we realize (see Figure 12-16) that RQ is the abscissa of point Q; that is, 3. RP is the abscissa of point P (10). Hence, the distance QP is $10 - 3$, or 7. In Figure 12-17 this distance is $x_2 - x_1$. How would you find the distance between two points on a line that is parallel to the x-axis?

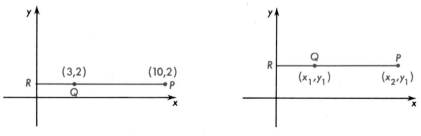

Figure 12-16.   Figure 12-17.

POSTULATE 35: The distance between two points on a line parallel to the

x-axis is the absolute value of the difference of their abscissas; that is, $|x_2 - x_1|$.

Postulates 34 and 35 enable us to find the distance between two points if the points are on a line that is parallel to either axis. But how is the distance between two points found if the points are on a line that is not parallel to either axis? This, we shall investigate now.

THEOREM 71: The distance between two points Q and P with coordinates (x_1, y_1) and (x_2, y_2) is given by the formula

$$d = \sqrt{(x_2 - x_1)^2 + (y_2 - y_1)^2}$$

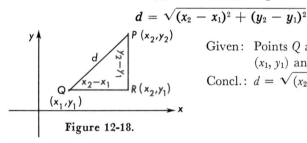

Given: Points Q and P with coordinates (x_1, y_1) and (x_2, y_2)

Concl.: $d = \sqrt{(x_2 - x_1)^2 + (y_2 - y_1)^2}$

Figure 12-18.

ANALYSIS: By drawing lines through P and Q that are parallel to the y and x axes respectively, it can easily be shown that $\angle R$ is a right angle; the proof of this is left for you to do. The abscissa of point R will have to be the same as that of point P since both points are equidistant from the y-axis. Similarly, the ordinate of point R is the same as that of point Q, as both points are equidistant from the x-axis. Hence, the coordinates of R are (x_2, y_1). Since it is possible to find RP and QR by Postulates 34 and 35, we can determine the measure of QP by the theorem of Pythagoras.

PROOF	STATEMENTS	REASONS
1. Let $\overleftrightarrow{PR}$ be the line through P that is parallel to the y-axis.		1. Parallel postulate
2. Let $\overleftrightarrow{QR}$ be the line through Q that is parallel to the x-axis.		2. Same as 1
3. Coordinates of P are (x_2, y_2)		3. Given
4. Coordinates of Q are (x_1, y_1)		4. Given
5. Coordinates of R are (x_2, y_1)		5. See analysis.
6. $\angle R$ is a right angle.		6. Proof left for you to do.
7. $RP = |y_2 - y_1|$		7. Postulate 34
8. $QR = |x_2 - x_1|$		8. Postulate 35
9. $(QR)^2 = (QR)^2 + (RP)^2$		9. Theorem of Pythagoras
10. $d^2 = |x_2 - x_1|^2 + |y_2 - y_1|^2$ or $d = \sqrt{(x_2 - x_1)^2 + (y_2 - y_1)^2}$		10. Substitution postulate

Notice that we did not include the negative sign of the radical when we took the square root of both sides of the equation. The distance between two points will always be considered to be a positive number. Similarly, the absolute bars were dropped from $|x_2 - x_1|^2$ and $|y_2 - y_1|^2$ for the square of any number is always positive.

Illustration 1:

Find the distance between the points $(2, 3)$ and $(-4, 11)$.

METHOD: By the distance formula

$$d = \sqrt{(2 + 4)^2 + (3 - 11)^2}$$
$$d = \sqrt{(6)^2 + (-8)^2}$$
$$d = \sqrt{36 + 64}$$
$$d = \sqrt{100}$$
$$d = 10$$

To save time, we immediately changed the sign of x_1, or -4, and avoided writing the distance in the cumbersome form of

$$d = \sqrt{[2 - (-4)]^2 + (3 - 11)^2}$$

Illustration 2:

Show that the points $(2, 3)$, $(17, 10)$, and $(8, -5)$ are the vertices of an isosceles triangle.

METHOD: By the distance formula

$$d_1 = (17 - 2)^2 + (10 - 3)^2 \qquad d_2 = (17 - 8)^2 + (10 + 5)^2$$
$$= (15)^2 + (7)^2 \qquad\qquad\quad = (7)^2 + (15)^2$$
$$= 274 \qquad\qquad\qquad\qquad = 274$$

Since the measures of two of the sides of the triangle are equal, then by the reverse of the definition of an isosceles triangle we can conclude that the triangle is isosceles.

Our next objective will be to determine the coordinates of the point that divides a line segment with known endpoints into segments whose measures have any desired ratio.

THEOREM 72: **The coordinates of the point that will divide the line segment whose endpoints are (x_1, y_1), (x_2, y_2) into the ratio of $m:n$ are given by the formulas**

$$a = \frac{m\,x_2 + n\,x_1}{m + n}, \qquad b = \frac{m\,y_2 + n\,y_1}{m + n}$$

Figure 12-19.

Given: Points P and Q with coordinates (x_2, y_2) and (x_1, y_1)

$$\frac{QR}{RP} = \frac{m}{n}$$

Concl.: $a = \dfrac{m\,x_2 + n\,x_1}{m + n}$

$b = \dfrac{m\,y_2 + n\,y_1}{m + n}$

ANALYSIS: As in the previous proof, lines are drawn through P parallel to the y-axis and through R and Q parallel to the x-axis. The abscissas of S and T are the same as that of P. The ordinate of S is the same as the ordinate of R, while the ordinate of T is the same as that of Q. The theorem concerning a line being parallel to one side of a triangle and hence dividing the other two sides into two equal ratios will enable us to set up an equation through which we can find the coordinate b.

PROOF | STATEMENTS	REASONS
1. $\dfrac{QR}{RP} = \dfrac{m}{n}$	1. Given
2. $\overleftrightarrow{RS} \parallel \overleftrightarrow{QT}$	2. See analysis.
3. $\dfrac{QR}{RP} = \dfrac{TS}{SP}$	3. If a line is parallel to one side of a triangle, then the ratios of the measures of corresponding segments of the other two sides will be equal.
4. $\dfrac{TS}{SP} = \dfrac{m}{n}$	4. Substitution postulate
5. $TS = b - y_1$† $SP = y_2 - b$†	5. Postulate 34
6. $\dfrac{b - y_1}{y_2 - b} = \dfrac{m}{n}$	6. Same as 4
7. $\therefore nb - ny_1 = my_2 - mb$ $mb + nb = my_2 + ny_1$ $b(m + n) = my_2 + ny_1$ $b = \dfrac{my_2 + ny_1}{m + n}$	7. The product of the means of a proportion is equal to the product of the extremes, and the laws of algebra.

In the same way, had a line been drawn through R parallel to the y-axis, it could have been shown that

$$a = \frac{mx_2 + nx_1}{m + n}$$

Although these formulas may appear quite foreboding, they are really very simple to apply. This will be shown in the following illustration.

Illustration:

Determine the coordinates of the point that will divide the line segment joining the points $(-3, 7)$ and $(4, 1)$ into the ratio of $2:3$. The point $(-3, 7)$ will be one of the endpoints of the smaller segment.

METHOD: The very first thing to do is to draw a rough sketch of the figure. In addition to writing down the coordinates of the two points, write in the

† The absolute bars were not used for both of these numbers are positive.

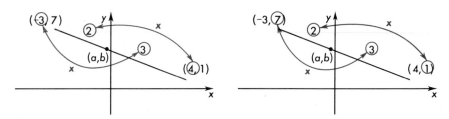

Figure 12-20.   Figure 12-21.

numbers 2 and 3 on those segments that will bear the ratio of 2:3. Then, applying the formula for finding the abscissa, we obtain

$$a = \frac{2(4) + 3(-3)}{2 + 3} = \frac{8 - 9}{5} = \frac{-1}{5}$$

Notice how in Figure 12-20 the arrows point to the numbers that are used in each product. In Figure 12-21 we see that the value of the ordinate, b, is found in the very same way.

$$b = \frac{2(1) + 3(7)}{2 + 3} = \frac{2 + 21}{5} = 4\tfrac{3}{5}$$

Hence, the coordinates of the point are $(\tfrac{-1}{5}, 4\tfrac{3}{5})$

Probably the most important application of Theorem 72 is to enable us to determine the coordinates of the midpoint of a line segment when the coordinates of the endpoints of the line segment are known.

THEOREM 73: **The coordinates of the midpoint of a line segment whose endpoints are (x_1, y_1) and (x_2, y_2) are given by the formulas**

$$a = \frac{x_1 + x_2}{2}, \qquad b = \frac{y_1 + y_2}{2}$$

ANALYSIS: Since the point (a, b) is the midpoint of the line segment, the values of m and n in the formulas given in Theorem 72 are identically the same. Hence, the ratio of $\frac{m}{n}$ can be written as $\frac{m}{m}$, or $\frac{1}{1}$. When we replace m and n by 1 and 1 in the formulas of Theorem 72, they become

$$a = \frac{1x_2 + 1x_1}{1 + 1} = \frac{x_2 + x_1}{2}$$

$$b = \frac{1y_2 + 1y_1}{1 + 1} = \frac{y_2 + y_1}{2}$$

Illustration:

If $A(-4, 3)$, $B(-7, 1)$, and $C(-9, -3)$ are the vertices of a triangle, determine the length of the median from A to $\overline{BC}$.

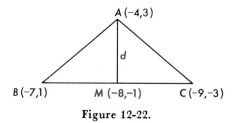

Figure 12-22.

METHOD: As always, a rough sketch is made of the figure; notice that there is no need to draw the coordinate axes. Finding the coordinates of M can be done mentally by adding -7 to -9, then dividing this sum by 2. Similarly, adding 1 to -3 gives us a sum of -2; dividing this by 2, we obtain the -1 that is shown as the ordinate of the midpoint. The length of the median, $\overline{AM}$, is simply the distance from A to M. This is found by using the distance formula.

$$d = \sqrt{(-4 + 8)^2 + (3 + 1)^2} = \sqrt{(4)^2 + (4)^2}$$
$$d = \sqrt{16 + 16} = \sqrt{32}$$
$$d = 4\sqrt{2}$$

Before giving you an opportunity to apply the formulas just developed, we would like to illustrate the power of our new tool. Although we have but scratched the surface of coordinate geometry, it is possible for us to prove at this early stage that the diagonals of a parallelogram bisect each other.

METHOD:

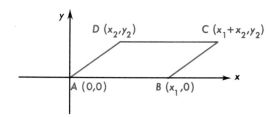

Figure 12-23.

Since we are free to place the parallelogram in any position we desire, it is best to so place it that one vertex will be at the origin, while one side will lie along the x-axis. Vertex B is labeled as $(x_1, 0)$. Turning next to point D, since it has no relation to point A, we express its coordinates as (x_2, y_2). With point C, however, we must be more careful. Since its distance from the x-axis is the same as that of point D, its ordinate must also be y_2. Being a parallelogram, the length of $\overline{DC}$ must be the same as that of $\overline{AB}$. But $AB = x_1$. In order that DC be equal to x_1 also, the abscissa of C will have to be $x_1 + x_2$. By applying Postulate 35, page 385, the length of $\overline{DC}$ can be verified as being x_1.

By the midpoint formulas

$$\text{coordinates of the midpoint of } \overline{DB} \text{ are } \left(\frac{x_1 + x_2}{2}, \frac{y_2}{2}\right)$$

$$\text{coordinates of the midpoint of } \overline{AC} \text{ are } \left(\frac{x_1 + x_2}{2}, \frac{y_2}{2}\right)$$

Hence, $\overline{DB}$ and $\overline{AC}$ bisect each other.

Your first reaction to this "proof" is very likely to be a shrug of your shoulders followed by a long period of bewildered silence. Let's backstep to see just what has been accomplishèd. We have shown that the midpoint of $\overline{DB}$ is exactly the same point as the midpoint of $\overline{AC}$. Hence, this point is common to the two line segments. This, in turn, implies that these segments must intersect at each of their midpoints. Therefore, they bisect each other!

EXERCISES

1. Determine the distance between each of the following pairs of points. Leave answers in radical form unless you have a square root table available.
    (a) $(6, 8)$, $(6, 12)$ (b) $(-5, -2)$, $(-1, -2)$
    (c) $(-2, -15)$, $(4, -7)$ (d) $(-14, 2)$, $(-2, -3)$
    (e) $(0, 7)$, $(-6, 4)$ (f) $(-5a, a)$, $(3a, a)$

2. (a) Find the distance from the point $(-12, 5)$ to the origin.
    (b) Find the lengths of the sides of a triangle whose vertices are $(2, 4)$, $(6, 1)$, $(11, 13)$.
    (c) Find the lengths of the sides of a triangle whose vertices are $(-3, 5)$, $(2, 0)$, $(-1, -2)$.

3. Show that the points $(-5, 2)$, $(7, 4)$, and $(2, -3)$ are the vertices of an isosceles triangle.

4. Show that the points $(-3, 7)$, $(3, -1)$, and $(4, 6)$ are the vertices of a right triangle. (See problem 8, page 370.)

5. Show that the diagonals of a rectangle whose vertices are $(0, 0)$, $(0, 6)$, $(8, 6)$, and $(8, 0)$ are congruent.

6. (a) Find the fourth vertex of the rectangle if three of its vertices are $(0, 0)$, $(a, 0)$, and $(0, b)$.
    (b) Prove that the diagonals of this rectangle are congruent.

7. Determine the coordinates of the midpoint of each of the following line segments.
    (a) $(0, 0)$, $(8, 6)$ (b) $(5, 4)$, $(11, 14)$
    (c) $(-2, 7)$, $(6, 3)$ (d) $(-9, -4)$, $(-1, 6)$

(e) (5, 8), (14, 17)   (f) (−3, 9), (−2, −12)

(g) (−7, −10), (−7, −1)   (h) (−a, −b), (0, 0)

(i) (a, b), (2a, −2b)

8. The vertices of a triangle are (−2, 6), (0, 10), and (8, −3). Find the midpoint of each of the sides.

9. The vertices of a triangle are $A(6, 4)$, $B(2, 1)$, and $C(8, 1)$.

(a) Find the lengths of the sides of the triangle.

(b) Find the coordinates of the midpoint of $\overline{BC}$.

(c) Find the length of the median from A to $\overline{BC}$.

10. The line segment joining the points (6, 14) and (2, −2) is divided into four congruent parts. Find the coordinates of the points of division.

11. The vertices of the parallelogram $ABCD$ are $A(−1, 4)$, $B(2, 8)$, $C(7, 3)$, and $D(4, −1)$. Find the point at which the diagonals bisect each other.

12. One endpoint of a line segment is (7, −2), while the coordinates of the midpoint are (1, −5). Find the coordinates of the other endpoint.

13. The line segment with endpoints $A(3, −2)$ and $B(−5, 6)$ is extended its own length through point B to point C. What are the coordinates of point C?

14. $A(3, 5)$ is the midpoint of the diagonals of a parallelogram. If $B(−5, 2)$ and $C(7, −4)$ are two of the vertices of this parallelogram, find the coordinates of the other two vertices.

15. Find the coordinates of the point that will divide each of the following line segments into the ratio indicated. The ratio will be of the measure of the left segment to the measure of the right segment.

(a) (0, 0), (5, 0); 2:3   (b) (6, 10), (12, −2); 1:2

(c) (−2, 5), (6, −4); 3:1   (d) (−10, −8), (2, −3); 5:2

(e) (−6, 0), (−5, 10); 3:5   (f) (−5, 4), (3, 4); 2:1

16. The vertices of a triangle are $A(5, 8)$, $B(1, −2)$, and $C(7, 6)$.

(a) Find the coordinates of the midpoints of $\overline{AB}$ and $\overline{AC}$.

(b) Find the length of the line segment joining the midpoints of $\overline{AB}$ and $\overline{AC}$.

(c) Find the length of $\overline{BC}$.

(d) What conclusion can you draw in terms of your answers to b and c?

17. Using $A(2x_2, 2y_2)$, $B(0, 0)$, and $C(2x_1, 0)$ as the vertices of a triangle, prove that the measure of the line segment joining the midpoints of the sides $\overline{AB}$ and $\overline{AC}$ is equal to one-half the measure of side $\overline{BC}$.

18. The vertices of an isosceles trapezoid are $A(0, 0)$, $B(12, 0)$, $C(10, 6)$, and $D(2, 6)$.

   (a) Show that the measure of the line segment joining the midpoints of the nonparallel sides is equal to one-half the sum of the measures of the bases. (This line segment is called the median of a trapezoid.)

   (b) Show that the diagonals of this trapezoid are congruent.

   (c) Show that the line segment joining A to the midpoint of $\overline{BC}$ is congruent to the line segment joining B to the midpoint of $\overline{AD}$.

   (d) Show that the line segments joining the midpoints of the sides in order form a parallelogram. (Hint: Use Theorem 40.)

19. $A(0, 0)$, $B(6, 4)$, and $C(8, 2)$ are the vertices of a triangle.

   (a) What are the coordinates of the point that divides the median from A to $\overline{BC}$ into the ratio of $2:1$? (The ratio is taken in the direction from A to $\overline{BC}$.)

   (b) Determine the coordinates of the point that divides the median from B to $\overline{AC}$ into the ratio of $2:1$.

   (c) Determine the coordinates of the point that divides the median from C to $\overline{AB}$ into the ratio of $2:1$.

   (d) In view of the answers that you have found for a, b, and c, what conclusion seems to be true concerning the medians of a triangle?

20.* **(a)** Following the method used in Problem 19, prove that the medians of a triangle are concurrent; that is, that they meet at a point. (Hint: Use (x_1, y_1), (x_2, y_2), and (x_3, y_3) as the vertices of the triangle.)

   (b) After examining the coordinates of the point of concurrency that you have found in answer to (a), formulate a statement expressing how to determine the coordinates of the point of concurrency of the medians of any triangle if the coordinates of the vertices are known.

21. **(a)** $A(-10, -3)$ and $B(5, 7)$ are two points. Find the coordinates of a third point, P, on the segment AB such that $AP:PB = 2:3$.

   (b) Find the coordinates of a third point, Q, on the line AB but not on the segment AB such that $AQ:QB = 2:3$. The point P found in (a) is said to divide the line segment *internally* into the ratio of $2:3$, while the point Q found now divides the line segment *externally* into the ratio of $2:3$.

22. The vertices of an isosceles triangle are given by the points $A(0, 0)$, $B(4a, 0)$, $C(2a, 2b)$.

   (a) Which of the three points A, B, and C are the endpoints of the base?

   (b) Prove that the medians to the legs of this isosceles triangle are congruent.

   (c) Prove that the line segments from the midpoint of the base to the midpoints of the legs are congruent.

   (d) Can you give any reason why the coordinates of the vertices in this problem were chosen as they were?

23. Two of the vertices of an equilateral triangle are $(0, 0)$ and $(2a, 0)$. What will the coordinates of the third vertex have to be if it falls in the first quadrant?

Parallelism and Perpendicularity

   Two of the important topics discussed in synthetic geometry concerned themselves with parallelism and perpendicularity of two lines. We would like to take another look at these topics, but from an analytic standpoint. This can be done, though, only after an understanding of the term *slope* has been established.

   We have often heard people speak of a hill as having a "steep" slope or a "gradual" slope; yet precisely what did they mean? Are the slopes of the hills in Figures 12-24 and 12-25 "steeper" than that of Figure 12-26?

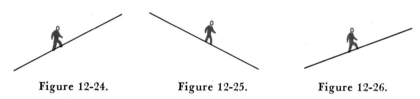

| Figure 12-24. | Figure 12-25. | Figure 12-26. |

Is it possible to distinguish between the slopes of the hills in Figures 12-24 and 12-25; that is, in Figure 12-24 we seem to be going uphill, while in Figure 12-25 our direction is downhill? To answer these questions, the mathematician has defined the slope of a hill in terms of a ratio:

$$\text{slope of a hill} = \frac{\text{rise}}{\text{run}}$$

   Let us examine our three hills to see exactly what this means. The "rise" of a hill is the change in our vertical position as we move from the bottom to the top of the hill or from the top to the bottom. The "run" is the distance we moved horizontally in traveling from the bottom to the top of the hill or from the top to the bottom. By measuring the "rise" and "run" in Figure 12-27 we discover that the "rise," or vertical change, is only two

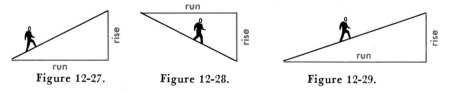

| Figure 12-27. | Figure 12-28. | Figure 12-29. |

units, while the "run," or horizontal change, is four units. Hence, we say that the slope of the hill in Figure 12-27 is

$$\text{slope}_1 = \frac{\text{rise}}{\text{run}} = \frac{2}{4} = \frac{1}{2}$$

In the same way, by measuring the "rise" and "run" in Figure 12-29 we note that they are 2 units and 6 units respectively, and, hence, the slope of that hill is

$$\text{slope}_3 = \frac{\text{rise}}{\text{run}} = \frac{2}{6} = \frac{1}{3}$$

In terms of these numbers, we can conclude that the slope of the first hill is greater than that of the third, for the fraction $\frac{1}{2}$ is greater than $\frac{1}{3}$.

The hill in Figure 12-28 presents a bit of a problem, for here the "rise" is actually negative. In going from the top of the hill to the bottom, the vertical position of the person has *decreased* two units, while his horizontal position has *increased* four units. Thus, the slope becomes

$$\text{slope}_2 = \frac{\text{rise}}{\text{run}} = \frac{-2}{4} = \frac{-1}{2}$$

Hence, it appears that the "rise" may be either positive or negative depending on whether the vertical change has been positive or negative. This, in turn, will determine the sign of the slope.

Now, how does all this tie in with our coordinate system? Rather than

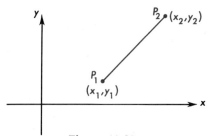

Figure 12-30.

considering hills and their slopes, we now investigate line segments and their slopes. Hence, we must ask ourselves two questions:

(1) How great is the "rise" between P_1 and P_2; that is, what is the extent of the vertical change?

(2) How great is the "run" between P_1 and P_2; that is, what is the extent of the horizontal change?

To answer both of these questions it is necessary to find the coordinates of the point where the line through P_2 parallel to the y-axis intersects the line through P_1 that is parallel to the x-axis.

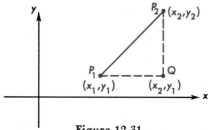

Figure 12-31.

Examining this diagram, we realize that the coordinates of Q will have to be (x_2, y_1). From this it follows that the "run" must be $(x_2 - x_1)$, while the "rise" is $(y_2 - y_1)$. This brings us to the point where we can safely formulate the definition of the slope of a line segment.

DEFINITION 70: The slope of a line segment whose endpoints are (x_1, y_1) and (x_2, y_2) is defined by the formula

$$m = \frac{y_2 - y_1}{x_2 - x_1}$$

Notice that this definition says no more than does our earlier description in terms of the "rise" and "run" of a hill. The letter "m" was used to represent the word slope; this is common practice. Also, in more advanced courses in mathematics you will find the symbol Δy (read delta y) replacing $y_2 - y_1$. Similarly, Δx is used to replace $x_2 - x_1$. Thus, all three of the expressions below represent the slope of a line segment.

$$m = \frac{y_2 - y_1}{x_2 - x_1} = \frac{\Delta y}{\Delta x}$$

Illustration:

If $A(3, 5)$, $B(-2, 7)$, and $C(8, -3)$ are the vertices of a triangle, then find the slope of the median from A to $\overline{BC}$.

METHOD: By applying the midpoint formula, we find that the coordinates of the midpoint of $\overline{BC}$ are

$$x_m = (-2 + 8)/2 = 3$$
$$y_m = (7 - 3)/2 = 2$$

Therefore the slope of the median from A to $\overline{BC}$ is

$$m = (y_2 - y_1)/(x_2 - x_1)$$
$$= (3 - 5)/(2 - 3)$$
$$= 2$$

Now we are prepared to prove several theorems on parallelism and perpendicularity.

THEOREM 74: **The slope of the line segment joining any two points on a line is equal to the slope of the line segment joining any other two points on the line.**

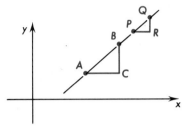

Given: $\overset{\leftrightarrow}{PR} \parallel \overset{\leftrightarrow}{AC} \parallel x$-axis

$\overset{\leftrightarrow}{QR} \parallel \overset{\leftrightarrow}{BC} \parallel y$-axis

Concl.: $\dfrac{BC}{AC} = \dfrac{QR}{PR}$

Figure 12-32.

ANALYSIS: The slope of the line segment AB is given by the ratio $\dfrac{BC}{AC}$, while that of PQ is the ratio $\dfrac{QR}{PR}$. By proving the triangles similar we can show the slopes to be equal.

PROOF

The proof is left for you to do.

Theorem 74 enables us to prove that if we start with a line, the slope of the line segment joining any two points will be equal to the slope of the line segment joining any other two points. Equally as important to us is a question closely related to this. It is, "Under what conditions will points be collinear?" This we plan to answer by the next theorem.

THEOREM 75: **Three points are collinear if the slope of the line segment joining two of the points is equal to the slope of the line segment joining either of these points to the third point.**

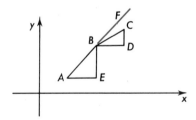

Given: $\overset{\leftrightarrow}{CD} \parallel \overset{\leftrightarrow}{BE} \parallel y$-axis

$\overset{\leftrightarrow}{BD} \parallel \overset{\leftrightarrow}{AE} \parallel x$-axis

$\dfrac{BE}{AE} = \dfrac{CD}{BD}$

Concl.: A, B, and C are collinear.

Figure 12-33.

ANALYSIS: The proof will be of the indirect variety. By assuming that A, B, and C are not collinear, we will be led to the inconsistency that $\angle FBD \cong \angle CBD$ and $\angle FBD \ncong \angle CBD$.

PROOF

By the law of the excluded middle one of the following statements must be true and no other possibility exists:

A, B, and C are collinear.

or

A, B, and C are not collinear.

Let us accept the possibility that A, B, and C are not collinear. Extend $\overleftrightarrow{AB}$ to some point F; in doing so $\overleftrightarrow{AB}$ will not pass through C, since we have accepted the possibility that A, B, and C are not collinear. Since $\overleftrightarrow{BD}$ is parallel to $\overleftrightarrow{AE}$, $\angle FBD \cong \angle BAE$. However, $\triangle BDC \sim \triangle AEB$ by the S.A.S. theorem on similarity; hence $\angle CBD \cong \angle BAE$. Therefore, it follows that $\angle FBD \cong \angle CBD$. However, from the postulate that the whole is greater than any of its parts, $m \angle FBD > m \angle CBD$. Thus, accepting the possibility that A, B, and C were not collinear has led to the logical inconsistency of the truth of both $\angle FBD \cong \angle CBD$ and $\angle FBD \ncong \angle CBD$. By the law of contradiction both cannot be true at the same time. Since $\angle FBD \ncong \angle CBD$ must be true as the result of a postulate, $\angle FBD \cong \angle CBD$ must be false, and, therefore, the statement "A, B, and C are not collinear" is also false. Hence, the statement "A, B, and C are collinear" is true, for it is the only remaining possibility.

Illustration:

Are the points $A(2, 1)$, $B(5, 0)$, and $C(26, -7)$ collinear?

METHOD: By applying Theorem 75 to show that the slope of $\overline{AB}$ is equal to the slope of $\overline{BC}$, we will be able to conclude that A, B, and C are collinear.

$$\text{slope of } \overline{AB} = m_1 = \frac{0 - 1}{5 - 2} = \frac{-1}{3}$$

$$\text{slope of } \overline{BC} = m_2 = \frac{-7 - 0}{26 - 5} = \frac{-7}{21} = \frac{-1}{3}$$

$\therefore m_1 = m_2$; hence, A, B, and C are collinear.

DEFINITION 71: The slope of a line is the slope of the line segment joining any two points on that line.

In view of Theorem 74 do you see why it is possible to say that the slope of a line is the slope of the line segment joining *any* two points rather than two *specific* points on the line?

THEOREM 76: If two lines are parallel, their slopes are equal.

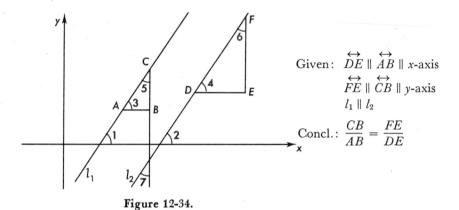

Given: $\overleftrightarrow{DE} \parallel \overleftrightarrow{AB} \parallel x$-axis

$\overleftrightarrow{FE} \parallel \overleftrightarrow{CB} \parallel y$-axis

$l_1 \parallel l_2$

Concl.: $\dfrac{CB}{AB} = \dfrac{FE}{DE}$

Figure 12-34.

ANALYSIS: As in the proof of Theorem 74, the slopes can be shown to be equal by proving $\triangle ABC \sim \triangle DEF$.

PROOF	(The reasons will be left for you to supply.)

1. $\overleftrightarrow{DE} \parallel \overleftrightarrow{AB} \parallel x$-axis
2. $\angle 3 \cong \angle 1$ and $\angle 4 \cong \angle 2$
3. $l_1 \parallel l_2$
4. $\angle 1 \cong \angle 2$
5. $\angle 3 \cong \angle 4$ (a)
6. $\angle 5 \cong \angle 7$

7. $\overleftrightarrow{FE} \parallel \overleftrightarrow{CB}$
8. $\angle 6 \cong \angle 7$
9. $\angle 5 \cong \angle 6$ (a)
10. $\therefore \triangle ABC \sim \triangle DEF$
11. $\dfrac{CB}{AB} = \dfrac{FE}{DE}$

THEOREM 77: If two lines have equal slopes, the lines are parallel.

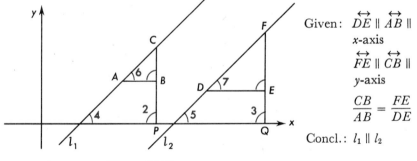

Given: $\overleftrightarrow{DE} \parallel \overleftrightarrow{AB} \parallel$ x-axis

$\overleftrightarrow{FE} \parallel \overleftrightarrow{CB} \parallel$ y-axis

$\dfrac{CB}{AB} = \dfrac{FE}{DE}$

Concl.: $l_1 \parallel l_2$

Figure 12-35.

ANALYSIS: l_1 will be shown parallel to l_2 by proving $\angle 4 \cong \angle 5$. To do this, the two angles will be shown congruent to $\angle$ 6 and 7 respectively. Hence, the proof revolves around the need to show that $\angle 6$ and $\angle 7$ are congruent. This can be done by proving $\triangle ABC \sim \triangle DEF$.

| **PROOF** | (The reasons will be left for you to supply.) |

1. $\overleftrightarrow{FE} \parallel \overleftrightarrow{CB}$
2. $\angle 2 \cong \angle 3$
3. $\overleftrightarrow{DE} \parallel \overleftrightarrow{AB} \parallel$ x-axis
4. $\angle ABC \cong \angle 2$ and $\angle DEF \cong \angle 3$
5. $\angle ABC \cong \angle DEF$ (a)
6. $\dfrac{CB}{AB} = \dfrac{FE}{DE}$

7. $\triangle ABC \sim \triangle DEF$
8. $\angle 6 \cong \angle 7$
9. $\angle 4 \cong \angle 6,\ \angle 5 \cong \angle 7$
10. $\therefore\ \angle 4 \cong \angle 5$
11. $\therefore\ l_1 \parallel l_2$

Illustration:

$A(-2, -5)$, $B(4, -7)$, $C(10, 9)$, and $D(-8, 13)$ are the vertices of a quadrilateral. Prove that the line joining the midpoints of $\overline{AB}$ and $\overline{BC}$ is parallel to the line joining the midpoints of $\overline{CD}$ and $\overline{DA}$.

METHOD: A sketch is made of the figure, and the coordinates of the midpoints are written on the diagram *at sight*.

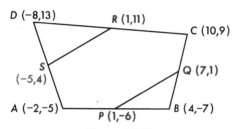

Figure 12-36.

$$\text{slope of } \overleftrightarrow{SR} = m_1 = \frac{11 - 4}{1 + 5} = \frac{7}{6}$$

$$\text{slope of } \overleftrightarrow{PQ} = m_2 = \frac{1 + 6}{7 - 1} = \frac{7}{6}$$

$\therefore\ m_1 = m_2$; hence, by Theorem 77 the lines are parallel.

It should be pointed out that it does not matter which of the points is considered the first point and which is the second. In either event the slope of the line segment will be the same. Thus, in the illustration above we found the slope of $\overleftrightarrow{SR}$ by considering S as the first point and R as the second. Had this been reversed, we would have obtained,

$$\text{slope of } \overleftrightarrow{RS} = m = \frac{4 - 11}{-5 - 1} = \frac{-7}{-6} = \frac{7}{6}$$

Thus, the slope of $\overleftrightarrow{SR}$ is the same as that of $\overleftrightarrow{RS}$.

When the slope of one line is $\frac{3}{4}$, while another is $\frac{4}{3}$, the slope of the second is said to be the *reciprocal* of the slope of the first, for the fraction $\frac{4}{3}$ is the reciprocal of $\frac{3}{4}$. Similarly, if the slope of one line is $\frac{2}{5}$ and the other $-\frac{5}{2}$, then the second slope is the *negative reciprocal* of the slope of the first. Thus, to find the negative reciprocal of a fraction, it is simply a matter of inverting the fraction and changing its sign. This information is needed for the next theorem. What is the negative reciprocal of $\frac{5}{9}$? Of $\frac{-3}{7}$? Of $-\frac{7}{4}$?

THEOREM 78: If two lines are perpendicular, the slope of one is the negative reciprocal of the slope of the other.

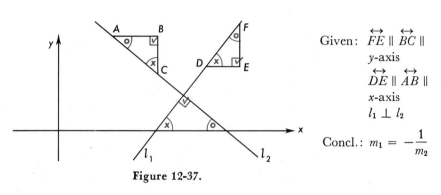

Given: $\overleftrightarrow{FE} \parallel \overleftrightarrow{BC} \parallel$
y-axis

$\overleftrightarrow{DE} \parallel \overleftrightarrow{AB} \parallel$
x-axis

$l_1 \perp l_2$

Concl.: $m_1 = -\dfrac{1}{m_2}$

Figure 12-37.

ANALYSIS AND PROOF: By showing that the corresponding angles are congruent as marked in the diagram, it can be proved $\triangle FED \sim \triangle ABC$, and, hence, it would follow that

$$\frac{FE}{DE} = \frac{AB}{CB} \tag{1}$$

Fortunately, $\dfrac{FE}{DE}$ is the slope of l_1, and, therefore, is m_1.

Thus, $$\frac{FE}{DE} = m_1 \tag{2}$$

The slope of l_2, however, involves more difficulty, for this slope is negative since the "rise" is a negative quantity. By placing a negative sign in front of m_2, it will become positive and, hence, have the same sign as $\dfrac{CB}{AB}$.

$$\therefore \frac{CB}{AB} = -m_2$$

$$\text{or } \frac{AB}{CB} = -\frac{1}{m_2} \tag{3}$$

Hence, by substituting both (2) and (3) in (1), we obtain

$$m_1 = -\frac{1}{m_2}$$

THEOREM 79: **If the slope of one line is the negative reciprocal of the slope of a second line, the lines are perpendicular.**

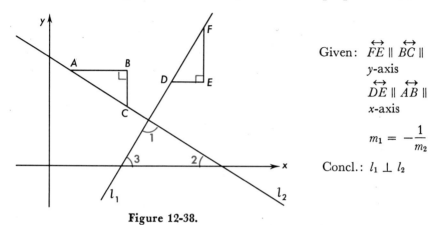

Given: $\overleftrightarrow{FE} \parallel \overleftrightarrow{BC} \parallel$
y-axis

$\overleftrightarrow{DE} \parallel \overleftrightarrow{AB} \parallel$
x-axis

$m_1 = -\dfrac{1}{m_2}$

Concl.: $l_1 \perp l_2$

Figure 12-38.

ANALYSIS: In a manner similar to that used in the proof of Theorem 77 we can show $\triangle FED \sim \triangle ABC$. Then to prove $l_1 \perp l_2$, $\angle 1$ will be shown to be congruent to $\angle E$, which is a right angle. Why is $\angle E$ a right angle? With $\angle 1$ a right angle, the lines will be perpendicular.

PROOF		(The reasons will be left for you to supply.)

Since the triangles are similar,	$\angle F \cong \angle A$
But $\overleftrightarrow{AB} \parallel$ x-axis, $\therefore$	$\angle 2 \cong \angle A$
Hence,	$\angle F \cong \angle 2$ (a)
But $\overleftrightarrow{DE} \parallel$ x-axis, $\therefore$	$\angle D \cong \angle 3$ (a)
Hence,	$\angle 1 \cong \angle E$
But,	$\angle E$ is a right angle.
$\therefore$	$\angle 1$ is a right angle.
Hence,	$l_1 \perp l_2$

Illustration:

Show that the diagonals of the rhombus whose vertices are $A(0, 0)$, $B(10, 0)$, $C(16, 8)$, and $D(6, 8)$ are perpendicular to each other.

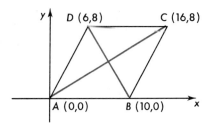

Figure 12-39.

METHOD: Using Figure 12-39, we find the slopes of $\overleftrightarrow{AC}$ and $\overleftrightarrow{DB}$ to see if one is the negative reciprocal of the other.

$$\text{slope of } \overleftrightarrow{AC} = m_1 = \frac{8-0}{16-0} = \frac{1}{2}$$

$$\text{slope of } \overleftrightarrow{DB} = m_2 = \frac{0-8}{10-6} = \frac{-8}{4} = \frac{-2}{1}$$

$$\therefore m_1 = -\frac{1}{m_2}; \text{ hence, by Theorem 79, } \overleftrightarrow{AC} \perp \overleftrightarrow{DB}.$$

There are several rather important omissions that we have made when discussing the slope of a line in the coordinate plane. These concern the slopes of lines that are parallel to either the x- or y-axis.

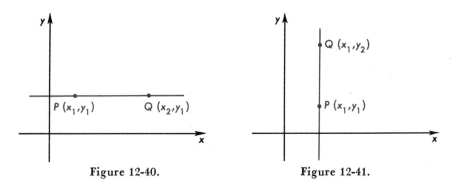

Figure 12-40.   **Figure 12-41.**

In Figure 12-40 we see that the slope of the line segment joining the points P and Q will be

$$m = \frac{y_1 - y_1}{x_2 - x_1} = \frac{0}{x_2 - x_1}$$

This will be interpreted to mean that there is *no* "rise" or vertical change in the line for any two points that may be selected on the line. That is, no matter how many units the abscissa may increase between two points on the line, the ordinate will not increase at all. In view of this, we will express a slope such as this in its simplest form of

$$\frac{0}{1}$$

for, as was said, whether x increases 1 unit or 1,000 units between two points on this line, the increase in y between these same two points will always remain 0.

Similarly, in Figure 12-41

$$m = \frac{y_2 - y_1}{x_1 - x_1} = \frac{y_2 - y_1}{0}$$

As before, this will simply be interpreted to mean that no matter how many units the ordinate may change between two points on this line, the change in the abscissa will always remain 0. As before, the simplest way of expressing a slope whose denominator is zero will be in the form of

$$\frac{1}{0}$$

We must impress upon you the fact that $\frac{1}{0}$ is *not* to be interpreted as a division problem, *for division by zero is impossible.* It should be interpreted only in terms of a "rise" and "run," as was done in the preceding paragraph.

The negative reciprocal of $\frac{1}{0}$ will be considered to be $\frac{-0}{1}$. Similarly, the negative reciprocal of $\frac{0}{1}$ will be $\frac{-1}{0}$. This interpretation will simplify a number of problems we will encounter.

EXERCISES

1. Determine the slope of the line that passes through each of the following pairs of points:

   (a) $(0, 0)$, $(5, 4)$ (b) $(0, 0)$, $(-3, 6)$
   (c) $(2, 5)$, $(10, 14)$ (d) $(-3, 4)$, $(6, -8)$
   (e) $(0, 4)$, $(8, -6)$ (f) $(5, -7)$, $(2, -10)$
   (g) $(-4, -3)$, $(-1, -8)$ (h) $(3, 7)$, $(9, 7)$

2. Find the slope of the line that is perpendicular to the line that passes through each of the following pairs of points:

   (a) $(2, 3)$, $(5, 14)$ (b) $(-4, 7)$, $(1, -6)$ (c) $(-8, -5)$, $(-2, -10)$

3. Which of the following sets of points are collinear?

   (a) $(0, -7)$, $(3, -1)$, $(-2, -11)$
   (b) $(0, 3)$, $(15, -8)$, $(-12, 10)$

4. What conclusion can be drawn concerning a line whose slope is 0?

5. $A(8, 6)$, $B(0, 0)$, and $C(12, 2)$ are the vertices of a triangle.

    (a) What is the slope of the line through C parallel to $\overleftrightarrow{AB}$?

    (b) What is the slope of the altitude from B to $\overline{AC}$?

    (c) What is the slope of the median from C to $\overline{AB}$?

    (d) What is the slope of the perpendicular bisector of $\overline{AB}$?

6. $A(1, 5)$, $B(5, 9)$, and $C(11, 1)$ are the vertices of a triangle.

    (a) Find the midpoints of $\overline{AB}$, $\overline{AC}$, and $\overline{BC}$.

    (b) Show that the line joining the midpoints of $\overline{AB}$ and $\overline{AC}$ is parallel to $\overleftrightarrow{BC}$.

    (c) Show that the line joining the midpoints of $\overline{AC}$ and $\overline{BC}$ is parallel to $\overleftrightarrow{AB}$.

7. $R(-2, 5)$, $S(0, 11)$, and $T(-6, -7)$ are the vertices of a triangle. Show that the line passing through the midpoints of $\overline{SR}$ and $\overline{ST}$ is parallel to $\overleftrightarrow{RT}$.

8. Prove that the line passing through the midpoints of two sides of a triangle is parallel to the third side. (Hint: Use the coordinates $(2a, 2b)$, $(2c, 2d)$, and $(2e, 2f)$ as the vertices of the triangle.)

9. Show that the line segments joining the points $(-4, -3)$, $(8, 2)$, $(11, 6)$, and $(-1, 1)$ taken in order form a parallelogram. (Hint: Use the reverse of the definition of a parallelogram.)

10. Show that the vertices in each of the problems below are the vertices of a right triangle. Do *not* use the distance formula.

    (a) $(5, 2)$, $(8, 9)$, $(10, 4)$ **(b)** $(-3, 1)$, $(-1, 20)$, $(5, 4)$

11. $A(-12, 0)$, $B(2, 0)$, $C(1, 5)$, and $D(-11, 5)$ are the vertices of an isosceles trapezoid.

    (a) Show that the line that passes through the midpoints of the non-parallel sides is parallel to the bases.

    (b) Show that the line that passes through the midpoints of the parallel sides is perpendicular to them.

12. (a) If $A(0, 0)$, $B(12, 0)$, and $D(2, 5)$ are three vertices of an isosceles trapezoid in which $\overleftrightarrow{AB}$ is the lower base, find the fourth vertex C so that the vertices will read in the order A, B, C, and D.

    (b) If $A(0, 0)$, $B(2a, 0)$, and $D(2b, 2c)$ are three vertices of an isosceles trapezoid where $\overleftrightarrow{AB}$ is the lower base, write the coordinates of the fourth vertex C so that the vertices will read in the order A, B, C, and D.

(c) Using the vertices in b, prove that the median of a trapezoid is parallel to the bases and equal to one-half their sum. (See Problem 18, page 392.)

13. $A(0, 0)$, $B(8, 0)$, $C(12, -6)$, and $D(-4, -4)$ are the vertices of a quadrilateral.

(a) Show that if the midpoints of the sides are joined in order, the quadrilateral will be a parallelogram.

(b) Show that if line segments are drawn between pairs of opposite midpoints, these line segments will bisect each other.

14. Prove that if the midpoints of the sides of any quadrilateral are joined in order, the quadrilateral formed will be a parallelogram. (Hint: Use $(2x_1, 2y_1)$, $(2x_2, 2y_2)$, $(2x_3, 2y_3)$, $(2x_4, 2y_4)$ as the vertices of the quadrilateral.)

15. $A(0, 0)$, $B(8, 0)$, $C(10, 4)$, and $D(2, 4)$ are the vertices of a parallelogram. If segments are drawn from B to M, the midpoint of $\overline{DC}$, and from D to N, the midpoint of $\overline{AB}$, then $BMDN$ will be a parallelogram.

16. $ABCD$ is a parallelogram where M and N are the midpoints of $\overline{DC}$ and $\overline{AB}$ respectively. Prove that $BMDN$ is a parallelogram. (Hint: Use $(0, 0)$, $(2a, 0)$, and $(2b, 2c)$ as the coordinates of A, B, and D; then find the coordinates for C in the same manner as you had for Problem 12b.)

17. The coordinates of a parallelogram are $A(3, 6)$, $B(6, 6)$, $C(12, 15)$, and $D(9, 15)$. Prove that if segments are drawn from D to the trisection points of $\overline{AC}$ and from B to these same points, that the quadrilateral formed will be a parallelogram.

18. Prove that if segments are drawn from a pair of opposite vertices of a parallelogram to the trisection points of the diagonal joining the remaining vertices, the quadrilateral formed will be a parallelogram. (Hint: Use $(0, 0)$, $(3a, 0)$, and $(3b, 3c)$ for the vertices A, B, and D; then find the coordinates of vertex C.)

■ Test and Review

1. Represent each of the following statements by an equation:

(a) The ordinate of a point is always 5.

(b) The abscissa of a point is always -7.

(c) The ordinate of a point is always equal to twice the abscissa.

(d) The abscissa of a point is always less than 10.

(e) The sum of the square of the abscissa and the square of the ordinate is always 25.

2. (a) A set of points lie on a line perpendicular to the y-axis. Which of the coordinates is the same for all points of the set?

   (b) How could you give a description for the points in this set by using symbols?

3. Determine the distance between each of the following pairs of points. Leave your answers in radical form.

   (a) $(3, 7)$, $(9, 2)$ (b) $(-5, -6)$, $(8, -3)$

4. Determine the coordinates of the midpoints of the line segments whose endpoints are

   (a) $(-2, -9)$, $(8, -3)$ (b) $(5a, b)$, $(2a, 3b)$

5. Find the coordinates of the point that will divide each of the following line segments into the ratio indicated. The ratio will be the measure of the left segment to the measure of the right segment.

   (a) $(0, 3)$, $(7, 12)$; $2:1$ (b) $(-5, 1)$, $(-2, -3)$; $1:4$

6. The three vertices of a triangle are $A(0, 2)$, $B(4, 10)$, and $C(12, -4)$.

   (a) Find the length of $\overline{AB}$.

   (b) Find the coordinates of the midpoint of $\overline{BC}$.

   (c) Find the length of the median from A to $\overline{BC}$.

   (d) Find the length of the line segment joining the midpoints of $\overline{CA}$ and $\overline{CB}$.

7. The coordinates of two consecutive vertices of a parallelogram are $(0, 2)$ and $(10, 4)$. If the point of intersection of the diagonals is $(6, 5)$, what are the other two vertices of the parallelogram?

8. Determine the slope of the line that passes through each of the following pairs of points.

   (a) $(0, 8)$, $(5, 2)$ (b) $(-3, 4)$, $(-2, -1)$

9. The vertices of a quadrilateral taken in consecutive order are $A(0, 0)$, $B(12, 2)$, $C(10, 6)$, and $D(4, 8)$.

   (a) Show that the line segment joining the midpoints of $\overline{BA}$ and $\overline{BC}$ is congruent to the line segment joining the midpoints of $\overline{DA}$ and $\overline{DC}$.

   (b) Show that the above line segments are parallel.

10. $A(1, 4)$, $B(-3, 8)$, and $C(5, 6)$ are the vertices of a triangle.

    (a) What is the slope of the line through A parallel to $\overleftrightarrow{BC}$?

    (b) What is the slope of the altitude from C to $\overline{AB}$?

    (c) What is the slope of the median from B to $\overline{AC}$?

    (d) Show that the line joining the midpoints of $\overline{AB}$ and $\overline{AC}$ is parallel to $\overleftrightarrow{BC}$.

11. (a) How do you interpret the statement that the slope of a line is 4?

(b) How do you interpret the statement that the slope of a line is $\frac{-3}{2}$?

(c) How do you interpret the statement that the slope of a line is $\frac{0}{1}$?

■ Try This For Fun

It was noted earlier that the distance between two "objects" was the measure of the shortest path between them. This path was investigated when the "objects" were two points of a plane or a point and a line of a plane. But what if the surface is not a plane? Is there anything that we, as students of plane geometry, can do to find the distance between two objects on a surface such as this? More often than not, the answer to this question is "No." There are, however, certain special situations in which it is possible for us to press the surface flat, then treat the problem as though it existed on a plane. One such case is described below.

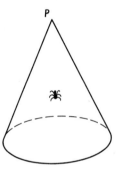

For reasons known only to himself, a spider built his web on the side of a cone. One rather hot day he emerged from his shelter and, in spite of his better judgement, decided to embark on a walk around the cone. Not wanting to overdo this, however, he felt that it would be best if he restricted his path to the shortest route that would enable him to see the back of the cone and return him to his home. To do this, he pictured the cone as being cut down the back, then pressed flat on the surface of a table. The path he decided to take was along the perpendicular from the nest to the cut $\overline{PB}$

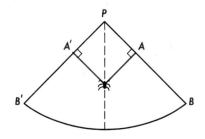

and back along a second perpendicular to $\overline{PB'}$. Remember, of course, that A and A' are the same point at the back of the cone.

(1) Can you prove that this is the shortest route?

(2) What path should the spider take if, when the cone was cut and pressed flat on the plane, the $\angle B'PB$ turned out to be a straight angle?

(3) Is there still a third situation that might arise when the cone is laid out flat in the plane?

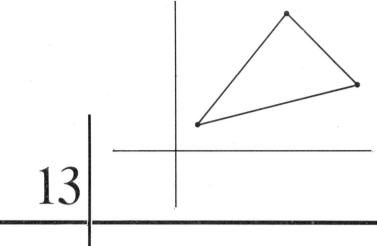

13

Coordinate Geometry
The Graph

OUR FIRST ENCOUNTER WITH A *SET* WAS during the very first few weeks of the course. A set, as we learned, may be any collection of elements where the elements are found by some rule. The mathematician prefers to say that the elements are determined by the conditions presented in the problem. Thus, the rule or conditions presented in the problem may be that the elements in the set must be the boys in the Conway family. The set would then be written as {Joe, Fred, William}. The elements listed in this set comply now with two requirements:

(1) All the names listed—that is, the elements in the set—are the boys in the Conway family.

(2) All the boys in the Conway family have their names listed in this set, that is, are elements in the set.

Notice that requirement 2 is the converse of requirement 1.

The elements in a set are frequently numbers. Specifically, if the conditions of the problem are that the elements be even numbers greater than 0 but less than 10, then the set would be

$$\{2, 4, 6, 8\}$$

And again we can say that

(1) All the numbers in the set are even numbers greater than 0 and less than 10.

(2) All the numbers that are even numbers greater than 0 and less than 10 are numbers in the set.

Frequently there will be sets of elements where all the elements, or *members*, cannot be listed. These are called infinite sets. Thus, had the rule in the previous problem been to determine the set whose members were even numbers greater than zero, it would be impossible to list all of them. To overcome this, we merely list a few and indicate that there are more to follow by using three dots:

$$\{2, 4, 6, 8, \ldots\}$$

In order to make certain that there is no doubt as to how the elements in the set were determined, we will express the description of the elements in the set as

$$\{x \mid x \text{ is an even number greater than zero}\}$$

This is read as

"The set of all x such that x is an even number greater than zero."

When expressed in this manner, we can see that the symbol x is designed to represent any element in the set. It may be the element 2, or 6, or 38, or 2,594; in fact, *any* even number greater than zero.

Our present concern is with sets whose elements are ordered pairs of numbers. Consider the set

$$\{(1, 5), (1, 6), (2, 5), (2, 6)\}$$

The conditions leading to this set of elements were that the first number in each pair had to be either 1 or 2, while the second number had to be either 5 or 6. This same set could have been written in the form,

$$\{(x, y) \mid x \text{ is either 1 or 2 and } y \text{ is either 5 or 6}\}$$

We would read this as

"The set of all ordered pairs of numbers (x, y) such that x is either 1 or 2 and y is either 5 or 6."

The importance to us of sets whose elements are pairs of numbers rests in the fact that every ordered pair of numbers represents a point in the

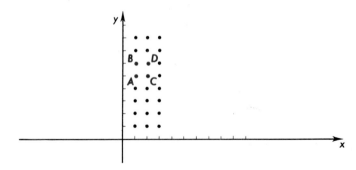

Figure 13-1.

coordinate plane and, conversely, every point in the coordinate plane represents a pair of ordered numbers. Hence, all sets consisting of ordered pairs of numbers can be represented by points in the coordinate plane. The set of elements $\{(1, 5), (1, 6), (2, 5), (2, 6)\}$ is pictured as A, B, C, and D in the plane of Figure 13-1. The points A, B, C, and D are called the *graph* of the set of elements $\{(1, 5), (1, 6), (2, 5), (2, 6)\}$.

DEFINITION 72: The graph of a set consisting of ordered pairs of numbers is the set of points whose coordinates are members of the original set.

Now let us examine all of this in terms of the following set:

$$\{(x, y)|y = 2x + 1\}$$

As before, this is read as

"The set of all ordered pairs of numbers (x, y) such that the second number in each pair is always 1 more than twice the first number."

When you studied algebra, you learned to determine such pairs of numbers by substituting values for x, then finding the corresponding value for y. Thus, when x is 1, the value of y will be 3. Some of these pairs of values were tabulated as

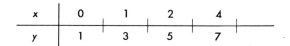

x	0	1	2	4
y	1	3	5	7

Now, we can express these pairs of values as the set of elements

$$\{(0, 1), (1, 3), (2, 5), (-4, -7), \ldots\}$$

where each of the elements in this set is restricted by the fact that it must satisfy the equation $y = 2x + 1$. The set of pairs of values that *satisfy an equation*—that is, make it true—is called the *solution set* of that equation. The pair of values $(5, 1)$ when used as replacements for x and y in the equation

$$y = 2x + 1$$

will make the left side 1 while the right side will be 11. Hence, $(5, 1)$ is *not* a member of the solution set of the equation $y = 2x + 1$. On the other hand, the elements listed in the set above are members of the solution set of this equation, for they will make this equation true.

The graph of the elements thus far found in the solution set of the equation $y = 2x + 1$ is pictured in Figure 13-2. Although this is a set consisting of infinitely many pairs of numbers, we have found only four of these pairs. This question then arises, "What would the graph of the solution set have been had we been able to express all the pairs of values in the solution set?" Examination of the four points leads us to suspect that the graph will consist of collinear points. This is what we now intend to prove.

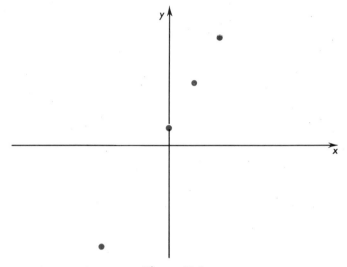

Figure 13-2.

Actually, our problem is twofold:

(1) Will all the pairs of values in the solution set of $y = 2x + 1$ represent collinear points?

(2) Will all the points on this line be elements in the solution set of $y = 2x + 1$?

We will attack each of these questions individually. To answer the first, we know by Theorem 75 that three points will be collinear if the slope of the line segment joining any two is equal to the slope of the line segment joining either of these to the third. Hence, we will let $A(x_1, y_1)$, $B(x_2, y_2)$, and $C(x_3, y_3)$ be any three pairs of values that are elements in the solution set. We would now like to show that they represent three collinear points. To do this by applying Theorem 75, we must show that

$$\frac{y_2 - y_1}{x_2 - x_1} = \frac{y_3 - y_2}{x_3 - x_2}$$

for these are the slopes of $\overline{AB}$ and $\overline{BC}$.

Since the three points are elements in the solution set of $y = 2x + 1$, then

$$\textbf{(1) } y_1 = 2x_1 + 1$$
$$\textbf{(2) } y_2 = 2x_2 + 1$$
$$\textbf{(3) } y_3 = 2x_3 + 1$$

Therefore, slope of $\overline{AB} = m_1 = \dfrac{y_2 - y_1}{x_2 - x_1} = \dfrac{(2x_2 + 1) - (2x_1 + 1)}{x_2 - x_1}$

$$= \frac{2x_2 + 1 - 2x_1 - 1}{x_2 - x_1} = \frac{2x_2 - 2x_1}{x_2 - x_1}$$

$$= \frac{2(x_2 - x_1)}{x_2 - x_1} = 2$$

Similarly, slope of $\overline{BC} = m_2 = \dfrac{y_3 - y_2}{x_3 - x_2} = \dfrac{(2x_3 + 1) - (2x_2 + 1)}{x_3 - x_2}$

$$= \dfrac{2x_3 + 1 - 2x_2 - 1}{x_3 - x_2} = \dfrac{2x_3 - 2x_2}{x_3 - x_2}$$

$$= \dfrac{2(x_3 - x_2)}{x_3 - x_2} = 2$$

Thus, $m_1 = m_2$, and hence, A, B, and C are collinear.

To answer question 2, we change its form to one that we can handle more easily. That is, will *all* the points on the line that passes through two members of the solution set also be members of the solution set?† To prove this, let $A(x_1, y_1)$ and $B(x_2, y_2)$ be two points in the solution set of the equation $y = 2x + 1$. We are now called upon to show that a point such as $D(x_4, y_4)$ that is on the line determined by points A and B will satisfy the equation $y = 2x + 1$. This will be true if

$$y_4 = 2x_4 + 1 \tag{1}$$

By Theorem 74 we know that the slope of the line segment joining any two points on a line is equal to the slope of the line segment joining any other two points. Hence,

$$\text{slope of } \overline{DB} = \text{slope of } \overline{BA}$$

$$\frac{y_4 - y_2}{x_4 - x_2} = \frac{y_2 - y_1}{x_2 - x_1}$$

But points A and B are in the solution set; therefore,

$$y_1 = 2x_1 + 1 \quad \text{and} \quad y_2 = 2x_2 + 1$$

Hence

$$\frac{y_4 - y_2}{x_4 - x_2} = \frac{(2x_2 + 1) - (2x_1 + 1)}{x_2 - x_1}$$

$$\frac{y_4 - y_2}{x_4 - x_2} = \frac{2x_2 + 1 - 2x_1 - 1}{x_2 - x_1}$$

$$\frac{y_4 - y_2}{x_4 - x_2} = \frac{2x_2 - 2x_1}{x_2 - x_1}$$

$$\frac{y_4 - y_2}{x_4 - x_2} = 2$$

Therefore

$$y_4 - y_2 = 2x_4 - 2x_2$$
$$y_4 - (2x_2 + 1) = 2x_4 - 2x_2$$
$$y_4 - 2x_2 - 1 = 2x_4 - 2x_2$$
$$y_4 = 2x_4 + 1$$

And this is what we had planned to prove. (See (1) above.)

† Notice that we are using the words "points" and "pairs of values" interchangeably. This is often done since there is a one-to-one correspondence between them.

EXERCISES

1. Give the rule or description for finding the elements in each of the following sets:
   (a) $\{1, 3, 5, 7, 9\}$ (b) $\{5, 10, 15, 20\}$
   (c) $\{7, 8, 9, 10, 11\}$ (d) $\{3, 6, 9, 12, \ldots\}$
   (e) $\{(1, 1), (1, 2), (1, 3), (1, 4)\}$ (f) $\{(3, 1), (3, 2), (4, 1), (4, 2)\}$

2. How would you read each of the following expressions?
   (a) $\{x \mid x \text{ is a whole number}\}$
   (b) $\{x \mid 2x + 1 = 6\}$
   (c) $\{x \mid x > 3\}$
   (d) $\{x \mid x < 5 \text{ and } x \text{ is a natural number}\}$
   (e) $\{x \mid 3x > x + 2\}$
   (f) $\{(x, y) \mid x + y = 5\}$
   (g) $\{(x, y) \mid y = 3x - 2\}$

3. Find four ordered pairs of numbers in each of the following sets:
   (a) $\{(x, y) \mid x + y = 4\}$ (b) $\{(x, y) \mid 2x - y = 5\}$
   (c) $\{(x, y) \mid 2x + 3y = 6\}$ (d) $\{(x, y) \mid x^2 + y^2 = 25\}$

4. Find four ordered pairs of numbers in the solution set of each of the following equations and graph these four points:
   (a) $y = x + 3$ (b) $x + 2y = 4$
   (c) $3x + y = 7$ (d) $x^2 + y^2 = 100$

5. For each of the equations below, find three points in its solution set. Using Theorem 75, determine whether these points are collinear.
   (a) $y = 3x - 2$ (b) $x = 2y + 3$
   (c) $2x - 3y = 6$ (d) $x^2 - y^2 = 16$

■ The Straight Line

The analysis in the preceding section leads us to the following definition:

DEFINITION 73: The graph of an equation is the graph of the solution set of that equation.

Having accepted the property that a definition is reversible, we have at our disposal, through Definition 73, two important principles:

(1) The coordinates of every point of the graph of an equation is an element of the solution set of that equation.
(2) Every element of the solution set of an equation is the coordinates of a point of the graph of the equation.

One of the simplest and yet one of the most important graphs is that of the equation of the form

$$ax + by = c$$

In the previous section we proved that the graph of a particular form of this equation, $y = 2x + 1$, was a straight line. What are the values of a, b, and c in this equation? Now we plan to show that every equation having the form $ax + by = c$ will be a straight line. The pattern of proof will be identical with that used in showing the graph of $y = 2x + 1$ to be a straight line. Since this is so, our first objective will be to write the equation $ax + by = c$ so that it resembles the equation $y = 2x + 1$.

$$ax + by = c$$
$$by = -ax + c$$

$$y = -\frac{a}{b}x + \frac{c}{b} \quad \text{(Assume } b \neq 0.\text{)}$$

As $-\frac{a}{b}$ and $\frac{c}{b}$ are constants, we will simplify the appearance of this equation by replacing them by m and k.

$$y = mx + k$$

Again, we are confronted with proving two properties:

(1) All points in the solution set are collinear.
(2) All points lying on the line joining any two points in the solution set are also in the solution set.

PROOF—PART 1

Let $A(x_1, y_1)$, $B(x_2, y_2)$, and $C(x_3, y_3)$ be points in the solution set of the equation $y = mx + k$. We will now show that these points are collinear.

(1) $y_1 = mx_1 + k$ **(2)** $y_2 = mx_2 + k$ **(3)** $y_3 = mx_3 + k$

$$\text{slope of } \overline{AB} = \frac{y_2 - y_1}{x_2 - x_1} = \frac{(mx_2 + k) - (mx_1 + k)}{x_2 - x_1} = \frac{mx_2 - mx_1}{x_2 - x_1}$$

$$= \frac{m(x_2 - x_1)}{x_2 - x_1} = m$$

$$\text{slope of } \overline{BC} = \frac{y_3 - y_2}{x_3 - x_2} = \frac{(mx_3 + k) - (mx_2 + k)}{x_3 - x_2} = \frac{mx_3 - mx_2}{x_3 - x_2}$$

$$= \frac{m(x_3 - x_2)}{x_3 - x_2} = m$$

Hence, slope of $\overline{AB}$ = slope of $\overline{BC}$

Therefore, the three points A, B, and C are collinear. (See Theorem 75.)

PROOF—PART 2

Since this proof is identical to that presented on page 413 (except the symbols m and k replace the symbols 2 and 1), it will be left for you to do.

Now let us examine what would have happened had b been equal to 0 in the equation $ax + by = c$. Were this so, then

$$ax + 0y = c$$
$$ax = c$$

and therefore

$$x = c/a$$

The equality $x = c/a$ is simply a direction stating that the point will always be c/a units from the vertical axis.† For this to be so, the point will have to be on a line parallel to the y-axis. Hence, even were $b = 0$, the equation $ax + by = c$ would still represent a line.

Before leaving the proof of this theorem, it is imperative to point out that as a by-product of Part 1 of the proof we have shown that the slope of the line segment joining any two points in the solution set of the equation $y = mx + k$ is m. By definition, though, the slope of a line is the slope of the line segment joining any two points on the line. Hence, the slope of the line $y = mx + k$ is m. But how is m found? It is the coefficient of x when the equation is solved for y. To illustrate, to find the slope of the line

$$3y + 2x = 6$$

solve the equation for y:

$$3y = -2x + 6$$
$$y = -\tfrac{2}{3}x + 2$$

Hence, $m = -2/3$, and therefore the slope of the line $3y + 2x = 6$ is $-2/3$.

In summary, we have proved

THEOREM 80: (1) The graph of any equation of the form $ax + by = c$ will be a line.

(2) Every line can be represented by an equation of the form $ax + by = c$.

Now we come to the mechanics of finding the equation of a line. No matter what the conditions of the problem, the equation of a line will *always* be found by applying Theorem 74; that is, the slope of the line segment joining any two points of a line is equal to the slope of the line segment joining any other two points of the line. This will be indicated henceforth by writing $m_1 = m_2$.

† See page 380.

Illustration 1:

Determine the equation of the line that passes through the points $A(2, 3)$ and $B(4, -1)$.

METHOD: Let $C(x, y)$ represent the coordinates of a third point on the line joining the points A and B. Then, since

$$m_1 = m_2$$

$$\text{slope } \overline{BC} = \text{slope } \overline{AB}$$

$$\frac{y + 1}{x - 4} = \frac{3 + 1}{2 - 4}$$

$$\frac{y + 1}{x - 4} = \frac{4}{-2}$$

$$\frac{y + 1}{x - 4} = \frac{2}{-1}$$

$$-y - 1 = 2x - 8$$

$$7 = 2x + y \quad \text{or} \quad 2x + y = 7$$

Illustration 2:

Determine the equation of the line that passes through the point $A(-5, 1)$ and is perpendicular to the line $2x + 3y = 4$.

METHOD: The slope of the line $2x + 3y = 4$ is found by solving the equation for y and examining the coefficient of x:

$$3y = -2x + 4 \qquad\qquad (1)$$

$$y = -\tfrac{2}{3}x + \tfrac{4}{3}$$

slope of (1): $-2/3$

$\therefore$ slope of a line perpendicular to (1): $3/2$

Let $B(x, y)$ be a second point on the line that passes through $A(-5, 1)$ and is perpendicular to $2x + 3y = 4$. Then, since

$$m_1 = m_2$$

$$\text{slope of } \overline{AB} = \text{slope of line perpendicular to } 2x + 3y = 4$$

$$\frac{y - 1}{x + 5} = \frac{3}{2}$$

$$3x + 15 = 2y - 2$$

$$3x - 2y = -17$$

Illustration 3:

Prove that the points $A(1, 5)$, $B(-2, 6)$, and $C(0, -3)$ are not collinear.

METHOD: Let $D(x, y)$ be any point on the line joining the points A and B. Then,

$$m_1 = m_2$$

$$\text{slope } \overline{DB} = \text{slope } \overline{AB}$$

$$\frac{y-6}{x+2} = \frac{5-6}{1+2}$$

$$\frac{y-6}{x+2} = \frac{-1}{3}$$

$$3y - 18 = -x - 2$$

$$x + 3y = 16$$

If point $C(0, -3)$ is on the line passing through A and B, it will be an element in the solution set of its equation. Hence,

$$0 + 3(-3) \overset{?}{=} 16$$
$$-9 \neq 16$$

$\therefore$ C, A, and B are not collinear.

EXERCISES

1. In each of the following problems, determine the equation of the line that passes through the two points that are given.
   (a) $(0, 2)$, $(3, 4)$ (b) $(4, 6)$, $(8, 2)$
   (c) $(1, 5)$, $(0, 9)$ (d) $(-2, 8)$, $(3, 10)$
   (e) $(-5, -2)$, $(0, -5)$ (f) $(-1, 7)$, $(3, -3)$

2. Determine the equation of the line that passes through each of the following points and has the slope indicated.
   (a) $(2, 3)$; slope $= 2/5$ (b) $(0, 5)$; slope $= -1/2$
   (c) $(-4, 6)$; slope $= -3/4$ (d) $(-3, -4)$; slope $= 4$
   (e) $(5, -3)$; slope $= 0$ (f) $(0, 2)$; slope $= -1$

3. Determine the equation of the line under each of the following conditions:
   (a) Passes through the origin and the point (a, b).
   (b) Intersects the x-axis at $x = 3$ and the y-axis at $y = -3$.
   (c) Parallel to the x-axis and passes through $(2, 8)$.
   (d) Parallel to the y-axis and passes through $(-5, -2)$.
   (e) Passes through the origin and has a slope of 1.
   (f) Intersects the x-axis at $x = 4$ and has a slope of $-5/3$.

4. Find the equation of the line that passes through the point $(4, 1)$ and is parallel to the line that passes through the points $(-5, 7)$ and $(2, 3)$.

5. Find the equation of the line that passes through the point $(-2, -2)$ and is perpendicular to the line that passes through the points $(1, 3)$ and $(-5, 0)$.

6. $A(0, 3)$, $B(6, -1)$, and $C(4, 7)$ are the vertices of a triangle.

    (a) Find the equation of the line that passes through A and is parallel to $\overleftrightarrow{BC}$.

    (b) Find the equation of the line that passes through C and is perpendicular to $\overleftrightarrow{AB}$.

    (c) Find the equation of the altitude from B to $\overline{AC}$.

    (d) Find the equation of the median from A to $\overline{BC}$.

    (e) Find the equation of the perpendicular bisector of $\overline{AB}$.

    (f) Find the equation of the line that passes through the midpoints of $\overline{AB}$ and $\overline{AC}$.

7. Which of the following sets of points are collinear? Justify your answer.

    (a) $\{(2, 3), (5, 8), (-4, -7)\}$ **(b)** $\{(2, 1), (-3, 5), (-6, -1)\}$

8. Determine the slope of each of the following lines:

    (a) $y = 3x + 4$ **(b)** $y = -2x + 5$ **(c)** $x + y = 7$

    (d) $2y - 3x = 5$ **(e)** $2x + y = 3$ **(f)** $3x - 4y = 5$

    (g) $ax + by = c$ **(h)** $3y = 4\dagger$ **(i)** $5x = 2\dagger$

9. Find the equation of each of the following lines:

    (a) Passes through $(2, 1)$ and is parallel to the line $5x + y = 6$.

    (b) Passes through $(-3, 1)$ and is perpendicular to the line $3x - 4y = 5$.

    (c) Passes through $(-2, -3)$ and is parallel to the line $2y = -5$.

    (d) Passes through $(4, -1)$ and is perpendicular to the line $x = -7$.

10. Prove that the lines $10x - 4y = 3$ and $5x = 2y$ are parallel.

11. Are the lines $3x + 2y = 5$ and $3x - 2y = 1$ perpendicular to each other? Justify your answer.

12. Prove that the point $(5, -4)$ lies on the line $4x - 3y = 32$.

13. What is the equation of the perpendicular bisector of the line segment joining the points $(6, -2)$ and $(4, 8)$?

14. $A(2, 4)$, $B(6, 10)$, and $C(10, 3)$ are the vertices of an isosceles triangle where C is the vertex of the vertex angle.

    (a) Show that the perpendicular bisector of the base passes through C.

    (b) Show that the altitude to the base bisects the base.

    (c) Show that the median to the base is perpendicular to the base.

■ Intersection of Two Sets

        Knowing how to determine the equation of a line places us in the position of being able to prove several important geometric relations.

† See pages 402–403.

What these relations are can best be illustrated through the use of the problem below.

Illustration:

Prove that the perpendicular bisectors of the sides of the triangle $A(-3, 5)$, $B(3, 3)$, and $C(11, 19)$ are concurrent; that is, have a point in common.

METHOD: A rough sketch is drawn at the very outset. The coordinates of

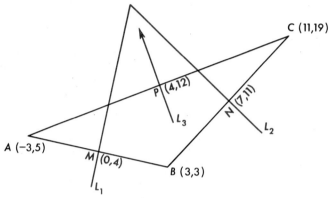

C (11,19)

P (4,12)

N (7,11)

L_3

L_2

A (−3,5)

M (0,4)

B (3,3)

L_1

Figure 13-3.

the midpoints of the sides are determined mentally and placed in the diagram. To find the slopes of L_1, L_2, and L_3, we must first determine the slope of $\overline{AB}$, $\overline{BC}$, and $\overline{CA}$.

$$\text{slope of } \overline{AB} = \frac{3-5}{3+3} = \frac{-1}{3}; \quad \text{slope of } L_1 = 3/1$$

$$\text{slope of } \overline{BC} = \frac{19-3}{11-3} = 2; \quad \text{slope of } L_2 = -1/2$$

$$\text{slope of } \overline{CA} = \frac{19-5}{11+3} = 1; \quad \text{slope of } L_3 = -1$$

$$L_1: \quad \frac{y-4}{x-0} = \frac{3}{1}; \quad 3x = y - 4; \quad 3x - y = -4$$

$$L_2: \quad \frac{y-11}{x-7} = \frac{-1}{2}; \quad 2y - 22 = -x + 7; \quad x + 2y = 29$$

$$L_3: \quad \frac{y-12}{x-4} = -1; \quad y - 12 = -x + 4; \quad x + y = 16$$

Using the methods of algebra, we find the common element to L_1 and L_2:

$$L_1: \quad 3x - y = -4$$
$$L_2: \quad x + 2y = 29$$

$$L_1: \quad 6x - 2y = -8$$
$$L_2: \quad x + 2y = 29$$

$$7x = 21$$
$$\therefore x = 3$$

and hence

$$y = 13$$

You may have called this pair of values—(3, 13)—the simultaneous solution to the two equations $3x - y = -4$ and $x + 2y = 29$. At the present time we prefer to refer to this pair of values as the *intersection of the solution sets* of these equations. This simply means that (3, 13) will be a common element to the solution sets of both $3x - y = -4$ and $x + 2y = 29$. Geometrically, however, the graph of the solution set of each of these equations is a straight line. Hence, the pair of values (3, 13) represents the coordinates of the intersection of the two graphs of the equations. Thus, the intersection of the solution sets of two equations has two interpretations:

(1) Algebraic: It is a pair of values that is common to both solution sets.
(2) Geometric: It is a point of the graphs of both equations.

Thus far we have shown that L_1 and L_2 intersect at the point (3, 13). We are now faced with the problem of demonstrating that L_3 also passes through this point. If (3, 13) is a point on L_3, then this pair of values must be an element in the solution set of the equation of L_3. Hence, it is simply necessary to determine whether (3, 13) satisfies the equation $x + y = 16$.

$$x + y = 16$$
$$3 + 13 \stackrel{?}{=} 16$$
$$16 = 16$$

Since (3, 13) does satisfy the equation of L_3, we can now conclude that L_1, L_2, and L_3 are concurrent.

There are times when the intersection of two sets is sought but can not be found. This will occur when the lines are parallel. If the lines are parallel, there will be no point that is common to the two graphs; and hence, there will be no element that is common to the two solution sets. It is possible to tell at a glance whether the solution sets of the equations of two lines have no intersection. Should the slopes of these two lines be equal, then, except for one condition, the lines will be parallel. Therefore, there will be no common elements to the solution sets of these equations. Equal slopes, however, may imply that the lines coincide; and hence, further investigation may be necessary. If the lines coincide, how many elements will there be in the intersection of the two sets?

Geometrically, three possibilities exist when trying to find the intersection of the solution sets of two equations whose graphs are straight lines:

(1) The lines intersect at one point; these are called *consistent* equations.
(2) The lines are parallel; these are called *inconsistent* equations.
(3) The lines coincide; these are called *dependent* equations.

How many elements will there be in the intersection of the solution sets in each of these situations?

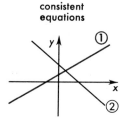

consistent
equations

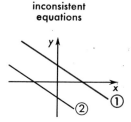

inconsistent
equations

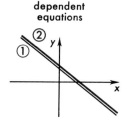

dependent
equations

Figure 13-4.

EXERCISES

1. Determine the intersection of the solution sets of each of the following pairs of equations:

(a) $x + y = 7$
$2x - y = 2$

(b) $x - 3y = -17$
$x + 2y = 8$

(c) $2x - y = 2$
$x + 2y = -4$

2. Determine the point of intersection of the graphs of each of the following pairs of equations:

(a) $2x + y = -6$
$2y - x = 8$

(b) $x = -2y$
$2x - 3y = 21$

3. State whether each of the following pairs of equations are consistent, inconsistent, or dependent:

(a) $6x - 9y = 5$
$4x - 6y = 7$

(b) $5x + 2y = 1$
$y = 3x - 4$

(c) $x + y = 5$
$y = x - 3$

(d) $5x = 9 - 10y$
$6y = 13 - 3x$

(e) $7x - 21y = 14$
$2x - 6y = 4$

(f) $3x - 5y = 4$
$5x = 3y + 4$

4. Show that the lines $x - y = 4$, $2x - 5y = 17$, and $x + 2y = -5$ are concurrent.

5. Determine the equation of the line that passes through the point $(4, -1)$ and the intersection of the two lines $3x - y = 4$ and $x + 2y = 13$.

6. $A(6, 10)$, $B(0, 0)$, and $C(6, 4)$ are the vertices of a triangle. Prove that the perpendicular bisectors of the sides of this triangle are concurrent.

7. $A(0, 0)$, $B(8, 6)$, and $C(4, 12)$ are the vertices of a triangle. Prove that the medians of this triangle are concurrent.

8. $A(0, 0)$, $B(8, 0)$, and $C(6, 2)$ are the vertices of a triangle. Prove that the altitudes of this triangle are concurrent.

9. $A(2, 5)$, $B(12, 3)$, and $C(8, 9)$ are the vertices of a right triangle where $\angle C$ is the right angle. Prove that the midpoint of the hypotenuse lies on the perpendicular bisectors of the legs.

10. The vertices of an isosceles triangle are $A(2, 3)$, $B(6, 11)$, and $C(8, 5)$ where C is the vertex of the vertex angle. Prove that the altitude to the base, the median to the base, and the perpendicular bisector of the base coincide. (Hint: Show that the equations of all three lines are the same.)

11.* Determine the distance from the point $(5, 6)$ to the line $x + 2y = 2$. (Hint: Determine the equation of the perpendicular from the point to the line.)

12.* $A(5, -1)$, $B(1,1)$, and $C(5, -11)$ are the vertices of a triangle. Determine the length of the altitude from A to $\overline{BC}$.

■ Analytic Proofs of Problems from Synthetic Geometry

      Among the problems that you were called upon to investigate in this chapter were a number that you had proved earlier by synthetic methods. The purpose of this unit is to present to you a great many problems for which you have given synthetic proofs. Now, however, you will be asked to give analytic proofs for these same problems. Though not necessarily true in all cases, you will find that in most of the situations presented here the analytic proof is somewhat simpler than the synthetic proof had been.

Illustration:

      Prove that the line drawn from one of the vertices of a parallelogram to the midpoint of one of the opposite sides is a trisector of a diagonal of the parallelogram.

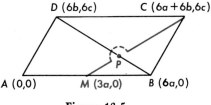

D (6b,6c)   C (6a +6b,6c)

P

A (0,0)   M (3a,0)   B (6a,0)

Figure 13-5.

METHOD: Let $A(0, 0)$, $B(6a, 0)$, $C(6a + 6b, 6c)$, and $D(6b, 6c)$ be the four vertices of the parallelogram. Our attack will be to find the coordinates of point P, one of the trisection points of $\overline{DB}$, and to show that this point satisfies the equation of $\overleftrightarrow{CM}$. The coordinates of M, the midpoint of $\overline{AB}$, were found mentally.

$$\text{abscissa of } P\dagger = \frac{2(6a) + 1(6b)}{2 + 1} = \frac{12a + 6b}{3} = 4a + 2b$$

$$\text{ordinate of } P\dagger = \frac{2(0) + 1(6c)}{2 + 1} = \frac{6c}{3} = 2c$$

coordinates of P: $(4a + 2b, 2c)$

$$\text{equation of } \overleftrightarrow{CM}: \quad \frac{y - 0}{x - 3a} = \frac{6c - 0}{6a + 6b - 3a}$$

$$\frac{y}{x - 3a} = \frac{2c}{a + 2b}$$

Substituting the coordinates of P in this equation,

$$\frac{2c}{4a + 2b - 3a} \overset{?}{=} \frac{2c}{a + 2b}$$

$$\frac{2c}{a + 2b} = \frac{2c}{a + 2b}$$

Since P satisfies the equation of $\overleftrightarrow{CM}$, $\overleftrightarrow{CM}$ will pass through a trisection point of $\overline{DB}$ and, hence, be one of the trisectors of $\overline{DB}$.

EXERCISES

1. Prove that the diagonals of a square are perpendicular to each other. Let $A(0, 0)$, $B(a, 0)$, $C(a, a)$, and $D(0, a)$ be the vertices of the square.
2. Prove that the diagonals of a rhombus are perpendicular to each other. Let $A(0, 0)$, $B(5a, 0)$, $C(8a, 4a)$, and $D(3a, 4a)$ be the vertices of the rhombus. (Can you prove that these points must be the vertices of a rhombus?)
3. Prove that the midpoint of the hypotenuse of a right triangle is equidistant from the three vertices. Let $A(2a, 0)$, $B(0, 2b)$, and $C(0, 0)$ be the vertices of the triangle.
4. Prove that the line joining the midpoints of the diagonals of a trapezoid is parallel to the bases. Let $A(0, 0)$, $B(2a, 0)$, $C(2b, 2c)$, and $D(2d, 2c)$ be the vertices of the trapezoid.
5. Prove that the measure of the line segment joining the midpoints of the diagonals of a trapezoid is equal to one-half the difference of the measures of the bases. See Problem 4 for the vertices.
6. Prove that the diagonals of an isosceles trapezoid are congruent. Let $A(-2a, 0)$, $B(2a, 0)$, $C(2c, 2d)$, and $D(-2c, 2d)$ be the vertices.

† See page 386.

7. Prove that if line segments are drawn joining the midpoints of consecutive sides of an isosceles trapezoid, these segments will be congruent. See Problem 6 for the vertices.

8. Prove that if a line passes through the midpoint of one side of a triangle and is parallel to the second side, then it will pass through the midpoint of the third side.

9. Prove that if a line bisects one of the nonparallel sides of a trapezoid and is parallel to the bases, then it bisects the other of the nonparallel sides. See Problem 4 for the vertices and use the method illustrated on pages 423–424.

10. Prove that if line segments are drawn between the midpoints of opposite sides of a quadrilateral, they will bisect each other. Let $A(0, 0)$, $B(2x_2, 0)$, $C(2x_3, 2y_3)$, and $D(2x_4, 2y_4)$ be the vertices of the quadrilateral.

11. Prove that the perpendicular bisector of the lower base of an isosceles trapezoid is also the perpendicular bisector of the upper base. See Problem 6 for the vertices.

12. Prove that if the nonparallel sides of an isosceles trapezoid are extended, they will be concurrent with the perpendicular bisector of the lower base. See Problem 6 for the vertices.

13. Prove that if the diagonals of a quadrilateral bisect each other, the quadrilateral is a parallelogram. (Hint: Use as vertices the values for A, B, and M shown below; then prove that the opposite sides are parallel.)

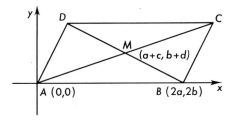

14. Prove that the sum of the squares of the measures of the sides of a parallelogram is equal to the sum of the squares of the measures of its diagonals. Let $A(0, 0)$, $B(a, 0)$, $C(a + c, d)$, and $D(c, d)$ be the vertices of the parallelogram.

15.* Prove that the altitudes of a triangle are concurrent. Let $A(0, a)$, $B(0, b)$, and $C(c, 0)$ be the vertices of the triangle.

The Graphs of Inequalities

Thus far we have considered only those situations in which the elements in the solution set yielded a set of points that fell on a line. There are conditions, however, under which the graph of the solution set will consist of the points in a half-plane or possibly the points enclosed within a region of the coordinate plane.

To illustrate, consider the open sentence

$$x > 3$$

As before, we can look upon this as a direction stating that the point must be more than three units to the right of the vertical, or y-axis. Since no requirements were placed on how far the points must be from the x-axis, the second element, or ordinate, in each ordered pair can be any value we desire. Thus, a few of the pairs of elements in the solution set of $x > 3$ will be

$$\{(4, 0), (4, -10), (5, 17), (5, 246), (9, -578), \ldots\}$$

What must be true of the first coordinate in each ordered pair? What must be true of the second coordinate?

To answer the question "Where do these points lie?", we first graph the equation $x = 3$.

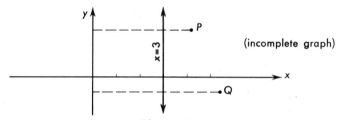

Figure 13-6.

Any point on this graph, the red line, will be 3 units from the y-axis. On the other hand the distance from point P to the y-axis is greater than 3 units; hence, the coordinates of P will be an element in the solution set of the inequality

$$x > 3$$

Furthermore, the point P itself is a point of the graph of the solution set. Similarly, the distance from Q to the y-axis is greater than 3 units, thus making Q a point of the graph. In addition, the distance from any point to the right of the line $x = 3$ to the y-axis will be greater than 3 units; therefore, all points in this half-plane will be points of the graph of $x > 3$. This graph is shown as the shaded area of the coordinate plane in Figure 13-7.

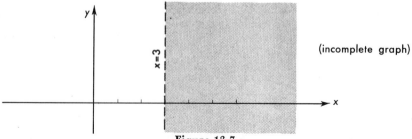

Figure 13-7.

To indicate the fact that the points on the line $x = 3$ are not elements in the solution set, the red line was drawn as a *dotted line*. If the points on this line were to be included in the graph, it would have been drawn as a solid line.

In the same way, the solution set of the open sentence

$$y \leq 7$$

will consist of all ordered pairs of numbers in which the second coordinate is equal to or less than 7. The sentence $y \leq 7$ implies that there are two types of replacements for y under which this sentence will be true. These replacements are

    (1) That y be 7.
    (2) That y be less than 7.

The graph of the solution set of $y \leq 7$ is the set of points in the half-plane below the line $y = 7$ and this line itself. Each of the points on the line $y = 7$

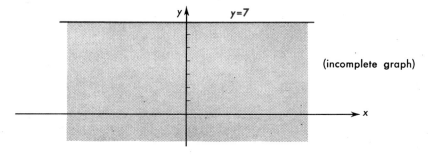

Figure 13-8.

conforms with the first replacements for y, while the points in the half-plane below $y = 7$ fulfills the second requirement. Notice that in Figure 13-8 the line graph $y = 7$ was drawn as a solid line, for it is to be included in the graph.

We have examined graphs consisting of half-planes that fell to either the right or left of a vertical line and half-planes above or below a horizontal line. What would occur, however, if the graph of the equality were not parallel to either axis? Before it is possible to answer this question, it will be necessary to formulate several assumptions on inequalities similar to those developed earlier for equalities.

POSTULATE 36: If $a > b$

then $a + c > b + c$

This symbolic relation is often expressed as

    "If equals are added to unequals, the sums will be unequal in the same order."

As an illustration, we know that 9 is greater than 7. Were we to add 3 to both 9 and 7, the sum of 9 and 3 (12) would be greater than the sum of 7 and 3 (10). That is,

If	$9 > 7$
then	$9 + 3 > 7 + 3$
or	$12 > 10$

What are the replacements for a, b, and c in this illustration?

The words "same order" as used in the statement above implies that if the left side of the inequality is larger than the right side at the outset, then after addition takes place, the left side will still be larger than the right side.

Postulate 36 is helpful in simplifying inequalities of the form $x - 7 > 4$. Thus,

$$x - 7 > 4$$
$$x - 7 + 7 > 4 + 7$$
$$x > 11$$

By examining the inequality $x > 11$, we are made aware of those numbers that are elements in the solution set of the original inequality $x - 7 > 4$. That is, any number greater than 11 will make the left side of this inequality greater than the right side.

POSTULATE 37: If $\qquad$ $a > b$

then $\qquad$ $a - c > b - c$

This symbolic relation is often expressed as

"If equals are subtracted from unequals, the differences will be unequal in the same order."

As an illustration,

$$9 > 7$$
$$9 - 3 > 7 - 3$$
or $\qquad$ $6 > 4$

What replacements were used for a, b, and c?

Postulate 37 is used to simplify the form of inequalities such as $x + 7 > 4$, for

$$x + 7 > 4$$
$$x + 7 - 7 > 4 - 7$$
$$x > -3$$

POSTULATE 38: If $\qquad$ $a > b$

then $\qquad$ $\dfrac{a}{c} > \dfrac{b}{c}$ where $c > 0$

This symbolic relation is often expressed as

"If unequals are divided by *positive* equals, the quotients will be unequal in the same order."

As an illustration,

$$15 > 6$$

$$\frac{15}{3} > \frac{6}{3}$$

$$5 > 2$$

What replacements were used for a, b, and c? Were c negative in this illustration, how would our conclusion been affected? What would happen were c equal to zero?

This postulate is used to simplify the form of an inequality such as $4x > 20$. Thus,

$$4x > 20$$

$$\frac{4x}{4} > \frac{20}{4}$$

$$x > 5$$

With these assumptions as a foundation, we are prepared to graph the inequality $x + 2y > 10$. Let us first consider the graph of the equality $x + 2y = 10$. Each point on the line, such as P, satisfies the condition that

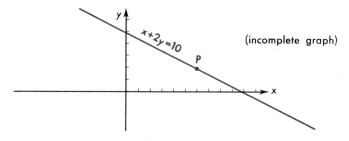

Figure 13-9.

$$x \text{ be equal to } 10 - 2y \qquad (1)$$

To illustrate by using P, when y is replaced by 2, the value of x in equation (1) is 6, while the value of the abscissa of the point P in the graph is also 6. By using Postulate 37 the form of the inequality

$$x + 2y > 10$$

can be changed to

$$x > 10 - 2y$$

This implies that

$$x \text{ must be greater than } 10 - 2y \qquad (2)$$

When y was replaced by 2, we found that the value of $10 - 2y$ was 6 and, hence, the value of x on the line was 6. From our information in (2), we see that x must now be greater than 6 when y is equal to 2. Where will these points fall? The points for which y is 2 and x is greater than 6 will appear

Illustration:

Determine the intersection of the solution sets of the open sentences:

$$\textbf{(1)} \quad 2x + 3y \geq 12$$
$$\textbf{(2)} \quad x - 4y > 4$$

METHOD: Following the pattern outlined, we will first graph the equalities $2x + 3y = 12$ and $x - 4y = 4$.

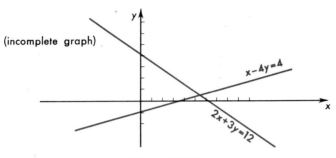

Figure 13-14.

Solving (1) for x, we obtain

$$2x \geq 12 - 3y$$

$$x \geq \frac{12 - 3y}{2}$$

This implies that the points of the graph will fall in the half-plane "to the right" of the line $2x + 3y = 12$ and, also, on the line itself.

Solving (2) for y, we obtain

$$x - 4 > 4y$$

$$\frac{x - 4}{4} > y$$

Thus, the graph of the second inequality will be the points of the half-plane "below" the line $x - 4y = 4$. In solving for y, $4y$ was added to both sides of the inequality. This was done to make the coefficient of y a positive quantity so that Postulate 38 could be applied.

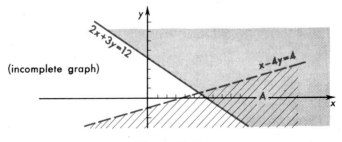

Figure 13-15.

The points in the region marked A, being in both half-planes, will be points of the graphs of both inequalities. Hence, the points in the *cross-hatched*, or doubly shaded region, are elements in the intersection of the solution sets of the two inequalities. Notice that whereas half of the line $2x + 3y = 12$ is included in the intersection, none of the line $x - 4y = 4$ is included.

In this illustration, the first inequality was solved for x, while the second was solved for y. Although both can be solved for the same variable, the graph of the intersection is much clearer and neater if one inequality is solved for one of the variables, while the other is solved for the other variable.

EXERCISES

1. Using Postulates 36, 37, and 38, determine the greatest or least replacement value for x so as to make each of the following open sentences true. Give two other values in the solution set of each of these inequalities.
   (a) $2x \geq 10$ (b) $24 \leq 3x$
   (c) $5x - 1 \geq 29$ (d) $7x - 36 \leq 4x$
   (e) $9x - 25 \geq 11x + 7$ (f) $4(x - 3) \leq 5x + 2$

2. Graph each of the following inequalities:
   (a) $x < 10$ (b) $y \geq -5$
   (c) $x + y > 4$ (d) $2x - y \leq 6$
   (e) $y - 3x > 12$ (f) $4y - x < 8$
   (g) $2x - 3y \geq 6$ (h) $5x + 4y \leq 20$

3. By graphing, determine the intersection of the solution sets of the following pairs of inequalities:

   (a) $\begin{cases} x > 4 \\ y < -2 \end{cases}$ (b) $\begin{cases} x < 0 \\ x + y \geq 2 \end{cases}$

   (c) $\begin{cases} y \geq -1 \\ x - 2y < 4 \end{cases}$ (d) $\begin{cases} x - y > 5 \\ 3x + y < 6 \end{cases}$

   (e) $\begin{cases} 2x + y \leq 4 \\ y - 3x \geq 9 \end{cases}$ (f) $\begin{cases} 2x + 3y > 12 \\ 5x - 2y < 10 \end{cases}$

4. Determine the intersection of each of the following systems of inequalities:

   (a) $\begin{cases} x > 0 \\ y > 0 \\ x + y < 10 \end{cases}$ (b) $\begin{cases} x < 0 \\ y < 0 \\ x + y > -4 \end{cases}$

   (c) $\begin{cases} x \geq 2 \\ y \leq 5 \\ x - y \leq 2 \end{cases}$ (d) $\begin{cases} x + 3 \leq 0 \\ y + 5 \geq 0 \\ x - 2y \geq 0 \end{cases}$

   (e) $\begin{cases} x + y \leq 8 \\ 10x + y \geq 10 \\ x + 10y \geq 10 \end{cases}$ (f) $\begin{cases} x + y \geq 0 \\ 2x - 3y \leq 6 \\ x + 2y \leq 3 \end{cases}$

■ Locus of Points

A very important topic in mathematics and one closely related to what we have been discussing is the topic known as the *locus of points.*†

DEFINITION 74: The locus of points is the set of those points and only those points that satisfy certain given conditions.

Should the conditions that determine these points be described by an equation or an inequality, then the definition implies that the graph of this description will be the locus. Thus, let us say that the conditions describing the locus of points is

$$\{(x, y) \mid x = 3\} \tag{A}$$

This, you recall, was read as "The set of all points with coordinates (x, y) such that the abscissa of each of these points would always be 3." The graph of this set of points is the line parallel to the y-axis and 3 units to the right of it. Hence, the locus of points fulfilling the conditions specified in (A) is merely the graph of the elements in (A).

Similarly, if the locus was described by the conditions

$$\{(x, y) \mid 2x - 3y < 12\}$$

then the locus would be the points in the half-plane "to the left" of the line $2x - 3y = 12$.

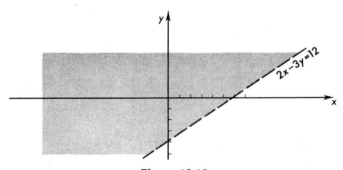

Figure 13-16.

Actually, the definition of the locus of points calls for two requirements to be fulfilled:

(1) That every point that satisfies the given conditions be in the locus.
(2) That every point in the locus should satisfy the given conditions.

Fortunately, this is exactly the relationship that exists between a graph and the equality or inequality leading to that graph: every element in the solution set is a point of the graph or locus, and every point of the graph

† Locus is a Latin word meaning *place;* hence, *locus of points* means *place of points.*

or locus is an element in the solution set. Thus, in the illustration above every ordered pair of values in the set

$$\{(x, y) \mid 2x - 3y < 12\}$$

will lie in the half-plane to the "left" of the line $2x - 3y = 12$, and every point in this half-plane can be represented by a pair of values in this set.

In many cases the description of the locus or set is not given by an equation or an inequality but by some narrative statement. Thus,

"Find the locus or set of points that are equidistant from the points $(1, 0)$ and $(5, 8)$."

Under these circumstances it is necessary for us to rewrite this description in terms of set symbols and then simplify the equality or inequality through the use of our postulates.

METHOD: Our first objective is to draw a rough sketch based on the descrip-

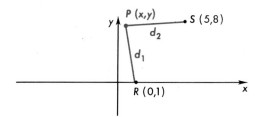

Figure 13-17.

tion and allow the ordered pair (x, y) to represent any point of the locus. In terms of this diagram the description of the set can be rewritten as

(1) $\{(x, y) \mid d_1 = d_2\}$

Now, it is merely a matter of simplifying this expression:

(2) $\{(x, y) \mid \sqrt{(x - 0)^2 + (y - 1)^2} = \sqrt{(x - 5)^2 + (y - 8)^2}\}$
(3) $\{(x, y) \mid x^2 + (y - 1)^2 = (x - 5)^2 + (y - 8)^2\}$
(4) $\{(x, y) \mid x^2 + y^2 - 2y + 1 = x^2 - 10x + 25 + y^2 - 16y + 64\}$
(5) $\{(x, y) \mid 10x - 2y + 16y = 25 + 64 - 1\}$
(6) $\{(x, y) \mid 10x + 14y = 88\}$
(7) $\{(x, y) \mid 5x + 7y = 44\}$

Thus, we have transformed the description for finding the elements of the set from the narrative form to that of the simple equation $5x + 7y = 44$. The graph of this equation is a line. Therefore, what we have proved thus far is that all the points that are equidistant from the points $(0, 1)$ and $(5, 8)$ must be points of this line. However, it is possible that there may be some points of this line that are not equidistant from these two points. Hence, we must now show that every point of the line $5x + 7y = 44$ must be equidistant from the points $(0, 1)$ and $(5, 8)$.

Fortunately, we had proved in Theorem 80 that every element in the solution set of $5x + 7y = 44$ is on a line and every point on this line is an element in the solution set of $5x + 7y = 44$. But by retracing our steps in the proof above, we find that the description $5x + 7y = 44$ is but another form, or equivalent form, of the description

(2) $\sqrt{(x - 0)^2 + (y - 1)^2} = \sqrt{(x - 5)^2 + (y - 8)^2}$

Hence, the points on the line are also elements in the solution set of equation (2). However, this equation indicates that the distance from each point (x, y) on the line to $(0, 1)$ is always equal to the distance from (x, y) to $(5, 8)$. This is what we had hoped to show. In summary, then, the locus or set of points that are equidistant from the point $(0, 1)$ and $(5, 8)$ are all the points on the line $5x + 7y = 44$.

Generally speaking, for the problems we will encounter on locus, once we have found the description leading to the graph, it will not be necessary for us to prove that all points of this graph fulfill the conditions of the problem. This will be so without proof, for each step in our proofs are retraceable similar to what we had done in the illustration just completed. The only retraceable step that is questionable is when we had moved from step 3 back to step 2 (see Proof, page 435). In doing this it was necessary to take the square root of each side of the equation. Thus, the point might be raised as to why the negative square root was not used. It was simply because we had agreed that distance would always be a positive number.

There are several things that are of interest about the line $5x + 7y = 44$ in this illustration. By solving the equation for y and examining the coefficient of x, we see that the slope of this line is $-5/7$. The slope of the segment RS is $7/5$. Thus, the locus turned out to be a line that is perpendicular to the line segment joining the two points $(0, 1)$ and $(5, 8)$. Furthermore, the coordinates of the midpoint of $\overline{RS}$—$(5/2, 9/2)$—satisfy the description of the locus:

$$5x + 7y = 44$$
$$5(5/2) + 7(9/2) \stackrel{?}{=} 44$$
$$25/2 + 63/2 \stackrel{?}{=} 44$$
$$44 = 44$$

Therefore, the locus is not only the line perpendicular to $\overleftrightarrow{RS}$, but this line also turns out to be the bisector of $\overline{RS}$.

The description of a locus is sometimes given in terms of a compound sentence. Thus,

"Find the locus of points that are more than two units from the line $x = 6$ and also equidistant from the points $(0, 1)$ and $(5, 8)$."

Loci of this form are called *compound loci*.† In reality they involve nothing more than the intersection of two sets. Symbolic descriptions of each of the sets are formulated from the narrative descriptions. This is then followed by finding the graph of their intersection.

† Plural of locus is *loci*.

METHOD: Starting with the first description,

A = the set of points that are more than two units from the line $x = 6$

$A = \{(x, y) \mid x > 8 \text{ or } x < 4\}$

The description in set A came from the fact that the points had to be more than two units from the line $x = 6$. Since these points can lie on either side of $x = 6$, the description must include the fact that x may be either greater than 8 or less than 4.

The second description was analyzed in the preceding illustration and led to the set

$$B = \{(x, y) \mid 5x + 7y = 44\}$$

Hence, the problem resolves itself to one of determining the intersection† of set A with set B. Symbolically, this is expressed as $A \cap B$ and is read as

               (1) The intersection of A and B

or

               (2) A intersects B.

The shaded region in the graph in Figure 13-18 represents those points that are more than two units from the line $x = 6$. The line $5x + 7y = 44$

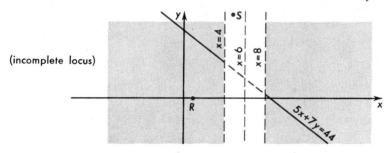

(incomplete locus)

Figure 13-18.

represents those points that are equidistant from the points $(0, 1)$ and $(5, 8)$. Hence, the points that are both two units away from the line $x = 6$ and equidistant from $(0, 1)$ and $(5, 8)$ are in that part of the line $5x + 7y = 44$ that lies to the right of the line $x = 8$ and to the left of the line $x = 4$. The points of these sections of the line $5x + 7y = 44$ represent $A \cap B$.

EXERCISES

1. Using set symbols, rewrite the description of each of the following loci:
   (a) The locus of points that are four units to the right of the vertical axis.
   (b) The locus of points that are three units below the horizontal axis.
   (c) The locus of points that are four units to the right of the line $x = 8$.
   (d) The locus of points that are five units below the line $y = 3$.

† See page 11.

(e) The locus of points that are more than two units to the right of the y-axis.

(f) The locus of points that are more than seven units above the x-axis.

(g) The locus of points that are more than three units to the right of the line $x = 8$.

(h) The locus of points that are more than two units from the line $y = 6$.

(i) The locus of points that are more than five units from the line $x = 3$.

(j)* The locus of points that are less than three units from the line $x = 5$.

2. Draw each locus in problem 1.

3. Using set symbols, rewrite the description of each of the following loci:

(a) The locus of points that are a distance of five units from the origin.

(b) The locus of points that are a distance of R units from the origin.

(c) The locus of points that are a distance of seven units from the point $(4, 6)$.

(d) The locus of points that are a distance of R units from the point (h, k).

4. (a) Using set symbols, express the locus of points that are equidistant from the points $(0, 2)$ and $(10, 4)$.

(b) Draw this locus.

(c) Prove that this locus is the perpendicular bisector of the line segment joining the two points.

5. Using set symbols, express the locus of points that are equidistant from the two points in each of the problems below:

(a) $(-5, 0)$ and $(5, 0)$ (b) $(0, -7)$ and $(0, 7)$

(c) $(2, 5)$ and $(12, 5)$ (d) $(-6, -3)$ and $(-6, 9)$

(e) $(1, 0)$ and $(5, 2)$ (f) $(-3, 4)$ and $(5, 8)$

(g) $(-2, -6)$ and $(0, -14)$ (h) $(-1, -7)$ and $(6, -4)$

(i) (a, b) and $(2a, -2b)$

6. Draw each locus in Problem 5.

7. (a) Using set symbols, express the locus of points such that the difference of the squares of the distances from the points $A(0, 0)$ and $B(4, 5)$ is always 4.

(b) By simplifying the description of the set in part (a), show that this locus is a line.

(c) Prove that this locus is a line that is perpendicular to the line determined by the points A and B.

(d) Graph the locus found in (b).

8. Using set symbols, express the locus of points such that the difference of the squares of the distances from any point of the locus to

(a) $(3, 5)$ and $(7, 5)$ is always 6 units.

(b) $(-4, 6)$ and $(-4, -2)$ is always 2 units.

(c) $(0, 0)$ and $(-5, -8)$ is always 4 units.

(d) $(-2, 4)$ and $(3, 7)$ is always -3 units.

9. **(a)** By simplifying each of the descriptions in Problem 8, show that each of these loci is a line.

   (b) Graph each of the loci in Problem 8.

10. **(a)** Using set symbols, express the following locus as a problem in which the intersection of two sets is to be found:

   "Find the locus of points that are two units to the right of the vertical axis and four units above the horizontal axis."

   (b) Graph the intersection of the two sets found in part (a).

11. Draw the locus in each of the following problems:

   (a) What is the locus of points that is more than two units to the left of the vertical axis and more than two units above the horizontal axis?

   (b) What is the locus of points that is more than four units to the right of the vertical axis and on the line $x - 2y = 4$?

   (c) What is the locus of points that is more than three units from the horizontal axis and on the line $x + y = 0$?

   (d) What is the locus of points that is two units from the x-axis and equidistant from the points $(0, 0)$ and $(6, 0)$?

   (e) What is the locus of points that is more than three units from the line $y = 7$ and equidistant from the points $(-2, 4)$ and $(4, 6)$?

   (f) What is the locus of points that is less than four units from the line $x = -8$ and equidistant from the points $(-1, 2)$ and $(3, 8)$?

   (g) What is the locus of points that is equidistant from the points $(0, 0)$ and $(6, 0)$ and also equidistant from the points $(2, 4)$ and $(4, 10)$?

12. Prove that the locus of points equidistant from two fixed points is the perpendicular bisector of the line segment joining the two points. Let $(0, 0)$ and $(2a, 2b)$ be the two fixed points.

13. **(a)** What is the distance from the point $(6, 4)$ to the y-axis?

   (b) What is the distance from the point (x, y) to the y-axis?

   (c) Using set symbols, express the locus of points such that the distance from each of these points to the y-axis is equal to its distance to the point $(6, 4)$.

14. Using set symbols, express the locus of points such that the distance from each of these points to the point $(6, 0)$ is equal to its distance to the line $x = 2$.

15. Using set symbols, express the locus of points such that the distance from each of these points to the point (0, 4) is four times its distance to the x-axis.

16. (a) Using set symbols, express the locus of points such that the slope of the line segment joining any of these points to the point (2, 3) is 1/2.

   (b) By simplifying the description of this set, show that the locus will be a line.

   (c) Graph the locus found in (b).

■ The Circle

Thus far we have considered only the properties of lines from an analytic standpoint. There was, however, another figure that was examined briefly in synthetic geometry that we would like to analyze at this time in coordinate geometry. This figure is the circle. You may recall that by definition a circle is a set of points such that line segments drawn from all points of this set to a fixed point are congruent. Had we preferred, the definition of a circle could have been given in the equivalent form of

ALTERNATIVE DEFINITION 36: A circle is the set or locus of points that are a fixed distance from a fixed point.

Examination of this definition will reveal that it is identically the same as the previous one. The new definition, however, enables us to apply set symbolism to describe the set of points that lie on the circle.

Illustration:

Using set symbols, describe the circle wherein the fixed point is (2, 3) and the fixed distance is 7 units.

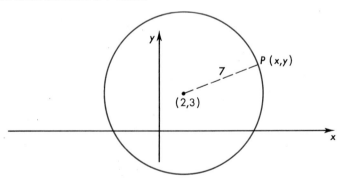

Figure 13-19.

METHOD: In terms of the definition of a circle, this problem can be rewritten as

(1) This circle is the set of points such that each of these points is 7 units from the fixed point (2, 3).

(2) $C = \{(x, y) \mid \sqrt{(x - 2)^2 + (y - 3)^2} = 7\}$

(3) $C = \{(x, y) \mid (x - 2)^2 + (y - 3)^2 = 49\}$

In step (2), the expression on the left side of the equality sign simply represents the distance from any point in the set to the point (2, 3). By the conditions of the problem this distance was always to be 7; hence, the equality between the radical and the 7. Step (3) was found by squaring both sides of the equality. The equality in step (3) is called the *equation of the circle* for this problem. In exactly the same way we are now going to develop the equation of the circle where the fixed point may be any point in the coordinate plane and the fixed distance is any given distance.

THEOREM 81: The equation of a circle whose center is (h, k) and whose radius is R is

$$(x - h)^2 + (y - k)^2 = R^2$$

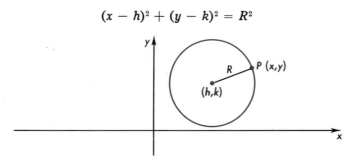

Figure 13-20.

PROOF

On the basis of the definition made earlier we know that the fixed distance is the radius of the circle, while the fixed point is the center of the circle. Hence,

(1) This circle is the set of points such that each point is R units from the fixed point (h, k).

(2) $C = \{(x, y) \mid \sqrt{(x - h)^2 + (y - k)^2} = R\}$

(3) $C = \{(x, y) \mid (x - h)^2 + (y - k)^2 = R^2\}$

Thus, points that are R units from (h, k) are elements in the solution set of

$$(x - h)^2 + (y - k)^2 = R^2 \tag{1}$$

What we have shown, thus far, is that each point of the circle must be an element in the solution set of equation (1). Now it is necessary to show that each element in the solution set of equation (1) is a point on the circle with center (h, k) and radius R. This can be done rather easily by simply reversing the steps in our proof. Thus,

$$(x - h)^2 + (y - k)^2 = R^2 \qquad (1)$$

$$\sqrt{(x - h)^2 + (y - k)^2} = R \qquad (2)$$

Equation (2) indicates that every element (x, y) in the solution set of (1) is a point whose distance from (h, k) is always R. But this is exactly what we mean by a circle with center (h, k) and radius R!

Your attention must be called to one point of this proof. In finding the square roots of both sides of the equality, the negative sign was not used. This was avoided, for we had agreed that distance would always be considered as a positive number.

The application of this theorem to problems is extremely simple.

Illustration:

Find the equation of the circle whose center is at the point $(2, -3)$ and whose radius is 5 units.

METHOD: This problem entails simply writing the general form of the equation of the circle. This is the form found in Theorem 81. The letters h and k are then replaced by 2 and -3, and R by 5.

Thus,
$$(x - h)^2 + (y - k)^2 = R^2$$
$$(x - 2)^2 + (y + 3)^2 = 25$$

Just a word of caution: be careful to change the signs of the coordinates of the center when substituting them in the general form of the equation of the circle.

Should the center of the circle be at the origin, the equation of the circle will become

$$(x - h)^2 + (y - k)^2 = R^2$$
$$(x - 0)^2 + (y - 0)^2 = R^2$$
$$x^2 + y^2 = R^2 \text{ (General equation of a circle with center at origin.)}$$

Just as earlier we had shown that the graph of the equation of the form $ax + by = c$ was a line, so we are prepared now to prove a comparable theorem relating to circles.

THEOREM 82: The graph of every equation of the form

$$Ax^2 + Ay^2 + Bx + Cy + D = 0 \qquad (1)$$

will be a circle.

ANALYSIS: To prove this, we will show that every point in the solution set of this equation is a fixed distance from a fixed point. This will imply, on the basis of the reverse of the definition of a circle, that the graph of the solution set is a circle.

PROOF

Dividing both sides of equation (1) by A,

$$x^2 + y^2 + \frac{B}{A}x + \frac{C}{A}y + \frac{D}{A} = 0$$

Since B/A, C/A, and D/A are constants, we will replace each of them with other constants so as to simplify our work.

Let $B/A = 2p$, $C/A = 2q$, $D/A = s$

Then, $x^2 + y^2 + 2px + 2qy + s = 0$

$$(x^2 + 2px + \underline{?}\,) + (y^2 + 2qy + \underline{?}\,) = -s$$

To determine the missing term, we complete the square of each trinomial, remembering, of course, to add the same quantity to the right side of the equality.

$$(x^2 + 2px + p^2) + (y^2 + 2qy + q^2) = p^2 + q^2 - s$$
$$(x + p)^2 + (y + q)^2 = p^2 + q^2 - s$$
$$\sqrt{(x + p)^2 + (y + q)^2} = \sqrt{p^2 + q^2 - s} \qquad (2)$$

Since the left side of the equation above represents the distance from the point (x, y) to the point $(-p, -q)$, this equation simply expresses the fact that each point (x, y) in the solution set is a fixed distance

$$\sqrt{p^2 + q^2 - s}$$

from the fixed point $(-p, -q)$. Hence, the graph of the points in the solution set of equation (1) will be a circle.

Examine the right side of equation (2). If $p^2 + q^2$ were equal to s, what would be the value of $p^2 + q^2 - s$? Hence, what would be the radius of this circle be? Under these conditions the only element in the solution set will be the center $(-p, -q)$. Thus, the circle will consist of only one point. A circle such as this is called a *point circle*. Similarly, if $p^2 + q^2$ were less than s, the quantity under the radical would be negative.† In this event the radius of the circle will be an imaginary number. Circles such as these are called *imaginary circles*.

Illustration 1:

Find the radius and the coordinates of the center of the circle whose equation is

$$x^2 + y^2 - 8x + 2y - 3 = 0$$

METHOD: Since the equation is of the form stated in Theorem 82, its graph will be a circle. By rewriting it in the general form shown in Theorem 81, we can easily determine the radius and the coordinates of the center.

† This statement is true only if s is a positive number.

$$(x^2 - 8x + \underline{\ ?\ }) + (y^2 + 2y + \underline{\ ?\ }) = 3$$
$$(x^2 - 8x + 16) + (y^2 + 2y + 1) = 3 + 16 + 1$$
$$(x - 4)^2 + (y + 1)^2 = 20$$

Comparing this with the general form

$$(x - h)^2 + (y - k)^2 = R^2$$

we can say that

coordinates of center: $(4, -1)$; radius $= \sqrt{20} = 2\sqrt{5}$

There is but one further matter that we have to investigate. This is the situation that arises when we encounter inequalities with reference to circles.

Illustration 2:

Determine the locus of points that are less than 7 units from the point $(3, 4)$.

METHOD: Rewriting the problem, we obtain

(1) C is the set of points such that the distance from each of these points to the point $(3, 4)$ is less than 7 units.

(2) $C = \{(x, y) \mid \sqrt{(x - 3)^2 + (y - 4)^2} < 7\}$

(3) $C = \{(x, y) \mid (x - 3)^2 + (y - 4)^2 < 49\}$

Were the inequality sign in the third description replaced by an equality sign, the graph of this set would be the circle with center $(3, 4)$ and radius 7. Hence, each point on the circle would be 7 units from the center $(3, 4)$.

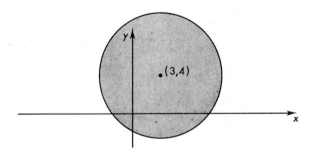

Figure 13-21.

The conditions of this problem state that the points in the set must be less than 7 units from $(3, 4)$. Hence, these points will lie within the circle. Thus, the region shaded in red will represent the locus of points that are less than 7 units from the point $(3, 4)$.

Similarly, were we required to determine the locus of points that were more than 7 units from the point $(3, 4)$, these points would lie outside the circle.

Illustration 3:

Find the locus of points that are more than 4 units from the line $x = 8$ and less than 6 units from the point $(8, 7)$.

METHOD: Using set symbols,

$$A = \{(x, y) \mid x > 12 \text{ or } x < 4\}$$
$$B = \{(x, y) \mid \sqrt{(x - 8)^2 + (y - 7)^2} < 6\}$$

Our problem is to find $A \cap B$. Rewriting B, we obtain

$$B = \{(x, y) \mid (x - 8)^2 + (y - 7)^2 < 36\}$$

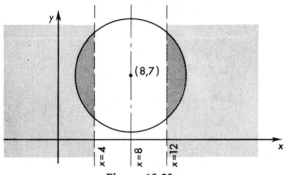

Figure 13-22.

The points to the right of $x = 12$ and to the left of $x = 4$ are in set A. The points within the circle are in set B. Hence, the intersection of A and B are points in the region shaded in red. The points in this region are more than 4 units from the line $x = 8$ and less than 6 units from the point $(8, 7)$.

EXERCISES

1. Determine the equation of each of the following circles:
   (a) Center $(0, 2)$, radius 5   (b) Center $(3, 0)$, radius 4
   (c) Center $(2, 5)$, radius 1   (d) Center $(-3, 1)$, radius 6
   (e) Center $(5, -3)$, radius $\sqrt{5}$ (f) Center $(-1, -5)$, radius $2\sqrt{3}$

2. Find the equation of the circle
   (a) Whose center is the origin and passes through the point $(6, 0)$.
   (b) Whose center is the origin and passes through the point $(0, -5)$.
   (c) Whose center is $(6, 0)$ and passes through the origin.
   (d) Whose center is $(0, -8)$ and passes through the origin.
   (e) Whose center is $(4, 6)$ and passes through the point $(4, 10)$.
   (f) Whose center is $(2, 3)$ and passes through the point $(-4, 3)$.
   (g) Whose center is $(4, -5)$ and passes through the origin.
   (h) Whose center is $(3, 5)$ and passes through the point $(-1, 2)$.

3. Determine the center and radius of each of the following circles:
   (a) $x^2 + y^2 - 6x - 16 = 0$
   (b) $x^2 + y^2 + 8y + 7 = 0$
   (c) $x^2 + y^2 - 4x - 6y - 23 = 0$
   (d) $x^2 + y^2 + 10x - 12y + 60 = 0$
   (e) $2x^2 + 2y^2 - 16x + 12y - 48 = 0$
   (f) $3x^2 + 3y^2 - 6x + 48y - 105 = 0$

4. Show that the point $(2, -5)$ lies on the circle $(x - 3)^2 + (y + 4)^2 = 2$.

5. Show that the point $(-3, 1)$ lies on the circle $x^2 + y^2 + 4x - 10y + 12 = 0$.

6. (a) Using set symbols, express the locus of points such that the sum of the squares of the distances from each of those points to the points $(0, 0)$ and $(6, 0)$ is 36.
   (b) Show that this locus is a circle.
   (c) Show that the center of this circle is the midpoint of the line segment joining the two points.
   (d) Explain how the locus would have been affected had the sum of the squares of the distances been 18 rather than 36.
   (e) Explain how the locus would have been affected had the sum of the squares of the distances been less than 18 rather than 36.
   (f) If the *difference* of the squares had been 36, rather than the sum of the squares, what would the locus have been?

7. (a) Show that the locus of points such that the distance from each of these points to the point $(-2, 0)$ is twice its distance to the point $(2, 0)$ is a circle.
   (b) Find the center and radius of this circle.

8. Use the diagram at the right to prove each of the following problems. The center of the circle is the origin.

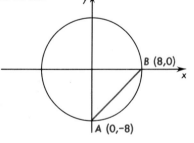

   (a) Prove that the radius drawn to the midpoint of $\overline{AB}$ is perpendicular to $\overleftrightarrow{AB}$.
   (b) Prove that the perpendicular bisector of $\overline{AB}$ passes through the center of the circle.

9. (a) Express with set symbols and then draw the locus of points that are less than 5 units from the point $(2, 1)$.

(b) What will be the locus of points that are more than 5 units from the point $(2, 1)$?

10. Draw the locus of points that are less than 10 units from the origin and also on the line $x = y$.

11. Draw the locus of points that are more than 5 units to the right of the y-axis and less than 10 units from the point $(7, 2)$.

12. (a) Draw the locus of points that are 8 units from the origin and equidistant from the points $(0, -2)$ and $(2, 0)$.
    (b) Draw the locus of points that are less than 8 units from the origin and equidistant from the points $(0, -2)$ and $(2, 0)$.
    (c) Draw the locus of points that are more than 8 units from the origin and equidistant from the points $(0, -2)$ and $(2, 0)$.

13. (a) Draw the locus of points that are less than 2 units from the point $(8, 10)$ and more than 6 units from the line $y = 10$.
    (b) Draw the locus of points that are more than 2 units from the point $(8, 10)$ and less than 6 units from the line $y = 10$.

14.* Draw the locus of points that are either less than 2 units from the point $(8, 10)$ or more than 6 units from the line $y = 10$.

■ Test and Review

1. How would you read each of the following expressions?
   (a) $\{x \mid x + 4 = 7\}$
   (b) $\{(x, y) \mid y > 2x + 3\}$

2. Find two ordered pairs of numbers in $\{(x, y) \mid 3x + y = 10\}$.

3. Find two ordered pairs of numbers in the solution set of

$$2x - y > 4$$

4. Determine the equation of each of the lines under the conditions given.
   (a) Passes through the points $(2, 5)$ and $(0, -4)$.
   (b) Passes through the point $(-1, 2)$ and has a slope of $2/3$.
   (c) Passes through the origin and the point $(4, -1)$.
   (d) Intersects the x-axis at $x = -3$ and has a slope of -1.
   (e) Parallel to the y-axis and passes through the point $(2, -1)$.

5. $A(-3, 2)$, $B(1, -4)$, and $C(7, 6)$ are the vertices of a triangle.
   (a) Find the equation of the median from A to $\overline{BC}$.
   (b) Find the equation of the perpendicular bisector of $\overline{BC}$.
   (c) Find the equation of the altitude from B to $\overline{AC}$.

6. Is the following set of points collinear? Justify your answer.

$$\{(-2, 5), (0, 2), (-6, 11)\}$$

7. **(a)** Find the equation of the line that passes through $(-4, 2)$ and is parallel to the line $3x + y = 4$.

   (b) Find the equation of the line that passes through the origin and is perpendicular to the line $x - 2y = 5$.

8. The vertices of an isosceles triangle are $A(3, -5)$, $B(20, 4)$, and $C(1, 7)$ where $\angle B$ is the vertex angle. Prove that the altitude to the base is also the median to the base.

9. **(a)** Find the intersection of the solution sets of the following two equations: $5x - y = -11$ and $2x + 5y = 1$.

   (b) Interpret the ordered pair of numbers that you found as your answer to part (a).

10. Will the graphs of the following two equations be parallel, intersect, or be coincident?

$$2x - 4y = 7$$
$$7x = 14y - 5$$

11. Prove that the medians of the triangle whose vertices are $A(0, 4)$, $B(6, 0)$, and $C(2, 8)$ are concurrent.

12. Prove that the diagonals of a rectangle are congruent.

13. Prove that the line segments joining a vertex of a square to the midpoints of the opposite sides trisect the diagonal of the square that is not drawn from that vertex. Let $(0, 0)$, $(2a, 0)$, $(2a, 2a)$, and $(0, 2a)$ be the four vertices of the square.

14. Determine the element in the solution set of $3x + 12 \leq 4x$ that has the least value.

15. By graphing, determine the intersection of the solution sets of the following pair of equations:

$$x > -5 \quad \text{and} \quad y + 3x \leq 1$$

16. Using set symbols, rewrite the description of each of the following loci:

   (a) The locus of points that are 3 units to the left of the vertical axis.

   (b) The locus of points that are more than 5 units above the horizontal axis.

   (c) The locus of points that are more than 2 units from the line $x = 7$.

   (d) The locus of points that are a distance of 2 units from the point $(2, 6)$.

   (e) The locus of points that are less than 4 units from the origin.

   (f) The locus of points that are equidistant from the points $(-5, 4)$ and $(7, 8)$.

   (g) The locus of points such that the difference of the squares of its distances from any point of the locus to the points $(-3, -2)$ and $(1, 6)$ is always 3.

17. (a) Draw the locus of points that are 5 units from the vertical axis and equidistant from the points $(-4, 1)$ and $(6, -5)$.

(b) Draw the locus of points that are less than 5 units from the origin and 2 units from the horizontal axis.

18. Determine the equation of the circle under each of the following conditions.

(a) center $(1, -4)$; radius 2.

(b) center $(1, -3)$; passes through the origin.

19. Determine the center and radius of the circle whose equation is

$$x^2 + y^2 - 4x + 6y - 36 = 0$$

20. Draw the locus of points that are more than 5 units and less than 10 units from the origin.

■ Try This For Fun

When light strikes a shiny surface, such as a mirror, it is reflected from that surface in a way so that the angle at which it makes contact with the surface is congruent to the angle at which it leaves the surface. In the drawing below, the light ray $\overrightarrow{BA}$ made contact with the mirror

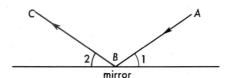

forming the $\angle 1$. When it bounced off the mirror, the light ray $\overrightarrow{BC}$ formed the $\angle 2$ with the surface such that $\angle 2 \cong \angle 1$.

This simple piece of information can help us find the height of an object whose base is inaccessible to us. Can you prove that the height of the flag pole below is

$$x = \frac{h \cdot AB}{AC - DB}$$

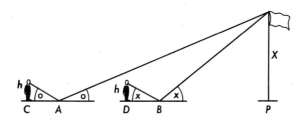

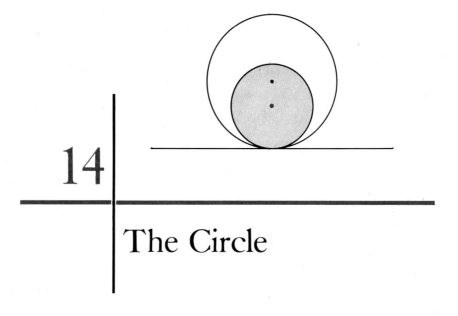

14 | The Circle

MANY OF THE PROPERTIES OF A CIRCLE CAN be developed far more easily through the processes of synthetic geometry rather than coordinate geometry. Hence, to formulate these principles, we are going to return to the methods of proof used earlier in the course.

As usual, it will be necessary to define our terms before proceeding.

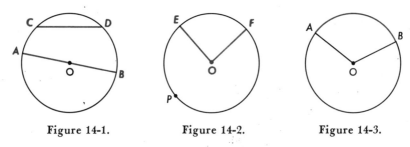

| Figure 14-1. | Figure 14-2. | Figure 14-3. |

DEFINITION 75: A chord of a circle is a line segment whose endpoints are two points of the circle.

In Figure 14-1 the line segment CD is a chord of circle O. Segment AB is also a chord of circle O; however, it is a special chord since it passes through the center of the circle. What is its name?

DEFINITION 76: A diameter of a circle is a chord such that one of its points is the center of the circle.

DEFINITION 77: A central angle of a circle is an angle whose vertex is the center of the circle.

In Figure 14-2 $\angle EOF$ is a central angle of the circle O. By having an understanding of the central angle at our disposal, it is possible to define an arc of a circle.

DEFINITION 78: A minor arc AB of circle O where A and B are points of that circle is the union of the points A and B and the points of the circle in the interior of central angle AOB.

In Figure 14-3 the points marked in red are the points of the minor arc AB of circle O. Each of these points are in the interior of $\angle AOB$ and each is a point of circle O. In addition, points A and B are also points of minor arc AB.

DEFINITION 79: A major arc AB of a circle O where A and B are points of that circle is the union of the points A and B and the points of the circle in the exterior of central angle AOB.

In Figure 14-3 the points of circle O that are drawn in black will be the points of major arc AB. Each of these points is in the exterior of $\angle AOB$ and each is on circle O. Points A and B themselves are points of the arc, too.

DEFINITION 80: A semicircle AB of a circle O where A and B are endpoints of a diameter of this circle is the union of the points A and B and the points on the circle in the half plane on one side of $\overleftrightarrow{AB}$.

All three of these terms—the minor arc, the major arc, and the semicircle—are referred to as arcs of a circle. The symbol $\frown$ is used to represent the word *arc*. Confusion immediately arises, for by $\overset{\frown}{EF}$ (read as *arc EF*) in Figure 14-2, do we mean the minor arc or major arc? Henceforth, should we refer to the $\overset{\frown}{EF}$, we will be speaking of the minor arc EF, not the major arc. Should it be necessary to call attention to the major arc EF, this will be done by either referring to it as *major arc EF* or by naming another point on the circle and calling the arc, $\overset{\frown}{EPF}$ (see Figure 14-2). There are times when more than two letters are employed to name a minor arc also. Thus,

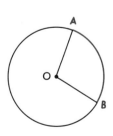

Figure 14-4.

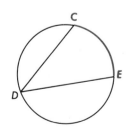

Figure 14-5.

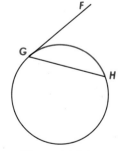

Figure 14-6.

in Figure 14-1 $\overgroup{AD}$ may be called $\overgroup{ACD}$, or $\overgroup{CB}$ may be called $\overgroup{CDB}$. The letters that appear in the first and last positions are the names of the end-points of the arc.

In Figure 14-4 $\overgroup{AB}$ is said to be the intercepted arc of $\angle AOB$. In Figure 14-5 $\overgroup{CE}$ is the intercepted arc of $\angle CDE$; and in Figure 14-6 $\overgroup{GH}$ is the intercepted arc of $\angle FGH$. Thus,

DEFINITION 81: An arc of a circle intercepted by an angle is an arc such that each side of the angle contains at least one endpoint of the arc and all points of the arc other than the endpoints are in the interior of the angle.

In Figure 14-4 endpoint A of $\overgroup{AB}$ fell on side OA, while endpoint B fell on side OB. It is possible for one endpoint to fall on both sides of the angle, for in Figure 14-6 point G is a point of both $\overrightarrow{GF}$ and $\overrightarrow{GH}$.

A one-to-one correspondence exists between the chords of a circle and the *minor* arcs of that circle. Thus, in Figure 14-7 there is only one minor

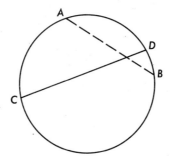

Figure 14-7.

arc that bears the name $\overgroup{CD}$ and but one chord CD. Similarly, there is but one $\overgroup{AB}$ and one chord whose endpoints are A and B. Hence, we refer to $\overline{AB}$ as corresponding to $\overgroup{AB}$; and, conversely, $\overgroup{AB}$ corresponds to $\overline{AB}$.

In order to make it possible to relate the measure of an arc to the measure of the central angle that intercepted that arc, the following definition was devised:

DEFINITION 82: **(1)** The measure of a minor arc or a semicircle is the measure of the central angle that intercepts that arc.

　　　　　　(2) The measure of a major arc is 360 minus the measure of the minor arc having the same endpoints as the major arc.

Thus, if in Figure 14-8 $m \angle AOB$ was 50, the measure of $\overgroup{AB}$ (written as $m \overgroup{AB}$) would also be 50. In Figure 14-9, where central angle 1 is a straight angle, the $m \overgroup{ACB}$ is 180. Similarly, $m \overgroup{BDA}$ is also 180. Hence, it appears that the arc consisting of the entire circle O will have a measure of 360.

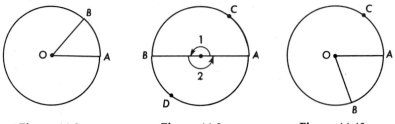

Figure 14-8.   Figure 14-9.   Figure 14-10.

Since we did not admit to the existence of angles greater than a straight angle in our work, it was necessary to define the measure of a major arc as we did, for no central angle less than a straight angle could intercept a major arc. Hence, to find in Figure 14-10 the measure of $\widehat{ACB}$ we would first determine the measure of $\widehat{AB}$ and subtract this value from 360, which is the measure of the entire circle. Therefore, if $m \angle AOB$ in Figure 14-10 is 70, then the $m \widehat{AB} = 70$ and $m \widehat{ACB} = 360 - 70$, or 290.

Earlier it had been pointed out that $m \angle AOB = 70$ could be expressed as the statement that $\angle AOB$ was an angle of 70 degrees where the degree was the unit of measure for the size of an angle. In the same way, if $m \widehat{AB} = 70$, then $\widehat{AB}$ is said to be an arc of 70 degrees. However, to distinguish the unit of measure for the angle from that of the arc, we call the former the *angular degree*, while the latter is the *arc degree*.

Other than the fact that the angular degree and the arc degree are units of measure for two different geometric figures, there is another very, very important difference between them. Whereas, by definition two angles having equal measures are congruent, this relationship will generally not be the case for arcs having equal measures! Consider Figure 14-11. If $\angle AOB$

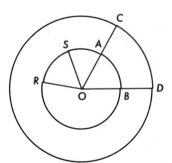

Figure 14-11.

was an angle of 60 angular degrees, this would imply that both $\widehat{AB}$ and $\widehat{CD}$ are arcs of 60 arc degrees. Obviously, to say that these arcs are congruent would stretch the imagination excessively! The statement that $\widehat{AB}$ is an arc of 60 arc degrees implies merely that it is $\frac{60}{360}$, or $\frac{1}{6}$, of its circle in size.

In the same way $\overset{\frown}{CD}$ is $\frac{1}{6}$ of the size of its own circle. And although equal in the number of arc degrees in their measures, the two arcs are far from equal in inches, or feet, or any linear unit. However, were both the measure of $\overset{\frown}{AB}$ and the measure of $\overset{\frown}{RS}$ in circle O equal to 60, it would seem that we should say that $\overset{\frown}{AB} \cong \overset{\frown}{RS}$, for both are $\frac{1}{6}$ the size of the same circle. First, however, it would be well to define congruent arcs before trying to prove this.

DEFINITION 83: Congruent circles are circles whose radii are congruent.

DEFINITION 84: Congruent arcs are arcs in the same or congruent circles that have equal measures.

Now we are prepared to prove the relationship stated above.

THEOREM 83: If two central angles of a circle are congruent, then their intercepted arcs are congruent.

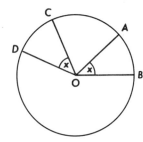

Given: $\angle AOB \cong \angle COD$ in $\odot$ O
Concl.: $\overset{\frown}{AB} \cong \overset{\frown}{CD}$

Figure 14-12.

PROOF STATEMENTS	REASONS
1. $\angle AOB \cong \angle COD$ in $\odot$ O	1. Given
2. $m \angle AOB = m \angle COD$	2. Def. of congruent angles
3. $m \overset{\frown}{AB} = m \angle AOB$	3. Def. of the measure of an arc
4. $m \overset{\frown}{CD} = m \angle COD$	4. Same as 3
5. $m \overset{\frown}{AB} = m \overset{\frown}{CD}$	5. If two numbers are equal to two equal numbers, then they are equal to each other.
6. $\overset{\frown}{AB} \cong \overset{\frown}{CD}$	6. Two arcs of equal measures are congruent arcs. (Reverse of definition of congruent arcs)

THEOREM 84: If two arcs of a circle are congruent, then the central angles intercepting these arcs are congruent.

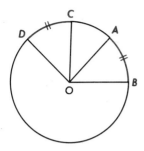

Figure 14-13.

Given: $\overset{\frown}{AB} \cong \overset{\frown}{CD}$ in $\odot$ O

Concl.: $\angle AOB \cong \angle COD$

PROOF	(The reasons will be left for you to supply.)

1. $\overset{\frown}{AB} \cong \overset{\frown}{CD}$ in $\odot$ O
2. $m \overset{\frown}{AB} = m \overset{\frown}{CD}$
3. $m \angle AOB = m \overset{\frown}{AB}$

4. $m \angle COD = m \overset{\frown}{CD}$
5. $m \angle AOB = m \angle COD$
6. $\angle AOB \cong \angle COD$

THEOREM 85: If in a circle two chords are congruent, their corresponding arcs are congruent.

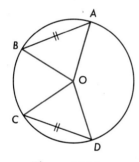

Figure 14-14.

Given: $\overline{AB} \cong \overline{CD}$ in $\odot$ O

Concl.: $\overset{\frown}{AB} \cong \overset{\frown}{CD}$

PROOF	STATEMENTS	REASONS
	1. Let $\overset{\leftrightarrow}{OA}$ be the line through points O and A. The same for $\overset{\leftrightarrow}{OB}$, $\overset{\leftrightarrow}{OC}$, and $\overset{\leftrightarrow}{OD}$.	1. There exists one and only one line through two points.
	2. $\overline{AB} \cong \overline{CD}$ (s)	2. Given
	3. $\overline{OA} \cong \overline{OC}$ (s)	3. The radii of a circle are congruent.
	4. $\overline{OB} \cong \overline{OD}$ (s)	4. Same as 3
	5. $\triangle OAB \cong \triangle OCD$	5. S.S.S.
	6. $\angle AOB \cong \angle COD$	6. Def. of $\cong$ polygons
	7. $\overset{\frown}{AB} \cong \overset{\frown}{CD}$	7. Theorem 83

THEOREM 86: If in a circle two arcs are congruent, their corresponding chords are congruent.

PROOF

The proof of this theorem is very much the same as that for
Theorem 85. It will be left for you to do.

Theorems 83 and 84 show the relationship that exists between central
angles and their intercepted arcs. On the other hand, Theorems 85 and 86
point up how chords are related to their corresponding arcs. In summary,

A. To prove arcs of a   **B.** To prove chords of   **C.** To prove central
circle congruent: a circle congruent: angles of a circle
                                                          congruent:

    (1) Prove chords   **(1)** Prove arcs   **(1)** Prove arcs
       congruent   congruent   congruent

or

    (2) Prove central
       angles congru-
       ent

The definitions of such terms as "bisector of an arc" or "midpoint
of an arc" are similar to these definitions with reference to a line segment.
In the work that follows, an understanding of these definitions is assumed.

Illustration:

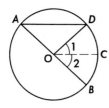

Given: C midpoint of $\overset{\frown}{BD}$ in $\odot O$

Concl.: $\overset{\leftrightarrow}{AD} \parallel \overset{\leftrightarrow}{OC}$

| **PROOF** | (The reasons will be left for you to supply.) |

1. C midpoint of $\overset{\frown}{BD}$
2. $\overset{\frown}{BC} \cong \overset{\frown}{CD}$
3. $\angle 1 \cong \angle 2$
4. $m \angle DOB = m \angle 1 + m \angle 2$
5. $\overline{OA} \cong \overline{OD}$
6. $\angle A \cong \angle D$

7. $m \angle DOB = m \angle A + m \angle D$
8. $m \angle A + m \angle D = m \angle 1 + m \angle 2$
9. $m \angle A + m \angle A = m \angle 2 + m \angle 2$
   or $2m \angle A = 2m \angle 2$
10. $\angle A \cong \angle 2$
11. $\overset{\leftrightarrow}{AD} \parallel \overset{\leftrightarrow}{OC}$

EXERCISES

$$\boxed{A}$$

1. Given: $\triangle ABC$ is isosceles
with $\overline{AB} \cong \overline{AC}$
Concl.: $\overset{\frown}{ABC} \cong \overset{\frown}{ACB}$

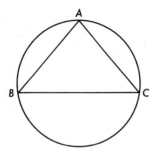

Given: $\overset{\frown}{BAD} \cong \overset{\frown}{CDA}$ **2.**
Concl.: $\overline{AB} \cong \overline{CD}$

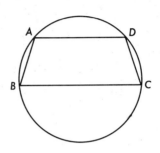

3. Given: $\angle A \cong \angle D$
$\overline{BE} \cong \overline{CE}$
Concl.: $\overset{\frown}{ABC} \cong \overset{\frown}{DCB}$

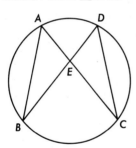

Given: $\odot O$ with $\overset{\frown}{AB} \cong \overset{\frown}{CD}$ **4.**
Concl.: $\angle A \cong \angle B$

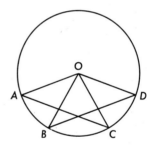

5. Given: $\overset{\frown}{AB} \cong \overset{\frown}{CD}$
Concl.: $\angle B \cong \angle C$

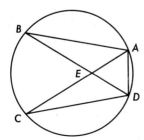

Given: $\odot O$ with C the mid-   **6.**
point of $\overset{\frown}{AB}$
Concl.: $\overleftrightarrow{OC} \perp \overleftrightarrow{AB}$

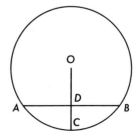

7. Given: ⊙O with diameter
AB
$\angle CBA \cong \angle DBA$
Concl.: $\overset{\frown}{CA} \cong \overset{\frown}{DA}$

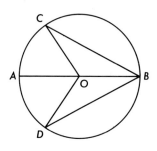

8. Given: Circles A and B with
$\overset{\leftrightarrow}{AB}$ the line drawn
between the centers
Concl.: E midpt. of $\overset{\frown}{CED}$
F midpt. of $\overset{\frown}{CFD}$

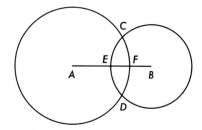

9. Given: ⊙O with $\overline{DB}$ a diam.
$\overset{\leftrightarrow}{AB} \parallel \overset{\leftrightarrow}{CO}$
Concl.: C is the midpoint
of $\overset{\frown}{AD}$.

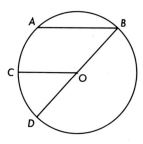

10. Given: P midpt. of $\overset{\frown}{APB}$
Q midpt. of $\overset{\frown}{AQB}$
Concl.: $\overset{\leftrightarrow}{PQ} \perp$ bi. $\overline{AB}$

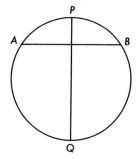

11. Given: P midpt. of $\overset{\frown}{AB}$ in ⊙O
Q midpt. of $\overset{\frown}{CD}$
Concl.: $\overset{\leftrightarrow}{AB} \parallel \overset{\leftrightarrow}{CD}$

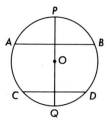

12. Given: ⊙O with $\overset{\leftrightarrow}{AB} \parallel \overset{\leftrightarrow}{CD}$
P midpt. of $\overset{\frown}{AB}$
Concl.: Q midpt. of $\overset{\frown}{CD}$

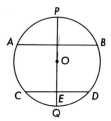

13. Given: $\overset{\frown}{AD} \cong \overset{\frown}{BC}$

    Concl.: $\triangle EDC$ is isosceles.

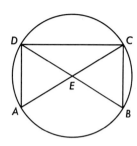

Given: $\odot O$ with D the mid- **14.**

    point of $\overline{AB}$

    C is the midpoint of

    $\overset{\frown}{AB}$.

Concl.: $\overset{\leftrightarrow}{OD}$ passes

    through C.

    (Hint: See page 184.)

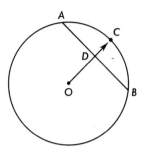

15.* Given: Circle O

    C is the midpoint

    of $\overset{\frown}{AB}$.

    D is the midpoint

    of $\overline{AB}$.

Concl.: D lies on $\overset{\leftrightarrow}{OC}$.

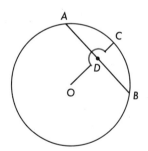

Given: Circles A and B **16.***

    P is the midpoint

    of $\overset{\frown}{CPD}$.

    Q is the midpoint

    of $\overset{\frown}{CQD}$.

Concl.: $\overset{\leftrightarrow}{QP}$ passes through A.

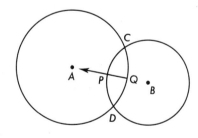

$$\boxed{B}$$

1. If the vertices of an equilateral triangle lie on a circle, they will divide the circle into three congruent arcs.
2. If the vertices of a parallelogram lie on a circle, then the diagonals will be congruent.

3. A diameter of a circle bisects the circle.†

4. The line joining the midpoint of a chord to the midpoint of its corresponding arc is perpendicular to the chord.

5. From the outer endpoint of a radius perpendicular segments are drawn to two other radii. If the perpendicular segments are congruent, then the two arcs cut off by the three radii are congruent.

6. A central angle intercepts an arc on the circle. If from the midpoint of the arc perpendicular segments are drawn to the sides of the angle, then these segments are congruent.

7. A radius perpendicular to a chord bisects the chord and its corresponding arc.†

8. If the measures of two central angles of a circle are unequal, the measures of their intercepted arcs will be unequal. (Hint: Use the indirect proof.)

9. If two chords of a circle are not congruent, their corresponding arcs will not be congruent.

10. If two arcs of a circle are not congruent, their corresponding chords will not be congruent.

11. If from a point on a circle two chords are drawn so as to make congruent angles with the radius drawn to this point, then the arcs corresponding to the chords will be congruent.

12. The line joining the midpoint of a chord to the midpoint of its corresponding arc passes through the center of the circle.

13. If two congruent chords intersect within a circle, then the segments of one will be congruent to the corresponding segments of the other.

14. If two circles intersect, the perpendicular bisector of the chord that is common to the two circles passes through the centers of the two circles.

■ Chords Equidistant from the Center of a Circle

Thus far we have but one method for showing chords of a circle to be congruent. A second method, to be presented in this unit, will depend upon our ability to show that the chords of the circle are equidistant from the center of the circle. As you recall, the distance from a point to a line is the measure of the perpendicular line segment drawn from that point to the line.‡ Thus, to say that point P is equidistant from lines a and b is to imply three things:

$$(1)\ \overleftrightarrow{PR} \perp a \qquad (2)\ \overleftrightarrow{PS} \perp b \qquad (3)\ \overline{PR} \cong \overline{PS}$$

Similarly, were we asked to prove that P is equidistant from lines a and b, we would know that

† These problems often appear as theorems.
‡ See page 378.

$$(1) \overleftrightarrow{PR} \perp a \quad \text{and} \quad (2) \overleftrightarrow{PS} \perp b$$

while the conclusion would be

$$\overline{PR} \cong \overline{PS}$$

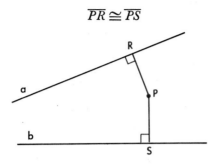

Figure 14-15.

THEOREM 87: If two chords are equidistant from the center of a circle, they are congruent.

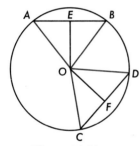

Figure 14-16.

Given: $\odot O$ with $\overline{OE} \cong \overline{OF}$

$$\overleftrightarrow{OE} \perp \overleftrightarrow{AB}$$

$$\overleftrightarrow{OF} \perp \overleftrightarrow{CD}$$

Concl.: $\overline{AB} \cong \overline{CD}$

ANALYSIS: By proving $\triangle OBE \cong \triangle ODF$, we can show $\overline{BE} \cong \overline{DF}$. In the same way $\triangle OAE$ can be shown congruent to $\triangle OCF$, and hence, $\overline{EA} \cong \overline{FC}$. Then by applying the addition postulate it will follow that $\overline{AB} \cong \overline{CD}$.

| PROOF | (The reasons will be left for you to supply.) |

1. Let $\overleftrightarrow{OB}$ be the line through points O and B.

2. Same for $\overleftrightarrow{OA}$, $\overleftrightarrow{OD}$, and $\overleftrightarrow{OC}$

3. $\overline{OE} \cong \overline{OF}$ (*l*)

4. $\overleftrightarrow{OE} \perp \overleftrightarrow{AB}$

5. $\angle OEB$ is a right angle.

6. $\overleftrightarrow{OF} \perp \overleftrightarrow{CD}$

7. $\angle OFD$ is a right angle.

8. $\overline{OB} \cong \overline{OD}$ (*h*)

9. $\triangle OBE \cong \triangle ODF$

10. $\overline{BE} \cong \overline{DF}$

In the same way, $\triangle OAE$ can be shown congruent to $\triangle OCF$.

11. $\overline{EA} \cong \overline{FC}$

12. $\overline{AB} \cong \overline{CD}$

The converse of Theorem 87 is also quite important. Its proof, however, is dependent upon the following statement.

THEOREM 88: A radius perpendicular to a chord bisects the chord and its corresponding arc.

PROOF

You were asked to prove this relation in Problem 7, page 460; hence, its proof will not be given now.

THEOREM 89: If two chords of a circle are congruent, they are equidistant from the center of that circle.

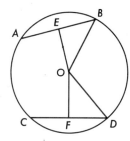

Figure 14-17.

Given: $\odot O$ with $\overline{AB} \cong \overline{CD}$

$\overleftrightarrow{OE} \perp \overleftrightarrow{AB}$

$\overleftrightarrow{OF} \perp \overleftrightarrow{CD}$

Concl.: $\overline{OE} \cong \overline{OF}$

ANALYSIS: By using Theorem 88 and the postulate that halves of congruent segments are congruent, it can be shown that $\overline{BE}$ and $\overline{DF}$ are congruent. With this piece of information it will follow that $\triangle OBE \cong \triangle ODF$ and, hence, $\overline{OE} \cong \overline{OF}$.

| **PROOF** | (The reasons will be left for you to supply.) |

1. Let $\overleftrightarrow{OB}$ be the line through points O and B.

2. Same for $\overleftrightarrow{OD}$

3. $\overleftrightarrow{OE} \perp \overleftrightarrow{AB}$

4. $\overleftrightarrow{OE}$ bisects $\overline{AB}$. (Theorem 88)

5. $\overleftrightarrow{OF} \perp \overleftrightarrow{CD}$

6. $\overleftrightarrow{OF}$ bisects $\overline{CD}$.

7. But, $\overline{AB} \cong \overline{CD}$

8. $\therefore \overline{BE} \cong \overline{DF}$ (*l*)

9. $\angle OEB$ is a right angle.

10. $\angle OFD$ is a right angle.

11. $\overline{OB} \cong \overline{OD}$ (*h*)

12. $\triangle OBE \cong \triangle ODF$

13. $\overline{OE} \cong \overline{OF}$

All principles developed in this chapter with reference to a single circle will hold as well for congruent circles. As an exercise, prove Theorems 85, 86, 87, and 89 by using two congruent circles rather than the same circle.

EXERCISES

A

1. Given: $\odot O$ with $\overleftrightarrow{OC} \perp \overleftrightarrow{AE}$
$\overline{AB} \cong \overline{DE}$

Concl.: $\triangle OBD$ is isosceles.

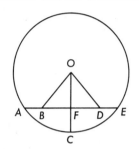

Given: $\odot O$ with $\overleftrightarrow{OC} \perp \overleftrightarrow{AB}$ **2.**

Concl.: $\overrightarrow{CO}$ bisects $\angle ACB$.

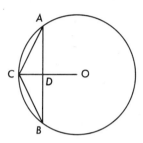

3. Given: $\odot O$ with $\overleftrightarrow{AD} \perp \overleftrightarrow{BC}$

Concl.: $\triangle ABC$ is isosceles.

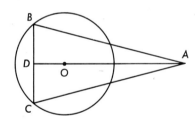

Given: $\odot O$ with $\overline{BA} \cong \overline{BC}$ **4.**
$\overleftrightarrow{OD} \perp \overleftrightarrow{AB}$
$\overleftrightarrow{OE} \perp \overleftrightarrow{CB}$

Concl.: $\overrightarrow{BO}$ bisects $\angle ABC$.

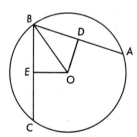

5. Given: $\odot O$ with $\overleftrightarrow{AO} \perp \overleftrightarrow{BO}$
$\overleftrightarrow{CO} \perp \overleftrightarrow{AB}$

Concl.: $\triangle OCB$ is isosceles.

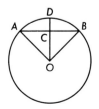

Given: $ABCD$ is an isos. trap.   **6.**
with $\overline{AB} \cong \overline{DC}$ in $\odot O$.

Concl.: $\overline{AC}$ and $\overline{BD}$ are equidistant from O.

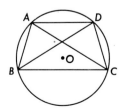

7. Given: $\odot O$ with $\overline{AB} \cong \overline{AC}$
$\overset{\leftrightarrow}{OD} \perp \overset{\leftrightarrow}{AB}$
$\overset{\leftrightarrow}{OE} \perp \overset{\leftrightarrow}{AC}$
Concl.: $\triangle ADE$ is isosceles.

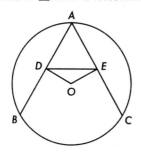

Given: $\odot O$ with $\overline{EF} \cong \overline{CD}$ **8.**
$\overset{\leftrightarrow}{OA} \perp \overset{\leftrightarrow}{CD}$
$\overset{\leftrightarrow}{OB} \perp \overset{\leftrightarrow}{EF}$
Concl.: $\angle OAB \cong \angle OBA$

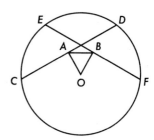

9. Given: $\odot O$ with $\overline{OA} \cong \overline{OB}$
$\overset{\leftrightarrow}{OA} \perp \overset{\leftrightarrow}{CD}$
$\overset{\leftrightarrow}{OB} \perp \overset{\leftrightarrow}{EF}$
Concl.: $\overset{\frown}{CE} \cong \overset{\frown}{FD}$

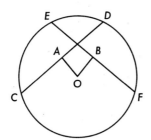

Given: $\odot O$ with $\overline{AB} \cong \overline{DC}$ **10.**
$\overset{\leftrightarrow}{OE} \perp \overset{\leftrightarrow}{PA}$
$\overset{\leftrightarrow}{OF} \perp \overset{\leftrightarrow}{PD}$
Concl.: $\overset{\rightarrow}{PO}$ bisects $\angle APD$.

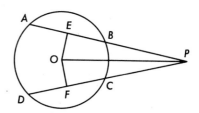

11. Given: $\odot O$ with $\overline{AC} \cong \overline{BD}$
Concl.: $\overset{\frown}{AE} \cong \overset{\frown}{BF}$

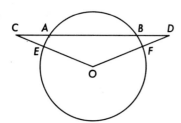

Given: $\odot O$ with $\overset{\leftrightarrow}{AB} \parallel \overset{\leftrightarrow}{CD}$ **12.**
$\overline{AB} \cong \overline{CD}$
P midpt. of $\overline{AB}$
Concl.: $\overline{OP} \cong \overline{OQ}$

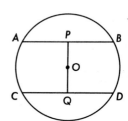

13. Given: $\odot O$ with $\overline{CE} \cong \overline{DF}$

$\overleftrightarrow{OA} \perp \overleftrightarrow{CE}$

$\overleftrightarrow{OB} \perp \overleftrightarrow{DF}$

Concl.: $\overrightarrow{GO}$ bisects $\angle CGD$.

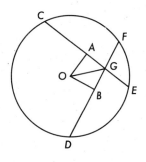

14. Given: Point O is the center of both circles. Line l intersects the circles in points A, B, C, and D.

Concl.: $\overline{AB} \cong \overline{CD}$ (Hint: Let $\overleftrightarrow{OP}$ be the perpendicular from O to l.)

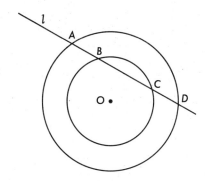

15. Given: $\odot O$ with $\overleftrightarrow{AC} \parallel \overleftrightarrow{DB}$

$\overline{AOB}$ is a diameter.

Concl.: $\overline{AC} \cong \overline{DB}$ (Hint: Let $\overleftrightarrow{OP}$ be the perpendicular from O to $\overleftrightarrow{AC}$, and $\overleftrightarrow{OR}$ be the perpendicular from O to $\overleftrightarrow{DB}$.)

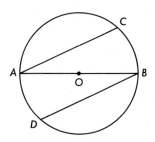

16. * Given: $\odot O$ with $\overline{AB} \cong \overline{DC}$

Concl.: $\overline{PB} \cong \overline{PC}$ (Hint: Let $\overleftrightarrow{OR}$ be the perpendicular from O to $\overleftrightarrow{PB}$, and $\overleftrightarrow{OQ}$ be the perpendicular from O to $\overleftrightarrow{PC}$.)

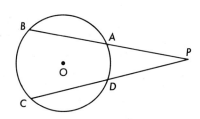

$\boxed{B}$

1. The vertices of a triangle lie on a circle. If the sides of the triangle are equidistant from the center of the circle, then the triangle is equilateral.
2. If from opposite endpoints of a diameter chords are drawn so as to form congruent angles with the diameter, then the arcs corresponding to these chords will be congruent.
3. Two chords intersect within a circle. If the diameter drawn to the point of intersection bisects the angle formed by the chords, then the chords are congruent. (Hint: Prove that the chords are equidistant from the center of the circle.)
4. If two congruent chords are extended until they intersect outside the circle, then the extended segments will be congruent. Assume that the chords are not segments of parallel lines.
5. If two chords of a circle are not congruent, then they are not equidistant from the center of the circle. (Hint: Use the indirect proof.)
6. If two chords of a circle are not equidistant from the center of a circle, then they are not congruent.
7.* If a diameter bisects two chords of a circle, then the chords are parallel.
8.* If a diameter bisects one of two parallel chords of a circle, then it bisects the other also.
9.* The midpoints of congruent chords of a circle will lie on the same circle.

■ Tangents and Secants

There are but two more lines that we need to consider in connection with the properties of a circle.

DEFINITION 85: A tangent to a circle is a line that has but one point in common with the circle.

DEFINITION 86: A secant to a circle is a line that has two distinct points in common with a circle.

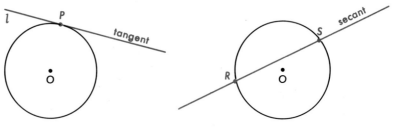

Figure 14-18.   Figure 14-19.

In Figure 14-18 the point P that is common to the circle and the tangent is called the *point of tangency*, or the *point of contact*. Should we think of this in terms of our understanding of sets, we can consider the elements in set O as the points on circle O. Similarly, the elements in set l are the points on line l. Thus, if $O \cap l$—that is, the intersection of O and l—is but one element, then l is a tangent to the circle. However, should $O \cap l$ be two elements as in Figure 14-19, then the line l will be a secant. What if the intersection of O and l be the null set; that is, contain no elements? This would imply that the line had no points in common with the circle and, hence, would have no connection to it.

DEFINITION 87: Tangent circles are two circles that are tangent to the same line at the same point on that line.

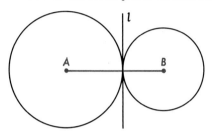   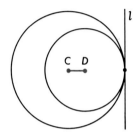

Figure 14-20.   Figure 14-21.

The two circles in both Figures 14-20 and 14-21 are tangent circles. Should the line segment that joins the centers of the two circles intersect the common tangent line, as it does in Figure 14-20, then the circles are said to be *tangent externally*. If it does not, as in Figure 14-21, then the circles are *tangent internally*.

Two circles can be tangent to the same line but not at the same point on that line. This is the situation that exists in each of the drawings below. In Figure 14-22, there are four lines that are *common tangents* to circles A and B. The line AB joining the two centers is called the *line of centers*. If the common tangents intersect line segment AB, as they do in Figure 14-22, they are said to be *common internal tangents*. If they do not intersect segment AB, such as l and m, they are *common external tangents*.

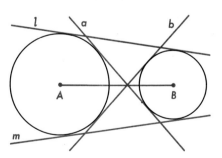   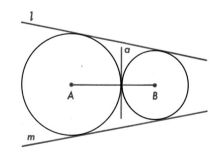

Figure 14-22.   Figure 14-23.

21. Given: $\overleftrightarrow{PB}$ tangent to circles C and D at B and A respectively.

Concl.: $PC:PD = BC:AD$

Given: $\overline{PA}$ and $\overline{PB}$ are tangent segments to circle O. **22.** *

Concl.: $(PA)^2 = PO \cdot PC$

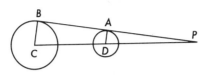

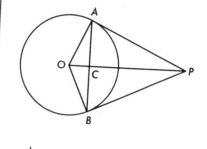

23. Using the diagram at the right, find the length of the tangent segment PA.

24. Using the method illustrated above, find the length of the tangent segment from the point given to each of the following circles:

(a) $(x - 2)^2 + (y - 3)^2 = 25$, $P(7, 6)$
(b) $(x + 1)^2 + (y - 2)^2 = 16$, $P(4, -4)$
(c) $(x + 3)^2 + (y + 1)^2 = 9$, $P(-3, 4)$
(d) $x^2 + y^2 = 10$, $P(5, 7)$
(e) $x^2 + y^2 + 2x + 4y - 20 = 0$, $P(10, 5)$
(f) $x^2 + y^2 - 6x + 2y - 14 = 0$, $P(6, -9)$
(g) $x^2 + y^2 - 8y - 9 = 0$, $P(5, 4)$. (What can be said of point P in this problem?)

25. (a) What are the coordinates of the center of the circle whose equation is $(x - 3)^2 + (y - 5)^2 = 25$.
(b) Show that the point $(7, 2)$ is a point of this circle.
(c) How will the tangent to the circle at this point be related to the radius to this point?
(d) What is the slope of the radius to the point $(7, 2)$?
(e) What is the slope of the tangent to the circle at the point $(7, 2)$?
(f) What is the equation of the tangent to this circle at the point $(7, 2)$?

(g) What is the equation of the tangent to this circle at the point $(-1, 2)$?

$$\boxed{B}$$

1. If two tangent segments are drawn to a circle from an external point, then the line passing through that point and the center of the circle bisects the angle formed by the tangent segments.

2. If two circles are tangent externally, then the common internal tangent bisects the common external tangent segment.

3. If two circles are congruent, the line of centers bisects either common internal segment.

4. The common internal tangent segments of two circles are congruent.

5. If two lines are tangent to a circle at the endpoints of a diameter, then they are parallel.

6. The point of intersection of the line segment joining the centers of two noncongruent circles with a common internal tangent segment will divide the two segments into equal ratios.

7. The common internal tangents of two noncongruent circles intersect at a point such that the ratio of the segments of one is equal to the ratio of the corresponding segments of the other.

8. If the common internal tangents are drawn to two noncongruent circles, then the secant passing through the points of contact of the first circle is parallel to the secant passing through the points of contact of the second circle.

9.* If the sides of a triangle are tangent to a circle, then the perpendiculars to the sides at their points of contact with the circle will be concurrent; that is, meet at a point.

10.* The line of centers of two noncongruent circles will pass through the point of intersection of their common external tangent.

■ The Sphere

The circle in plane geometry has its counterpart in the sphere in space geometry. As we move through this unit, notice the similarity that exists between the principles developed here and those developed earlier in this chapter.

DEFINITION 90: A sphere is a closed surface such that each point on this surface is a fixed distance from a fixed point. (Compare this with the
definition of a circle.)

As in the case of the circle, the *fixed distance is the radius of the sphere,*
while the *fixed point is the center of the sphere.*

**THEOREM 94: If a plane and a sphere have more than one point in
common, these points will lie on a circle.**

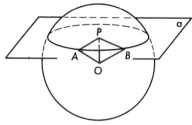

Given: Sphere O
       Plane a intersects O such that
       two of the points they have in
       common are A and B.

Concl.: All points that a and O have in
       common lie on a circle.

Figure 14-34.

ANALYSIS: We will show that point B and point A are each the same fixed
distance from P. Since they represent any two points that a and O have in
common, then all points in common to the two will be that same fixed distance from P. Hence, by the reverse of the definition of a circle these points
will lie on a circle.

PROOF STATEMENTS	REASONS
1. Sphere O with point B, a point that plane a and sphere O have in common.	1. Given
2. Let $\overleftrightarrow{OP}$ be the perpendicular from point O to a.	2. From a given point not on a given plane there can be no more than one line perpendicular to the given plane. (See Problem 2, page 288.)
3. Let $\overleftrightarrow{PB}$ be the line through P and B; let $\overleftrightarrow{OB}$ be the line through O and B	3. There exists one and only one line through two points.
4. $\overleftrightarrow{OP} \perp \overleftrightarrow{PB}$	4. Def. of a line perpendicular to a a plane
5. $\angle OPB$ is a right angle.	5. Def. of perpendicular lines
6. $\triangle OPB$ is a right triangle.	6. Rev. of def. of a right triangle
7. $(BP)^2 = (OB)^2 - (OP)^2$	7. Theorem of Pythagoras

In the same manner, had any other point A common to a and O been
selected, it could be shown that

8. $(AP)^2 = (OA)^2 - (OP)^2$	8. Same as 7
9. $OA = OB$	9. Def. of a sphere
10. $\therefore (AP)^2 = (OB)^2 - (OP)^2$	10. Substitution postulate

Thus, each point that a and O have in common can be shown to be a distance of $\sqrt{(OB)^2 - (OP)^2}$ from P. Hence, by the reverse of the definition of a circle the points common to the two fall on a circle.

If we analyze the previous proof, we will notice that point P is the center of the circle on which the points of intersection lie. Thus, by this proof we have shown also that

THEOREM 95: If a plane intersects a sphere, the perpendicular drawn from the center of the sphere to the plane will pass through the center of the circle on which the points of intersection lie.

Now let us turn to tangency as related to a sphere.

DEFINITION 91: A tangent plane to a sphere is a plane that has one and only one point in common with the sphere. (Compare this definition with that of a line tangent to a circle.)

As before, the point that the tangent plane has in common with the sphere is called the *point of tangency*, or the *point of contact*. Since a sphere is considered as a set of points, O, and a plane as a set of points, p, then the definition of a tangent plane implies that $O \cap p$ will have but one element, the point of tangency. Similarly, if O and p have more than one point in common, then according to Theorem 94 $O \cap p$ will be a set of points that lie on a circle.

POSTULATE 40: At a given point on a sphere there exists one and only one plane that is tangent to the sphere. (Compare this with Postulate 39.)

THEOREM 96: A plane perpendicular to a radius of a sphere at its outer endpoint is tangent to the sphere.

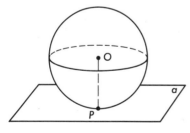

Given: Sphere O with P the outer endpoint of radius OP.

$\overleftrightarrow{OP} \perp a$

Concl.: Plane a is tangent to the sphere.

Figure 14-35.

ANALYSIS: The analysis and proof of this theorem are almost identical to that used to prove Theorem 90. The difference arises only in the fact that the word *sphere* replaces the word *circle*, and *plane* replaces *line*.

PROOF

By the law of the excluded middle one of the following statements is true and no other possibility exists:

P is the only point that a has in common with sphere O.

or

P is not the only point that a has in common with sphere O.

Let us accept the possibility that P is not the only point that a has in common with O; then let Q be another of these points. Also, let $\overleftrightarrow{OQ}$ be the line that passes through O and Q. The two intersecting lines OP and OQ determine a plane. This plane intersects plane a in the line l. $\overleftrightarrow{OP} \perp l$ by definition of a line perpendicular to a plane. Hence, $\angle 1$ and $\angle 2$ are right angles. Therefore, $\angle 1 \cong \angle 2$. But $\overline{OP} \cong \overline{OQ}$ by definition of a sphere. Hence, $\angle 3 \cong \angle 2$.

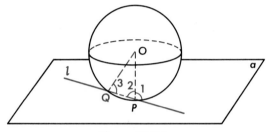

Figure 14-36.

In view of this, $\angle 1 \cong \angle 3$. However, we have a theorem that an exterior angle of a triangle must be greater than either of the remote interior angles. This would imply that $m \angle 1 > m \angle 3$. Therefore, accepting the possibility that P is not the only point a has in common with sphere O led to the logical inconsistency of the truth of $\angle 1 \cong \angle 3$ and $\angle 1 \ncong \angle 3$. By the law of contradiction both cannot be true at the same time. Since $\angle 1 \ncong \angle 3$ must be true, for it is the result of a theorem, then $\angle 1 \cong \angle 3$ must be false. Therefore, the statement that P is not the only point that a has in common with sphere O is also false. Hence, the statement that P is the only point that a has in common with sphere O is true, for it is the only remaining possibility.

The proofs of the next two theorems are very much the same as those for Theorems 91 and 92. They will be left for you to do.

THEOREM 97: **A radius drawn to the point of contact of a plane tangent to a sphere is perpendicular to the plane.**

THEOREM 98: **If a plane is tangent to a sphere, then a line perpendicular to the plane at the point of contact will pass through the center of the sphere.**

EXERCISES

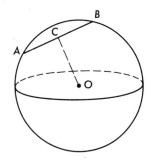

$$\boxed{\textbf{A}}$$

1. Given: O is the center of the sphere.

   C is the midpoint of $\overline{AB}$.

   Concl.: $\overleftrightarrow{OC} \perp \overleftrightarrow{AB}$

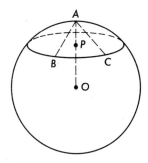

2. Use the same diagram as in Problem 1.

   Given: O is the center of the sphere.

   $\overleftrightarrow{OC} \perp \overleftrightarrow{AB}$

   Concl.: C is the midpoint of $\overline{AB}$.

3. Given: O is the center of the sphere.

   P is the center of the circle.

   Concl.: $\overline{AB} \cong \overline{AC}$ (Hint: Draw $\overleftrightarrow{PB}$

   and $\overleftrightarrow{PC}$.)

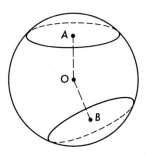

4. Given: O is the center of the sphere.

   A and B are the centers of two circles of the sphere.

   $\overline{OA} \cong \overline{OB}$

   Concl.: $\odot A \cong \odot B$ (Hint: See definition of congruent circles.)

5. Use the same diagram as in Problem 4.

   Given: O is the center of the sphere.

   A and B are the centers of two circles of the sphere.

   $\odot A \cong \odot B$

   Concl.: $\overline{OA} \cong \overline{OB}$

1. If two chords are equidistant from the center of a sphere, then the two chords are congruent. (Hint: See proof of Theorem 87.)
2. If two chords of a sphere are congruent, then they are equidistant from the center of the sphere. (Hint: Use Problem A-2 and see the proof of Theorem 89.)
3. Tangent segments from an external point to a sphere are congruent.
4. If a line is drawn from the center of a sphere perpendicular to a tangent plane, then it passes through the point of tangency. (Hint: Use the indirect proof.)

■ The Relation Between Angles and Arcs

Earlier in this chapter we discussed the relation that existed between the measure of a central angle and that of its intercepted arc. In reality, the measure of every angle whose sides intercept arcs on a circle is in some way related to the measures of these arcs.

Quite often in this section we will speak of points lying "within a circle" or "outside a circle." Although all of us have an intuitive understanding of these terms, it would be best were they defined formally.

DEFINITION 92: The interior of a circle is the set of points such that if a line was drawn through any given point of the set it would intersect the circle in two distinct points where the given point would be between the points of intersection.

DEFINITION 93: The exterior of a circle is the set of points of the plane that are neither interior points or points of the circle.

Henceforth, whenever the phrase "inside a circle" or "within a circle" is used, it will refer to the set of points of the interior of a circle. Similarly, the phrase "outside a circle" refers to the points of the exterior of the circle.

The vertex of an angle may lie in any one of four different positions relative to the circle: either (1) at the center, (2) within the circle, (3) on

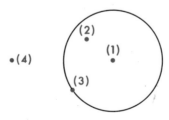

Figure 14-37.

the circle, or (4) outside of the circle. The relation between the angle and its intercepted arcs will depend upon which of the four positions the vertex of the angle takes. Should the vertex fall at the center of the circle, then, being a central angle, its measure will be equal to the measure of its intercepted arc. This we know from Definition 82. It is to the angles whose vertices fall in the remaining three positions that we turn our attention.

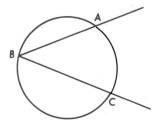

Figure 14-38.

In the Figure 14-38 $\angle ABC$ is said to be an *inscribed angle*, and it is said to be inscribed in $\overset{\frown}{ABC}$. The endpoints of the arc, A and C, are points of the sides of the angle, while the vertex of the angle, point B, is a point that lies somewhere on the arc "between" the endpoints A and C. Formally, it is defined as

DEFINITION 94: An inscribed angle in an arc is an angle such that each endpoint of the arc is a point on each side of the angle, while the vertex of the angle is a point on the arc not coincident with an endpoint.

THEOREM 99: The measure of an inscribed angle is equal to one-half the measure of its intercepted arc.

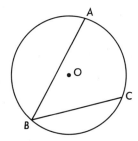

Given: Inscribed $\angle B$

Concl.: $m \angle B = \frac{1}{2} m\, AC$

Figure 14-39.

ANALYSIS: Having no more than the measure of a central angle upon which to base our proof, we are forced to consider the proof of this theorem under three different circumstances. The first of these, obviously, must be in terms of a central angle. Each of the others will be in terms of the conclusions drawn in the first proof.

Case 1

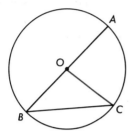

Given: Inscribed $\angle B$ with side $\overrightarrow{BA}$ passing through center O

Concl.: $m \angle B = \frac{1}{2} m \widehat{AC}$

Figure 14-40.

PROOF │ STATEMENTS	REASONS
1. Let $\overleftrightarrow{OC}$ be the line through points O and C.	1. Why?
2. $m \angle AOC = m \widehat{AC}$	2. The measure of a central angle is equal to the measure of its intercepted arc.
3. $m \angle AOC = m \angle B + m \angle C$	3. The measure of an exterior angle of a triangle is equal to the sum of the measures of the remote interior angles.
4. $m \angle B + m \angle C = m \widehat{AC}$	4. Why?
5. $\overline{OB} \cong \overline{OC}$	5. Why?
6. $\angle B \cong \angle C$	6. Why?
7. $m \angle B + m \angle B = m \widehat{AC}$ or, $2 m \angle B = m \widehat{AC}$	7. Why?
8. $m \angle B = \frac{1}{2} m \widehat{AC}$	8. Halves of equals are equal.

Case 2

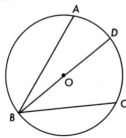

Given: Inscribed $\angle ABC$ with center O in the interior of $\angle ABC$

Concl.: $m \angle ABC = \frac{1}{2} m \widehat{AC}$

Figure 14-41.

PROOF	STATEMENTS	REASONS
1. Let $\overset{\leftrightarrow}{BO}$ be the line through points B and O.		1. Why?
2. $m \angle ABD = \frac{1}{2} m \overset{\frown}{AD}$		2. Case 1
3. $m \angle DBC = \frac{1}{2} m \overset{\frown}{DC}$		3. Case 1
4. $m \angle ABC = \frac{1}{2} m \overset{\frown}{AC}$		4. Addition postulate

Case 3

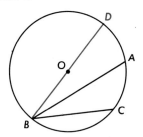

Given: Inscribed $\angle ABC$ with center O in the exterior of $\angle ABC$

Concl.: $m \angle ABC = \frac{1}{2} m \overset{\frown}{AC}$

Figure 14-42.

PROOF	STATEMENTS	REASONS
1. Let $\overset{\leftrightarrow}{BO}$ be the line through points B and O.		1. Why?
2. $m \angle DBC = \frac{1}{2} m \overset{\frown}{DC}$		2. Case 1
3. $m \angle DBA = \frac{1}{2} m \overset{\frown}{DA}$		3. Case 1
4. $m \angle ABC = \frac{1}{2} m \overset{\frown}{AC}$		4. Subtraction postulate

THEOREM 100: An angle inscribed in a semicircle is a right angle.

ANALYSIS: The proof of this theorem follows directly from the previous theorem. If an angle is inscribed in a semicircle, the arc it intercepts will be a semicircle. Since the measure of a semicircle is 180, the measure of the inscribed angle intercepting this arc will be 90 and, hence, a right angle.

The proof of Theorem 100 makes possible the proof of another theorem concerning the relation of the measure of an angle to the measure of its intercepted arc. Once again the vertex falls on the circle. Now, however, only one of the sides of the angle is a chord of the circle. The other side is a ray that is tangent to the circle at the endpoint of the ray. Before turning the page, try to draw this angle.

THEOREM 101: The measure of an angle formed by a tangent and a chord is equal to one-half the measure of its intercepted arc.

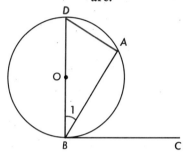

Given: $\odot O$ with $\overleftrightarrow{BC}$ tangent to O at point B

Concl.: $m \angle ABC = \frac{1}{2} m \widehat{AB}$

Figure 14-43.

ANALYSIS: To arrive at the conclusion, it is necessary to relate $\angle ABC$ to an inscribed angle that intercepts $\widehat{AB}$. This is done by drawing $\overleftrightarrow{BO}$ and introducing $\angle D$ into the problem. Our objective will be to prove $\angle D \cong \angle ABC$.

PROOF STATEMENTS	REASONS
1. Let $\overleftrightarrow{BO}$ be the line through points B and O; let $\overleftrightarrow{AD}$ be the line through A and D.	1. Why?
2. $\widehat{DAB}$ is a semicircle.	2. Rev. of def. of a semicircle.
3. $\angle DAB$ is a right angle.	3. An angle inscribed in a semicircle is a right angle.
4. $\angle D$ is complementary to $\angle 1$.	4. The acute angles of a right triangle are complementary. (See Theorem 53.)
5. $\overleftrightarrow{BC}$ is a tangent to $\odot O$ at point B.	5. Given
6. $\overleftrightarrow{DB} \perp \overleftrightarrow{BC}$	6. Why?
7. $\angle DBC$ is a right angle.	7. Why?
8. $\angle ABC$ is complementary to $\angle 1$.	8. Why?
9. $\angle ABC \cong \angle D$	9. Why?
10. $m \angle D = \frac{1}{2} m \widehat{AB}$	10. The measure of an inscribed angle is equal to one-half the measure of its intercepted arc.
11. $m \angle ABC = \frac{1}{2} m \widehat{AB}$	11. Why?

We can turn our attention now to those situations in which the vertex of an angle falls either outside the circle or inside the circle, but not at the center.

THEOREM 102: If the vertex of an angle falls within a circle, the measure of the angle is equal to one-half the sum of the measures of the two arcs intercepted by the sides of the angle and that of its vertical angle.

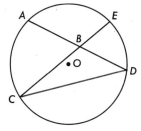

Given: $\angle ABC$ whose vertex lies within circle O

Concl.: $m \angle ABC = \frac{1}{2}(m \overset{\frown}{AC} + m \overset{\frown}{ED})$

Figure 14-44.

PROOF	STATEMENTS	REASONS
1.	Let $\overset{\leftrightarrow}{CD}$ be the line through points C and D.	1. Why?
2.	$m \angle ABC = m \angle D + m \angle C$	2. The measure of an exterior angle of a triangle is equal to the sum of the measures of the remote interior angles.
3.	$m \angle D = \frac{1}{2} m \overset{\frown}{AC}$	3. Why?
4.	$m \angle C = \frac{1}{2} m \overset{\frown}{ED}$	4. Why?
5.	$m \angle ABC = \frac{1}{2} m \overset{\frown}{AC} + \frac{1}{2} m \overset{\frown}{ED}$ or, $m \angle ABC = \frac{1}{2}(m \overset{\frown}{AC} + m \overset{\frown}{ED})$	5. Substitution postulate

THEOREM 103: If the vertex of an angle falls outside a circle and the sides of the angle intercept arcs on the circle, then the measure of the angle is equal to one-half the difference of the measures of the arcs intercepted by the sides of the angle.

ANALYSIS: There are three different cases under which the vertex can lie outside the circle. Although the proofs are very much the same, each will be examined separately.

Case 1

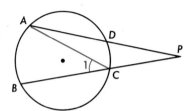

Figure 14-45.

Given: $\overline{PA}$ and $\overline{PB}$ are secant segments to circle O.

Concl.: $m \angle P = \frac{1}{2}(m \widehat{AB} - m \widehat{DC})$

PROOF	STATEMENTS	REASONS
1. Let $\overleftrightarrow{AC}$ be the line through points A and C.		1. Why?
2. $m \angle P + m \angle A = m \angle 1$		2. Theorem on the exterior angle of a triangle.
3. $m \angle P = m \angle 1 - m \angle A$		3. If equals are subtracted from equals, the differences are equal.
4. $m \angle 1 = \frac{1}{2} m \widehat{AB}$		4. Why?
5. $m \angle A = \frac{1}{2} m \widehat{DC}$		5. Why?
6. $\therefore m \angle P = \frac{1}{2} m \widehat{AB} - \frac{1}{2} m \widehat{DC}$ or, $m \angle P = \frac{1}{2}(m \widehat{AB} - m \widehat{DC})$		6. Substitution postulate.

Case 2

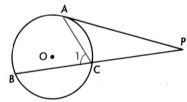

Figure 14-46.

Given: $\overline{PA}$ is a tangent segment to $\odot O$.
$\overline{PB}$ is a secant segment to $\odot O$.

Concl.: $m \angle P = \frac{1}{2}(m \widehat{AB} - m \widehat{AC})$

PROOF	(The reasons are left for you to supply.)

1. Let $\overleftrightarrow{AC}$ be the line through points A and C.
2. $m \angle P + m \angle A = m \angle 1$
3. $m \angle P = m \angle 1 - m \angle A$

4. $m \angle 1 = \frac{1}{2} m \widehat{AB}$
5. $m \angle A = \frac{1}{2} m \widehat{AC}$
6. $m \angle P = \frac{1}{2} m \widehat{AB} - \frac{1}{2} m \widehat{AC}$
   or, $m \angle P = \frac{1}{2}(m \widehat{AB} - m \widehat{AC})$

Case 3

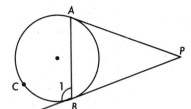

Given: $\overline{PA}$ and $\overline{PB}$ are tangent segments to circle O.

Concl.: $m \angle P = \frac{1}{2}(m \overset{\frown}{ACB} - m \overset{\frown}{AB})$

Figure 14-47.

PROOF

The proof is left for you to complete.

In terms of the angles *we have examined*, we can summarize the relationship between the measure of an angle and the measures of its intercepted arcs as follows:

(1) If the vertex of the angle lies at the *center of the circle*:
The measure of the angle is equal to the measure of its intercepted arc.

(2) If the vertex of the angle lies *within the circle* but not at the center:
The measure of the angle is equal to one-half the sum of the measures of its intercepted arc and that of its vertical angle.

(3) If the vertex of the angle *lies on the circle*:
The measure of the angle is equal to one-half the measure of its intercepted arc.

(4) If the vertex of the angle *lies outside the circle*:
The measure of the angle is equal to one-half the difference of the measures of its intercepted arcs.

EXERCISES

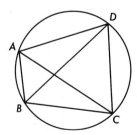

1. Given: $m \overset{\frown}{DC} = 100$, $m \overset{\frown}{AD} = 70$,
$\qquad m \overset{\frown}{AB} = 60$

Find the measure of each of the following angles:
(a) $\angle DAC$ **(b)** $\angle BCD$ **(c)** $\angle BAC$
(d) $\angle ADC$ **(e)** $\angle ACB$ **(f)** $\angle ABC + \angle ADC$

2. Given: Circle O with $m \stackrel{\frown}{AC} = 80$

         $\overleftrightarrow{DE}$ tangent to $\odot O$ at C

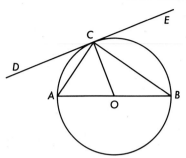

Find the measure of each of the following angles:

(a) $\angle AOC$ (b) $\angle ABC$ (c) $\angle BAC$ (d) $\angle ACB$

(e) $\angle ECB$ (f) $\angle OCE$ (g) $\angle OCD$ (h) $\angle ACE$

3. Given: $m \stackrel{\frown}{AB} = 120$, $m \stackrel{\frown}{DC} = 80$

        $m \angle BAC = 50$, $\overleftrightarrow{FG}$ tangent

        at C

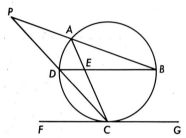

Find the measure of each of the following angles:

(a) $\angle BDC$ (b) $\angle ACD$ (c) $\angle PCF$

(d) $\angle ACG$ (e) $\angle AEB$ (f) $\angle P$

4. Use the diagram at the right to answer each of the following questions:

(a) $m \angle P = 30$, $m \stackrel{\frown}{DC} = 40$,

    $m \stackrel{\frown}{AB} = ?$

(b) $m \angle P = 55$, $m \stackrel{\frown}{DC} = 70$,

    $m \stackrel{\frown}{AB} = ?$

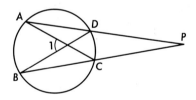

(c) $m \angle P = 50$, $m \stackrel{\frown}{AB} = 140$,

    $m \stackrel{\frown}{DC} = ?$

(d) $m \angle P = 20$, $m \stackrel{\frown}{AB} = 70$, $m \stackrel{\frown}{DC} = ?$

(e) $m \angle 1 = 65$, $m \stackrel{\frown}{AB} = 85$, $m \stackrel{\frown}{DC} = ?$

(f) $m \angle 1 = 55$, $m \stackrel{\frown}{DC} = 30$, $m \stackrel{\frown}{AB} = ?$

(g) $m \angle 1 = 60$, $m \stackrel{\frown}{AB} = 80$, $m \angle P = ?$

(h) $m \angle 1 = 75$, $m \stackrel{\frown}{DC} = 65$, $m \angle P = ?$

(i) $m \angle P = 25$, $m \stackrel{\frown}{DC} = 30$, $m \angle 1 = ?$

(j) $m \angle P = 35$, $m \stackrel{\frown}{AB} = 100$, $m \angle 1 = ?$

(k) $m \angle A = 20$, $m \angle 1 = 70$, $m \angle P = ?$

(l)* $m \angle 1 = 80$, $m \angle P = 50$, $m \stackrel{\frown}{AB} = ?$

5. Given: $m \angle C = 85$, $m \widehat{AD} = 100$,

$m \widehat{CD} = 110$, $\overleftrightarrow{PE}$ tangent to

circle at A

Find the value of each of the following:

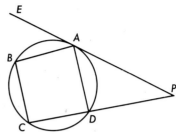

(a) $m \angle P$ ... **(b)** $m \angle ABC + m \angle ADC$

6. Given: $m \widehat{BC} = 85$, $m \widehat{CD} = 120$,

$m \angle 1 = 70$

E is the midpoint of $\widehat{BA}$.

Find the measure of $\angle P$.

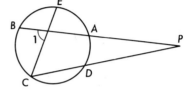

7. Prove: If the vertices of a quadrilateral lie on a circle, then the opposite angles are supplementary. (This statement often appears as a theorem.)

8. The measure of the angle formed by two tangents to a circle from an external point is 40. Find the measure of each of the arcs of the circle whose endpoints are the points of tangency.

9. The two tangents from an external point to a circle are perpendicular to each other. Show that the major arc whose endpoints are the points of tangency is three times as large as the minor arc with these same endpoints.

10. Using the diagram at the right where $\overline{AB}$ is a diameter, prove that $\angle P \cong \angle Q$.

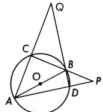

■ Applications of the Theorems on Angle Measurement

The theorems that were proved in the preceding section have wide application to much of the work we developed earlier in the course; in particular, the section on similarity. Before we investigate illustrations of this, there is one theorem yet to be presented that will help simplify the proofs of many problems.

THEOREM 104: If inscribed angles of a circle intercept the same arc, then they are congruent.

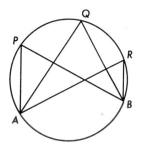

Given: Inscribed ⊿ P, Q, and R intercept $\widehat{AB}$.
Concl.: $\angle P \cong \angle Q \cong \angle R$

Figure 14-48.

PROOF	STATEMENTS	REASONS
1. Inscribed ⊿ P, Q, and R intercept $\widehat{AB}$.		1. Given
2. $m \angle P = \frac{1}{2} m \widehat{AB}$, $m \angle Q = \frac{1}{2} m \widehat{AB}$, $m \angle R = \frac{1}{2} m \widehat{AB}$		2. Why?
3. $\angle P \cong \angle Q \cong \angle R$		3. Rev. of def. of congruent angles

Illustration 1:

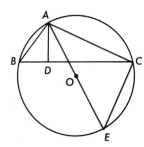

Given: In $\triangle ABC$, $\overline{AD}$ is an altitude
to $\overline{BC}$.
$\overline{AE}$ is a diameter.
Concl.: $AB \cdot AC = AD \cdot AE$

Figure 14-49.

ANALYSIS: By proving $\triangle ABD \sim \triangle AEC$ it will follow that $AB:AE = AD:AC$. Our conclusion will then be an immediate consequence of this proportion.

PROOF	STATEMENTS	REASONS
1. $\overline{AD}$ is altitude to $\overline{BC}$.		1. Given
2. $\overleftrightarrow{AD} \perp \overleftrightarrow{BC}$		2. Def. of an altitude
3. $\angle ADB$ is a right angle.		3. Def. of perpendicular lines
4. $\overline{AE}$ is a diameter.		4. Given
5. $\angle ACE$ is a right angle.		5. An angle inscribed in a semicircle is a right angle.

6. $\angle ADB \cong \angle ACE$
7. $\angle B \cong \angle E$

6. Why?
7. If inscribed angles of a circle intercept the same arc, then they are congruent.

8. $\triangle ABD \sim \triangle AEC$
9. $AB:AE = AD:AC$
10. $AB \cdot AC = AD \cdot AE$

8. A.A. theorem on similarity
9. Def. of similar polygons
10. The product of the means of a proportion is equal to the product of the extremes.

Illustration 2:

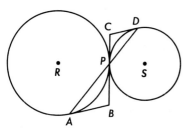

Figure 14-50.

Given: Circles R and S tangent to $\overleftrightarrow{BC}$ at P

$\overleftrightarrow{CD}$ tangent to S at D

$\overleftrightarrow{BA}$ tangent to R at A

Concl.: $\overleftrightarrow{AB} \parallel \overleftrightarrow{CD}$

ANALYSIS: By showing $\angle D$ to be congruent to $\angle A$, $\overleftrightarrow{AB}$ will be parallel to $\overleftrightarrow{CD}$.

PROOF STATEMENTS	REASONS
1. Circles R and S tangent to $\overleftrightarrow{BC}$ at P	1. Given
2. $\overleftrightarrow{CD}$ tangent to S at D $\overleftrightarrow{BA}$ tangent to R at A	2. Given
3. $m \angle CPD = \frac{1}{2} m \widehat{PD}$ $m \angle D = \frac{1}{2} m \widehat{PD}$	3. The measure of an angle formed by a tangent and a chord is equal to one-half the measure of its intercepted arc.
4. $\angle D \cong \angle CPD$	4. Why?
5. $m \angle BPA = \frac{1}{2} m \widehat{PA}$ $m \angle A = \frac{1}{2} m \widehat{PA}$	5. Same as 3
6. $\angle A \cong \angle BPA$	6. Why?
7. But, $\angle CPD \cong \angle BPA$	7. Why?
8. Hence, $\angle D \cong \angle A$	8. Why?
9. $\therefore \overleftrightarrow{AB} \parallel \overleftrightarrow{CD}$	9. Why?

EXERCISES

1. Given: Circle O

Concl.: $AE:ED = BE:EC$

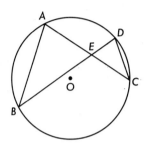

Given: $\overline{PB}$ and $\overline{PC}$ are   **2.**
secant segments.

Concl.: $PA:PD = PC:PB$

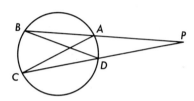

3. Given: $\overleftrightarrow{ED} \perp \overleftrightarrow{AD}$

$\odot O$ with $\overline{AB}$ a diameter

Concl.: $AC:ED = AB:BE$

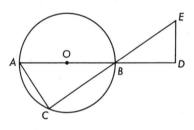

Given: $\overline{PA} \cong \overline{PD}$ **4.**

Concl.: $\overline{AB} \cong \overline{DC}$ (Hint:

Draw $\overleftrightarrow{AC}$ and $\overleftrightarrow{DB}$.)

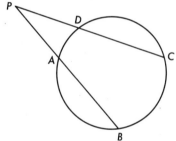

5. Given: $\overrightarrow{BD}$ bisects $\angle ABC$.

Concl.: $AB \cdot DC =$
$AE \cdot DB$

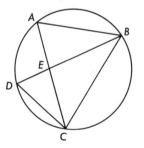

Given: $\overline{AB} \cong \overline{BC} \cong \overline{CD}$ **6.**

Concl.: $\overrightarrow{PB}$ and $\overrightarrow{PC}$ trisect
$\angle APD.$

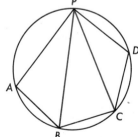

7. Given: $\overleftrightarrow{CA}$ tangent to circle
to A

M is the midpoint
of $\overparen{AB}$.

$\overleftrightarrow{MS} \perp \overleftrightarrow{AC}$

$\overleftrightarrow{MR} \perp \overleftrightarrow{AB}$

Concl.: $\overline{MR} \cong \overline{MS}$ (Hint:

Draw $\overleftrightarrow{AM}$.)

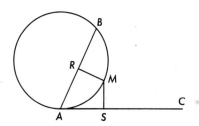

Given: $\triangle ABC$ is isosceles
with $\overline{AB} \cong \overline{AC}$.

$\overline{AC}$ is a diameter
of $\odot O$.

Concl.: D is the midpoint of
$\overline{BC}$. (Hint: Draw
$\overleftrightarrow{AD}$.)

8.

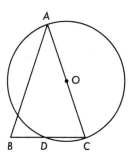

9. Given: $\overline{PA}$ is a tangent
segment.

Concl.: $AB:CA = PA:PC$

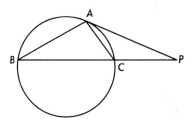

Given: C is the midpoint
of $\overparen{AD}$.

Concl.: $AB:EA = BC:AC$

10.

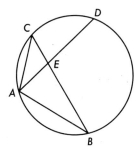

11. Given: $\overparen{AD} \cong \overparen{AE}$

$\overparen{DF} \cong \overparen{EG}$

Concl.: $\triangle ABC$ is isos.

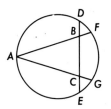

Given: $\odot O$ with $\overleftrightarrow{AC} \perp \overleftrightarrow{EG}$

Concl.: $AE \cdot AD = AG \cdot AF$

12.

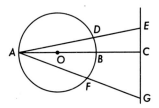

13. Given: $\overleftrightarrow{PQ}$ tangent to circle
at C
$\overleftrightarrow{RS} \parallel \overleftrightarrow{PQ}$
Concl.: $CA:CB = CE:CD$

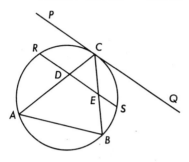

Given: Circles P and Q tan-   **14.**
gent to $\overleftrightarrow{AF}$ at A
Concl.: $\overleftrightarrow{BC} \parallel \overleftrightarrow{DE}$

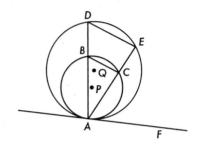

15. Given: Circles P and Q tangent to $\overleftrightarrow{AC}$ at A
$\overleftrightarrow{AE}$ intersects $\odot P$ at
D and $\odot Q$ at E.
$\overleftrightarrow{BD}$ tangent to P at D
$\overleftrightarrow{CE}$ tangent to Q at E
Concl.: $\overleftrightarrow{DB} \parallel \overleftrightarrow{EC}$

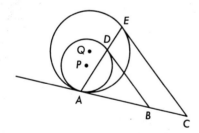

Given: Circles R and S tan-   **16.**
gent to $\overleftrightarrow{EF}$ at P
Concl.: $CD:AB = PD:PB$

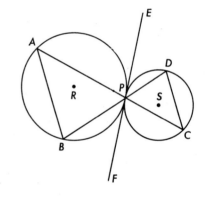

17. Given: $\odot O$ with tangent
segment PA
Concl.: $(AC)^2 = PC \cdot CB$

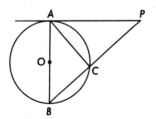

Given: Three intersecting   **18.**[*]
circles
Concl.: $\overleftrightarrow{EP}$ passes through F.
(Hint: Use indirect
proof.)

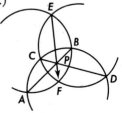

19. Given: $\overline{CA}$ tangent segment to circle F

$\overline{DA}$ tangent segment to circle E

Concl.: $(AB)^2 = BC \cdot BD$

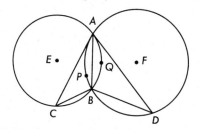

20. Given: A is the midpoint of $\overset{\frown}{DE}$.

Concl.: $AB \cdot AG = AC \cdot AF$

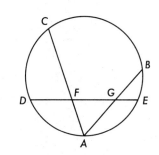

21. Given: $\overset{\leftrightarrow}{PED}$ common external tangent to ⊚ A and B at E and D

$\overset{\leftrightarrow}{PAB}$ is the line of centers.

Concl.: $\overset{\leftrightarrow}{CD} \parallel \overset{\leftrightarrow}{FE}$ (Hint: Draw $\overset{\leftrightarrow}{BD}$ and $\overset{\leftrightarrow}{AE}$.)

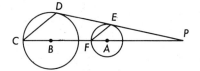

22. Given: ⊚ R and S tangent to l at P

$\overset{\leftrightarrow}{CD}$ tangent to ⊙ R at E

Concl.: $\overset{\rightarrow}{PE}$ bisects $\angle CPD$. (Hint: Prove $\angle 1 \cong \angle 2$.)

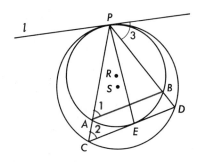

23. Given: $\overline{AC}$ is a diameter of ⊙ E.

$\overline{AD}$ is a diameter of ⊙ F.

$\overline{AB}$ is the common chord to ⊚ E and F.

Concl.: C, B, and D are collinear. (Hint: Draw $\overset{\leftrightarrow}{CB}$ and $\overset{\leftrightarrow}{BD}$; then prove that $\angle CBD$ is a straight angle.)

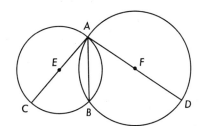

1. If the vertices of an isosceles triangle lie on a circle, then the tangent at the vertex of the vertex angle bisects the exterior angle at this point.
2. If from any point on a circle a perpendicular line segment is dropped to a diameter, then the square of the measure of the perpendicular is equal to the product of the measures of the segments of the diameter.
3. If parallel lines intersect a circle, they will cut off congruent arcs on the circle.* There are three cases that exist; you are to prove all three.

   (a) Case 1: The parallel lines are secants.
   (b) Case 2: The parallel lines are tangents.
   (c) Case 3: One of the parallel lines is a tangent, while the other is a secant.

4. If two chords intersect within a circle such that one bisects the other, then the square of the measure of one of the segments of the bisected chord is equal to the product of the measures of the segments of the other chord.
5. A line segment is drawn through the point of tangency of two externally tangent circles terminating at points of each of the circles. If tangents are drawn to each of the circles at these points, then the tangents are parallel.

■ Chords, Tangent Segments, and Secant Segments

Several of the problems in the preceding exercises have wide application in numerical situations. In view of this they will be established as theorems, and illustrations of when they can be applied will be presented.

THEOREM 105: **If two chords intersect within a circle, the product of the measures of the segments of one will be equal to the product of the measures of the segments of the other.**

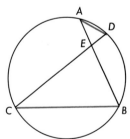

Given: Chords $\overline{AB}$ and $\overline{CD}$ intersect at E.

Concl.: $AE \cdot EB = CE \cdot ED$

Figure 14-51.

PROOF	(The reasons will be left for you to supply.)

1. Let $\overleftrightarrow{AD}$ be the line through points A and D.	4. $\angle AED \cong \angle CEB$
	5. $\triangle AED \sim \triangle CEB$
2. Let $\overleftrightarrow{CB}$ be the line through points C and B.	6. $AE:CE = ED:EB$
	7. $\therefore\ AE \cdot EB = CE \cdot ED$
3. $\angle C \cong \angle A$	

THEOREM 106: **If a tangent segment and a secant segment are drawn to a circle from an external point, then the square of the measure of the tangent segment is equal to the product of the measures of the secant segment and its external portion.**

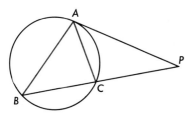

Given: Tangent segment PA
            Secant segment PB
Concl.: $(PA)^2 = PB \cdot PC$

Figure 14-52.

ANALYSIS: Note that the *external portion* of a secant segment is that segment between the external point and the first point of intersection with the circle. In Figure 14-52 it is the segment PC. The *internal portion* is the segment between the points of intersection of the secant with the circle. By proving $\triangle PAC \sim \triangle PBA$ the conclusion will follow.

PROOF	(The reasons will be left for you to supply.)

1. Let $\overleftrightarrow{AC}$ be the line through points A and C.	5. $m \angle PBA = \frac{1}{2} m \widehat{AC}$
	6. $\angle PAC \cong \angle PBA$
2. Let $\overleftrightarrow{AB}$ be the line through points A and B.	7. $\triangle PAC \sim \triangle PBA$
	8. $PA:PB = PC:PA$
3. $\angle P \cong \angle P$	9. $\therefore\ (PA)^2 = PB \cdot PC$
4. $m \angle PAC = \frac{1}{2} m \widehat{AC}$	

THEOREM 107: If two secant segments are drawn to a circle from an external point, then the product of the measures of one of these segments and its external portion is equal to the product of the measures of the other with its external portion.

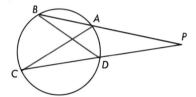

Given: $\overline{PB}$ and $\overline{PC}$ are secant segments.

Concl.: $PB \cdot PA = PC \cdot PD$

Figure 14-53.

| PROOF | (The reasons are left for you to supply.) |

1. Let $\overleftrightarrow{BD}$ be the line through points B and D.

2. Let $\overleftrightarrow{CA}$ be the line through points C and A.

3. $\angle P \cong \angle P$

4. $\angle B \cong \angle C$
5. $\triangle PBD \sim \triangle PCA$
6. $PB:PC = PD:PA$
7. $PB \cdot PA = PC \cdot PD$

Had the tangent segment in Figure 14-53 been drawn from point P to the circle, then $(PR)^2 = PB \cdot PA$; also, $(PR)^2 = PC \cdot PD$. In fact,

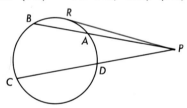

Figure 14-54.

$(PR)^2$ would be equal to the product of any secant segment from point P with its external portion. Since each of these products is equal to $(PR)^2$, we say that from a fixed point *the product of the measure of a secant segment with the measure of its external portion is constant*. Notice that as the secant seg-

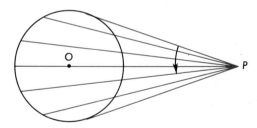

Figure 14-55.

ment rotates counterclockwise about the point P, its length increases until it reaches a certain position and then it begins to decrease. What is that position? How do you account for the fact that although the secant segment grows larger, its product with its external segment remains the same?

Illustration 1:

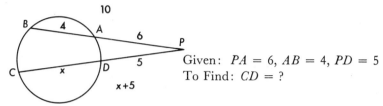

Given: $PA = 6$, $AB = 4$, $PD = 5$
To Find: $CD = ?$

Figure 14-56.

METHOD: It is advisable to label all six segments in Figure 14-56 before applying the theorem needed; in this case it is Theorem 107.

$$PB \cdot PA = PC \cdot PD$$
$$10 \cdot 6 = (x + 5) \cdot 5$$
$$60 = 5x + 25$$
$$35 = 5x$$
$$7 = x \text{ or } CD$$

Illustration 2:

In a circle whose diameter is 10 inches, how far from the center is a chord that is 8 inches long?

METHOD:

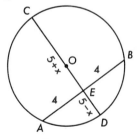

Figure 14-57.

Using Theorem 105: $CE \cdot ED = AE \cdot EB$ (Why is $\overline{AE} \cong \overline{EB}$?)

$$(5 + x)(5 - x) = 4 \cdot 4$$
$$25 - x^2 = 16$$
$$25 - 16 = x^2$$
$$9 = x^2$$
$$3 = x$$

Illustration 3:

Two secant segments are drawn to a circle from an external point. If the secant segments are congruent, then their internal portions are congruent.

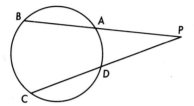

Figure 14-58.

Given: $\overline{PB} \cong \overline{PC}$

Concl.: $\overline{AB} \cong \overline{DC}$

PROOF STATEMENTS	REASONS
1. $PB \cdot PA = PC \cdot PD$	1. Theorem 107
2. $PB = PC$	2. Given
3. $\therefore PA = PD$	3. Division postulate
4. $\therefore AB = DC$	4. Subtraction postulate (Step 3 from step 2.)

EXERCISES

1. Use the figure at the right for each of the following problems:

(a) $CE = 9$, $ED = 4$, $AE = 12$, $EB = ?$
(b) $AE = 12$, $EB = 4$, $ED = 3$, $CE = ?$
(c) $CD = 18$, $ED = 6$, $EB = 8$, $AE = ?$
(d) $AB = 10$, $AE = 6$, $ED = 2$, $CD = ?$
(e) $CD = 16$, $ED = 6$, $EB = 3$, $AB = ?$
(f) $AB = 16$, $CE = 32$, $AE = EB$, $ED = ?$
(g)† $AE = 3$, $EB = 2$, $CD = 7$, $CE = ?$
(h)† $CD = 15$, $CE = 12$, $AB = 13$, $EB = ?$

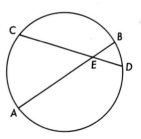

† The solution of a quadratic equation by factoring is required for this problem.

2. Use the figure at the right for each of the following problems:

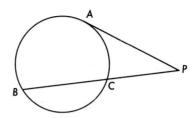

Given: $\overline{PA}$ is a tangent segment.
$\overline{PB}$ is a secant segment.

(a) $PA = 8, PB = 32, PC = ?$ (b) $PC = 2, PB = 8, PA = ?$
(c) $PC = 3, CB = 24, PA = ?$ (d) $PA = 8, PC = CB, PC = ?$
(e) $PA = 6, PC = 4, CB = ?$ (f) $PA = 4, PC = CB, CB = ?$
(g)† $PA = 2, BC = 3, PB = ?$ (h)† $PA = 8, BC = 30, PC = ?$

3. Use the figure at the right for each of the following problems:

(a) $PA = 5, PB = 8, PD = 4,$
$PC = ?$
(b) $PA = 6, AB = 4, PD = 5,$
$CD = ?$
(c) $CD = 8, PD = 2, PA = 4,$
$PB = ?$

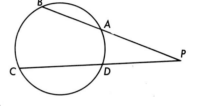

(d) $PC = 16, CD = 13, PB = 12,$
$AB = ?$
(e)† $PB = 6, PA = 4, CD = 5,$
$PD = ?$
(f)† $PC = 12, PD = DC, AB = 1,$
$PB = ?$

4. In the diagram at the right, $\overset{\frown}{PQ}$ is an
arc of a circular race track where M
is the midpoint of $\overset{\frown}{PQ}$ and R is the
midpoint of $\overline{PQ}$. If $PQ = 120$ (feet)
and $MR = 10$ (feet), what is the diameter of the track?

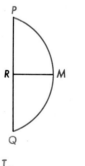

5. A circular play area is being laid
out in a field. The points P, R, and Q
have been found such that $PS = 24$
(feet), $PQ = 66$ (feet), and $RS = 12$
(feet). If T is to be another point on
the circle, how far from R will it lie?

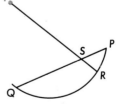

6. Two secant segments are drawn to a circle from an external point.
The length of one of these secants is 9 inches, while its internal portion

---

† The solution of a quadratic equation by factoring is required for this problem.

is 1 inch in length. If the circle bisects the other secant segment, how long is it?

7. To a circle whose diameter is 20 inches a tangent segment is drawn from a point that is 20 inches from the center of the circle. How long is the tangent segment?

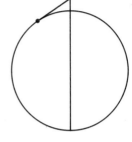

8. The diameter of the earth is approximately 8,000 miles. An astronaut is at a point 100 miles above the surface of the earth. Assuming that he can see that far, what is the farthest point on earth he would be able to see from his position?

9. A surveyor places his transit along the line tangent to the circle at point A such that $PA = 200$ (feet). He locates another point B on the circle and finds $PB = 80$ (feet). If a third point, C, on the circle lies along $\overleftrightarrow{PB}$, how far from point B will it be?

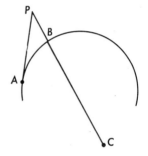

10. If in the figure at the right $AG = CG$ and $PF = 4$, $FD = 8$, $PE = 3$, $AC = 12$, then what is the measure of $\overline{EG}$?

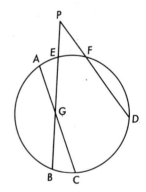

11. A circular archway is to be built such that the distance between the endpoints of the arch is to be 14 times as long as the height of the arch. If the radius of the circle of this arch is 20 feet, how high is the arch?

12. A tangent segment and a secant segment are drawn to a circle from an external point. The measure of the tangent segment is twice that of the external portion of the secant segment. What is the measure of the tangent segment if the measure of the internal portion of the secant segment is nine?

13.* The measure of a chord of a circle is 14. A point is selected on the chord so that its distance from one end of the chord is 8, while its distance from the center of the circle is 4. What is the measure of the chord that is perpendicular to the radius that passes through this point? (This chord is the shortest chord that can be drawn through this point.)

$$\boxed{B}$$

1. Given: Chords $\overline{AB}$ and $\overline{CD}$
             intersect at E.
             $AE = ED$
    Concl.: $AB = CD$

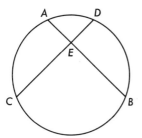

Given: Secant segments **2.**
       $\overline{PB}$ and $\overline{PC}$
       $PB = PC$
Concl.: $AB = DC$

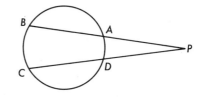

3. Given: Ⓢ O and R tangent
        to $\overset{\leftrightarrow}{PQ}$ at Q
    Concl.: $PB \cdot PA =$
        $PD \cdot PC$

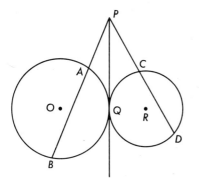

Given: $\overline{PD}$ common secant **4.**
       segment to Ⓢ O and R
       $\overline{PA}$ tangent segment
       to O
       $\overline{PB}$ tangent segment
       to R
Concl.: $PA = PB$

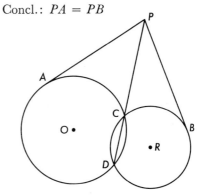

5. Given: $\overline{PD}$ common secant segment to ⓈⒸ O and R

$\overline{PB}$ secant segment to O

$\overline{PF}$ secant segment to R

Concl.: $PB \cdot PA = PF \cdot PE$

Given: P is the point of intersection of common secant segments $\overline{PC}$ and $\overline{PE}$.

$\overline{PA}$ tangent segment to O

$\overline{PB}$ tangent segment to S

Concl.: $PA = PB$

6.

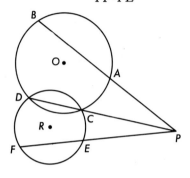

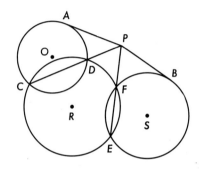

7. Given: $\overleftrightarrow{AB}$ common external tangent to ⓈⒸ O and R

$\overleftrightarrow{CE}$ common secant

Concl.: $\overleftrightarrow{CE}$ bisects $\overline{AB}$.

Given: $\overline{PC}$ and $\overline{PD}$ are secant segments.

$\overline{PA} \cong \overline{PB}$

O is the center of the circle.

Concl.: $\overleftrightarrow{PO} \perp \overleftrightarrow{CD}$ (Hint: Draw $\overleftrightarrow{OD}$ and $\overleftrightarrow{OC}$.)

8.

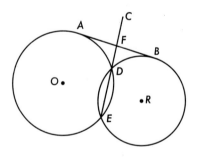

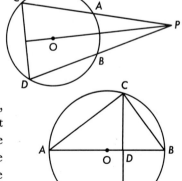

9. Using the diagram at the right, prove the theorem that in a right triangle the square of the measure of the altitude to the hypotenuse is equal to the product of the measures of the segments of the hypotenuse. (Theorem 69)

10. Using the diagram at the right, prove the theorem that in a right triangle with an altitude to the hypotenuse, the square of the measure of either leg is equal to the product of the measures of the entire hypotenuse and the segment on the hypotenuse adjacent to that leg. (Theorem 68)

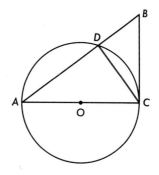

11. Using the diagram at the right, prove the theorem of Pythagoras; that is,

$$(PO)^2 = (OA)^2 + (PA)^2$$

(Hint: Write PB as $PO - OB$ and PC as $PO + OC$).

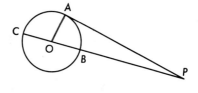

12. * Using the diagram at the right, prove that the square of the measure of the bisector of an angle is given by the following formula:

$$(AD)^2 = AB \cdot AC - BD \cdot DC$$

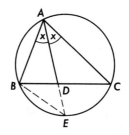

13. Given: Points A, C, and B lie on circle O.

$$AE \cdot EB = CE \cdot ED$$

Concl.: Point D lies on circle O. (Hint: Use indirect proof.)

Given: Points A, B, and C lie on circle O. **14.**

$$PB \cdot PA = PD \cdot PC$$

Concl.: Point D lies on circle O.

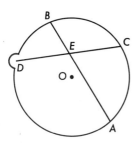

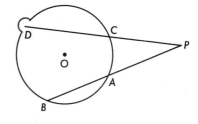

15. * Given: ⊚ *O* and *R* with secants
PABC and *PDEF*

Concl.: $\overset{\leftrightarrow}{AD} \parallel \overset{\leftrightarrow}{CF}$ (Hint: Prove
△*PAD* ∼ △*PCF.*)

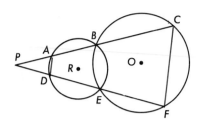

16. Given: Sphere *O* with secant
segments $\overline{PB}$ and $\overline{PD}$
intersecting sphere at
A and *C*

Concl.: *PB·PA* =
PD·PC

Given: Sphere *O*   **17.**
$\overline{PA}$ tangent segment
$\overline{PD}$ secant segment
intersecting sphere
at *C* and *D*

Concl.: $(PA)^2 = PD \cdot PC$

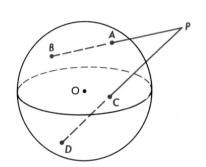
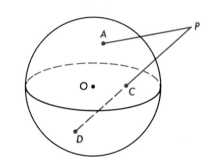

■ **Test and Review**

A

1. Given: $m \overset{\frown}{AB} = 110$
$m \angle DBC = 30$
$\overset{\leftrightarrow}{EF}$ is tangent at *A.*

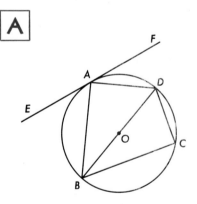

Find the measure of each of the following:

(a) ∠*ADB*   **(b)** ∠*EAB*   **(c)** $\overset{\frown}{BC}$
(d) ∠*BAD*   **(e)** ∠*ADC*   **(f)** $\overset{\frown}{AC}$
(g) ∠*EAD*   **(h)** ∠*BAF*   **(i)** $m \angle ABC + m \angle ADC$

2. Use the diagram at the right to answer each of the following questions:

(a) $m \ \widehat{BC} = 100$, $m \ \widehat{AD} = 40$, $m \ \angle P = ?$

(b) $m \ \widehat{BC} = 120$, $m \ \widehat{AD} = 30$, $m \ \angle BEC = ?$

(c) $m \ \widehat{AB} + m \ \widehat{CD} = 160$, $m \ \angle AED = ?$

(d) $m \ \angle BDC = 75$, $m \ \angle ABD = 25$, $m \ \angle P = ?$

(e) $m \ \angle P = 30$, $m \ \widehat{AD} = 100$, $m \ \widehat{BC} = ?$

(f) $m \ \angle BEC = 115$, $m \ \angle P = 75$, $m \ \widehat{AD} = ?$

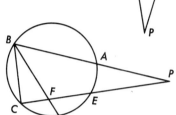

3. Given: D is the midpoint of $\widehat{CE}$.

$m \ \widehat{CD} = 60$

$m \ \angle BFC = 85$

$m \ \angle DBA = 70$

Find the measure of $\angle P$.

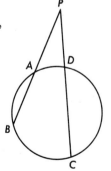

4. In a circle at the right $CD = 10$, $DE = 4$, $BE = 12$. Find BA.

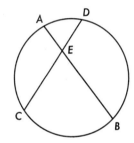

5. In the circle at the right $PA = 9$, $AB = 3$, $PD = 6$. Find DC.

6. In the circle at the right $\overline{PA}$ is a tangent segment whose measure is 12. If the measure of $\overline{PB}$ is 8, then what is the measure of $\overline{BC}$?

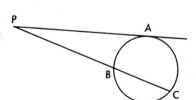

7. The measures of the radii of two concentric circles are 10 and 8 respec-

tively. What is the measure of a chord of the larger circle that is tangent to the smaller circle?

8. The measures of the radii of two circles that are tangent externally are 8 and 3 respectively. What is the distance between the points of tangency of one of their common external tangents?

9. The measures of the diameters of two circles that are tangent internally are 18 and 8 respectively. What is the length of the tangent segment from the center of the larger circle to the smaller circle?

10. In the diagram at the right $\overline{PE}$ is a tangent segment. If $PA = 4$, $AB = 6$, what is PE?

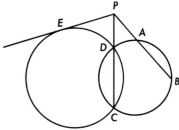

11. A point is 4 units from the center of a circle. A secant segment is drawn from that point to the circle such that the measure of the external portion is 3 while the internal portion is 1. What is the radius of the circle?

12. The measure of an angle formed by two tangents to a circle is 90. If the radius of the circle is 8, how far is the point from the center of the circle?

$$\boxed{\text{B}}$$

Prove each of the following:

1. Given: $\odot O$ with C the
            midpoint of $\overparen{AB}$
            $\overleftrightarrow{CD} \perp \overleftrightarrow{OA}$
            $\overleftrightarrow{CE} \perp \overleftrightarrow{OB}$

Concl.: $\overline{CD} \cong \overline{CE}$

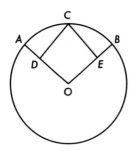

Given: $\odot O$ with diameter   **2.**
         $\overline{AB}$ extended to C
         $\overleftrightarrow{DC} \perp \overleftrightarrow{AC}$

Concl.: $AB \cdot AC =$
         $AE \cdot AD$

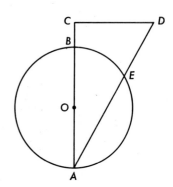

3. Given: Secant segments
$\overline{PC}$ and $\overline{PD}$

Concl.: $\dfrac{PA}{PC} = \dfrac{PF}{PD}$

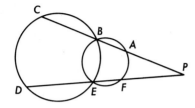

Given: $\odot O$ with $\overline{PA}$ and   **4.**
$\overline{PB}$ tangent segments
$\overline{BC}$ is a diameter.

Concl.: $\overleftrightarrow{AC} \parallel \overleftrightarrow{PO}$ (Hint:
Prove M to be the
midpoint of $\overparen{AB}$.)

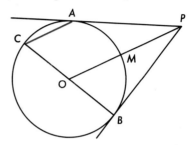

5. Given: $\overparen{AD} \cong \overparen{EB}$

C is the midpoint of $\overparen{BD}$.

Concl.: $\overline{BR} \cong \overline{DS}$

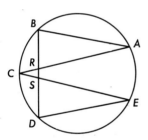

Given: $\overleftrightarrow{AB} \parallel \overleftrightarrow{CD}$ **6.**
$\overleftrightarrow{EF}$ passes through
center of $\odot O$.
$\overline{OE} \cong \overline{OF}$

Concl.: $\overline{AB} \cong \overline{CD}$

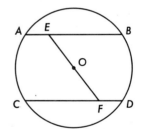

7. Given: $\circledS\ A$ and B

$\overleftrightarrow{AB}$ bi. $\overline{CD}$ and $\overline{EF}$.

Concl.: $\overleftrightarrow{CD} \parallel \overleftrightarrow{EF}$

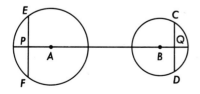

Given: $\odot O$ **8.**
Concl.: $AE \cdot EB =$
$(CO)^2 - (OE)^2$
(Hint: $CE = CO + OE$
$ED = CO - OE$)

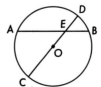

9. Given: $\overleftrightarrow{AB} \perp \overleftrightarrow{BC}$
$\overleftrightarrow{DC} \perp \overleftrightarrow{BC}$

Concl.: $\overline{AB} \cong \overline{DC}$

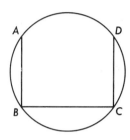

10. Given: Circle O with
$\overline{AB} \cong \overline{CD}$

Concl.: $\overline{AE} \cong \overline{DE}$ (Hint: Draw perpendiculars from O and prove triangles congruent.)

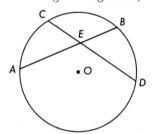

11. Given: $\odot O$ with $\overline{EA}$ and $\overline{CB}$ tangent segments

Concl.: $(AB)^2 = AE \cdot BC$

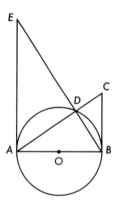

12.* Given: $\overleftrightarrow{AB}$ and $\overleftrightarrow{CD}$ are common external tangents.
$\overleftrightarrow{HG}$ is the common internal tangent.

Concl.: $\overline{AB} \cong \overline{GH}$

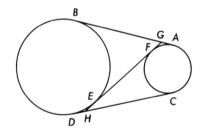

$\boxed{C}$

Prove each of the following statements:

1. If the endpoints of two perpendicular diameters are joined in order, the quadrilateral formed will be a square.

2. The perpendicular bisector of a chord passes through the center of the circle.

3. The diagonals of an equilateral pentagon inscribed within a circle are congruent. (The vertices of the pentagon are points of the circle.)

4. If from the endpoints of a diameter perpendiculars are drawn to any secant of the circle, then the points of intersection of the perpendiculars with the secant will be equidistant from the center of the circle.

5. If two chords intersect within a sphere, then the product of the measures of the segments of one is equal to the product of the measures of the segments of the other.

■ Try This For Fun

A question that often arises in the minds of students is the possibility that when a chord of a circle is doubled in measure will its distance from the center become only half as great? Should a chord be selected at random, then the answer is a most emphatic "No!" However, if we make our choice a bit more carefully, there do exist chords in every circle for which this is true. These are the chords whose measures are the same as their distances from the center of the circle. Can you prove that this is so for these chords?

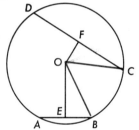

Given: $OE = AB$, $\overleftrightarrow{OE} \perp \overleftrightarrow{AB}$

$CD = 2AB$, $\overleftrightarrow{OF} \perp \overleftrightarrow{CD}$

Concl.: $OF = \frac{1}{2}OE$

(Hint: Let $OE = 2a$.)

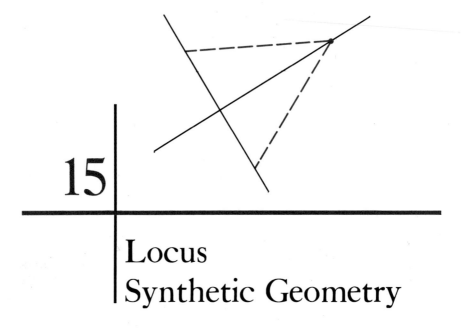

15

Locus
Synthetic Geometry

OUR FIRST ENCOUNTER WITH THE TERM *locus* was in connection with the study of analytic geometry. We are going to take another look at this area of our work; now, however, it will be from a synthetic point of view rather than an analytic.

By definition, *the locus of points was the set of points and only those points that satisfied certain given conditions.* Thus, if the locus is a line, the definition implies that two properties will hold:

(1) Every point on the line satisfies the given conditions.

(2) Every point that satisfies the given conditions lies on the line.

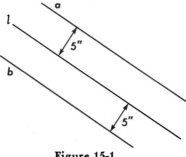

Figure 15-1.

Before plunging into the formal study of locus, let us examine several problems from an intuitive point of view. That is, let us determine what to us seems to be the set of points that fulfill the requirements without handicapping ourselves with the necessity of trying to justify our answer.

Illustration:

What is the locus of points that are five inches from a given line?

ANSWER: The locus or set of points that are five inches from a given line are two lines, one on each side of the given line, parallel to it and five inches from it. (See Figure 15-1.)

In answering the question in this illustration, we have, in reality, made two assertions, neither of which we have attempted to prove.

(1) All points on a and b are five inches from l.

(2) All points that are five inches from l lie on either line a or line b.

EXERCISES

Discuss *informally* the answer to each of the following problems:

1. What is the locus of points in a plane that are 10 inches from a given point?

2. What is the locus of points in space that are 10 inches from a given point?

3. What is the set of points in a plane that are equidistant from two parallel lines?

4. In regard *only* to the points in your classroom,
   (a) What is the set of points that are 7 feet from the front wall?
   (b) What is the set of points that are 8 feet from the wall containing the windows?
   (c) What is the set of points that are both 7 feet from the front wall and 8 feet from the wall containing the windows?
   (d) What is the locus of points that are equidistant from the ceiling and floor of the room?

5. What is the locus of points in space that are 7 feet from a given plane? How does this problem differ from Problem 4 (a)?

6. What is the locus of points in a plane that are more than 6 inches from a given point?

7. What is the locus of points in space that are less than 10 inches from a given point?

8. What is the set of points outside a
circle in a plane that are 10 inches
from the circle? (The distance from a
point to a circle is the external portion of the secant segment drawn
from that point through the center
of the circle.)

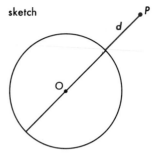

sketch

9. What is the set of points in space inside a sphere of radius 25 inches
that are 10 inches from the sphere?
10. When in a plane a coin rolls along one side of a line, what is the locus
of the center of the coin?
11. A dime is rolled around a half-dollar; what is the locus of the center
of the dime?
12. Two points A and B are 10 inches apart. Consider your answer to each
of the following questions in terms of coplaner points only:
   (a) What is the locus of points that are 8 inches from A and 8 inches
   from B?
   (b) What is the locus of points that are 5 inches from A and 5 inches
   from B?
   (c) What is the locus of points that are 2 inches from A and 2 inches
   from B?
   (d) What is the locus of points that are less than 8 inches from A and
   less than 8 inches from B?
   (e) What is the locus of points that are less than 8 inches from A and
   8 inches from B?
13. Two parallel lines l and m are 6 inches apart. Point P is a point on l.
Consider your answer to each of the following questions in terms of
coplaner points only:
   (a) What is the set of points equidistant from l and m and 5 inches
   from P?
   (b) What is the set of points equidistant from l and m and 3 inches
   from P?
   (c) What is the set of points equidistant from l and m and 2 inches
   from P?
   (d) What is the set of points equidistant from l and m and less than
   4 inches from P?
   (e) What is the set of points equidistant from l and m and less than
   3 inches from P?
14. What is the locus of points that are on a given plane and 5 feet from a
second given plane?

■ Theorem, Converse, Inverse, and Contrapositive

Earlier in our work it was pointed out that in order to justify a set of points as fulfilling the conditions set up in the problem, it is necessary to prove that

(1) Each point in the set fulfilled the requirements of the problem.
and
(2) Each point that fulfilled the requirements was an element in the set.

In analytic geometry we were extremely fortunate, for there the description of the set of points was given by an equation. Hence, it immediately followed that all points on the graph of this equation satisfied this equation, while all the points that satisfied the equation fell on its graph. This is the relation between a graph and its equation. Now, however, we are faced with the problem of not only having to name what we believe the locus to be but also justifying this by proving the two properties stated above.

To illustrate, let us say that we are required to determine the set of points that are equidistant from points A and B in Figure 15-2. An intelligent

A •

• B

Figure 15-2.

guess would be that the set of points equidistant from A and B is the perpendicular bisector of $\overline{AB}$. To justify our conviction, we are faced with having to prove two things. The first is that

(1) Every point equidistant from A and B is a point on the perpendicular bisector of $\overline{AB}$.

This, however, is not enough, for our guess implied more than that which is stated in (1). By (1) we have merely shown that those points that are equidistant from A and B have to be points on the line that is the perpendicular bisector of $\overline{AB}$. This perpendicular bisector contains many points, and although we have shown that *some* of its points are equidistant from A and B, it may have many others that are not equidistant from A and B. Thus, points P, Q, and R that we know to be equidistant from A and B lie on the perpendicular bisector of $\overline{AB}$. Points W and S that are also on the perpendicular bisector of $\overline{AB}$, however, may not be equidistant from A and B. Hence, the second part of our proof consists in showing that

(2) Every point on the perpendicular bisector of $\overline{AB}$ is equidistant from points A and B.

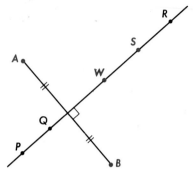

Figure 15-3.

Examination of statements (1) and (2) reveals that they are simply a statement and its converse. Thus, justifying a set of points as fulfilling the requirements of a given problem necessitates proving a theorem and its converse.

Although the term *converse* had been used a number of times earlier in the text, only a rather weak description had been made of the word. It had been pointed out that the converse of a theorem was a statement in which the "given data" and the "conclusion" of the original theorem had been interchanged. But what if the given data contained many pieces of information, and, in addition, we were asked to draw several conclusions? Do we interchange all of the given data with all the conclusions or with only part? In reality, should we interchange any piece of given data with any one of the conclusions, a converse statement will follow. Thus, an original statement may have many converses depending on the number of pieces of given data and the number of conclusions. None or perhaps even all of these converses may be true. The number that are true will depend on how many can be proved to be so.

Normally, the given data is listed in terms of angle bisectors, or perpendicular lines, or isosceles triangles, while the conclusion is considered in terms of parallel lines, or congruent triangles, or similar triangles. To make our discussion as general as possible, we will consider the given data as, "Item A," "Item B," and "Item C," while the conclusion will be called "Item D." Thus, the statement of a theorem in terms of these items will be

"If 'Item A,' 'Item B,' and 'Item C' are true,
then 'Item D' is true."

Or, even more concisely, this can be stated as

"If A, B, and C are true, then D is true."

In terms of these symbols, a converse of the above statement will be

"If A, B, and D are true, then C is true."

Can you write at least two other converses to the original statement?

Many of the theorems in the past and, even more important, those concerned with locus consist of merely one piece of given data and one conclusion. It is to this type of statement that we now turn our attention. Its form will be that of the conditional statement with which we are familiar:

$$\text{If } p \text{ then } q.$$

Thus, in the statement

(1) "If two angles are right angles, then the two angles are congruent" p is the antecedent (Two angles are right angles) while q is the consequent (The two angles are congruent).

Early in the year we proved the truth of statement (1). Now we are interested in knowing what effect the truth of this statement has on statements such as

(2) "If two angles are congruent, then the two angles are right angles."
(3) "If two angles are not right angles, then the two angles are not congruent."
(4) "If two angles are not congruent, then the two angles are not right angles."

Statements (2), (3), and (4) are called respectively the converse, inverse, and contrapositive to statement (1). Notice that the antecedent and consequent of the inverse are the contradictory statements to the antecedent and consequent of the original statement (1).

In general, our present objective is to investigate the relation that exists between the following four conditional statements:

(1) If p then q.   (original statement)
(2) If q then p.   (converse of original statement)
(3) If $\sim p$ then $\sim q$.†   (inverse of original statement)
(4) If $\sim q$ then $\sim p$.   (contrapositive of original statement)

The ideas we are trying to develop can be expressed quite clearly through the use of the Venn diagram. In Figure 15-5 we have shaded those elements that are members of the set p. In Figure 15-6 the region shaded

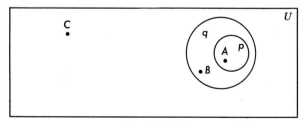

Figure 15-4.

† Recall that $\sim q$ is the contradictory statement to q and is read as "not q."

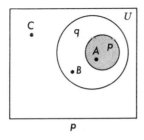

Figure 15-5.

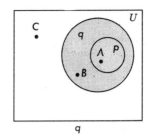

Figure 15-6.

contains those elements that are in set q; in Figure 15-7 it was the elements in set $\sim p$, while in Figure 15-8 it was those in $\sim q$. Each of these figures

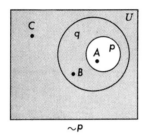

Figure 15-7.

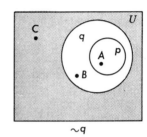

Figure 15-8.

expresses diagramatically the *truth* of the original statement

"If p then q."

Now, based on the truth of this statement, what will these diagrams tell us of the truth of the remaining three statements?

We will first examine

"If q then p."

Notice in Figure 15-6 that although some of the elements of q are contained in p, such as element A, not all the elements of q are in p. In particular, element B is not in p. Thus, it appears that we cannot say that

"If q then p"

must be true on the basis of the truth of

"If p then q."

This could also have been seen by examining the two statements:

(1) If two angles are right angles, then the two angles are congruent.
(2) If two angles are congruent, then the two angles are right angles.

Although we had proved the truth of the first, the second may not be true, for if two angles are congruent, they may be straight angles rather than right angles or, in fact, they may be any two angles having equal measures rather than right angles.

Examination of Figure 15-7 will give us a clue as to the truth of the inverse

(3) "If $\sim p$ then $\sim q$."

In Figure 15-7 we see that some of the elements that are not in $\sim p$, such as B, are in q. However, if statement 3 is to be true, then all the elements that are not in p cannot be in q. Thus, the truth of the original statement does *not* imply the truth of its inverse.

Figure 15-8 points out that all the elements that are not in q are also not in p. Thus, apparently, the truth of

(1) "If p then q"

implies also the truth of its contrapositive

(4) "If $\sim q$ then $\sim p$."

In the same way, were a Venn diagram to be drawn such as Figure 15-9

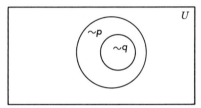

Figure 15-9.

it would be possible to demonstrate that the truth of the statement

"If $\sim q$ then $\sim p$"

would lead to the truth of the statement

"If p then q."

In Figure 15-9 all elements in p must be outside of circle ($\sim p$). By being outside of circle ($\sim p$), they are also outside of circle ($\sim q$). Hence, the elements of p are also elements of q. Thus, since Figure 15-9 implies the truth of

"If $\sim q$ then $\sim p$"

it also implies the truth of

"If p then q."

Two statements of the form

"If p then q"   and   "If $\sim q$ then $\sim p$"

are called *equivalent statements*. Equivalent statements are statements that are either *both* true or *both* false at the same time. It is not possible for one to be true while the other is false.

Returning again to the conditional statement

(1) "If two angles are right angles, then the two angles are congruent"

we see that its contrapositive

(4) If two angles are not congruent, then the two angles are not right angles."

will be true since the original statement was true.

But what of the converse and the inverse of a statement. Although the truth of neither follows from the truth of the original statement, can anything be said of the relationship that exists between them? Oddly enough, they, too, are equivalent statements. The truth of

"If q then p"   (converse)

gives rise to the Venn diagram in Figure 15-10. An element that is not in p

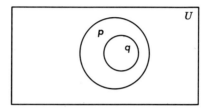

Figure 15-10.

would lie outside circle (p) and, hence, could not be an element of q. Thus, the truth of the converse leads to the truth of the inverse:

"If $\sim p$ then $\sim q$."

Similarly, the truth of

"If $\sim p$ then $\sim q$"

will imply the truth of

"If q then p"

Draw a Venn diagram to show why this would be so.

Based on this analysis, we will assume that

POSTULATE 41: The statements

"If p then q"   and   "If $\sim q$ then $\sim p$"

are equivalent statements.

Postulate 41 points out not only the equivalence of a statement and its contrapositive but also the equivalence of the converse and the inverse of a statement. In reality, the converse and the inverse of a statement can be considered as a statement and its contrapositive relative to each other, for

"If q then p"   and   "If $\sim p$ then $\sim q$"

are but a statement and its contrapositive.

Knowing these relations is very valuable, for there are times when it may be exceedingly difficult to prove a statement. However, proving its contrapositive may turn out to be a simple matter. Hence, the contrapositive is proved and the truth of the original statement immediately follows from Postulate 41.

EXERCISES

1. Given the fact that each of the following statements is true, write its converse, inverse, and contrapositive. State which of your statements is true without need for proof.
   (a) If it rains tomorrow, then I shall stay at home.
   (b) If the test is not difficult, then I shall receive a passing grade.
   (c) If I buy the book, then it is not expensive.
   (d) If at least 100 people do not purchase tickets, the show will not go on.
   (e) If two triangles are congruent, then an angle of one triangle is congruent to its corresponding angle in the other triangle.

2. Rewrite each of the following statements as conditional statements; then write the contrapositive of each.
   (a) Any citizen is eligible to run for Congress.
   (b) All Golden Brand candies are good to eat.
   (c) All of John's shirts are made from cotton.
   (d) A book that is written in Sanskrit does not sell in Harbor City.
   (e) A person who does not enjoy Shakespearean plays will not enjoy *Hamlet.*
   (f) A person who eats excessively will not lose weight.
   (g) Two tangent segments to a circle from an external point are congruent.

3. (a) Write the converse to the following statement: If a polygon is a triangle, then it has three sides.
   (b) Why is the converse of this statement true without need of proof?

4. (a) Using your postulates, prove the statement that "If $2x = 10$, then $x = 5$."
   (b) In view of the fact that you have proved this statement to be true, what other statement will be true without need of proof?
   (c) What is the converse of the statement in part (a)? Prove that the converse is also true.
   (d) In view of the fact that you have proved the converse of the statement in (a) to be true, what other statement will be true without need of proof?

5. (a) Write the converse, inverse, and contrapositive to the statement "If $\angle A$ and $\angle B$ are straight angles, then $\angle A \cong \angle B$."
   (b) In view of the theorems we have proved, which of the statements that you wrote in answer to part (a) are true?

6. Write the converse and inverse of each of the following statements:

(a) Any point on the perpendicular bisector of a line segment is equi-distant from the endpoints of the line segment.

(b) If a point is on the bisector of an angle, then it is equidistant from the sides of the angle.

(c) All points on a circle are a fixed distance from the center of the circle.

7. Justify why the converse, inverse, and contrapositive of any definition are true statements without the necessity of having to prove them to be.

Locus Theorems

There are basically only five theorems upon which the great bulk of the locus problems in synthetic geometry are based. Justifica-tion of each of these theorems, as you know, involves the proof of both a statement and its converse. For a few of these theorems it will be far easier to prove the inverse rather than the converse. From the information in the preceding unit, however, the truth of one will imply the truth of the other.

THEOREM 108: The locus of points equidistant from two fixed points is the perpendicular bisector of the line segment joining the two points. (First theorem on locus)

Part A—Proof of Statement

If a point is on the perpendicular bisector of the line seg-ment joining two fixed points, then it is equidistant from these two points. (See Theorem 17.)

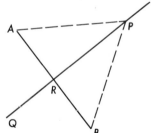

Given: $\overleftrightarrow{PQ} \perp \overleftrightarrow{AB}$

$\overleftrightarrow{PQ}$ bisects $\overline{AB}$.

P is any point on $\overleftrightarrow{PQ}$.

Concl.: $\overline{PA} \cong \overline{PB}$

Figure 15-11.

| PROOF | (The reasons will be left for you to supply.) |

1. $\overleftrightarrow{PQ} \perp \overleftrightarrow{AB}$
2. $\angle PRB$ and $\angle PRA$ are right angles.
3. $\angle PRB \cong \angle PRA$ (a)
4. $\overleftrightarrow{PQ}$ bisects $\overline{AB}$.

5. $\overline{AR} \cong \overline{RB}$ (s)
6. $\overline{PR} \cong \overline{PR}$ (s)
7. $\triangle PRA \cong \triangle PRB$
8. $\overline{PA} \cong \overline{PB}$

Part B—Proof of Converse

▬▬▬▬▬▬ If a point is equidistant from two fixed points, then it lies on the perpendicular bisector of the line segment joining these two points. (See Theorem 18.)

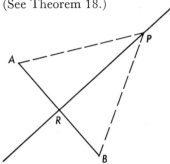

Given: $\overline{PA} \cong \overline{PB}$

P is any point equidistant from A and B.

Concl.: P is on the $\perp$ bisector of $\overline{AB}$.

Figure 15-12.

PROOF	(The reasons will be left for you to supply.)

1. $\overline{PA} \cong \overline{PB}$ (h)

2. Let $\overset{\leftrightarrow}{PR}$ be the perpendicular that exists from P to $\overset{\leftrightarrow}{AB}$.

3. $\angle PRA$ and $\angle PRB$ are right angles.

4. $\overline{PR} \cong \overline{PR}$ (l)

5. $\triangle PRA \cong \triangle PRB$

6. $\overline{RA} \cong \overline{RB}$

7. $\therefore \overset{\leftrightarrow}{PR}$ is the $\perp$ bisector of $\overline{AB}$.

Rather than prove the converse as we had in Part B, it would have been possible for us to have proved the inverse to justify the second half of the proof of this locus theorem. As a point of information, this will be done now.

Alternate Proof of Part B—Proof of Inverse

If a point is not on the perpendicular bisector of the line segment joining two fixed points, then it is not equidistant from these two points.

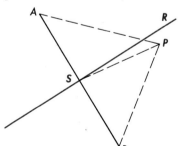

Given: $\overset{\leftrightarrow}{RS} \perp$ bisector of $\overline{AB}$

Point P does not lie on $\overset{\leftrightarrow}{RS}$.

Concl.: $\overline{PA} \cong \overline{PB}$

Figure 15-13.

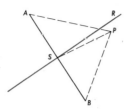

Figure 15-13.

PROOF

By the law of the excluded middle one of the following state-ments must be true and no other possibility exists:

$$\overline{PA} \not\cong \overline{PB} \quad \text{or} \quad \overline{PA} \cong \overline{PB}$$

Let us accept the possibility that $\overline{PA} \cong \overline{PB}$. Let $\overleftrightarrow{PS}$ be the line that exists through points P and S. By the S.S.S. congruency theorem it is possible to show that $\triangle PSA \cong \triangle PSB$. Hence, $\angle PSA \cong \angle PSB$, and, therefore, $\overleftrightarrow{PS} \perp \overleftrightarrow{AB}$. This would imply that $\angle PSA$ is a right angle. The Given Data, however, informs us that $\overleftrightarrow{RS} \perp \overleftrightarrow{AB}$; hence, $\angle RSA$ is a right angle. There-fore, $\angle PSA \cong \angle RSA$. However, by our postulate that the whole is greater than any of its parts, it follows that $\angle PSA \not\cong \angle RSA$. Therefore, accepting the possibility that $\overline{PA} \cong \overline{PB}$ led to the logical inconsistency of the truth of both $\angle PSA \cong \angle RSA$ and $\angle PSA \not\cong \angle RSA$. By the law of contradiction both cannot be true at the same time. Since $\angle PSA \not\cong \angle RSA$ is true, for it is the result of a postulate, then $\angle PSA \cong \angle RSA$ must be false, and so $\overline{PA} \cong \overline{PB}$ must also be false. Hence, $\overline{PA} \not\cong \overline{PB}$ is true, for it is the only remaining possibility.

THEOREM 109: The locus of points equidistant from two intersecting lines is the two lines that are the bisectors of the angles formed by these lines. (Second theorem on locus)

Part A—Proof of Statement

If a point is on the bisector of one of the angles formed by two intersecting lines, then it is equidistant from these lines.

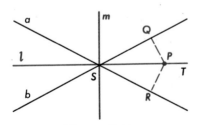

Given: $\overrightarrow{ST}$ is the bisector of an angle formed by a and b.

P is any point on $\overrightarrow{ST}$.

$\overleftrightarrow{PQ} \perp b$, $\overleftrightarrow{PR} \perp a$

Concl.: $\overline{PQ} \cong \overline{PR}$

Figure 15-14.

| PROOF | (The reasons will be left for you to supply.) |

1. $\overrightarrow{ST}$ bisects $\angle QSR$.
2. $\angle QSP \cong \angle RSP$ (a)
3. $\overline{PS} \cong \overline{PS}$ (s)
4. $\overleftrightarrow{PQ} \perp b$, $\overleftrightarrow{PR} \perp a$

5. $\angle PQS$ and $\angle PRS$ are right angles.
6. $\angle PQS \cong \angle PRS$ (a)
7. $\triangle PQS \cong \triangle PRS$
8. $\overline{PQ} \cong \overline{PR}$

Part B—Proof of Inverse

If a point is not on the bisector of one of the angles formed by two intersecting lines, then it is not equidistant from these lines.

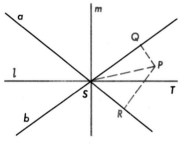

Given: $\overrightarrow{ST}$ is the bisector of an angle formed by a and b.

P is any point that is not on $\overrightarrow{ST}$.

$\overleftrightarrow{PQ} \perp b$, $\overleftrightarrow{PR} \perp a$

Concl.: $\overline{PQ} \not\cong \overline{PR}$

Figure 15-15.

PROOF

By the law of the excluded middle one of the following statements must be true and no other possibility exists:

$$\overline{PQ} \cong \overline{PR} \quad \text{or} \quad \overline{PQ} \not\cong \overline{PR}$$

Let us accept the possibility that $\overline{PQ} \cong \overline{PR}$. Let $\overleftrightarrow{PS}$ be the line through points P and S. By the hypotenuse-leg congruency theorem it is possible to show $\triangle PQS \cong \triangle PRS$. Hence, $\angle PSQ \cong \angle PSR$, and, therefore, $m \angle PSQ = \frac{1}{2} m \angle RSQ$. The Given Data, however, informs us that $\overrightarrow{ST}$ is the bisector of $\angle QSR$; therefore $m \angle TSQ = \frac{1}{2} m \angle RSQ$. Hence, $m \angle PSQ = m \angle TSQ$. However, by our postulate that the whole is greater than any of its parts, $m \angle PSQ \neq m \angle TSQ$. Therefore, accepting the possibility that $\overline{PQ} \cong \overline{PR}$ led to the logical inconsistency of the truth of both $m \angle PSQ = m \angle TSQ$ and $m \angle PSQ \neq m \angle TSQ$. By the law of contradiction both cannot be true at the same time. Since $m \angle PSQ \neq m \angle TSQ$ is true, for it is the result of a postulate, then $m \angle PSQ = m \angle TSQ$ must be false, and, hence, $\overline{PQ} \cong \overline{PR}$ is false. Therefore, $\overline{PQ} \not\cong \overline{PR}$ is true, for it is the only remaining possibility.

THEOREM 110: The locus of points at a fixed distance from a given line is two lines parallel to the given line at the fixed distance from it. (Third theorem on locus)

Part A—Proof of Statement

▆▆▆▆▆▆ If two lines are parallel to a given line such that two points, one on each line, are each a distance d from the given line, then all points on these lines are a distance d from the given line.

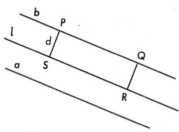

Given: $b \parallel l$, $a \parallel l$
P on line b at a distance d from l
Q is any other point on b.
$\overleftrightarrow{PS} \perp l$, $\overleftrightarrow{QR} \perp l$
Concl.: $QR = d$

Figure 15-16.

PROOF	(The reasons will be left for you to supply.)
1. $b \parallel l$	5. $PQRS$ is a parallelogram.
2. $\overleftrightarrow{PS} \perp l$	6. $\therefore QR = PS$
3. $\overleftrightarrow{QR} \perp l$	7. But $PS = d$
4. $\therefore \overleftrightarrow{PS} \parallel \overleftrightarrow{QR}$	8. $\therefore QR = d$

The same proof would apply for points on line a.

Part B—Proof of Inverse

▆▆▆▆▆▆ If two lines are parallel to a given line such that two points, one on each line, are each a distance d from the given line, then all points not on these lines are not a distance d from the given line.

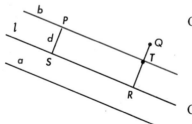

Given: $b \parallel l$, $a \parallel l$
P on line b at a distance d from l
Q is any point not on either a or b.
$\overleftrightarrow{PS} \perp l$, $\overleftrightarrow{QR} \perp l$
Concl.: $QR \neq d$

Figure 15-17.

PROOF

The proof is indirect as in Theorem 109. It will be left for you to complete.

THEOREM 111: **The locus of points equidistant from two given parallel lines is the perpendicular bisector of the segment that is the common perpendicular to these two lines.** (Fourth theorem on locus)

Part A—Proof of Statement

██████████ If a point is on the perpendicular bisector of the line segment that is the common perpendicular to two parallel lines, then it is equidistant from the two lines.

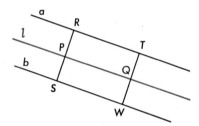

Given: $a \parallel l, b \parallel l$

$\overleftrightarrow{RS} \perp a, \overleftrightarrow{RS} \perp b$

$\overline{PR} \cong \overline{PS}$

Q is any other point on l.

Concl.: Q is equidistant from a and b.

Figure 15-18.

ANALYSIS: To prove that Q is equidistant from a and b, it is necessary to show that the perpendiculars from Q to a and b are congruent. In order to arrive at this, we allow $\overleftrightarrow{QT}$ to be the perpendicular from Q to a and then extend $\overleftrightarrow{QT}$ to intersect b. After proving that $\overleftrightarrow{QW}$ is perpendicular to b, we will show that $\overline{QT} \cong \overline{QW}$.

PROOF STATEMENTS	REASONS
1. $a \parallel b \parallel l$	1. Given
2. Let $\overleftrightarrow{QT}$ be the perpendicular from Q to a.	2. There exists one and only one perpendicular from a given point to a given line.
3. Extend $\overleftrightarrow{QT}$ until it intersects b at W.	3. A line can be extended as far as desired.
4. $\overleftrightarrow{QT} \perp b$	4. If a line is perpendicular to one of two parallel lines, it is also perpendicular to the other.
5. $\overline{PR} \cong \overline{PS}$	5. Given

6. $\overline{QW} \cong \overline{QT}$

6. If three or more parallel lines cut off congruent segments on one transversal, they cut off congruent segments on every transversal.

Part B—Proof of Inverse

████████████ If a point is not on the perpendicular bisector of the line segment that is the common perpendicular to two parallel lines, then it is not equidistant from the two lines.

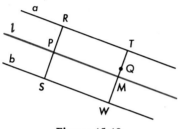

Figure 15-19.

Given: $a \parallel l$, $b \parallel l$
$\overset{\leftrightarrow}{RS} \perp a$, $\overset{\leftrightarrow}{RS} \perp b$
$\overline{PR} \cong \overline{PS}$
Q is any point not on l.

Concl.: Q is not equidistant from a and b.

PROOF

The proof is indirect as in Theorem 109. It will be left for you to complete.

THEOREM 112: The locus of points that are a fixed distance from a fixed point is a circle. (Fifth theorem on locus)

PROOF

This statement should not, strictly speaking, be called a theorem, for it is simply the alternative definition of a circle that had been given on page 440.

When you are confronted with a locus problem, it would be best to follow the pattern suggested below:

(1) Draw a diagram in which you have placed any two points of the set or locus.

(2) Prove some relation about these two points that falls under one of the five locus theorems.

(3) Write the proof in paragraph form similar to that used for the indirect proof.

Several illustrations will be given to present a clearer picture of this method of approach.

Illustration 1:

What is the locus of the midpoints of congruent chords of a circle?

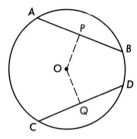

Figure 15-20.

Given: $\overline{AB} \cong \overline{CD}$ in circle O

       P is the midpoint of $\overline{AB}$.

       Q is the midpoint of $\overline{CD}$.

Concl.: To find the locus of the midpoints of congruent chords of circle O

PROOF

By allowing $\overleftrightarrow{OP}$ and $\overleftrightarrow{OQ}$ to be the lines through points O and P and through O and Q, we can show that $\overleftrightarrow{OP} \perp \overleftrightarrow{AB}$ and $\overleftrightarrow{OQ} \perp \overleftrightarrow{CD}$. Hence, $\overline{OP} \cong \overline{OQ}$ since congruent chords of a circle are equidistant from the center. Thus, the midpoints of congruent chords of a circle are a fixed distance from the center of the circle. Hence, their locus is a circle, for the set of points that are a fixed distance from a fixed point is a circle (fifth theorem on locus).

Illustration 2:

In a right triangle with a fixed hypotenuse what is the locus of the vertex of the right angle?

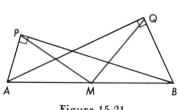

Figure 15-21.

Given: Right $\triangle APB$ with $\angle P$ the right angle

       Right $\triangle AQB$ with $\angle Q$ the right angle

Concl.: To find the locus of the vertices of the right angle of the right triangle where $\overline{AB}$ is the hypotenuse

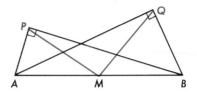

Figure 15-21.

PROOF

Let M be the midpoint of $\overline{AB}$ and let $\overset{\leftrightarrow}{PM}$ and $\overset{\leftrightarrow}{QM}$ be the lines through P and M and through Q and M. By Problem 10, page 274, we know that in $\triangle APB$ $\overline{MP} \cong \overline{MA}$ since the median to the hypotenuse is congruent to the segments of the hypotenuse. Similarly, in $\triangle AQB$ $\overline{MQ} \cong \overline{MA}$. Hence, $\overline{MP} \cong \overline{MQ}$. Thus, the vertices of these right triangles are a fixed distance from point M. Hence, their locus is a circle, for the set of points that are a fixed distance from a fixed point is a circle (fifth theorem on locus). Incidentally, since A and B lie on this circle and also on the hypotenuse, they will have to be excluded from the locus. Can you explain why?

EXERCISES

1. What is the locus of the centers of circles that are tangent to two parallel lines?
2. What is the locus of the centers of congruent circles that are tangent externally to a given circle?
3. What is the locus of the centers of congruent circles that are tangent to a given line?
4. What is the locus of the midpoints of the radii of a circle?
5. What is the locus of points that are equidistant from the sides of an angle?
6. What is the locus of the vertices of the vertex angles of isosceles triangles drawn on the same base?
7. Each of the radii of a circle is extended its own length. What is the locus of the endpoints of these extended segments?
8. What is the locus of points that are always a fixed distance from a fixed circle? (See Problem 8, page 516, for the distance from a point to a circle.)
9. What is the locus of the outer endpoint, not the point of tangency, of congruent tangent segments that are drawn to a circle?

10. What is the locus of the centers of circles that have a given line segment as a common chord?

11. What is the locus of the centers of circles that are tangent to both sides of a given angle?

12. In the diagram at the right what is the locus of the midpoints of all line segments whose endpoints are *P* and some point on *l*?

P
•

l _____

13. What is the locus of points that are equidistant from two opposite sides of a rectangle?

14. What is the locus of the midpoints of line segments whose endpoints lie in a pair of given parallel lines?

15.* Prove the theorem in space geometry that the locus of points that are equidistant from two fixed points is the plane that is the perpendicular bisector of the line segment joining these two points. Use the diagram below and the proof of Theorem 108 as a model.

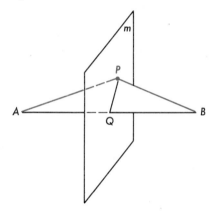

16. Write the statements of the theorems in space geometry that are comparable to Theorems 109, 110, 111, and 112. Do not prove these statements.

▪ Compound Loci in Synthetic Geometry

In our study of the intersection of two sets in analytic geometry, we found that this simply implied that we were searching for those elements that were common to the two sets.† These elements were either points in the coordinate plane or ordered pairs of values that represented these points. Now, however, the intersection of two sets, or loci, can only be *points* that are common to the two sets, for in synthetic geometry we do

† See page 419.

not consider the correspondence between points and ordered pairs of numbers.

Where previously the proof of a problem was shown in terms of the intersection of the solution sets of equalities or inequalities, now it must be given in terms of two of the five locus theorems. Several examples will be given to illustrate this point.

Illustration 1:

What is the locus of points that are equidistant from the points A and B and from the points C and D?

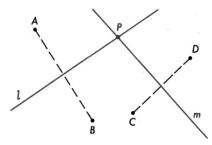

Figure 15-22.

PROOF

The set of points equidistant from points A and B is the perpendicular bisector of $\overline{AB}$, the line l. The set of points equidistant from points C and D is the perpendicular bisector of $\overline{CD}$, the line m. To find the points that are equidistant from the points A and B and also from the points C and D, it is necessary to find $l \cap m$; that is, the intersection of l and m. This is point P. Hence, P is equidistant from the points A and B and also equidistant from the points C and D.

Unfortunately the proof is not yet completed at this stage, for the points A, B, C, and D may take positions other than shown in the diagram above. Were the line segments AB and CD parallel, then l would be parallel to m. Hence, $l \cap m$ would be the null, or empty, set; that is, there would be no points that are common to the two loci. See Figure 15-23.

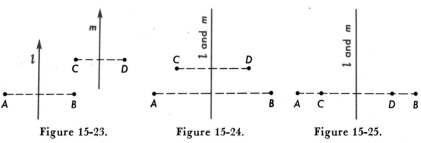

Figure 15-23.   **Figure 15-24.**   **Figure 15-25.**

Finally, if A, B, C, and D were so situated that the perpendicular bisector of $\overline{AB}$ was also the perpendicular bisector of $\overline{CD}$, then $l \cap m$ would be all the points on l or all the points on m. See Figures 15-24 and 15-25.

Illustration 2:

What is the locus of points that are a fixed distance from a fixed point and equidistant from the sides of a given angle?

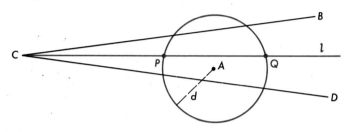

Figure 15-26.

PROOF

The set of points that are a fixed distance from the fixed point is a circle with the fixed point (A) as the center and the fixed distance (d) as the radius. The set of points equidistant from the sides of the angle is the bisector $(\overrightarrow{l})$ of the angle ($\angle BCD$). The set of points that is a fixed distance from A and equidistant from $\angle BCD$ is $\overrightarrow{l} \cap A$, or points P and Q. The placement of the fixed point and the given angle may be such that the possibilities shown in Figure 15-27 will exist.

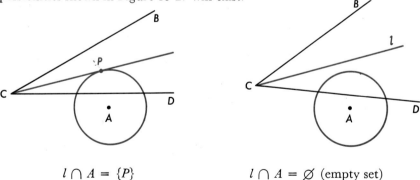

$$l \cap A = \{P\} \qquad\qquad l \cap A = \varnothing \text{ (empty set)}$$

Figure 15-27.

You may have noticed in our study of coordinate geometry that although we proved the concurrency of the medians of any triangle,† we

† See Problem 20, page 392.

avoided doing the same for either the perpendicular bisectors of the sides
of a triangle or the angle bisectors of a triangle. This omission was not an
oversight, but rather it was deliberate, since the proofs of the concurrency
of these lines are far simpler and far more elegant in synthetic geometry
than in coordinate geometry. The locus theorems provide us with the tools
that make this so.

**THEOREM 113: The perpendicular bisectors of the sides of a triangle
are concurrent at a point that is equidistant from the
vertices of the triangle.**

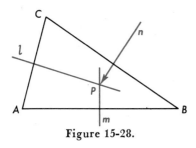

Given: l is the $\perp$ bisector of $\overline{AC}$.

m is the $\perp$ bisector of $\overline{AB}$.

n is the $\perp$ bisector of $\overline{BC}$.

Concl.: n passes through P (the point of
intersection of l and m).

Figure 15-28.

PROOF

The set of points that are equidistant from A and B is the
line m, the perpendicular bisector of $\overline{AB}$. Similarly, the set of points equidistant from A and C is l. Hence, P, the intersection of l and m, is equidistant
from A, B, and C. In particular, it is equidistant from B and C and, therefore, must be a point on n, for the locus of points equidistant from two fixed
points is the perpendicular bisector of the line segment joining these two
points.

The proof of this theorem depends upon the fact that l and m can be
shown to intersect at some point P. By using the indirect method of proof,
it is possible to show that if we accept the possibility that l does not intersect m, then $\overleftrightarrow{AC}$ would be perpendicular to m, for if a line is perpendicular
to one (l) of two parallel lines (l and m), then it is perpendicular to the other
also. Hence, $\overleftrightarrow{AC}$ would have to be parallel to $\overleftrightarrow{AB}$ as two lines perpendicular
to the same line are parallel. This, however, is in contradiction to the
Given Data that $\overline{AB}$ and $\overline{AC}$ have the point A in common. Thus, l must
intersect m, for the possibility that l does not intersect m led to contradictory
statements.

It may be interesting to you to compare the proof above with the one
you gave for Problem 18, page 190.

THEOREM 114: The bisectors of the angles of a triangle are concurrent at a point that is equidistant from the sides of the triangle.

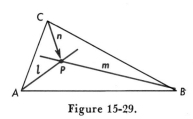

Figure 15-29.

Given: $\overrightarrow{l}$ bisects $\angle A$.

$\overrightarrow{m}$ bisects $\angle B$.

$\overrightarrow{n}$ bisects $\angle C$.

Concl.: $\overrightarrow{n}$ passes through P (the point of intersection of $\overrightarrow{l}$ and $\overrightarrow{m}$).

PROOF

The locus of points that are equidistant from $\overrightarrow{AC}$ and $\overrightarrow{AB}$ is the ray $\overrightarrow{l}$, the bisector of $\angle A$. Similarly, the locus of points equidistant from $\overrightarrow{BC}$ and $\overrightarrow{BA}$ is $\overrightarrow{m}$. Hence, P, the intersection of $\overrightarrow{l}$ and $\overrightarrow{m}$, is the point that is equidistant from $\overleftrightarrow{AB}$, $\overleftrightarrow{CA}$, and $\overleftrightarrow{CB}$. In particular, it is equidistant from $\overrightarrow{CA}$ and $\overrightarrow{CB}$ and, therefore, must be a point on $\overrightarrow{n}$, for the locus of points equidistant from the sides of an angle is the bisector of the angle.

As in Theorem 113 the proof of this theorem depends upon our ability to show that $\overrightarrow{l}$ and $\overrightarrow{m}$ intersect at some point P. This can be shown rather easily by the application of Pasch's Axiom.

EXERCISES

In each of the following problems you are to find the locus in terms of the conditions given. In addition, you are to draw diagrams showing the other possibilities that may arise. Specifically, follow the pattern presented in Illustration 2, page 535.

1. What is the locus of points that are equidistant from two parallel lines and lie on a third line?
2. What is the locus of points that are a fixed distance from a fixed point and lie on a given line?
3. What is the locus of points that are equidistant from the sides of an angle and lie on a given line?

4. What is the locus of points that are a fixed distance from a fixed line and lie on a given circle?

5. What is the locus of points that are equidistant from two fixed points and lie on a given circle?

6. What is the locus of points that are a fixed distance, d_1, from point A and a fixed distance, d_2, from point B?

7. What is the locus of points that are a fixed distance from the point of intersection of two intersecting lines and lie on these two lines?

8. What is the locus of points that are equidistant from two parallel lines and are at a fixed distance from a given point that lies on one of these lines?

9. What is the locus of points that are equidistant from two fixed points and are at a given distance from a given circle but lie outside the circle?

10. What is the locus of points that are equidistant from the points A and B and also from the points A and C? That is, what is the locus of points equidistant from three given points, A, B, and C?

11. What is the locus of points that are equidistant from two intersecting lines and are at a given distance from their point of intersection?

12. What is the locus of points that are a fixed distance from point A and equidistant from points A and B?

13.* Using the diagram at the right, prove that the bisectors of $\angle EAC$, $\angle DCA$, and $\angle ABC$ are concurrent.

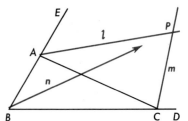

14.* Using the diagram at the right, prove that the altitudes of a triangle are concurrent. (Hint: Let $\overleftrightarrow{QR}$ be the line through A that is parallel to $\overleftrightarrow{BC}$. Same for $\overleftrightarrow{PQ}$ and $\overleftrightarrow{PR}$. Then use Theorem 113.)

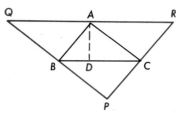

B

　　　　Discuss each of the following problems informally; no proof is required.

1. What is the locus of points that are less than a given distance from a fixed line and that lie on a second fixed line?

2. What is the locus of points that are greater than a given distance from a fixed line and that are equidistant from two fixed points? (See similar problem in Coordinate Geometry, pages 436–437.)

3. What is the locus of points that are less than a given distance from a given point and lie on a given line?

4. M is the midpoint of line segment AB. What is the locus of points that are not equidistant from A and B and are less than a given distance from M?

5. What is the locus of points that are equidistant from two parallel lines and less than a given distance from a given line?

6. What is the locus of points that are greater than a distance, d_1, from point A and also less than a distance of d_2 from point A? (Assume d_1 to be less than d_2.)

7. In space geometry what is the locus of points that are a fixed distance from a fixed point and lie on a given plane?

8. In space geometry what is the locus of points that are less than a fixed distance from a fixed point and lie on a given plane?

9. In space geometry, what is the locus of points that are a given distance, d_1, from a fixed point and at a given distance, d_2, from a fixed plane?

10. In space geometry what is the locus of points that are less than a distance, d_1, from a fixed point and at a given distance, d_2, from a fixed plane?

11. In space geometry what is the locus of points that are equidistant from two fixed points (see Problem 15 page 533) and equidistant from two parallel planes?

12. In space geometry what is the locus of points that are equidistant from two fixed points and less than a given distance from a given plane?

■ Straightedge and Compass Constructions

Closely allied to the work on loci is the topic of construction, for it enables us actually to draw the locus by using certain instruments. It may have occurred to you that the number of curves considered in this course has been rather limited. In fact, they have been limited to but two: the line† and the circle. No other curve was examined, not because of lack of space but rather because of the definition of plane geometry as agreed upon by Greek mathematicians:

Plane geometry is that branch of mathematics in which the only instruments permissible are the straightedge and compass.

As you well know, *the compass is the instrument used for drawing circles or arcs of circles. The straightedge, on the other hand, is the instrument for drawing lines.*

† We are assuming that a line can be considered as a special type of curve.

The straightedge is very much the same as the instrument you have come to know as the "ruler." However, unlike the ruler the straightedge has *no* markings on it. Hence, it cannot be used to measure the lengths of line segments.

A question such as "Can the bisector of an angle be constructed?" is largely meaningless until we are told what instruments we are permitted to use. If none are available, then by all means no construction is possible! However, in our work we will accept the Greek definition of geometry and consider that the only instruments that are both available and permissible are the straightedge and compass. Thus, the above question should be interpreted as "Can the bisector of an angle be constructed by using straightedge and compass only?" The answer to this question and others like it will be the subject of this unit.

In an earlier topic† we discussed the existence of certain lines or angles. The proofs of these "existence" statements were based on three postulates:

(1) A line may be extended as far as desired in either direction.

(2) There exists one and only one line through two points.

(3) At a given point on a given line there exists an angle whose vertex is the given point and one of whose sides is the given line such that this angle is congruent to any given angle.

In this unit we will reprove not only a few of the existence statements examined previously but also many more that we were unable to prove at that time. Now, however, our theorems will be phrased in the language of construction.

You may have wondered how it will be possible to construct congruent line segments without the aid of the markings on a ruler. The next theorem should answer that question.

THEOREM 115: **At a given point on a given line a line segment congruent to a given line segment can be constructed.**
(How would this theorem have been worded as an existence statement?)

Given: Line segment AB
          Line l containing point P
To Construct: A line segment on l at P
                      that is congruent to $\overline{AB}$

Figure 15-30.

METHOD:

(1) Using A as the center and a radius congruent to $\overline{AB}$, draw an arc of a circle.

† See page 255.

(2) With P as the center and the same radius, draw an arc of a circle intersecting l at Q.

(3) Then, $\overline{PQ} \cong \overline{AB}$

PROOF STATEMENTS	REASONS
1. $\odot A \cong \odot P$	1. Reverse of the definition of congruent circles
2. $\overline{PQ} \cong \overline{AB}$	2. Definition of congruent circles

THEOREM 116: At a given point on a given line an angle congruent to a given angle can be constructed.

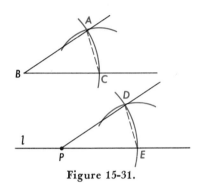

Given: $\angle B$
            Line l containing point P
To Construct: An angle at P, one of whose sides is l and that is congruent to $\angle B$.

Figure 15-31.

METHOD:

(1) Using B as the center and any convenient radius, draw an arc intersecting the sides of $\angle B$ at A and C.

(2) Using P as the center and the same radius as in step 1, draw an arc intersecting l at E.

(3) With C as the center and $\overline{CA}$ as a radius draw an arc.

(4) With E as the center and $\overline{CA}$ as a radius draw an arc intersecting the previous arc at D.

(5) Using the straightedge, draw $\overrightarrow{PD}$.

(6) Then $\angle DPE \cong \angle ABC$.

PROOF STATEMENTS	REASONS
1. Draw $\overleftrightarrow{AC}$ and $\overleftrightarrow{DE}$.	1. Why possible?
2. $\overline{BA} \cong \overline{PD}$ (s)	2. Def. of congruent circles
3. $\overline{BC} \cong \overline{PE}$ (s)	3. Same as 2
4. $\overline{CA} \cong \overline{ED}$ (s)	4. Same as 2
5. $\triangle ABC \cong \triangle DPE$	5. Why?
6. $\angle ABC \cong \angle DPE$	6. Why?

THEOREM 117: The perpendicular bisector of a line segment can be constructed.

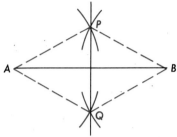

Given: Line segment AB
To Construct: The perpendicular bisector of $\overline{AB}$

Figure 15-32.

METHOD:

(1) Using A as a center and a radius whose measure is greater than one-half of AB, draw arcs above and below $\overleftrightarrow{AB}$.

(2) Using B as a center and the same radius as in step 1, draw arcs above and below $\overline{AB}$, intersecting the previous arcs in P and Q.

(3) Use the straightedge to draw $\overleftrightarrow{PQ}$.

(4) Then, $\overleftrightarrow{PQ}$ is the perpendicular bisector of $\overline{AB}$.

PROOF	STATEMENTS	REASONS
1. Draw $\overleftrightarrow{PA}$, $\overleftrightarrow{PB}$, $\overleftrightarrow{QA}$, and $\overleftrightarrow{QB}$.		1. Why possible?
2. $\overline{PA} \cong \overline{PB}$		2. Def. of congruent circles
3. $\overline{QA} \cong \overline{QB}$		3. Same as 2
4. $\overleftrightarrow{PQ}$ is the perpendicular bisector of $\overline{AB}$.		4. If two points are each equidistant from the endpoints of a line segment, then the line joining them will be the perpendicular bisector of the line segment.

THEOREM 118: The bisector of an angle can be constructed.

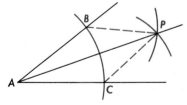

Given: $\angle A$
To Construct: The bisector of $\angle A$

Figure 15-33.

METHOD:

(1) Using A as a center and any convenient radius, draw an arc intersecting the sides of $\angle A$ at B and C.

(2) Using B as a center and a radius whose measure is greater than one-half of BC, draw an arc.

(3) Using C as a center and the same radius as used in step 2, draw an arc intersecting the one in step 2 at P.

(4) Use the straight edge to draw $\overleftrightarrow{AP}$.

(5) Then, $\overrightarrow{AP}$ bisects $\angle BAC$.

PROOF

The proof will be left for you to do.

THEOREM 119: At a given point on a given line a line perpendicular to this line can be constructed.

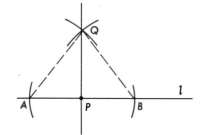

Given: Line l with point P on l
To Construct: A line perpendicular to l
at P

Figure 15-34.

METHOD:

(1) Using P as a center and any convenient radius, draw arcs intersecting l at A and B.

(2) Using A as a center and a radius whose measure is greater than AP, draw an arc above l.

(3) Using B as a center and the same radius as used in step 2, draw an arc intersecting the arc in step 2 at Q.

(4) Use the straightedge to draw $\overleftrightarrow{QP}$.

(5) Then, $\overleftrightarrow{QP} \perp l$

PROOF

The proof will be left for you to do.

THEOREM 120: From a given point not on a given line a line perpendicular to the given line can be constructed.

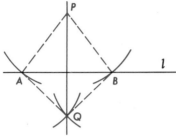

Given: Line *l* with *P* not on *l*
To Construct: A line from *P* perpendicular to *l*

Figure 15-35.

METHOD:

(1) Using *P* as a center and a radius whose measure is greater than the distance from *P* to *l*, draw arcs intersecting *l* at *A* and *B*.

(2) Using *A* as a center and a radius whose measure is greater than one-half of *AB*, draw an arc below *l*.

(3) Using *B* as a center and the same radius as used in step 2, draw an arc intersecting the arc in step 2 at *Q*.

(4) Use the straightedge to draw $\overleftrightarrow{PQ}$.

(5) Then, $\overleftrightarrow{PQ} \perp l$

PROOF

The proof will be left for you to do.

Illustration:

Construct an angle of 45°.

ANALYSIS: By using either Theorem 117, 119, or 120 a right angle can be constructed. Theorem 118 is then used to bisect that angle, thus obtaining an angle of 45°.

To avoid the necessity of having to write out the steps in your method of attack, simply draw the arcs of your circles large enough so that it is possible to determine what points had been used as the centers of the circles. Should this be done, an examination of your drawing is all that is necessary to understand the method you used to draw the diagram. Can you tell from the arcs in Figure 15-36 whether Theorem 117, 119, or 120 was used to construct the right angle?

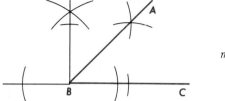

$m \angle ABC = 45$

Figure 15-36.

EXERCISES

1. **(a)** In Theorem 117, step 1, why was it necessary to use a radius whose measure was greater than one-half of AB?
   (b) In Theorem 119, step 2, why was it necessary to use a radius whose measure was greater than AP?
   (c) In Theorem 120, step 1, what represents the distance from P to l? Why must the measure of the radius be greater than this distance?

2. Construct a line segment equal to the sum of two given line segments.
3. Construct an angle equal to the difference of two given angles.
4. Divide a given line segment into four congruent segments.
5. Draw an obtuse angle and divide it into four congruent angles.
6. **(a)** Construct an angle of 135°.
   (b) Construct an angle of $22\frac{1}{2}°$.
   (c) Construct an angle of $67\frac{1}{2}°$.

7. If a and b are the measures of two given line segments where $a > b$, construct a line segment whose measure is equal to $\frac{1}{2}(a - b)$.
8. If $\angle A$ and $\angle B$ are two given angles, construct an angle whose measure is equal to $\frac{1}{2}(m \angle A + m \angle B)$.
9. Draw a triangle similar to the one at the right. Construct the median from C to $\overline{AB}$ in this triangle.

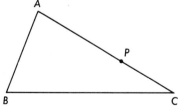

10. Draw a triangle similar to the one in Problem 9. Construct the line that is perpendicular to $\overleftrightarrow{AC}$ at point P.

11. Draw a triangle similar to the one in Problem 9. Construct the altitude from B to $\overline{AC}$.

12. Construct the angle bisectors of a triangle and find their point of concurrency.

13. (a) Construct the perpendicular bisectors of the sides of an acute triangle. Do the same for a right triangle and for an obtuse triangle.
    (b) What conclusion can be drawn concerning the point of concurrency in each case?

14. (a) Construct the altitudes to the sides of an acute triangle. Do the same for a right triangle and for an obtuse triangle.
    (b) What conclusion can be drawn concerning the point of concurrency in each case?

15. Construct the locus of points that are equidistant from two intersecting lines.

16. Construct the locus of points that are equidistant from two fixed points.

17. Construct the locus of points that are equidistant from two fixed points and at a given distance from a given point.

18. Construct the locus of points that are equidistant from two fixed points and equidistant from the sides of a given angle.

■ More About Construction with Straightedge and Compass

The great bulk of the problems on construction in plane geometry are based on the six construction theorems developed in the preceding unit. The key to determining how a particular construction can be done is to *sketch* the figure in completed form. An inspection of this drawing will lead to those construction theorems that must be applied. Application of this method will be made to the construction theorems in this unit.

THEOREM 121: Through a given point not on a given line a line can be constructed parallel to the given line.

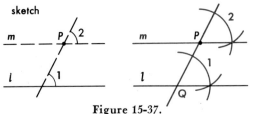

Given: Line l and point P not on l
To Construct: A line through P parallel to l

Figure 15-37.

ANALYSIS: By inspecting the completed sketch we realize that were $\angle 1 \cong \angle 2$, the lines would be parallel. Hence, the problem simplifies to the point of merely constructing an angle congruent to a given angle.

METHOD:

(1) Through *P* draw a line intersecting *l* at *Q*.

(2) On this line at point *P* construct an angle congruent to ∠*Q*.

(3) Then, *m* ∥ *l*

PROOF STATEMENTS	REASONS
1. ∠2 was constructed congruent to ∠1.	1. An angle congruent to a given angle can be constructed.
2. *l* ∥ *m*	2. If two lines are cut by a transversal such that the corresponding angles are congruent, then the lines are parallel.

Before developing the next two construction theorems, several definitions are necessary.

DEFINITION 95: An inscribed polygon in a circle is a polygon whose vertices are points of the circle.

DEFINITION 96: A circumscribed polygon about a circle is a polygon whose sides are tangent to the circle.

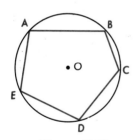

Figure 15-38.

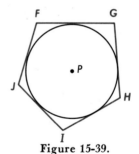

Figure 15-39.

ABCDE is an *inscribed polygon*, or circle *O* is said to be *circumscribed* about *ABCDE*.

FGHIJ is a *circumscribed polygon*, or circle *P* is said to be *inscribed* within *FGHIJ*.

Just as we refer to points that fall on the same line as being collinear points and points that are elements of the same plane as coplaner points, so, too, do we have a name for points that are members of the same circle. These points are called *concyclic* points. There are a number of interesting theorems that can be proved to show when points are concyclic—the most important of these being the one in which the vertices of a quadrilateral are concyclic if its opposite angles are supplementary. It is possible to word the following theorem as, *the vertices of a triangle are concyclic.*

THEOREM 122: A circle can be circumscribed about a given triangle.

sketch

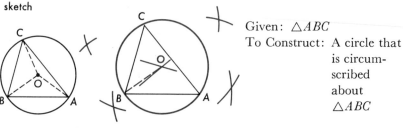

Given: $\triangle ABC$
To Construct: A circle that
is circum-
scribed
about
$\triangle ABC$

Figure 15-40.

ANALYSIS: By inspecting the completed sketch we realize that the center of the circle is equidistant from the three vertices of the triangle. This is a direct application of the theorem that the perpendicular bisectors of the sides of a triangle are concurrent at a point that is equidistant from the three vertices. The radius of the circle is then merely the line segment from the point of concurrency to any one of the vertices.

METHOD:

(1) Construct the perpendicular bisector of $\overline{BC}$.

(2) Construct the perpendicular bisector of $\overline{AC}$. This will intersect the line in step 1 at some point O.

(3) Using O as a center and $\overline{OB}$ as a radius, draw the circle.

PROOF

By using the indirect method of proof it is possible to show that points A and C must lie on the circle.

THEOREM 123: A circle can be inscribed within a given triangle.

sketch

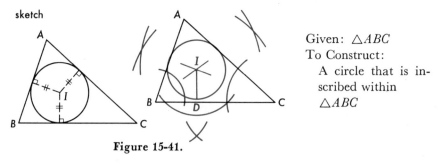

Given: $\triangle ABC$
To Construct:
A circle that is in-
scribed within
$\triangle ABC$

Figure 15-41.

ANALYSIS: By inspecting the completed sketch we realize that the center of the circle is equidistant from the three sides of the triangle. This is a direct application of the theorem that the bisectors of the angles of a triangle are concurrent at a point that is equidistant from the sides of the triangle.

The radius of the circle, as seen in the sketch, is the length of the perpendicular segment from the center to any one of the sides.

METHOD:

(1) Construct the bisector of $\angle ABC$.

(2) Construct the bisector of $\angle ACB$. This will intersect the line in step 1 at some point I.

(3) Construct the perpendicular from I to $\overleftrightarrow{BC}$.

(4) Using $\overline{ID}$ as a radius, draw the circle.

PROOF

The proof rests upon the need to show that both $\overleftrightarrow{AB}$ and $\overleftrightarrow{AC}$ are tangent to the circle. It will be left for you to do.

The remaining construction theorems are concerned with the ability to construct triangles when you are given certain parts of these triangles. In reality, they are but the five congruence statements couched in the language of construction theorems.

The need for a simple way to refer to the line segments and angles connected with a triangle gave rise to the following symbols:

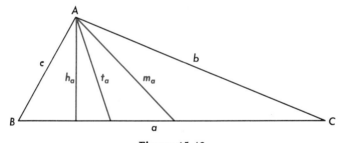

Figure 15-42.

(1) For the angles of a triangle the capital letters A, B, and C are used.

(2) The side opposite $\angle A$ is called side a; similarly, b lies opposite $\angle B$, and c opposite $\angle C$.

(3) The *altitude* to side a is h_a, while that to side b is h_b, etc.

(4) The *angle bisector* of $\angle A$ is t_a, while that of $\angle B$ is t_b, etc.

(5) The *median* to side a is m_a, while that to side b is m_b, etc.

Thus, to be given a, b, and C would imply that we know two sides of a triangle and also the angle included between these sides. Similarly, if the given data were h_b, t_b, and c, it would imply that line segments were given for the altitude and angle bisector to one side of a triangle; in addition, one of the sides of the triangle was given; however, it was not the side to which the altitude and bisector were drawn.

THEOREM 124: A triangle can be constructed if given two sides and the angle included between these two sides (*a*, *b*, *C*).

Given: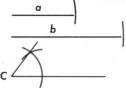

To Construct: A triangle with the above elements

sketch

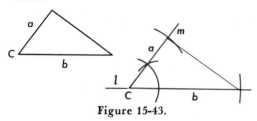

Figure 15-43.

METHOD:

(1) On line *l* select point *C*.
(2) With *C* as one endpoint construct a line segment congruent to *b*.
(3) At *C* construct an angle congruent to ∠*C*.
(4) With *C* as one endpoint construct a line segment on *m* that is congruent to *a*.
(5) Draw the line segment joining the endpoints of *a* and *b*.

THEOREM 125: A triangle can be constructed if given two angles and the side included between these two angles (*B*, *C*, *a*).

Given: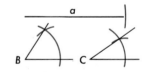

To Construct: A triangle with the above elements

sketch

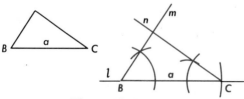

Figure 15-44.

METHOD:

    (1) On line l select point B.

    (2) At B construct a line segment congruent to a.

    (3) At B construct an angle congruent to $\angle B$.

    (4) At C construct an angle congruent to $\angle C$.

    (5) The intersection of m and n will be the third vertex of the triangle.

ANALYSIS: This construction is possible only if $\angle B$ and $\angle C$ are so given that $m \angle B + m \angle C < 180$. Were the $m \angle B + m \angle C$ either equal to or greater than 180, there would exist a contradiction with the theorem that the sum of the measures of *all* the angles of a triangle must be 180. In this situation the sum of the measures of *only two* of them would be either 180 or greater than 180. This can not be so.

THEOREM 126: A triangle can be constructed if given three sides (a, b, c).

Given:

To Construct: A triangle with the above elements

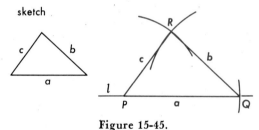

Figure 15-45.

METHOD:

    (1) On line l select point P.

    (2) At P construct a line segment congruent to a.

    (3) Using P as a center and c as a radius, draw an arc above line l.

    (4) Using Q as a center and b as a radius, draw an arc to intersect the arc in step 2 at some point R.

    (5) Draw $\overleftrightarrow{RP}$ and $\overleftrightarrow{RQ}$.

    (6) $\triangle RPQ$ is the required triangle.

ANALYSIS: This construction is possible only if a, b, and c are so given that the sum of any two of these segments is greater than the third. Examination of the *Sketch* reveals the fact that any side of the triangle must be smaller than the sum of the other two sides since the shortest path between two vertices of the triangle is the line segment joining them.

THEOREM 127: A triangle can be constructed if given two angles and a side opposite one of them (A, B, a).

Given:

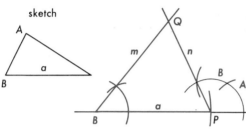

To Construct: A triangle with the above element

sketch

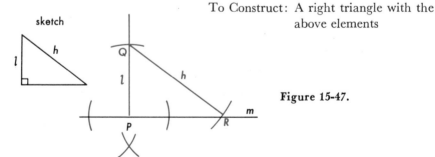

Figure 15-46.

ANALYSIS: By examining the *Sketch* we realize that the third angle of the triangle can be found by subtracting the sum of $m \angle A$ and $m \angle B$ from a straight angle. To save time this construction is done at the third vertex of the triangle.

This construction is possible only if $m \angle A + m \angle B < 180$.

METHOD:

   (1) On line l select point P.
   (2) At point P construct a line segment congruent to a.
   (3) At point P construct an angle equal to the sum of angles A and B.
   (4) At B construct an angle congruent to $\angle B$.
   (5) The intersection of m and n will be the third vertex of the triangle.

THEOREM 128: A right triangle can be constructed if given the hypotenuse and one of the legs.

Given:

To Construct: A right triangle with the above elements

sketch

Figure 15-47.

METHOD:

(1) At point P on line m construct a perpendicular to m.

(2) With P as one endpoint construct a line segment congruent to l on the perpendicular constructed in step 1.

(3) Using Q as a center and h as a radius, draw an arc intersecting m at R.

(4) Draw $\overleftrightarrow{QR}$.

(5) Then $\triangle QPR$ is the required triangle.

ANALYSIS: This construction is possible only if $h > l$. Can you justify why this should be so?

In applying the five construction theorems just proved to problem situations, it is best to draw a sketch of the completed figure. One of the triangles in this drawing will be such that it can be constructed by using one of these five theorems. Mark this triangle in red and under it write the letters of the construction theorem you plan to use. Once you have completed the construction of this triangle, the remaining vertices of the figure you have been asked to construct can usually be found rather easily.

Illustration 1:

Construct an isosceles triangle given a leg and the altitude to the base.

Given:

To Construct: An isosceles triangle with the above elements

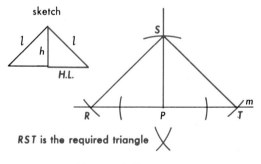

Figure 15-48.

ANALYSIS: Examination of the *Sketch* revealed that the triangle at the right in this sketch can be constructed under the hypotenuse-leg construction theorem. After this triangle was constructed, the third vertex was found by using S as the center of a circle and l as the radius. An arc was drawn intersecting m at point R. This is the third vertex of the isosceles triangle.

Illustration 2:

Construct a triangle given m_a, a, and b.

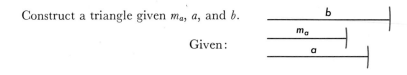

Given:

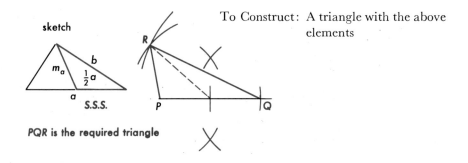

To Construct: A triangle with the above elements

PQR is the required triangle

Figure 15-49.

ANALYSIS: Examination of the *Sketch* revealed that the triangle at the right in this *Sketch* can be constructed under the *S.S.S.* construction theorem, where b, m_a, and $\frac{1}{2}a$ are the three sides. With this triangle completed, there was no need to find the third vertex, P, for it was already there as the leftmost point of segment a.

EXERCISES†

A

1. Construct an isosceles triangle under the conditions listed.
   (a) Given a leg and the vertex angle.
   (b) Given a leg and the base.
   (c) Given the base and a base angle.
   (d) Given the base and the median to the base.
   (e) Given a leg and the bisector of the vertex angle.
   (f) Given the altitude to the base and one of the base angles.
   (g)* Given the base and the altitude to one of the legs.

† No proof is required for any of the problems in this group of exercises.

2. Construct a right triangle under the conditions listed.
  (a) Given the legs.
  (b) Given a leg and the acute angle adjacent to that leg.
  (c) Given a leg and the acute angle opposite that leg.
  (d) Given the hypotenuse and one of the acute angles.
  (e) Given one leg and the median to the other leg.

3. Construct an equilateral triangle under the conditions listed.
  (a) Given one side.
  (b) Given an altitude. (Hint: Find a 60° angle by constructing any equilateral triangle.)
  (c) Given a bisector of one of the angles.

4. Construct a triangle under the conditions listed.

(a) a, h_c, c	**(b)** c, h_b, B	**(c)** a, b, h_c
(d) a, b, m_b	**(e)** b, t_a, A	**(f)** t_a, A, B
(g) h_a, m_a, a	**(h)** h_c, t_c, C	**(i)** h_b, t_b, c
(j) A, B, h_a	**(k)** h_a, t_a, B	**(l)** A, C, h_b
(m) t_b, B, h_a	**(n)** h_b, m_b, A	**(o)*** m_a, m_b, c

5. Construct a parallelogram under the conditions listed.
  (a) Given two sides and an angle.
  (b) Given the diagonals and an angle included between them.
  (c) Given the diagonals and one side.
  (d) Given sides a and b and the altitude to side b. (An altitude of a parallelogram is the common perpendicular to a pair of parallel sides.)

6. Construct a square
  (a) Given a side.
  (b) Given a diagonal.

7. Construct a rhombus
  (a) Given a side and an angle.
  (b) Given a side and a diagonal.
  (c) Given the diagonals.
  (d) Given an angle and the diagonal to the vertex of that angle.

8. Construct a quadrilateral given sides a, b, c, and d, and also the angle between sides a and b.

9. Draw a circle similar to the one at the right and construct a tangent to the circle at point P. (Hint: See Theorem 90.)

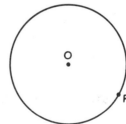

10. Construct a chord through a point within a circle such that this point will be the midpoint of the chord. (Hint: See Theorem 88.)

11. Draw a diagram similar to the one at the right and construct a tangent to circle O that is parallel to line l.

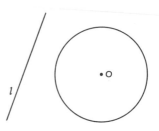

12. Construct a circle that has a radius a and is tangent to circle O at point P.

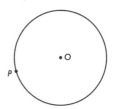

13. Construct a circle through three noncollinear points. (Hint: See Theorem 122.)

14. (a) Using the markings on the diagram below as a guide, divide a line segment into three congruent line segments.

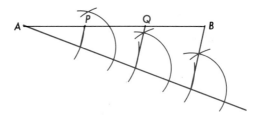

(b) What theorem must be used to justify the conclusion that

$$\overline{AP} \cong \overline{PQ} \cong \overline{QB}$$

15.* Construct an isosceles triangle given its perimeter and the altitude to the base. (Hint: Construct the altitude at the midpoint of the perimeter; then analyze your sketch.)

16.* Construct a right triangle given the hypotenuse and the altitude to the hypotenuse.

1. Construct the locus of points that are a given distance, d, from a fixed line.

2. Construct the locus of points that are equidistant from two parallel lines.

3. Construct the locus of points that are equidistant from two fixed points and also equidistant from two parallel lines.

4. Construct the locus of points that are a given distance, a, from a fixed point and also a given distance, b, from a fixed line.

5. Construct the locus of points that are equidistant from two intersecting lines and also equidistant from two parallel lines.

■ Test and Review

1. Given the fact that each of the following statements is true, write its converse, inverse, and contrapositive. Indicate which of your statements is true without need of proof.

(a) If John goes to the movie tonight, then I shall go.

(b) If a subject is not difficult, then Bill does not enjoy it.

(c) If $\overleftrightarrow{AB}$ bisects $\overline{CD}$, $\overrightarrow{AB}$ will not bisect $\angle A$.

2. State as a conditional statement the contrapositive of

"A person who does not like mathematics
should not plan to be an engineer."

3. (a) Give the definition of a right angle as a conditional statement.

(b) Write the inverse of the definition of a right angle.

4. (a) If the converse and the inverse of a statement are true, will this imply that the original statement is also true? Justify your answer.

(b) If the contrapositive of a statement is true, does this imply that the original statement is also true? Justify your answer.

5. Write three converse statements with reference to the statement

"If $\overline{PA} \cong \overline{PB}$ and $\overline{QA} \cong \overline{QB}$, then $\overleftrightarrow{PQ} \perp \overleftrightarrow{AB}$."

Answer each of the following questions without formal proof:

1. What is the locus of the centers of circles that are tangent to a given line at a given point of that line?

2. What is the locus of the centers of congruent circles that are tangent internally to a given circle?

3. What is the locus of the centers of all congruent circles that pass through a fixed point?

4. What is the locus of the midpoints of all line segments whose endpoints are one of the vertices of a triangle and any point of the side opposite that vertex?

5. What is the locus of the points of intersection of the diagonals of a rhombus that have a fixed segment as a side?

6. What is the locus of the midpoint M of $\overline{AB}$ where points A and B are always points of each side of right angle C and $m\ \overline{AB}$ is fixed?

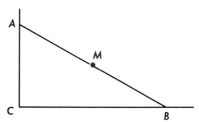

7. What is the locus of the centers of circles that are tangent to a given circle at a given point of that circle?

8. What is the locus of points that are equidistant from the centers of two congruent intersecting circles?

9. What is the locus of points that are equidistant from the sides of an angle and lie on another given angle?

10. What is the locus of points that are equidistant from the sides of an angle and also equidistant from two parallel lines?

11. What is the locus of points that are a fixed distance from a given point and equidistant from the endpoints of a given line segment?

12. What is the locus of points that are equidistant from the vertices of a rectangle?

13. What is the locus of points that are equidistant from the vertices of an isosceles trapezoid?

14. What is the locus of points that are equidistant from the sides of a rhombus?

Using straightedge and compass only, complete the construction in each of the following problems:

1. Construct a triangle under the conditions given.

    (a) a, c, m_a (b) h_b, t_b, a

2. Construct a rectangle given a base and a diagonal.

3. Construct a rhombus given one of its angles and the diagonal to the vertex of its next consecutive angle.

4. Construct an isosceles trapezoid given the lower base, a leg, and an upper base angle.

5. Construct a rectangle given a side and one of the angles formed by the diagonals.
6. Divide a line segment into five congruent segments.
7. Using a straightedge and compass, find the point on *l* that is equidistant from points *A* and *B*.

8. Construct the locus of points that are equidistant from the sides of an angle and at a fixed distance from a fixed line.
9. Through a given point construct a line that intersects a given line in an angle of a given measure.
10. Through a given point construct a line that will cut off congruent segments on the sides of a given angle.

■ Try These For Fun

If the point of concurrency of the altitudes of a triangle is found and also the point of concurrency of the perpendicular bisectors of the sides, then the distance from the latter to a side is one-half the distance of the opposite vertex to the point of concurrency of the altitudes.

Can you prove this?

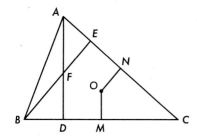

Given: Any triangle *ABC*

$\overleftrightarrow{OM}$ is the ⊥ bisector of $\overline{BC}$.

$\overleftrightarrow{ON}$ is the ⊥ bisector of $\overline{AC}$.

$\overline{AD}$ and $\overline{BE}$ are altitudes intersecting at *F*.

Concl.: $AF = 2\,OM$

Suggestion: Let circle *O* be the circle circumscribed about △*ABC*. Let $\overleftrightarrow{CP}$ be the line through *O*. Draw $\overleftrightarrow{PA}$ and $\overleftrightarrow{PB}$.

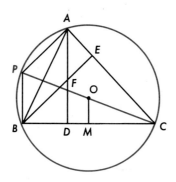

It would have been possible for us to have proved the relationships between a theorem, its converse, its inverse, and its contrapositive had we resorted to "truth tables." This is a device that logicians use to show the equivalence, or nonequivalence, of statements. By this scheme of things, "truth values" are assigned to any statement; that is, a statement is said to be either "True" or "False." Thus, the statement

p: "I shall pass this test"

is either a true statement or a false statement. We express this by saying that the truth values of p are T or F, and write this as

p
T
F

Figure 1

Were we now to examine a second statement,

q: "I shall receive a passing mark for this term"

the truth values of this statement would also be

q
T
F

Figure 2

Similarly, as we recall, if p represents "I shall pass this test," then $\sim p$ (read as *not* p) was interpreted as "I shall *not* pass this test." And it is possible for us to draw up a set of truth values for $\sim p$ based on the truth values of p. To illustrate, if p is true, then $\sim p$ would certainly have to be false; and when p is false, $\sim p$ must be true. This idea is expressed in a much, much more compact form by establishing a "truth table." What is the truth

p	$\sim p$
T	F
F	T

Figure 3

table relating q and $\sim q$?

Further, we might be interested in examining all the different combinations of truth values that exist between two distinct statements. Thus, they may both be true at the same time; they may both be false at the same time; or finally, one may be true when the other is false. Again resorting to truth tables, the picture would be

p	q
T	T
T	F
F	T
F	F

Figure 4

On the first line we note that when p is true, q is also true; on the second appears the possibility of p being true while q is false, and so on. These are the only combinations that exist between the truth values of p and q.

As a final step we would like to determine the truth values that should be assigned to the conditional statement

"If p then q"

Or as we had learned earlier, this statement can be expressed symbolically as

$$p \rightarrow q$$

Thus, if both p and q are true, would it be advisable to assert that "If p then q" is also true? Or, if both p and q are false, what truth value should be assigned to "If p then q"? Let us examine some definite statement before we try to commit ourselves. For instance, Miss Martin said to Joe,

"If you pass this test, then you will pass for the term"

where the statements p and q are

p: "You pass this test"
q: "You will pass for the term"

How should Joe interpret the teacher's honesty under each of the following conditions?

  A. (1) Joe passes the test. (p is true.)
      (2) Joe passes for the term. (q is true.)

He should certainly agree that Miss Martin told the truth, for this is exactly what she said would happen.

  B. (1) Joe passes the test. (p is true.)
      (2) Joe does not pass for the term. (q is false.)

It seems that Joe would be justified in his reaction that the teacher had not told the truth. Thus, if p is true and q is false, then "If p then q" is a false statement.

  C. (1) Joe does not pass the test. (p is false.)
      (2) Joe passes for the term. (q is true.)

Joe would joyously accept the passing grade and point out to all who would care to listen that the teacher said nothing about what would happen in the event he failed the test. Hence, since she is not telling a falsehood, she must be telling the truth! Thus, if p is false and q is true, then "If p then q" is true.

D. (1) Joe does not pass the test.   (p is false.)
    (2) Joe does not pass for the term.   (q is false.)

Joe is a sad young man indeed, for by his analysis in C, he has equally well justified that the teacher is still telling the truth in D for she had made no mention of the consequences should he fail the test. Thus, if p is false and q is false, then "If p then q" is true.

    The truth table for "If p then q" is accepted as

p	q	$p \rightarrow q$
T	T	T
T	F	F
F	T	T
F	F	T

Figure 5

Hence, the truth value of $p \rightarrow q$ is false only when p is true and q is false.

    To lend meaning to the background we have established, we first define *equivalent statements* as statements that have the same truth values. Hence, the question of the relation of a statement to its contrapositive merely reduces to, "Do these statements have the same truth values?" If so, then the truth of one implies the truth of the other or the falsity of one implies the falsity of the other. We have already determined the truth values of $p \rightarrow q$ (see Figure 5), and now let us do the same with its contrapositive $\sim q \rightarrow \sim p$

(1)   (2)   (3)   (4)   (5)

p	q	$\sim q$	$\sim p$	$\sim q \rightarrow \sim p$
T	T	F	F	T
T	F	T	F	F
F	T	F	T	T
F	F	T	T	T

Figure 6

    Columns (3) and (4) were based on the analysis given to arrive at Figure 3. To determine column (5), we examined columns (3) and (4) *only*, remembering that $\sim q \rightarrow \sim p$ is a false statement at no other time but when $\sim q$ is true and $\sim p$ is false. Now, should we compare the truth values of $p \rightarrow q$ with $\sim q \rightarrow \sim p$, we note that they are identically the same. That is, when p and q are both true, then $p \rightarrow q$ and $\sim q \rightarrow \sim p$ are also true;

similarly, when p is true and q is false, then $p \rightarrow q$ is false and so, too, is $\sim q \rightarrow \sim p$ false; and so on. Thus, $p \rightarrow q$ and its contrapositive $\sim q \rightarrow \sim p$ are equivalent statements.

(1) Can you prove that a statement and its converse are not equivalent statements? That is, $p \rightarrow q$ and $q \rightarrow p$ do not have the same truth values.

(2) Can you prove that a statement and its inverse are not equivalent statements? That is, $p \rightarrow q$ and $\sim p \rightarrow \sim q$ do not have the same truth values.

(3) Can you prove that the converse and the inverse of a statement are equivalent statements? That is, $q \rightarrow p$ and $\sim p \rightarrow \sim q$ are equivalent statements.

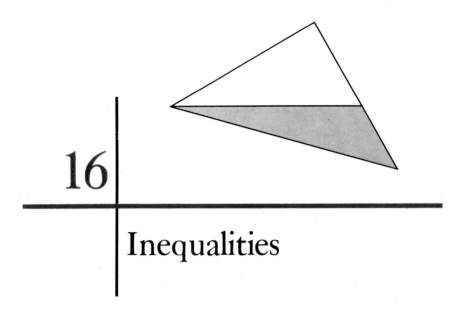

16

Inequalities

THUS FAR OUR STUDY OF SYNTHETIC GEOM-
etry has been concerned primarily with methods for showing conditions
under which quantities will be either equal or congruent to one another.
On those rare occasions when we have discussed the inequality of the measures of line segments or angles, it has been, to a large extent, only whether
they are unequal, not which of the two is the larger or which the smaller.

In this unit we plan to present six theorems that will enable us to prove
which of two line segments has the larger measure or which of two angles
has the larger measure. The postulates necessary for the proofs of these
theorems were presented earlier in our work. They are

POSTULATE 30: Given any two numbers a and b, one and only one of these
three relations must be true: $a > b$, $a = b$, $a < b$. (Existence and
Uniqueness of Order)

POSTULATE 31: Given any three numbers a, b, and c where $a > b$ and $b > c$,
then $a > c$. (Transitivity of Order)

The first of the theorems on inequalities is actually a form of the inverse
of the theorem on the base angles of an isosceles triangle. It does far more
for us, however, than merely justify that if the measures of two sides of a
triangle are unequal, the measures of the angles opposite them will be un-

equal. The theorem will specifically tell us which of the measures of the two angles is the larger.

Even in terms of the very little work that we have developed thus far in this chapter you may have noticed how cumbersome it was to word some of our statements. In order to greatly simplify the language to be used throughout this chapter, we will agree upon the following:

(1) Whenever we refer to the fact that one angle is larger than another, it will imply that the *measure* of the first angle is larger than the *measure* of the second angle.

(2) Whenever we refer to the fact that one line segment is larger than another, it will imply that the *measure* of the first line segment is larger than the *measure* of the second line segment.

THEOREM 129: If two sides of a triangle are unequal, the angles opposite them are unequal and the angle opposite the greater side is the greater angle.

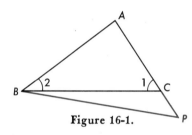

Given: $\triangle ABC$ with $AB > AC$
Concl.: $m \angle 1 > m \angle 2$

Figure 16-1.

PROOF STATEMENTS	REASONS
1. $\triangle ABC$ with $AB > AC$	1. Given
2. Let $\overleftrightarrow{AC}$ be extended to point P such that $AP = AB$.	2. A line can be extended as far as desired in either direction.
3. Let $\overleftrightarrow{BP}$ be the line through points B and P.	3. There exists one and only one line through two points.
4. $m \angle 1 > m \angle P$	4. The measure of an exterior angle of a triangle is greater than the measure of either of the remote interior angles.
5. $m \angle ABP = m \angle P$	5. Theorem on the base angles of an isosceles triangle.
6. $m \angle 1 > m \angle ABP$	6. Substitution postulate
7. But $m \angle ABP > m \angle 2$	7. The whole is greater than any of its parts.
8. $\therefore m \angle 1 > m \angle 2$	8. Postulate on transitivity of order (Postulate 31)

The converse of Theorem 129 is also true. Its proof, as we have often found to be the case with converse theorems, is by the indirect approach. Now, however, we will have to apply the assumption on the existence and uniqueness of order between two quantities rather than the law of the excluded middle. We are forced to take this position, for we are concerned with more than just the fact that two quantities are unequal but with which of these is the greater.

THEOREM 130: **If two angles of a triangle are unequal, the sides opposite them are unequal and the side opposite the greater angle is the greater side.**

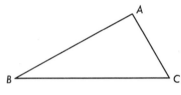

Given: $\triangle ABC$ with $m \angle C > m \angle B$
Concl.: $AB > AC$

Figure 16-2.

PROOF

By the postulate on the existence and uniqueness of order one of the following statements must be true and no other possibility exists:

(1) $AB > AC$,   (2) $AB = AC$,   or   (3) $AB < AC$

Order (1) will be shown to be true by proving that both order (2) and order (3) lead to contradictory statements.

Part 1

Let us accept the possibility that $AB = AC$. If this is so, then $m \angle C = m \angle B$, since if two sides of a triangle are congruent, the angles opposite them are congruent. The Given Data, however, states that $m \angle C > m \angle B$. Hence, accepting the possibility that $AB = AC$ led to the logical inconsistency of the truth of both $m \angle C \not> m \angle B$ and $m \angle C > m \angle B$. By the law of contradiction both cannot be true at the same time. Since $m \angle C > m \angle B$ must be true by virtue of the Given Data, then $m \angle C \not> m \angle B$ must be false, and so, therefore, is $AB = AC$ false.

Part 2

Let us now accept the possibility that $AB < AC$. If this is so, then $m \angle C < m \angle B$ by Theorem 129. But the Given Data states that $m \angle C > m \angle B$. Hence, the possibility that $AB < AC$ led again to the logical inconsistency of the truth of both $m \angle C \not> m \angle B$ and $m \angle C > m \angle B$.

Since $m \angle C > m \angle B$ must be true by virtue of the Given Data, then $m \angle C \not> m \angle B$ must be false, and so, therefore, is $AB < AC$ false.

Thus, we can conclude that $AB > AC$, for it is the only remaining possibility.

The next two theorems on congruency bear a resemblance to two of the congruency statements.

THEOREM 131: **If two sides of one triangle are congruent respectively to two sides of a second triangle but the included angle of the first triangle is greater than the included angle of the second triangle, then the third side of the first triangle is greater than the third side of the second triangle.**

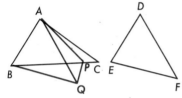

Figure 16-3.

Given: $\triangle ABC$ and DEF
$\overline{AB} \cong \overline{DE}$
$\overline{AC} \cong \overline{DF}$
$m \angle BAC > m \angle D$
Concl.: $BC > EF$

PROOF STATEMENTS	REASONS
1. $m \angle BAC > m \angle D$	1. Given
2. Within $\angle BAC$ construct $\overrightarrow{AQ}$ so that $\angle QAB \cong \angle D$. (a)	2. An angle congruent to a given angle can be constructed.
3. Extend $\overleftrightarrow{AQ}$ to point Q so that $\overline{AQ} \cong \overline{DF}$ (s). (The proof does not depend on whether Q falls in the interior or exterior of $\triangle ABC$.)	3. A line can be extended as far as desired in either direction.
4. Let $\overrightarrow{AP}$ be the bisector of $\angle QAC$.	4. Why possible?
5. Let $\overleftrightarrow{QP}$ be the line through points P and Q.	5. Why possible?
6. $\overline{AB} \cong \overline{DE}$ (s)	6. Given
7. $\triangle ABQ \cong \triangle DEF$	7. S.A.S.
8. $\overline{AQ} \cong \overline{DF}$	8. See statement 3.
9. $\overline{AC} \cong \overline{DF}$	9. Given
10. $\overline{AQ} \cong \overline{AC}$ (s)	10. Why?

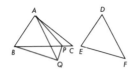

Figure 16-3.

11. $\angle QAP \cong \angle CAP$ (a)	11. Why?
12. $\overline{AP} \cong \overline{AP}$ (s)	12. Why?
13. $\triangle AQP \cong \triangle ACP$	13. S.A.S.
14. $\overline{PQ} \cong \overline{PC}$	14. Why?
15. In $\triangle BPQ$, $BP + PQ > BQ$	15. The shortest path between two points is the line segment joining the two points.
16. But $BQ = EF$	16. Why? (See step 7.)
17. And $PQ = PC$	17. Why? (See step 14.)
18. ∴ $BP + PC > EF$	18. Substitution postulate
19. But, $BP + PC = BC$	19. Def. of the sum of two segments
20. Hence, $BC > EF$	20. Same as 18

THEOREM 132: If two sides of one triangle are congruent respectively to two sides of a second triangle but the third side of the first triangle is greater than the third side of the second triangle, then the angle opposite the third side of the first triangle is greater than the angle opposite the third side of the second triangle.

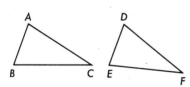

Figure 16-4.

Given: $\triangle ABC$ and DEF with
$\overline{AB} \cong \overline{DE}$
$\overline{AC} \cong \overline{DF}$
$BC > EF$
Concl.: $m \angle A > m \angle D$

PROOF

By the postulate on the existence and uniqueness of order one of the following statements must be true and no other possibility exists:

(1) $m \angle A > m \angle D$, **(2)** $m \angle A = m \angle D$, or **(3)** $m \angle A < m \angle D$

Order (1) will be shown to be true by proving that both order (2) and order (3) lead to contradictory statements.

Part 1

Let us accept the possibility that $m \angle A = m \angle D$. From the Given Data $\overline{AB} \cong \overline{DE}$ and $\overline{AC} \cong \overline{DF}$. Hence, by the *S.A.S.* congruence postulate it follows that $\triangle ABC \cong \triangle DEF$. Therefore, $BC = EF$. However, the Given Data states that $BC > EF$. Hence, accepting the possibility that $m \angle A = m \angle D$ led to the logical inconsistency of the truth of both $BC > EF$ and $BC \ngtr EF$. By the law of contradiction both cannot be true at the same time. Since $BC > EF$ is true by virtue of the Given Data, then $BC \ngtr EF$ must be false and, therefore, so must $m \angle A = m \angle D$ be false.

Part 2

Let us now accept the possibility that $m \angle A < m \angle D$. If this is so, and also $\overline{AB} \cong \overline{DE}$ and $\overline{AC} \cong \overline{DF}$, then by Theorem 131 $BC < EF$. Again, however, the Given Data states that $BC > EF$. Hence, accepting the possibility that $m \angle A < m \angle D$ led to the logical inconsistency of the truth of both $BC > EF$ and $BC \ngtr EF$. By the law of contradiction both cannot be true at the same time. Since $BC > EF$ is true by virtue of the Given Data, then $BC \ngtr EF$ must be false and, therefore, so must $m \angle A < m \angle D$ be false.

Hence, $m \angle A > m \angle D$ must be true, for it is the only remaining possibility.

The last two theorems to be proved on inequalities provides us with a tool for comparing the measures of chords of a circle. Their proof, however, is dependent upon a statement that we have not had.

THEOREM 133: If unequals are subtracted from equals, the differences will be unequal in the reverse order.

$$\text{Given: } a = b$$
$$c > d$$
$$\text{Concl.: } a - c < b - d$$

PROOF STATEMENTS	REASONS
1. $d < c$	1. Given
2. $b = a$	2. Given
3. $d - b < c - a$	3. If equals are subtracted from unequals, the differences will be unequal in the same order. (Postulate 37)
4. $a - c < b - d$	4. If equals are added to unequals, the sums will be unequal in the same order. (Both $a - c$ and $b - d$ were added to both sides of the inequality in step 3.)

A simple numerical illustration of this theorem is

$$10 = 10$$
$$7 > 2$$

Hence $10 - 7 < 10 - 2$

or $3 < 8$

Whereas 7 was greater than 2 with the greater quantity, 7, appearing on the left, after subtracting each of them from 10 and 10, the differences were such that the smaller quantity, 3, now appears on the left. Thus,

$$3 < 8$$

THEOREM 134: If two chords of a circle are unequal, then the greater chord is the smaller distance from the center.

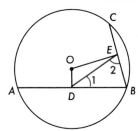

Given: $\overleftrightarrow{OD} \perp \overleftrightarrow{AB}$ in $\odot O$

$\overleftrightarrow{OE} \perp \overleftrightarrow{BC}$

$AB > BC$

Concl.: $OD < OE$

Figure 16-5.

ANALYSIS: Although the chords do not have to have an endpoint in common, for simplicity of proof they were drawn in that manner. In addition, this theorem will hold whether the chords appear in the same circle, as above, or in congruent circles.

PROOF	STATEMENTS	REASONS
1.	Let $\overleftrightarrow{DE}$ be the line through points D and E.	1. Why possible?
2.	$\overleftrightarrow{OD} \perp \overleftrightarrow{AB}$, $\overleftrightarrow{OE} \perp \overleftrightarrow{BC}$	2. Given
3.	$\overleftrightarrow{OD}$ bisects $\overline{AB}$; $\overleftrightarrow{OE}$ bisects $\overline{BC}$.	3. A radius perpendicular to a chord bisects the chord.
4.	But $AB > BC$	4. Given
5.	$\therefore DB > BE$	5. If unequals are divided by equals, the quotients will be unequal in the same order.
6.	$m \angle 2 > m \angle 1$	6. If two sides of a triangle are unequal, the angles opposite them are unequal, and the angle opposite the greater side is the greater angle.

7. $\angle ODB$ and $\angle OEB$ are right angles.	7. Def. of perpendicular lines
8. $m \angle ODB = m \angle OEB$	8. Why?
9. $m \angle OED < m \angle ODE$	9. If unequals ($m \angle 2$ and $m \angle 1$) are subtracted from equals ($m \angle ODB$ and $m \angle OEB$), the differences will be unequal in the reverse order.
10. $OD < OE$	10. Converse of reason 6

THEOREM 135: **If two chords of a circle are unequal, then the chord that is the greater distance from the center is the smaller chord.**

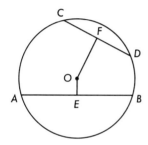

Given: $\overleftrightarrow{OE} \perp \overleftrightarrow{AB}$
$\overleftrightarrow{OF} \perp \overleftrightarrow{CD}$
$OE < OF$
Concl.: $AB > CD$

Figure 16-6.

PROOF

By the postulate on the existence and uniqueness of order one of the following statements must be true and no other possibility exists:

(1) $AB > CD$ **(2)** $AB = CD$ **(3)** $AB < CD$

Order (1) will be shown to be true by proving that both order (2) and order (3) lead to contradictory statements.

Part 1

Let us accept the possibility that $AB = CD$. From the theorem that congruent chords of a circle are equidistant from the center of the circle, it follows that $OE = OF$. However, the Given Data states that $OE < OF$. Hence, accepting the possibility that $AB = CD$ led to the logical inconsistency of the truth of both $OE = OF$ and $OE \neq OF$. By the law of contradiction, both can not be true at the same time. Since $OE < OF$ by virtue of the Given Data, then $OE = OF$ must be false and, therefore, so must $AB = CD$ be false.

Part 2

(The proof of this part is left for you to do.)

Illustration:

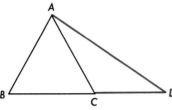

Given: $\triangle ABC$ is equilateral.
Concl.: $BD > AD$

Figure 16-7.

ANALYSIS: To show that $BD > AD$, it is necessary to prove that $\angle DAB > \angle B$.

PROOF	STATEMENTS	REASONS
1. $\triangle ABC$ is equilateral.		1. Given
2. $m \angle CAB = m \angle B$		2. An equilateral triangle is equiangular. (See Problem 20, page 152.)
3. $m \angle DAB > m \angle CAB$		3. The whole is greater than any of its parts.
4. $m \angle DAB > m \angle B$		4. Substitution postulate
5. $BD > AD$		5. If two angles of a triangle are unequal, the sides opposite them are unequal, and the side opposite the greater angle is the greater side.

EXERCISES

1. Given: $\triangle ACB$ is a right triangle with $\angle ACB$ the right angle.
Concl.: $AB > AC$
$AB > BC$

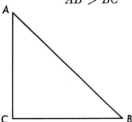

Given: $\angle ABC$ is an obtuse angle.
Concl.: $AC > AB$
$AC > CB$

2.

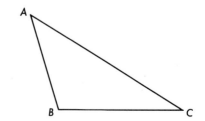

3. Given: △ABC is isosceles
with AB = AC.
$\overleftrightarrow{BA}$ extended to D
Concl.: BD > DC

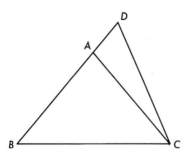

Given: △ABC is isosceles **4.**
with AB = AC.
$\overleftrightarrow{CD}$ drawn within
∠ACB
Concl.: DC > DB

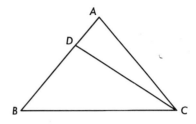

5. Given: △ABC is isosceles
with AB = AC.
$\overleftrightarrow{AB}$ extended to D
Concl.: m ∠ACD > m ∠D

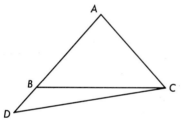

Given: $\overleftrightarrow{AB} \perp \overleftrightarrow{BD}$ **6.**
Concl.: AD > AC (Hint:
Prove that ∠1 is
obtuse.)

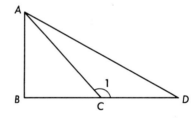

7. Given: $\overleftrightarrow{AB} \perp \overleftrightarrow{CD}$
BD > BC
Concl.: AD > AC (Hint:
Construct $\overline{BE} \cong \overline{BC}$)

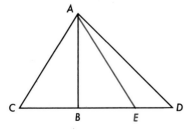

Given: AC > AB **8.**
$\overrightarrow{BD}$ bisects ∠ABC.
$\overrightarrow{CD}$ bisects ∠ACB.
Concl.: DC > DB

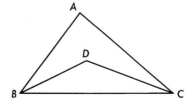

9. Given: $\triangle ABC$ is isosceles
with $\overline{AB} \cong \overline{AC}$.
$m \angle 1 > m \angle 2$
Concl.: $BD > DC$

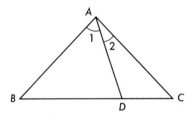

10. Given: $\triangle ABC$ is isosceles
with $\overline{AB} \cong \overline{AC}$.
$DC > BD$
Concl.: $m \angle DAC > m \angle DAB$

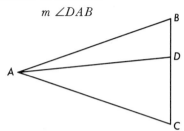

11. Given: $\overline{AM}$ is median to $\overline{BC}$.
$AC > AB$
Concl.: $m \angle AMC > m \angle AMB$

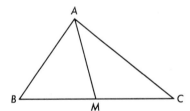

12. Given: M is the midpoint
of $\overline{BC}$.
$\overline{BD} \cong \overline{CE}$
$DM > EM$
Concl.: $AC > AB$

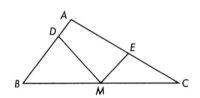

13. Given: $ABCD$ is a parallelogram.
$m \angle BAD > m \angle ADC$
Concl.: $BD > AC$

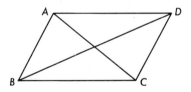

14. Given: $\overline{DB} \cong \overline{EC}$
$DC > BE$
Concl.: $AC > AB$

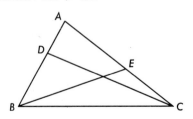

15. Given: $\overleftrightarrow{AO}$ intersects $\odot O$ at B.

Concl.: $AC > AB$ (Hint: Use Postulate 19.)

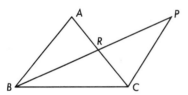

Given: Point P is any point in the interior of the triangle. **16.**

Concl.: $x + y + z > \frac{1}{2}(a + b + c)$ (Hint: Use Postulate 19.)

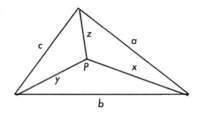

17. Given: $\triangle ABC$ is isosceles with $\overline{AB} \cong \overline{AC}$.

$\overleftrightarrow{BP}$ intersects $\overleftrightarrow{AC}$ at R.

Concl.: $PB > PC$

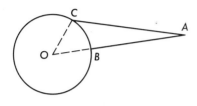

Given: $\triangle ABC$ is isosceles with $\overline{AB} \cong \overline{AC}$. **18.***

$\overleftrightarrow{AC}$ extended to D

Concl.: $BD > CD$ (Hint: Prove $m \angle 1 > m \angle 3$.)

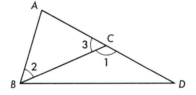

19. Given: $\odot O$ with $m \angle 2 > m \angle 1$

Concl.: $m \overset{\frown}{DC} > m \overset{\frown}{AB}$

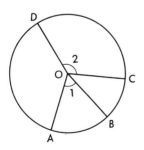

Given: M is the midpoint of $\overline{BC}$ in $\odot O$. **20.***

$\overleftrightarrow{OA} \perp \overleftrightarrow{DE}$

Concl.: $DE > BC$

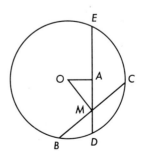

21. Given: ⊙O
Concl.: $m \angle PCB > m \angle PBC$
(Hint: Draw $\overleftrightarrow{OC}$.)

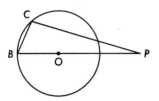

Given: ⊙O with $AC > AD$ **22.**
Concl.: $m \angle DAB > m \angle CAB$
(Hint: No other lines
are needed.)

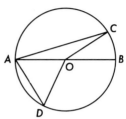

23.* If light, being reflected from
the mirror surface $\overline{BC}$, travels
from point A to point D, it
will take the path APD. Show
that this path is shorter than
any other path, such as AQD.

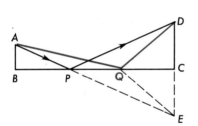

Given: $\overleftrightarrow{PQ} \perp$ plane a **24.**
$RQ > QS$
Concl.: $PR > PS$ (Hint:
Use same method
as in problem 7.)

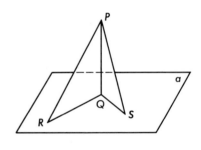

$\boxed{\text{B}}$

1. The sum of two sides of a triangle is greater than the third side. †

2. If a triangle is not isosceles, then a median to any side is greater than the altitude to that side.

3. (a) How would you express Problem 19 in Group A in the form of the statement of a theorem?

(b) Write the converse of your answer to Problem 3(a) and prove it.

4. Using the information in Problem 3(b), prove that if two minor arcs of a circle are unequal, then the chord corresponding to the larger arc is greater than the chord corresponding to the smaller arc.

5. Write the converse of Problem 4 and prove it.

† This problem often appears as a theorem.

6.* A point is in the interior of a circle but not at the center. The smallest chord that can be drawn through this point is the one that is perpendicular to the radius through the point. (Hint: Use Postulate 32.)

■ Test and Review

Prove each of the following:

1. Given: $\overleftrightarrow{AB}$ and $\overleftrightarrow{CD}$ intersect at E.

Concl.: $AB + CD > AD + CB$
(Hint: See Problem 1, page 576.)

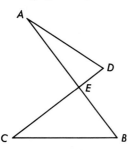

2. Given: $AC > AB$
D is any point of $\overline{BC}$.

Concl.: $AC > AD$

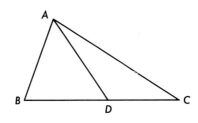

3. Given: $DC > AB$
$\overrightarrow{BD}$ bisects $\angle ABC$.

Concl.: $DC > DA$ (Hint: Prove $m \angle 1 > m \angle 2$.)

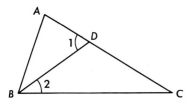

4. Given: $\odot O$ with $CD > EF$
$\overline{AC} \cong \overline{CB}$
$\overleftrightarrow{OA} \perp \overleftrightarrow{EF}$
$\overleftrightarrow{OB} \perp \overleftrightarrow{CD}$

Concl.: $m \angle ACO > m \angle BCO$

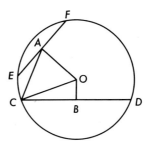

5. Given: *ABCD* is a rhombus.
    BC > *AC*
Concl.: *m* ∠*BAD* > *m* ∠*ADC*

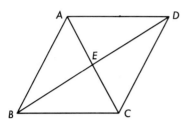

Given: *ABCD* is a paral- **6.**
    lelogram.
    m ∠*BAD* > *m* ∠*CBA*
Concl.: *BE* > *AE*

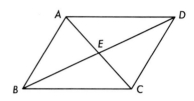

B

Prove each of the following statements:

1. The sum of the diagonals of a quadrilateral is less than the sum of the sides.

2. If a triangle is not isosceles, then the angle bisector of any angle of the triangle is greater than the altitude from that vertex.

3. If two oblique lines and a perpendicular are drawn to a plane from an external point, the greater oblique line will intersect the plane at a greater distance from the foot of the perpendicular than the smaller oblique line. (Hint: Use the indirect proof and apply Problem 24, page 576.)

▩ Try This For Fun

    For many, many hundreds of years mathematicians and pseudomathematicians have tried to solve three construction problems that have come to be known as the "Three Famous Problems of Antiquity." They are

 (1) The squaring of a circle.
 (2) The duplication of a cube.
 (3) The trisection of an angle.

Specifically, these are the problems:

 (1) Is it possible to construct a square whose area will be the same as the area of a given circle?
 (2) Is it possible to construct a cube whose volume is twice the volume of a given cube?
 (3) Is it possible to construct an angle whose measure is one-third the measure of a given angle?

Our first reaction is shocked surprise: of course it is possible to do these things! Why should mathematicians have been puzzled over these constructions for so long a time? Thus, in answer to problem (3) all we need do is measure the angle with a protractor, then but divide that number by 3 and, lo, we have an angle one-third the measure of the original angle! But hold, we have been too hasty and failed to listen to the statement of the complete problem. Not only must these figures be constructed but our freedom of movement has been severely restricted: these constructions must be done with the aid of only two instruments, the straightedge (no markings on the straightedge, please!) and the compass.

Mathematicians have proved by means beyond our present depth of the subject that these constructions are impossible with the restrictions placed upon them. Has this deterred the would-be angle trisectors from busily plying their trade? By all means, no! For year after year newspapers in various parts of the nation report the amazing success achieved by local Joe Spivis, the child prodigy, who has trisected the angle, succeeding where mathematicians for centuries have failed!

Let us take a look at one of these constructions.

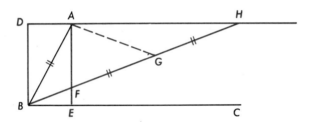

$\angle ABC$ is the given angle. At B construct $\overleftrightarrow{DB} \perp \overleftrightarrow{BC}$; at A construct $\overleftrightarrow{AE} \perp \overleftrightarrow{BC}$; at A construct $\overleftrightarrow{AH} \parallel \overleftrightarrow{BC}$. Hold the ruler at B and move it in a way such that $FH = 2\ AB$, then draw BH.

(1) Can you prove that $m \angle HBC = \frac{1}{3}m \angle ABC$?

(2) Where in the construction did we cheat and not use the instruments to which we were restricted?

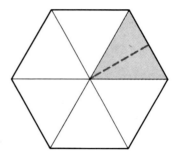

17

Areas of Polygons and Circles

MEASUREMENT, EXCEPT FOR VERY FEW SIT-
uations, is the process of comparing the object whose size we would like to
know to an object whose size we do know. The object whose size is known
is called a *standard unit*. It is determined, usually, by some governmental
decree or, possibly, by a mathematical definition. In any event, its size is
fixed and the measurement of other similar objects consists in determining
how many standard units are contained in the object being measured.

Thus, the measure of a line segment is a number that shows a comparison between this line segment and the standard unit called, perhaps, the
inch, the yard, the centimeter, or any one of many others. The statement
that the length of a line segment is 15 feet implies that the measure of this
segment is 15 times the measure of the standard unit called the foot. The
important feature, however, is the fact that both the object and the standard
unit are creatures of the same classifications; *they are both line segments*.

Now, let us turn to the subject matter of this chapter. Our first objective
is to determine a method for assigning a number to the region enclosed by
such curves or polygons as those below. Since the word "region" will appear
several times in this chapter, we should reach some understanding as to its
meaning. Although we can and will define a *triangular region*, defining the
regions such as in Figures 17-1 and 17-2 would involve us in more diffi-

580

culty than is warranted by the importance of this word. We will accept an intuitive understanding of the general term "region" based on the definition of a triangular region.

DEFINITION 97: A triangular region is the union of the sets of points consisting of the triangle and its interior.

 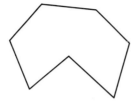 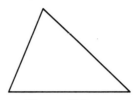

Figure 17-1.   Figure 17-2.   Figure 17-3.

In the illustration given earlier concerning the length of a line segment the standard unit belonged to the same classification, a line segment, as the object being measured. But to determine a unit of measure for the creatures above seems as though it would be an impossible task, for they obviously belong to different categories. It is not the objects themselves, however, for which we are seeking a standard of measure, but rather the region bounded by these creatures! Hence, any object that itself bounds part of the plane might act as our standard of measure. Several of these are pictured in Figure 17-4.

Figure 17-4.

Thus, the second of these might be called the triangular unit; the fourth, the circular unit; the fifth, the hexagonal unit. And to say that the size of the region bounded by the curve in Figure 17-1 is 9 triangular units would, as before, imply

(1) that the size of the region enclosed by the curve is 9 times as great as the region enclosed by the sides of the triangle or
(2) that the triangle can be made to fit exactly 9 times into the region enclosed by the curve.

Similar comparisons could be made were we to use any of the remaining four units. As you well know from other courses in mathematics, the *square unit* was selected to be the standard for measuring the size of the region bounded by closed curves or polygons.

DEFINITION 98: The area of the region enclosed by a curve or polygon is the number of square units contained within this region.

POSTULATE 42: If the intersection of two polygons is a line, then the area
of the region bounded by these polygons is the sum of the areas of the
two polygons.

It is important that we realize that just as the measure of a line segment
was a number, and the measure of an angle was a number, so too *is the area
of a region simply a number*. It is the number assigned to that region in terms
of the number of square units that are contained in the region. As you recall,
the measure of a line segment was the number assigned to that line segment
by the coordinate of one of its endpoints when the other endpoint was the
zero value on the number line.

To simplify the way of expressing ourselves, we shall henceforth speak
of finding the "area of a triangle" or the "area of a rectangle" rather than
the "area of a triangular region" or the "area of a rectangular region" as
we should.

As has been the case over and over again in the development of each
segment of this course, it has been necessary to assume certain properties
about some of the simpler figures. Having made these assumptions, we were
then in a position to prove more complex properties about more complex
figures. So, too, is our present problem. Of the many polygons whose area
we may have to investigate, the simplest of these is the rectangle.

Observation indicates that the number of square units in the rectangle
can be found by counting the number in the first row and then multiplying
this number by the number of rows. Thus, we would say that the area of
this rectangle is 24 (square inches) or that the area of this rectangle is

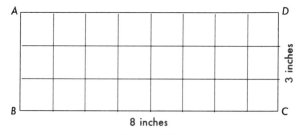

Figure 17-5.

24 times the area of 1 square inch. This same number, however, could have
been obtained by finding the product of the measure of its base, $\overline{BC}$, with
that of its altitude, $\overline{DC}$. Hence, we seem to be on fairly safe ground if we
assume that

POSTULATE 43: The area of a rectangle is equal to the product of the measures of its base and altitude.

It is important to realize that it is *not* 8 inches that is being multiplied
by 3 inches, *but simply 8 by 3*. This product, 24, being the area, implies either
(1) that there are *24* square inches in the region enclosed by the rectangle or

(2) that the region enclosed by the rectangle is *24* times as large as the region enclosed by 1 square inch.

EXERCISES

1. Find the area of a rectangle whose base is 10 yards 1 foot and whose altitude is 6 yards.
2. The floor of a rectangular living room was scraped and finished at 15 cents per square foot. The dimensions of the room are 18 feet by 12 feet 4 inches. What was the total cost of this work?
3. The dimensions of an asphalt tile are 9 inches by 9 inches. The tile selected to be laid on the floor of a rectangular den costs 9 cents per tile. Assuming no waste, what was the cost of the tiles for this room whose dimensions were 17'3'' by 12'6''?
4. If each square below is considered as a square unit, determine the approximate area of each of these figures.

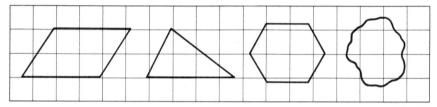

5. If each side of a square is *a* linear units in length, write a formula expressing the area of a square in terms of *a*.
6. (a) The dimensions of a rectangle are 32 inches by 2 inches. What is the length of the side of a square whose area is equal to that of this rectangle?
   (b) If the dimensions of the rectangle had been $8b$ by $2b$, what would the length of the side of the square have been?
7. (a) The area of a rectangle is 216 square feet. What is the base of the rectangle if its altitude is 18 feet?
   (b) If the area of the rectangle was $12a^2b$ square units, what would the altitude be if the base was $3a$ linear units?
8. Find the area of the rectangle whose diagonal is 39 inches and whose base is 36 inches.
9. Find the area of the square whose diagonal is 6 inches.
10. A rectangle is inscribed within a circle having a diameter of 26 inches. What is the area of the rectangle if its altitude is 10 inches?
11. (a) The bases of two rectangles are each 15 inches. If the altitude of the first is 7 inches while that of the second is 10 inches, what is the ratio of the areas of these rectangles?

(b) The bases of two rectangles are each *a* linear units. If the altitude of the first is *b* linear units while that of the second is *c* linear units, what is the ratio of the areas of these rectangles?

(c) Make up a statement showing what you have proved in part (b) of this problem.

12. Using the method presented in Problem 11(b), prove that if the altitudes of two rectangles are congruent, then the ratio of their areas is equal to the ratio of the measures of their bases.

13. The area of a square inscribed in a circle is 64 square inches. What is the radius of the circle?

14. The measure of the side of one square is three times the measure of the side of a second square. What is the ratio of their areas?

15. If the measure of the diagonal of a square is *a*, what is the area of the square in terms of *a*?

■ Area of the Parallelogram, the Triangle, and the Trapezoid

There are only three special polygons, other than the rectangle, whose areas are considered important enough to investigate. These polygons are the parallelogram, the triangle, and the trapezoid. The area of any other polygon is found by drawing lines so as to divide it into a combination of these four polygons.

You may have noticed that when we expressed the area of a rectangle, the statement was in terms of the "base" and "altitude" rather than in terms of the "sides." Normally we think of $\overline{BC}$ (see Figure 17-6) as being

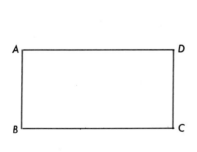

Figure 17-6.   Figure 17-7.

the base, while either $\overline{AB}$ or $\overline{DC}$ is the altitude. Had the rectangle been rotated 90° in a counterclockwise direction, as in Figure 17-7, the base would then appear to be $\overline{AB}$ and the altitude $\overline{BC}$. Thus, the roles of the measures of the segments would have been reversed. It is apparent, then, that any side of a rectangle can be considered as its base, while one of its adjacent sides is the altitude.

Similar considerations are made when we examine the areas of the parallelogram, the triangle, and the trapezoid. If in the parallelogram (Figure 17-8) $\overline{AB}$ is referred to as the base, then $\overline{EF}$, the common perpendicular segment to $\overline{AB}$ and $\overline{DC}$, is its corresponding altitude. If on the other hand $\overline{BC}$ is the base, then $\overline{GH}$ must be considered as the altitude of the parallelogram. In the same way, in Figure 17-9, any one of the sides of the

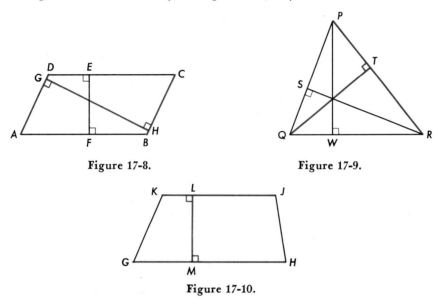

Figure 17-8. Figure 17-9.

Figure 17-10.

triangle can be considered as the base of the triangle. Once the base has been specified, then the altitude of the triangle is simply the altitude to that side. Thus, if $\overline{PR}$ is called the base, the altitude of the triangle would be $\overline{QT}$. If $\overline{RS}$ is the altitude of the triangle, what will the base be?

In a trapezoid, the bases, as before, are still the parallel sides, while the altitude is the common perpendicular segment to the bases. In Figure 17-10 the bases are $\overline{KJ}$ and $\overline{GH}$, while $\overline{LM}$ is the altitude.

Just a word about the symbols that will be used. The statement that the area of polygon $ABCD$ is equal to the area of polygon $XYZWT$ will be abbreviated to read as, $ABCD = XYZWT$. It is important to remember that this implies *only* that the areas of these two polygons are the same.

One further postulate still remains to be stated before it is possible to continue.

POSTULATE 44: If two triangles are congruent, then their areas are equal.

THEOREM 136: The area of a parallelogram is equal to the product of the measures of its base and corresponding altitude ($A = bh$).

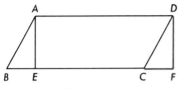

Figure 17-11.

Given: $\square ABCD$ with altitude $\overline{AE}$
Concl.: Area $\square ABCD = AD \cdot AE$

ANALYSIS: There is but one postulate at our disposal upon which to base the proof of this theorem. This concerns itself with the area of a rectangle. Hence, it is necessary to show that some relationship exists between the area of a parallelogram and that of the rectangle. This we will do by proving that $ABCD = AEFD$.

PROOF STATEMENTS	REASONS
1. $ABCD$ is a parallelogram.	1. Given
2. Let $\overleftrightarrow{DF}$ be the line through D parallel to $\overleftrightarrow{AE}$.	2. Why possible?
3. Extend $\overleftrightarrow{BC}$ until it intersects $\overleftrightarrow{DF}$.	3. Why possible?
4. $\overline{AE}$ is an altitude.	4. Given
5. $AEFD$ is a rectangle.	5. Reverse of def. of a rectangle
6. $\overline{AE} \cong \overline{DF}$ (l)	6. Opposite sides of a parallelogram are congruent.
7. $\overline{AB} \cong \overline{DC}$ (h)	7. Same as 6
8. $\triangle ABE \cong \triangle DCF$	8. H.L.
9. $\therefore \triangle ABE = \triangle DCF$	9. If 2 triangles are congruent, then their areas are equal.
10. $AECD = AECD$	10. Reflexive property of equality
11. $\triangle ABE + AECD = AECD + \triangle DCF$	11. Addition postulate
12. But $\triangle ABE + AECD = \square ABCD$	12. Postulate 42; see page 582.
13. $AECD + \triangle DCF =$ rectangle $AEFD$	13. Same as 12
14. $\therefore \square ABCD =$ rectangle $AEFD$	14. Substitution postulate
15. However, rectangle $AEFD = AD \cdot AE$	15. Why?
16. $\therefore ABCD = AD \cdot AE$	16. Substitution postulate

THEOREM 137: The area of a triangle is equal to one-half the product of the measures of its base and altitude ($A = \frac{1}{2}bh$).

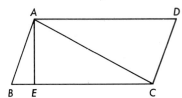

Given: $\triangle ABC$ with altitude $\overline{AE}$ to $\overline{BC}$
Concl.: Area $\triangle ABC = \frac{1}{2}(BC \cdot AE)$

Figure 17-12.

| **PROOF** | (The reasons will be left for you to supply.) |

1. Let $\overset{\leftrightarrow}{AD}$ be the line through A parallel to $\overset{\leftrightarrow}{BC}$.

2. Let $\overset{\leftrightarrow}{CD}$ be the line through C parallel to $\overset{\leftrightarrow}{AB}$.

3. $ABCD$ is a parallelogram.

4. $\overline{AE}$ is an altitude to $\overline{BC}$.

5. $\square ABCD = BC \times AE$

6. $\square ABCD = \triangle ABC + \triangle CDA$
7. $\triangle ABC + \triangle CDA = BC \cdot AE$
8. But $\triangle ABC \cong \triangle CDA$
9. $\therefore \triangle ABC = \triangle CDA$
10. $\triangle ABC + \triangle ABC = BC \cdot AE$
    or, $2\triangle ABC = BC \cdot AE$
11. Thus, $\triangle ABC = \frac{1}{2}(BC \cdot AE)$

THEOREM 138: The area of a trapezoid is equal to one-half the product of the measures of its altitude and the sum of the measures of its bases; $A = \frac{1}{2}h(b_1 + b_2)$.

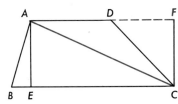

Given: Trapezoid $ABCD$ with altitude $\overline{AE}$ to the bases $\overline{AD}$ and $\overline{BC}$
Concl.: Area of trapezoid $ABCD = \frac{1}{2}AE(BC + AD)$

Figure 17-13.

| **PROOF** | (The reasons will be left for you to supply.) |

1. $\overline{AE}$ is an altitude to bases of trapezoid $ABCD$.

2. Let $\overset{\leftrightarrow}{AC}$ be the line through points A and C.

3. Extend $\overset{\leftrightarrow}{AD}$.

4. Let $\overset{\leftrightarrow}{CF}$ be the line through C perpendicular to $\overset{\leftrightarrow}{AF}$.

5. $\overset{\leftrightarrow}{AE} \parallel \overset{\leftrightarrow}{CF}$

6. $AECF$ is a parallelogram.
7. $AE = CF$
8. Area $\triangle CDA = \frac{1}{2}CF \cdot AD$
9. Area $\triangle CDA = \frac{1}{2}AE \cdot AD$
10. Area $\triangle ABC = \frac{1}{2}AE \cdot BC$
11. $\triangle ABC + \triangle CDA = \frac{1}{2}AE \cdot BC + \frac{1}{2}AE \cdot AD$
12. $ABCD = \triangle ABC + \triangle CDA$
13. $ABCD = \frac{1}{2}AE \cdot BC + \frac{1}{2}AE \cdot AD$ or,
    $ABCD = \frac{1}{2}AE(BC + AD)$

Illustration:

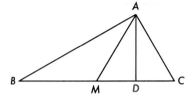

Given: $\triangle ABC$ with median $\overline{AM}$
Concl.: Area $\triangle AMB$ = area $\triangle AMC$

Figure 17-14.

PROOF	STATEMENTS	REASONS
1. Let $\overleftrightarrow{AD}$ be the line through A perpendicular to $\overleftrightarrow{BC}$.		1. Why possible?
2. $\overline{AM}$ is the median to $\overline{BC}$.		2. Given
3. M is the midpoint of $\overline{BC}$.		3. Def. of a median
4. $BM = MC$		4. Def. of a midpoint
5. $\triangle AMB = \frac{1}{2}BM \cdot AD$		5. Theorem on area of a triangle
6. $\triangle AMB = \frac{1}{2}MC \cdot AD$		6. Substitution postulate
7. $\triangle AMC = \frac{1}{2}MC \cdot AD$		7. Same as 5
8. $\triangle AMB = \triangle AMC$		8. Transitive property of equality

THEOREM 139: If two triangles have congruent bases and congruent altitudes, then their areas will be equal.

The proof of this theorem is very much the same as that of the illustration above. It will be left for you to do.

EXERCISES

1. Find the area of a triangle whose base is 42 inches and whose altitude is 17 inches.
2. (a) The legs of a right triangle are 5 and 12 respectively. Find the area of this right triangle.
   (b) Find the altitude to the hypotenuse of this right triangle.
3. If the hypotenuse and one leg of a right triangle are 52 and 48 respectively, find the area of the triangle.
4. Find the area of a rhombus whose diagonals are 16 and 20 respectively.
5. The area of a triangle is 195 square inches. If the altitude is 15 inches, what is the length of the base?
6. The altitude to the hypotenuse of a right triangle divides the hypotenuse

into two segments of 8 inches and 2 inches in length. Find the area of the triangle.

7. If a leg and the base of an isosceles triangle are 10 and 12 respectively, find the area of the triangle.

8. The hypotenuse of an isosceles right triangle is 8. Find the area of the triangle.

9. Find the area of an equilateral triangle under each of the following conditions:

    (a) if a side is 6 inches.   (b) if an altitude is 6 inches.

10. The length of the line segment from a point to the center of a circle is 25. If the diameter of this circle is 14, what is the area of the triangle whose sides are this segment, the tangent segment from this point, and the radius to the point of contact of the tangent?

11. The area of a rhombus is 442 square feet. If one of the diagonals is 34 feet, what is the length of the other diagonal?

12. Two sides of a triangle are 25 and 26, while the altitude to the third side is 24. Find the area of the triangle.

13. A triangle is inscribed in a circle such that one of its sides is a diameter of the circle. If the radius of the circle is 30.5 inches and one of the sides is 60 inches, find the area of the triangle.

14. Two adjacent sides of a parallelogram are 8 and 14 respectively. If the angle between them is 45°, what is the area of the parallelogram?

15. The bases of a trapezoid are 8 and 11 respectively, while the altitude is 6. Find the area of the trapezoid.

16. The area of a trapezoid is 42 square feet, while its upper and lower bases are 6 feet and 7 feet respectively. What is the length of the altitude of the trapezoid?

17. The median of a trapezoid is 25, while the altitude is 8. Find the area of the trapezoid. (Hint: See Problem 12(c), page 405.)

18. The area of a trapezoid is 480 square inches. If the altitude is 15 inches, what is the length of the median of the trapezoid?

19. The area of a trapezoid is 80 square feet. If the lower base is 11 feet and the altitude is 8 feet, what is the length of the upper base?

20. The upper and lower bases of an isosceles trapezoid are 10 and 16 respectively. If one of the lower base angles is 45°, what is the area of the trapezoid?

21. The upper and lower bases of an isosceles trapezoid are 20 and 36 respectively. If one of the nonparallel sides is 10, what is the area of the trapezoid?

22. The altitude of an isosceles trapezoid is equal to 4, while one of the congruent sides is 5. If the area of the trapezoid is 14, find the lengths of the upper and lower bases.

B

1. Given: *ABCD* is a parallelogram.
Concl.: $\triangle ABC = \triangle DBC$

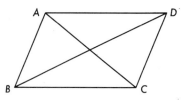

Given: *ABCD* is a trapezoid   **2.**
with $\overleftrightarrow{AD} \parallel \overleftrightarrow{BC}$.
Concl.: $\triangle ABC = \triangle DBC$

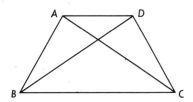

3. Given: *ABCD* is a parallelogram.
Concl.: $\triangle ABE = \triangle AED$

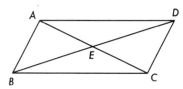

Given: *E* is any point on   **4.**
median $\overline{AD}$.
Concl.: $\triangle EBD = \triangle EDC$

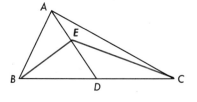

5. Using the same Given Data as in Problem 4, prove that $\triangle ABE = \triangle AEC$. (Hint: Use the information proved in Problem 4.)

6. Given: Median $\overline{AD}$ of
$\triangle ABC$ was extended
to point *E*.
Concl.: $\triangle ABE = \triangle ACE$

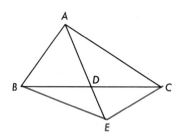

Given: $\overline{BE}$ is the median to $\overline{AC}$.   **7.**
$\overline{CD}$ is the median to $\overline{AB}$.
Concl.: $\triangle DBC = \triangle EBC$
(Hint: See Theorem
58.)

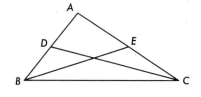

8. Given: *ABCD* is a parallelogram.

$\overleftrightarrow{AF} \perp \overleftrightarrow{BC}$

$\overleftrightarrow{AE} \perp \overleftrightarrow{CD}$

Concl.: $BC \cdot AF = CD \cdot AE$

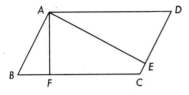

Given: $\overleftrightarrow{AD} \perp \overleftrightarrow{BC}$

$\overleftrightarrow{BE} \perp \overleftrightarrow{AC}$

Concl.: $BC \cdot AD = AC \cdot BE$

9.

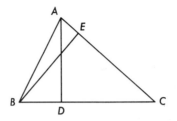

10. Given: *PQRS* is a $\square$.
M is the midpoint of $\overline{PS}$.

$\overleftrightarrow{RM}$ meets $\overleftrightarrow{QP}$ at *A*.

Concl.: $\triangle AQR = \square PQRS$
(Hint: Prove
$\triangle APM \cong \triangle RSM$
and use addition
postulate.)

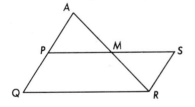

Given: $\odot I$ inscribed within $\triangle ABC$

Concl.: $\triangle ABC = \frac{1}{2}r(AB + AC + BC)$

11.

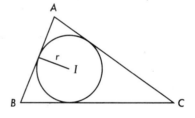

12. Given: *P* midpt. of $\overline{BD}$
Concl.: $ABCP = ADCP$

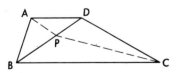

Given: $\overleftrightarrow{AC} \perp \overleftrightarrow{BD}$
Concl.: $ABCD = \frac{1}{2} AC \cdot BD$

13.

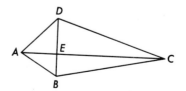

14. Given: $ABCD$ is a parallelogram.
M is the midpoint
of $\overline{AD}$.
N is the midpoint
of $\overline{BC}$.
Concl.: $BNDM = \frac{1}{2}ABCD$

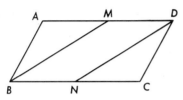

Given: $\overline{BE}$ is the median to $\overline{AC}$. **15.**
$\overline{CD}$ is the median to $\overline{AB}$.
Concl.:
(1) $\triangle BDF = \triangle CEF$
(See Problem 7.)
(2) $\triangle ABE = \triangle ACD$

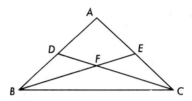

16. Given: $ABCD$ is a trapezoid
with $\overleftrightarrow{AD} \parallel \overleftrightarrow{BC}$.
$BC = 3AD$
Concl.: $\triangle DBC = 3\triangle BDA$

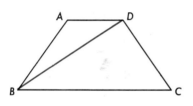

Given: $ABCD$ is a trapezoid **17.** *
with $\overleftrightarrow{AD} \parallel \overleftrightarrow{BC}$.
M is the midpoint
of $\overline{DC}$.
Concl.: $\triangle MDA + \triangle MCB$
$= \triangle MAB$
(Hint: Prove
$\triangle MDA + \triangle MCB$
$= \frac{1}{2}ABCD$.)

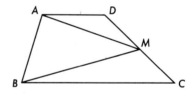

18. Given: $\overrightarrow{AD}$ bisects $\angle BAC$.
Concl.: $\triangle ABD : \triangle ACD =$
$AB : AC$

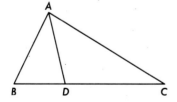

Given: D midpt. of $\overline{AB}$ **19.**
E midpt. of $\overline{AC}$
Concl.: $\triangle FBC = ADFE$

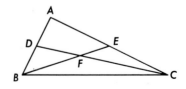

20. * Given: $\triangle ABC$ with medians $\overline{AM}$, $\overline{BN}$, and $\overline{CP}$ intersecting at G.

$\overset{\leftrightarrow}{GF} \perp \overset{\leftrightarrow}{BC}$

$\overset{\leftrightarrow}{AH} \perp \overset{\leftrightarrow}{BC}$

Concl.:

(1) $AH = 3GF$ (Hint: See Problems 19 and 20, page 392.)

(2) $\triangle GBC = \frac{1}{3}\triangle ABC$

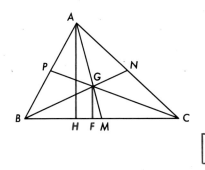

21. * Given: $ABCD$ is a parallelogram.

$\overset{\leftrightarrow}{CE}$ intersects $\overset{\leftrightarrow}{DA}$ at F.

Concl.:

(1) $\triangle DEC = \frac{1}{2}\square ABCD$

(2) $\triangle ADE = \triangle FEB$

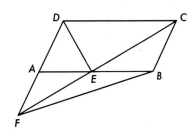

$\boxed{\text{C}}$

1. If two parallelograms have congruent bases, the ratio of their areas is equal to the ratio of the measures of their altitudes. †
2. If two parallelograms have congruent altitudes, the ratio of their areas is equal to the ratio of the measures of their bases. †
3. **(a)** Make up two statements similar to those in Problems 1 and 2 that refer to triangles rather than parallelograms.

   (b) Prove the statements that you wrote as your answer to part (a).
4. The area of a rhombus is equal to one-half the product of the measures of its diagonals.
5. If a line passes through the midpoint of a diagonal of a parallelogram, it will divide the parallelogram into two equal quadrilaterals.
6. The diagonals of a parallelogram will divide the parallelogram into four equal triangles.
7. * If two polygons are congruent, then their areas are equal. †
8. * If the three medians of a triangle are drawn to their point of concurrency, then the triangle will be divided into three equal triangles. (Hint: See Problem 20 in Group B.)

† This statement often appears as a theorem.

■ Areas of Similar Triangles

The areas of similar triangles bear a special relation to each other that is important enough in mathematics to be worthy of our attention. A comparison can be made of the areas of two similar triangles— or two similar polygons, in fact—without the necessity of having to find these areas. The next theorem will give us this tool.

THEOREM 140: The ratio of the areas of two similar triangles is equal to the ratio of the squares of the measures of any two corresponding sides.

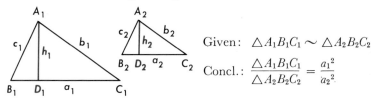

Given: $\triangle A_1B_1C_1 \sim \triangle A_2B_2C_2$

Concl.: $\dfrac{\triangle A_1B_1C_1}{\triangle A_2B_2C_2} = \dfrac{a_1{}^2}{a_2{}^2}.$

Figure 17-15.

PROOF	STATEMENTS	REASONS
1.	Let $\bar{h}_1$ be the perpendicular from A_1 to $\bar{a}_1$.	1. Why possible?
2.	Let $\bar{h}_2$ be the perpendicular from A_2 to $\bar{a}_2$.	2. Why possible?
3.	$\triangle A_1B_1C_1 = \frac{1}{2}a_1h_1$	3. Theorem on the area of a triangle
4.	$\triangle A_2B_2C_2 = \frac{1}{2}a_2h_2$	4. Same as 3
5.	$\dfrac{\triangle A_1B_1C_1}{\triangle A_2B_2C_2} = \dfrac{\frac{1}{2}a_1h_1}{\frac{1}{2}a_2h_2} = \dfrac{a_1}{a_2} \cdot \dfrac{h_1}{h_2}$	5. Division postulate
6.	But $\triangle A_1B_1C_1 \sim \triangle A_2B_2C_2$	6. Given
7.	$\therefore \dfrac{a_1}{a_2} = \dfrac{c_1}{c_2}$	7. Def. of similar polygons
8.	$\angle B_1 \cong \angle B_2$	8. Same as 7
9.	$\angle A_1D_1B_1 \cong \angle A_2D_2B_2$	9. Why?
10.	$\therefore \triangle A_1B_1D_1 \sim \triangle A_2B_2D_2$	10. A.A. theorem on similarity
11.	Hence, $\dfrac{h_1}{h_2} = \dfrac{c_1}{c_2}$	11. Same as 7
12.	$\therefore \dfrac{h_1}{h_2} = \dfrac{a_1}{a_2}$	12. Why? (See steps 11 and 7.)
13.	$\therefore \dfrac{\triangle A_1B_1C_1}{\triangle A_2B_2C_2} = \dfrac{a_1}{a_2} \cdot \dfrac{a_1}{a_2}$ or $\dfrac{\triangle A_1B_1C_1}{\triangle A_2B_2C_2} = \dfrac{a_1{}^2}{a_2{}^2}$	13. Substitution postulate (See step 5.)

It is interesting to note that had we replaced $\frac{a_1}{a_2}$ by $\frac{h_1}{h_2}$, rather than vice versa, step 13 would have been

$$\frac{\triangle A_1 B_1 C_1}{\triangle A_2 B_2 C_2} = \frac{h_1}{h_2} \cdot \frac{h_1}{h_2}$$

or

$$\frac{\triangle A_1 B_1 C_1}{\triangle A_2 B_2 C_2} = \frac{h_1{}^2}{h_2{}^2}$$

Hence, it appears that we have also proved that

THEOREM 141: The ratio of the areas of two similar triangles is equal to the ratio of the squares of the measures of any two corresponding altitudes.

These two theorems pave the way for the proofs of several theorems in space geometry. As usual, however, terms will have to be defined before we can proceed.

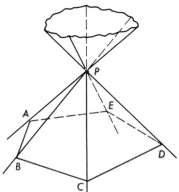

Figure 17-16.

DEFINITION 99: A pyramidal surface is a surface that is generated by a line that moves so as to always pass through a given point and always intersect a given polygon where the given point is not in the plane of the polygon.

In the figure above, the fixed point, P, is called the *vertex*, while the given polygon is $ABCDE$. Any one of the many positions that the moving line may assume is called an *element* of the surface. Notice that the surface extends above point P as well as below. Each of these two sections is called a *nappe* of the surface.

To define the term that we are seeking will require the need for another and final undefined term.

Solid

▰▰▰▰▰ Rather than attempt to describe the term *solid*, we will assume that all of us have a common understanding of it.

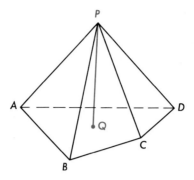

Figure 17-17.

DEFINITION 100: A pyramid is a solid bounded by one nappe of a pyramidal surface and a plane that intersects every element of this surface but does not contain the vertex of the surface.

DEFINITION 101: The base of a pyramid is the polygon formed as the intersection of the plane with the pyramidal surface.

DEFINITION 102: The altitude of a pyramid is the perpendicular segment that exists from the vertex to the plane of the base of the pyramid.

DEFINITION 103: A triangular pyramid is a pyramid whose base is a triangle.

It would seem as if we had gone to extraordinarily great lengths merely to build the background for one or two simple theorems. Unfortunately, as is the case in any area of the sciences, we can not speak intelligently unless we learn the language!

THEOREM 142: If a plane is parallel to the base of a triangular pyramid and intersects its pyramidal surface, but not the vertex, then the intersection will be a triangle similar to the base.

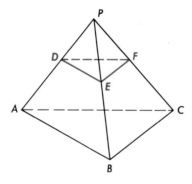

Given: Plane $DEF \parallel$ plane ABC

Concl.: $\triangle ABC \sim \triangle DEF$

Figure 17-18.

PROOF STATEMENTS	REASONS
1. Plane $DEF \parallel$ plane ABC	1. Given
2. $\overleftrightarrow{EF} \parallel \overleftrightarrow{BC}$	2. If a plane intersects two parallel planes, the lines of intersection are parallel. (Theorem 43, page 281)
3. $\angle PEF \cong \angle PBC$	3. Corresponding angles of parallel lines
4. $\angle PFE \cong \angle PCB$	4. Same as 3
5. $\therefore \triangle PEF \sim \triangle PBC$	5. A.A. theorem on similarity
6. Hence, $EF:BC = PE:PB$	6. Def. of similar polygons

In the same manner, by proving $\triangle PDE \sim \triangle PAB$ it will follow that

7. $DE:AB = PE:PB$	7. Same as 6
8. $\therefore EF:BC = DE:AB$	8. Transitive property of equality

Again, in the same manner it can be shown that

$$EF:BC = DE:AB = DF:AC$$

9. Hence, $\triangle ABC \sim \triangle DEF$	9. S.S.S. theorem on similarity

THEOREM 143: If a plane is parallel to the base of a triangular pyramid, then the ratio of the area of the triangle of intersection to the area of the base is equal to the ratio of the square of the distance of the plane from the vertex to the square of the measure of the altitude.

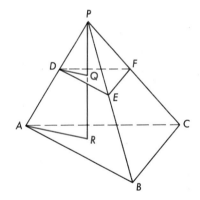

Given: Plane $DEF \parallel$ plane ABC

$\overleftrightarrow{PR} \perp$ plane ABC

Concl.: $\dfrac{\triangle DEF}{\triangle ABC} = \dfrac{(PQ)^2}{(PR)^2}$

Figure 17-19.

PROOF STATEMENTS	REASONS
1. Plane $DEF \parallel$ plane ABC	1. Given
2. $\overleftrightarrow{PR} \perp$ plane ABC	2. Given
3. $\overleftrightarrow{PR} \perp$ plane DEF	3. If a line is perpendicular to one of two parallel planes, it is perpendicu-

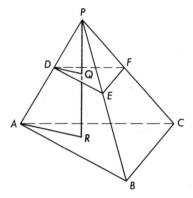

Figure 17-19.

ular to the other also. (Theorem 46, page 284)

4. $\overset{\leftrightarrow}{DQ} \parallel \overset{\leftrightarrow}{AR}$

4. If a plane intersects two parallel planes, the lines of intersection are parallel.

5. $\angle PQD \cong \angle PRA$ and $\angle PDQ \cong \angle PAR$

5. Why?

6. $\triangle PDQ \sim \triangle PAR$

6. *A.A.* theorem on similarity

7. $\dfrac{PQ}{PR} = \dfrac{PD}{PA}$

7. Def. of similar polygons

8. $\overset{\leftrightarrow}{DE} \parallel \overset{\leftrightarrow}{AB}$

8. Same as 4

9. $\angle PDE \cong \angle PAB$ and $\angle PED \cong \angle PBA$

9. Why?

10. $\triangle PDE \sim \triangle PAB$

10. Same as 6

11. $\dfrac{DE}{AB} = \dfrac{PD}{PA}$

11. Why?

12. $\dfrac{DE}{AB} = \dfrac{PQ}{PR}$

12. Transitive property of equality

13. But $\triangle DEF \sim \triangle ABC$

13. Theorem 142

14. $\therefore \dfrac{\triangle DEF}{\triangle ABC} = \dfrac{(DE)^2}{(AB)^2}$

14. The ratios of the areas of two similar triangles is equal to the ratio of the squares of the measures of any two corresponding sides.

15. Hence, $\dfrac{\triangle DEF}{\triangle ABC} = \dfrac{(PQ)^2}{(PR)^2}$

15. Substitution postulate

Illustration 1:

Two corresponding sides of two similar triangles are 6 inches and 8 inches respectively. If the area of the second triangle is 45 square inches, what is the area of the first triangle?

SOLUTION: $\dfrac{A_1}{A_2} = \dfrac{a_1^2}{a_2^2}$ (Theorem 140)

$\dfrac{A_1}{45} = \dfrac{6^2}{9^2} = \dfrac{6 \times 6}{9 \times 9} = \dfrac{2 \times 2}{3 \times 3} = \dfrac{4}{9}$

$A_1 = 20$

Illustration 2:

A triangular pyramid with an altitude of 20 inches has a base of 144 square inches. How far from the vertex must a plane be passed such that the area of the triangle of intersection will be 81 square inches?

SOLUTION: $\dfrac{A_1}{A_2} = \dfrac{d_1^2}{d_2^2}$ (Theorem 143)

$\dfrac{81}{144} = \dfrac{d_1^2}{20^2}$

$d_1^2 = \dfrac{20^2 \times 81}{144}$

$d_1 = 15$ inches

EXERCISES

1. What is the ratio of the areas of two similar triangles if two corresponding sides are respectively
   (a) 5 inches and 4 inches   (b) 2 inches and 6 inches
   (c) 10 feet and 20 feet   (d) 6 feet and 8 feet

2. What is the ratio of two corresponding sides of two similar triangles if their areas are respectively
   (a) 1 and 4   (b) 4 and 36

3. A plane is passed parallel to the base of a triangular pyramid. If the distance from the vertex of the pyramid to the plane and the altitude of the pyramid are given by the figures below, what is the ratio of the area of the triangle of intersection to the area of the base?
   (a) 14 feet and 35 feet   (b) 72 inches and 96 inches

4. A plane is passed parallel to the base of a triangular pyramid. If the area of the triangle of intersection and the area of the base are given

by the figures below, how does the distance from the vertex to the
plane compare with the altitude of the pyramid?

(a) 108 and 147   (b) 14 and 50

5. Two triangles are similar. If a side of one is four times a corresponding
   side of the other, what is the ratio of their areas?

6. Two triangles are similar. If the area of one is four times the area of
   the other, what is the ratio of any two corresponding sides?

7. If two corresponding altitudes of two similar triangles are in the ratio
   of 3:5, what is the ratio of their areas?

8. If the areas of two similar triangles are in the ratio of 5:9, what is
   the ratio of any two corresponding altitudes?

9. Two triangles are similar. If the area of one is 16 times the area of the
   other, what is the ratio of any two corresponding altitudes?

10. The angles of a triangle remain unchanged, but the sides of the triangle
    are doubled. What happens to the area of the triangle?

11. The area of a triangle is 63 square inches, while one of its sides is
    3 inches. In a similar triangle the side corresponding to the 3-inch side
    is 5 inches. What is the area of the second triangle?

12. The areas of two similar triangles are 48 and 60 square inches respec-
    tively. If a side of the first is 8 inches, what is the length of the side
    corresponding to this in the second triangle?

13. A plane is passed parallel to the base of a triangular pyramid such
    that the area of the base is 9 times the area of the triangle of intersec-
    tion. How far from the vertex does the plane intersect the altitude?

14. A plane is passed 4 feet from the vertex of a triangular pyramid whose
    altitude is 6 feet. If the area of the base of the pyramid is 108 square
    feet, what is the area of the triangular intersection?

15. A plane is passed parallel to the base of a triangular pyramid to make
    a cross section whose area is 56 square inches. If the base and altitude
    of the pyramid are 72 square inches and 12 inches respectively, what
    is the distance from the base to the plane?

16. * An altitude of one equilateral triangle is congruent to a side of another.
    What is the ratio of the areas of these two triangles?

$$\boxed{\text{B}}$$

1. If a line joins the midpoints of two sides of a triangle, it cuts off a triangle whose area is one-fourth of the area of the original triangle.

2. If two triangles are similar, then the ratio of their areas is equal to the

ratio of the squares of the measures of any pair of corresponding angle bisectors.

3. If two triangles are similar, then the ratio of their areas is equal to the ratio of the squares of the measures of any pair of corresponding medians.

4. Construct a triangle whose area is equal to one-sixteenth the area of a given triangle by drawing a line parallel to the base of the given triangle.

5. Given: $\angle A$ is an angle of $\triangle AEF$ and $\triangle ABC$.

   Concl.: $\dfrac{\triangle AEF}{\triangle ABC} = \dfrac{AF \cdot AE}{AC \cdot AB}$

   (Hint: Draw altitudes from E and B in each of the triangles.)

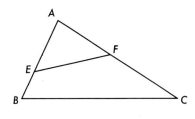

6. Given: Points D, B, and C are collinear.

   Concl.: $\dfrac{\triangle ABC}{\triangle DBE} = \dfrac{BA \cdot BC}{BE \cdot BD}$

   (Hint: Draw the altitudes from C and D in each of the triangles.)

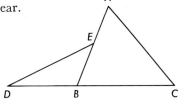

7. If the area of a triangle is one-half the product of the measures of two sides of the triangle, then the triangle is a right triangle. (Hint: Use the indirect method of proof.)

8. If two triangular pyramids have equal bases and congruent altitudes, then sections† made by planes parallel to the bases and equidistant from the vertices are equal.

9. Given: Plane $DEF \parallel$ plane ABC

   Concl.: $\dfrac{\triangle DEF}{\triangle ABC} = \dfrac{(VE)^2}{(VB)^2}$

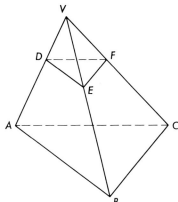

† A "section" of a plane and a solid is the intersection of the two.

10. Given: Plane $DEF \parallel$ plane ABC

$\overleftrightarrow{VP}$ is any line through V intersecting DEF and ABC in P and Q respectively.

Concl.: $\dfrac{\triangle DEF}{\triangle ABC} = \dfrac{(VP)^2}{(VQ)^2}$

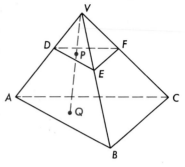

■ Areas of Regular Polygons

Our study of the areas of polygons has been limited to areas of either 3-gons or special 4-gons. What can be said of the areas of other polygons? In general, very little. If enough information is known, the polygon can always be divided into triangles and the area of the polygon can be found by computing the sum of the areas of all the triangles. There is, however, a special class of polygons whose areas can be found more readily.

Consider the circle below that has been divided into n congruent arcs.

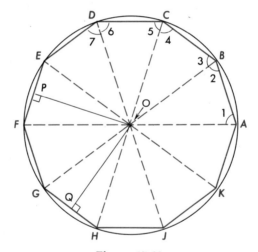

Figure 17-20.

To be as general as possible, we have stated the number as n rather than the 10 that you observe. Since the arcs are congruent, their corresponding chords are congruent and, hence, the polygon $ABCD$ . . . is equilateral. By drawing in the radii the triangles can readily be proved to be congruent by the *S.S.S.* congruency theorem. From this it would follow that $\angle 1 \cong \angle 3 \cong \angle 5 \cong \angle 7$ . . . and, too, that $\angle 2 \cong \angle 4 \cong \angle 6$ . . . . By the addition postulate $\angle ABC \cong \angle BCD \cong \angle CDE$ . . . ; hence, the polygon is, also, equiangular. Polygons such as these are called regular polygons.

DEFINITION 104: A regular polygon is a polygon that is both equilateral and equiangular.

In the illustration above we started with a circle and showed that there existed a regular polygon that was inscribed within a circle. The converse of this is also true; that is, *a circle can be circumscribed about a regular polygon.* Since we have no need for this statement, we do not intend to prove it.

Let us return to the regular polygon on page 602. Since all the triangles were shown to be congruent, the altitudes from point O, such as $\overline{OP}$ and $\overline{OQ}$, will be congruent. Each of these altitudes is called an *apothem* of this polygon; the point from which they are drawn is the *center* of the regular polygon. A radius, such as $\overline{OA}$ or $\overline{OB}$, is said to be the *radius of a regular polygon.* And the *perimeter*, of course, is the sum of the measures of the sides of the polygon.

THEOREM 144: The area of a regular polygon is equal to one-half the product of the measure of the apothem and the perimeter.

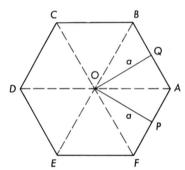

Figure 17-21.

Given: $ABCD \ldots$ is a regular polygon.
$\quad \quad \quad a$ is the measure of the apothem.
Concl.: Area of $ABCD \ldots = \frac{1}{2}ap$

PROOF STATEMENTS	REASONS
1. Let $\overleftrightarrow{OA}$ be the line through points O and A.	1. Why possible?
2. Same for $\overleftrightarrow{OB}, \overleftrightarrow{OC}, \ldots$	2. Same as 1
3. $\triangle OAB = \frac{1}{2}a \cdot AB$ $\triangle OBC = \frac{1}{2}a \cdot BC$ etc.	3. Area of a triangle
4. $\triangle OAB + \triangle OBC + \ldots = \frac{1}{2}a \cdot AB + \frac{1}{2}a \cdot BC + \ldots$	4. Addition postulate
5. Area of $ABCD \ldots = \triangle OAB + \triangle OBC + \ldots$	5. Why?
6. Area of $ABCD \ldots = \frac{1}{2}a(AB + BC + \ldots)$	6. Substitution postulate
7. $p = AB + BC + \ldots$	7. Definition of perimeter
8. Area of $ABCD \ldots = \frac{1}{2}ap$	8. Same as 6

Illustration:

What is the area of a regular hexagon, one of whose sides is 8?

METHOD: The perimeter can immediately be found as 48. Finding the apothem is a bit more involved. By drawing the radii of the hexagon, we find that each central angle is 60°. Since $\overline{OA} \cong \overline{OB}$, each of the angles

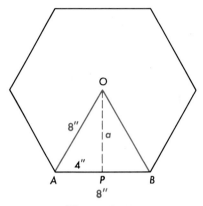

Figure 17-22.

OAB and OBA will also have to be 60°. Hence, $\triangle OAB$ is equiangular and, therefore, equilateral. Thus, $OA = 8$. The apothem $\overline{OP}$ bisects the base; therefore, $AP = 4$. Using the theorem of Pythagoras, a is found to be $4\sqrt{3}$. Hence,

$$\text{area} = \tfrac{1}{2}ap = \tfrac{1}{2} \cdot 4\sqrt{3} \cdot 48 = 96\sqrt{3}$$

EXERCISES

1. The perimeter and apothem of a regular polygon are 48 and 6 respectively. What is the area of the polygon?
2. Find the area of a regular hexagon if the length of one of its sides is
   (a) 10   (b) 16
   (c) 5   (d) 2a
3. If the radius of a regular hexagon is 12, what is the area of the hexagon?
4. If the apothem of a regular hexagon is $7\sqrt{3}$, what is the area of the hexagon?

† Leave answers in radical form.

5. The radius of a square is 3. What is the area of the square?

6. Find the area of an equilateral triangle if its radius is
   (a) 8   (b) 12
   (c) 7   (d) 2*a*

7. Find the area of an equilateral triangle if its apothem is
   (a) 6   (b) 24
   (c) 5   (d) *a*

8. A circle with a radius of 14 is inscribed within an equilateral triangle. Find the area of the triangle.

9. A circle with a radius of 9 is inscribed within a regular hexagon. What is the area of the hexagon?

10. A square is inscribed in a circle of radius R. What is the area of the square?

11. (a) A circle is inscribed within one square and circumscribed about another. If the radius of the circle is 6, what is the ratio of the area of the larger square to that of the smaller square?
    (b) If the radius of the circle is 2*a*, what is the ratio of the areas of the two squares?

12. A circle is inscribed within one regular hexagon and circumscribed about another. If the radius of the circle is 4, what is the ratio of the area of the larger hexagon to that of the smaller hexagon?

13. In the pyramid at the right, $ABCD$ is a regular polygon; in this case, a square. The altitude VP passes through the point of intersection of the diagonals. A pyramid such as this is called a *regular pyramid.* $\overline{VQ}$, the altitude in face VCD, is called the *slant height.* If $BC = 8$ and $VQ = 12$, what is the lateral surface area of the pyramid? (The lateral surface area will be the total surface area excluding the area of the base.)

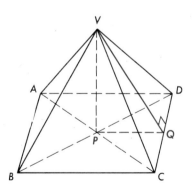

14. Refer to the pyramid above for each of the following problems:
    (a) $BC = 6$, $VQ = 10$. Find the total surface area.
    (b) $BC = 12$, $VP = 8$. Find the lateral surface area.
    (c) $BC = 8$, $m \angle PVQ = 45$. Find the lateral surface area.
    (d) $BC = a$, $VQ = s$. Find the total surface area.

15. (a) The base of a regular pyramid is a regular hexagon, each of whose

sides is 8. If the slant height of the pyramid is 10, what is the lateral surface area of the pyramid?

(b) What is the total surface area of this pyramid?

16. * The base of a regular pyramid is a regular hexagon, one of whose sides is 6. If the altitude of the pyramid is 5, what is the lateral surface area of the pyramid?

17. * The base of a regular pyramid is an equilateral triangle, one of whose sides is 12. If the altitude of the pyramid is 2, what is the total surface area of the pyramid?

$$\boxed{\text{B}}$$

1. A radius of a regular polygon bisects the angle to which it is drawn.

2. The perpendicular bisector of a side of a regular hexagon passes through the center of its circumscribed circle.

3. If two regular polygons have the same number of sides, then they are similar.

4. If two regular polygons have the same number of sides, then the ratio of the measures of their radii is equal to the ratio of the measures of their apothems.

5. A square and a regular hexagon are inscribed within the same circle. Prove: The ratio of the measure of a side of the square to the measure of a side of the hexagon is $\sqrt{2}:1$.

6. Prove: The lateral surface area of a regular pyramid is equal to one-half the product of the measure of the slant height and the perimeter of the base.

■ Circumference of a Circle

We could not very well leave the topic concerning the regular polygon without showing how some of its properties can be extended to formulate properties of the circle. Notice in Figure 17-23 what appears to be happening when the number of sides of a regular polygon is increased from 4 to 8 to 16 and finally to 32. As the number of sides increases, the

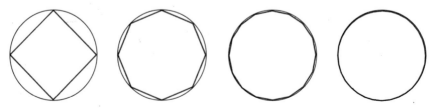

Figure 17-23.

polygon itself resembles more and more the circle in which it is inscribed. Yet no matter how large the number of sides may be, the polygon will always differ from the circle, for the sides of a polygon are line segments while any portion of a circle between two points of the circle must be an arc of that circle.

Mathematicians frequently encounter situations such as this where for "all practical purposes" one quantity can be made to so closely resemble another that a replacement of one for the other is permitted. Thus, in the situation here, as the number of sides of the regular polygon is increased, the perimeters of the polygons approach closer and closer to the circumference of the circle. If this is so, and it seems reasonable to suspect that it is, then the mathematician would say, "Why bother to pursue this endless sequence of numbers representing the perimeters! These numbers can be made to differ so little from the circumference of the circle itself that for all practical purposes we may as well use the circumference of the circle to represent the perimeter of the regular polygon when the number of sides of that polygon is very, very large." . . . And of course we have assumed that you recall from your work in elementary mathematics that,

DEFINITION 105: The circumference of a circle is the measure of the circle (in linear units).

In view of our analysis it seems that we would not be going too far astray by postulating the following,

POSTULATE 45: When the number of sides of a regular polygon inscribed in a circle is very large, then the circumference of the circle can be used as a replacement for the perimeter of the polygon.

Our discussion above has been on an extremely elementary level. Some day you may examine this topic much more thoroughly in the subject called calculus. The topic is the *theory of limits* which, needless to say, is quite beyond the scope of our work at this time. Postulate 45, however, enables us to prove the theorem below. This theorem, in turn, leads us to a method for finding the circumference of a circle.

THEOREM 145: In any two circles the ratio of the circumference to the radius of the first is equal to the ratio of the circumference to the radius of the second.

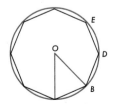

Given: $\odot O$ and $\odot P$ where C_O and C_P represent the circumference of each respectively.

Concl.: $C_O:OA = C_P:PQ$

PROOF	STATEMENTS	REASONS
1. Let regular polygons of n sides be inscribed in each of the circles.	1. A regular polygon of n sides can be inscribed in a circle.
2. $OA = OB$	2. The radii of a circle are congruent.
3. $PQ = PR$	3. Same as 2
4. $OA:PQ = OB:PR$	4. Division Postulate
5. $m \widehat{AB} = m \widehat{BD} = m \widehat{DE} = \ldots = \dfrac{360}{n}$	5. If in a circle two chords are congruent, their corr. arcs are congruent.
6. $m \angle AOB = \dfrac{360}{n}$	6. The measure of a central angle of a circle is the measure of the minor arc it intercepts. (Rev. of Def. 82.)
7. $m \widehat{QR} = m \widehat{RS} = m \widehat{ST} = \ldots = \dfrac{360}{n}$	7. Same as 5
8. $m \angle QPR = \dfrac{360}{n}$	8. Same as 6
9. $\angle AOB \cong \angle QPR$	9. Transitive Property
10. $\triangle AOB \sim \triangle QPR$	10. S.A.S. Theorem on Similarity
11. $AB:OA = QR:PQ$	11. Def. of similar triangles
12. $n(AB):OA = n(QR):PQ$	12. Multiplication Postulate
13. But $n(AB) = p_1$ and $n(QR) = p_2$	13. Def. of perimeter of a regular polygon
14. $p_1:OA = p_2:PQ$	14. Substitution Postulate

Now if we allow the number of sides in the two polygons to remain equal but become very large, then

| 15. $C_O:OA = C_P:PQ$ | 15. Postulate 45 |

We have just shown that the ratio of the circumference of a circle to the measure of its radius is always the same no matter what the size of the circle may be. Thus, we can set this ratio equal to a constant that we will call 2π (read as *two pi*). Therefore,

$$\frac{C}{r} = 2\pi$$

Hence, by applying the multiplication postulate we find that,

$$C = 2\pi r$$

This is the formula frequently used for finding the circumference of a circle.

But what is the value of the symbol π? It was approximated by Archimedes, an ancient Greek mathematician, to fall somewhere between $3\frac{10}{71}$ and $3\frac{10}{70}$. More recently, mathematicians have approximated π far more accurately. This symbol can never be expressed as an exact number—either in the form of a terminating or a non-terminating decimal. But approximations do exist that will give as great a degree of accuracy as one might desire. Some of these approximations are,

$$3, \ 3.14, \ 3.1416, \ 3.1415927, \ 3.14159265359$$

There is also, of course, the improper fraction that you may have used in elementary school: $\frac{22}{7}$.

Illustration 1:

What is the circumference of a circle whose diameter is 20 inches?

METHOD: The formula for the circumference of a circle calls for the measure of the radius. By dividing the measure of the diameter by 2 we find that the measure of the radius is 10 (inches). Hence,

$$C = 2\pi r$$
$$= 2\pi(10)$$
$$= 20\pi$$

Unless otherwise called for, the answer is usually left in terms of π.

By applying the commutative property of multiplication, it is possible to rewrite the formula for the circumference of a circle as,

$$C = \pi 2r$$

Then, by realizing that the measure of the diameter of a circle is twice the measure of the radius of the circle, it is possible to replace $2r$ by d. This will lead to the following variation of the formula that is often used.

$$C = \pi d$$

We would like to take a moment now to tie together the two measures that we have created for a circle. On the one hand we created the arc degree (see page 453) wherein we state arbitrarily that the measure of *every* circle is 360 arc degrees. On the other hand we have just discovered that the circumference of any circle can be found by using the formula $C = 2\pi r$. The arc degree unit is what is called a *non-denominate unit*. In reality, the arc degree is not a unit in the sense of such things as the pound, the yard, or the gallon—for it is not fixed in size. To say that an arc contains 60 arc degrees is merely to draw a comparison between the length of that arc and the length of the entire circle. In this case it would imply that the arc is $\frac{60}{360}$ of the length of the circle. Thus its length is shown to be some fraction of the length of the circle rather than some definite quantity. However, by saying that an arc is 6 *inches* we are applying an *absolute unit* as its measure. Now we have indicated that the arc—if stretched tight—will be 6 times as long as the linear unit called the *inch*. As we know, the inch is a very definite length.

Consider now the arc AB whose measure in arc degrees is n. We want to determine the number of linear units in this arc. To do this we realize that an arc of n arc degrees has a length $\frac{n}{360}$ of the length of its circle. Since the length of a circle is but another name for the circumference of the circle, arc AB is $\frac{n}{360}$ of $2\pi r$, where r is the measure of the radius of the circle of which $\overset{\frown}{AB}$ is an arc. Using symbols, this can be expressed as,

$$m \overset{\frown}{AB} = n$$

therefore, the length of $\overset{\frown}{AB} = \frac{n}{360}$ of its circle

hence, the length of $\overset{\frown}{AB} = \frac{n}{360} \cdot 2\pi r$

THEOREM 146: The length of an arc of a circle is given by the formula,

$$l = \frac{n}{360} \cdot 2\pi r$$

where n is the number of arc degrees in the arc and r is the number of linear units in the radius of the circle.

Illustration 2:

If the radius of a circle is 5 inches, find the length of an arc of this circle whose central angle has a measure of 40.

METHOD: Since the measure of the central angle is 40, the measure of the arc is 40. Hence, by Theorem 146,

$$l = \frac{n}{360} \cdot 2\pi r$$

$$= \frac{40}{360} \cdot 2\pi 5$$

$$= \frac{10}{9} \pi \text{ (inches)}$$

EXERCISES

(Unless otherwise stated, leave all answers in terms of π.)

1. Find the circumference of each of the following circles.
   (a) $r = 20$ (b) $r = 5\frac{1}{2}$
   (c) $d = 16$ (d) $d = 6\frac{1}{4}$

2. Find the length of each of the following arcs.
   (a) $m \overset{\frown}{AB} = 60$; radius is 10 inches
   (b) $m \overset{\frown}{AB} = 90$; radius is 12 inches

(c) $m \ \widehat{AB} = 150$; radius is 25 feet

(d) $m \ \widehat{AB} = 120$; diameter is 40 feet

(e) $m \ \widehat{AB} = 80$; diameter is 35 feet

3. One of the sides of a square is 8 inches long. The square is inscribed in a circle.

(a) What is the radius of the circle?

(b) What is the circumference of the circle?

(c) What is the length of an arc of the circle cut off by one of the sides of the square?

4. An equilateral triangle is inscribed in a circle. If the apothem of the triangle is 5 inches, what is the length of an arc of the circle that is cut off by one of the sides of the triangle?

5. An isosceles right triangle is inscribed in a circle.

(a) If the length of the hypotenuse of the triangle is 10 feet, what is the length of the arc cut off by one of the legs?

(b) If the length of one of the legs of the triangle is 10 feet, what is the length of the arc cut off by this leg?

6. A wheel travels the distance of its circumference in one revolution.

(a) How far will a bicycle having a 28 inch diameter wheel travel if the wheel makes 1,000 revolutions? (Use $\frac{22}{7}$ as the approximation for π.)

(b) How many revolutions will a wheel of this bicycle make during a trip of 1 mile? (Use $\frac{22}{7}$ as the approximation for π.)

7. An arc of a circle has a measure of 30 arc degrees and is 5π inches in length.

(a) What is the radius of the circle?

(b) What is the circumference of the circle?

8. The back wheel of a motor bike is placed on a stand and spun about its axle. The diameter of the wheel is 22 inches. How far does a point on the wheel travel when a spoke on the wheel rotates through an angle of 72 degrees?

9. A rope is stretched around the two pulley wheels as shown in the diagram. How many feet of rope will be needed? (See problem 10, page 370.)

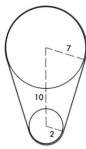

10. The "30th parallel" on the earth's
    surface is a circle determined as
    shown in the diagram.

    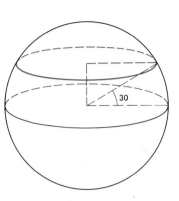

    (a) If the diameter of the earth is
        approximately 8,000 miles, what
        is the circumference of the 30th
        parallel? (Use 3.14 as the approxi-
        mation for π.)

    (b) During one day the earth makes
        one revolution about its axis. How
        many miles per hour is a tree trav-
        eling if it is located on the 30th
        parallel?

    (c) How much faster would the tree
        in (b) be traveling if it were lo-
        cated along the equator?

11. A circle is inscribed in a square one of whose sides is 12 inches. Find
    the length of the arc whose endpoints are two successive points of
    tangency.

    (a) If the polygon had been an equilateral triangle, what would the
        length of the arc have been?

    (b) If the polygon had been a regular hexagon, what would the length
        of the arc have been?

12. Imagine the earth to be a perfect sphere and consider a thin sheet
    of metal drawn tightly about the surface at the equator where the
    circumference is approximately 24,000 miles. The length of the metal
    is increased by 50 feet. It is then held away from the surface by the
    same distance throughout the 24,000 miles. Is it possible for a man
    who is 6 feet tall to stand beneath the metal sheet? Justify your answer.

■ Area of a Circle

Examine Figure 17-20 on page 602 and imagine the num-
ber of sides of the regular polygon to increase indefinitely. What conclusion
did we draw concerning the perimeter of the polygon when this occurs?
What do you believe will occur to the radius of the polygon under this
condition? And finally, what will happen to the apothem $\overline{OQ}$?

Actually, nothing will happen to the radius of the polygon for the radius
of the polygon is also the radius of the circle, and as the polygon approaches
the circle in appearance, the radius of the circle does not alter. However,
the apothem of the polygon becomes closer and closer to being the radius

of the circle as the number of sides increases. We need just such a postulate before it is possible to prove a theorem relating to the area of a circle.

POSTULATE 46: When the number of sides of a regular polygon inscribed in a circle is very large, then the measure of the radius of the circle can be used as a replacement for the measure of the apothem of the polygon.

THEOREM 147: The area of a circle is given by the formula,

$$A = \pi r^2$$

PROOF

Through our analysis on page 602 we know that it is possible to inscribe a regular polygon within a circle. The area of this polygon is given by the formula,

$$A = \tfrac{1}{2}ap$$

where a is the measure of the apothem and p is the perimeter of the polygon. Now, by making the number of sides of the polygon sufficiently large,

by Postulate 45,	C can replace p
and by Postulate 46,	r can replace a
Hence,	$A = \tfrac{1}{2}rC$
but since,	$C = 2\pi r$
then,	$A = \tfrac{1}{2}r \cdot 2\pi r$
or	$A = \pi r^2$

And this is what we set out to prove.

Illustration:

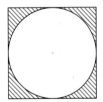

In the figure at the right, a circle is inscribed in a square one of whose sides is 8 inches. Find the area of the shaded region.

METHOD:

Area of square = 8 × 8 = 64 sq. in.
Area of circle = πr^2 = $\pi \cdot 4^2$ = 16π sq. in.
Area of shaded region = $(64 - 16\pi)$ sq. in.

Before completing our discussion of area as related to a circle, it would seem only natural that we examine the area of a region such as the "pie slice" pictured in Figure 17-24. Earlier our discussion led from the circumference of a circle to the length of an arc of a circle—the arc being but a section of the circumference. Now our discussion is leading us from the area of a circle to the "pie slice"—where the "pie slice" is but a section of the area of the circle.

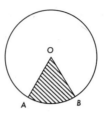

Figure 17-24.

Obviously, the actual name of this region is not a "pie slice" but rather, a *sector of a circle.*

DEFINITION 106: A sector of a circle O is the union of the sets of points consisting of $\overline{OA}$, $\overline{OB}$, $\overparen{AB}$ and the set of points in the interior of $\angle AOB$ where the distance from each of these points to O is less than $\overline{OA}$.

In finding the formula for the area of a sector of a circle we must apply a slight variation of Postulate 45. That is, not only is it possible to replace the perimeter of a regular inscribed polygon with the circumference of the circle when the number of sides become sufficiently large but we are also able to replace any fraction of that perimeter by an equal fraction of the circumference. Thus, intuitively we might gather from Figure 17-25 that as the

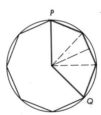

Figure 17-25.

number of sides of the regular polygon increases the sum of the measures of the sides between points P and Q would come very close to the measure in linear units of $\overparen{PQ}$. But the sum of the areas of the region bounded by the red line segments is,

$$A = \tfrac{1}{2}at$$

where a is the measure of the apothem and t is the sum of the measures of the sides from P to Q. Hence, as the number of sides of the polygon increases, a can be replaced by r and t can be replaced by

$$\frac{n}{360} \cdot 2\pi r$$

since this expression represents the number of linear units in the length of the arc of a circle (see Theorem 146). Hence,

$$A = \frac{1}{2}r \cdot \frac{n}{360} \cdot 2\pi r$$

or,
$$A = \frac{n}{360} \cdot \pi r^2$$

THEOREM 148: **The area of a sector of a circle is given by the formula,**

$$A = \frac{n}{360} \cdot \pi r^2$$

where n is the number of arc degrees in the arc and r is the measure of the radius of the circle.

Illustration:

A square inscribed in a circle has a side of 6 inches. Find the area of the region bounded by a side of the square and its corresponding arc.

ANALYSIS: Our problem resolves to one in which we are seeking the area of the shaded region in the diagram. To do this we will find the area of $\triangle OAB$ and the area of the sector bounded by the radii $\overline{OA}$ and $\overline{OB}$ and the arc $\overparen{AB}$. Then the difference between these areas will be the area of the region we have been asked to determine.

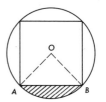

METHOD: Since the sides of the square are congruent, their corresponding arcs will be congruent and hence, the measure of each arc is 90. In view of this, $m\angle AOB = 90$ and by using the Theorem of Pythagoras we can find that $OA = \frac{6}{\sqrt{2}}$.

Hence,   Area of sector $= \frac{n}{360} \cdot \pi r^2$

$$= \frac{90}{360} \cdot \pi \cdot \left(\frac{6}{\sqrt{2}}\right)^2$$

$$= \frac{1}{4} \cdot \pi \cdot \frac{36}{2}$$

$$= \frac{9\pi}{2} \text{ square inches}$$

Also,   Area of $\triangle OAB = \frac{1}{2}OA \cdot OB$

$$= \frac{1}{2} \cdot \frac{6}{\sqrt{2}} \cdot \frac{6}{\sqrt{2}}$$

$$= 9 \text{ square inches}$$

Therefore, the area of the shaded region is,

$$A = \frac{9\pi}{2} - 9$$

$$= \frac{9\pi - 18}{2} \text{ square inches}$$

The shaded region in the illustration above is called a *segment of a circle*.

EXERCISES

(Leave all answers in terms of π unless otherwise stated.)

1. Find the area of each of the following circles.

    (a) $r = 7$ **(b)** $r = 4\frac{1}{2}$ **(c)** $d = 24$ **(d)** $d = 15$

2. Find the area of each of the following sectors of a circle.

	Measure of Arc	Radius of Circle
(a)	60	8 inches
(b)	40	12 inches
(c)	90	$4\frac{1}{2}$ inches
(d)	120	$3\frac{1}{4}$ inches

3. Using 3.14 as the approximate value of π, find the approximate area of the segment of the circle in the illustration on page 615.

4. An arc of a circle has a measure of 90. Find the area of the segment of the circle bounded by this arc and its corresponding chord if the radius of the circle is 16 inches.

5. (a) An isosceles right triangle is inscribed in a circle that has a diameter of 10 inches. Find the area of the segment of the circle bounded by one of the legs of the triangle and its corresponding arc.

    (b) If the right triangle in **(a)** had been a "30–60 degree" right triangle, what would be the area of the segment bounded by the shorter leg and its corresponding arc? (See problem 10, page 370.)

6. (a) A regular hexagon is inscribed in a circle that has a radius of 12 feet. Find the area of the segment of the circle bounded by a side of the hexagon and its corresponding arc.

    (b) If the polygon in **(a)** had been an equilateral triangle, what would the area of the segment have been?

7. The shaded region bound by two concentric circles is called an *annulus*.

    (a) Find the area of an annulus if the radius of the larger circle is 10 inches while the radius of the smaller circle is 7 inches.

    (b) Show that the area of an annulus can be expressed by the formula,

$$A = \pi(R - r)(R + r)$$

where R is the measure of the radius of the larger circle and r is the measure of the radius of the smaller circle.

8. **(a)** A sector of a circle has an arc of 40 degrees. If the area of the sector is 5π, what is the area of the circle?

   (b) A circle has an area of 36π square feet. What is the area of a sector of this circle if the arc of the sector is 20 degrees?

9. Using the dimensions shown, find the area of the shaded region of each of the figures below.

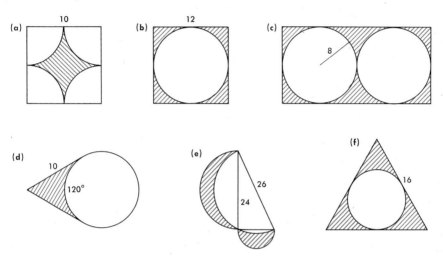

10. **(a)** Show that the ratio of the areas of two circles is equal to the ratio of the squares of their corresponding radii.

    (b) Show that the ratio of the areas of two circles is equal to the ratio of the squares of their corresponding circumferences.

11. Show that the area of a circle can be expressed by the formula $A = \frac{1}{4}\pi d^2$ where d is the measure of the diameter of the circle.

$$\boxed{\text{B}}$$

Prove each of the following statements.

1. The area of the circle circumscribed about a square is twice the area of the circle inscribed within the square.

2. The area of a circle circumscribed about an equilateral triangle is four times the area of the circle inscribed within the triangle.

3. In a right triangle if semicircles are constructed on each of the sides as a diameter, then the area of the semicircle on the hypotenuse is equal to the sum of the areas of the semicircles on the two legs.

4. Prove that the area of the annulus at the right is equal to $\pi(AC)^2$.

5. In the diagram at the right, $\overline{AC}$ is a diameter of the larger circle while $\overline{AB}$ and $\overline{BC}$ are diameters of the smaller circles. Prove that the area of the shaded region is equal to the area of the unshaded region. (See problem 11 of group A.)

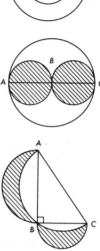

6.* Prove that the area of $\triangle ABC$ is equal to the area of the shaded region in the figure at the right, where $\overline{AB}$ and $\overline{BC}$ are diameters of the smaller semicircles and AC is a diameter of the largest semicircle.

◼ Test and Review

A

1. (a) Find the area of a right triangle, one of whose legs is 12, while the hypotenuse is 13.
   (b) Find the altitude to the hypotenuse of this triangle.

2. The altitude to the hypotenuse of an isosceles right triangle is 8. Find the area of the triangle.

3. (a) The ratio of the measures of two corresponding sides of two similar triangles is $3:5$. Find the ratio of their areas.
   (b) The ratio of the areas of two similar triangles is $27:64$. Find the ratio of the measures of a pair of corresponding sides.

4. A rectangle and a parallelogram have equal areas. The base and altitude of the rectangle are 16 and 12 respectively. If the measure of the base of the parallelogram is to the measure of the base of the rectangle as $5:8$, then what is the altitude of the parallelogram?

5. (a) Find the area of a parallelogram if its sides are 8 and 12 respectively, while the measure of the angle formed by these sides is 45.
   (b) If the measure of the angle were 30, what would the area be?
   (c) If the measure of the angle were 60, what would the area be?

6. The coordinates of the vertices of a triangle are $(0, 0)$, $(8, 0)$, and $(5, 7)$. Find the area of the triangle.

7. The side of a regular 8-gon is b. If the measure of the apothem is a, express the area of the polygon in terms of a and b.

8. The tangent segments to a circle from an external point form an angle of 120°. If the radius of the circle is 6, what is the area of the triangle whose sides are the two tangent segments and the line segment joining the points of tangency?

9. The measure of the lower base of an isosceles trapezoid exceeds the measure of the upper base by 8, while the measure of each of the non-parallel sides is 5. If the area is 36, what is the measure of each base?

10. The measures of two sides of a triangle are 10 and 12, while measure of the angle formed by these sides is 30. Find area of the triangle.

11. (a) Find the area of a regular hexagon if the length of one of its sides is 6.
   (b) Find the area of a regular hexagon if the length of its apothem is 10.
   (c) Find the measure of the side of a regular hexagon if its area is $108\sqrt{3}$.

12. (a) The upper and lower bases of an isosceles trapezoid are 18 and 24. If the lower base angles are 45°, what is area of the trapezoid?
   (b) If the lower base angle were 30°, what would the area be?
   (c) If the lower base angle were 60°, what would the area be?

13. A plane is passed parallel to the base of a pyramid in which this base is an equilateral triangle. The measure of the altitude of the pyramid is 4, while the distance from the vertex to the plane is 3. If the area of the base is 64, what is the measure of a side of the intersection?

14. Find circumference and area of the circle whose diameter is 18 feet.

15. A "30–60 degree" right triangle is inscribed in a circle. If the side opposite the 30 degree angle is 5 cm, find length of its corresponding arc.

16. (a) Show that the ratio of the circumferences of two circles is equal to the ratio of the measures of their corresponding diameters.
   (b) If the measure of the radius of one circle is 3 times the measure of the radius of a second circle, how do their circumferences compare?
   (c) How do the areas of the two circles in (b) compare?

17. A square, one of whose sides is 8 feet, is inscribed in a circle. Find area of segment bounded by a side of the square and its corresponding arc.

18. Two tangent segments are drawn from an external point to a circle having a diameter of 10 inches. The angle formed by the rays of these two segments has a measure of 60. Find the area of the region bounded by the tangent segments and the minor arc of the circle.

B

Prove each of the following:

1. Given: $ABCD$ is a $\square$.
  Concl.: $\triangle ABP = \triangle ADP$

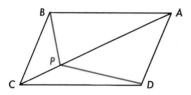

Given: E is the midpoint **2.**
    of $\overline{AD}$.
Concl.: $\triangle ABC = \triangle DBC$

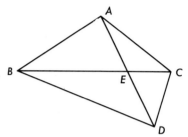

3. Given: $\overline{AD}$ is the median to $\overline{BC}$.
    E is the midpoint of $\overline{AD}$.
  Concl.: $\triangle ABE = \triangle DCE$

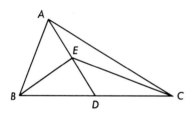

Given: Quadrilateral $ABCD$ **4.**
    with diagonal $\overline{BD}$
    $\overline{BF} \cong \overline{DE}$
Concl.: $ABCE = AFCD$

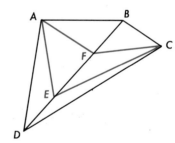

5. Given: $ABCD$ is a $\square$.
  Concl.: $\triangle PAB + \triangle PDC =$
    $\frac{1}{2}ABCD$

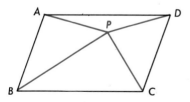

Given: $ABCD$ is a $\square$. **6.**
    M is the midpoint
    of $\overline{BD}$.
Concl.: $ABME = CFMD$

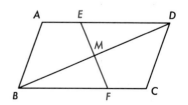

Prove each of the following statements:

1. If the altitudes of a triangle are congruent, then the triangle is equilateral.
2. The median to a side of a triangle separates the triangle into two equal triangles.
3. The product of the measures of the legs of a right triangle is equal to the product of the measures of the hypotenuse and the altitude to the hypotenuse.
4. The sum of the measures of the perpendiculars from any point within an equilateral triangle to the sides is equal to the measure of an altitude of the triangle.
5. If two regular polygons have the same number of sides, then the ratio of their areas is equal to the ratio of the squares of the measures of any two corresponding sides.
6. The area of a sector of a circle is equal to one-half the measure of the radius times the length of the arc of the sector.

■ Try This For Fun

At the time we studied the theorem of Pythagoras, it was pointed out that the early proofs of this theorem were very likely those that relied on the areas of polygons. The figure below was supposedly the one used by Leonardo DaVinci, the famous Italian painter, to prove this theorem. Using his diagram, can you prove that, "The square *on* the hypotenuse of a right triangle is equal to the sum of the squares *on* the legs"?

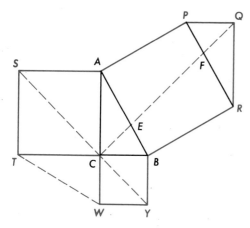

Given: Right $\triangle ACB$ with $\angle ACB$ the right angle.
$\overleftrightarrow{PQ} \parallel \overleftrightarrow{BC}$
$\overleftrightarrow{RQ} \parallel \overleftrightarrow{AC}$
Concl.: $ABRP = ASTC + CBYW$
(These are the squares on each of the sides.)

Suggestion: Prove $ABYS \cong APQC$ and $TSYW \cong RQCB$.

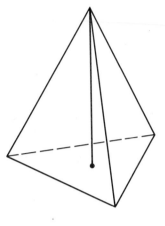

18 | Volumes

IT SEEMS ONLY NATURAL THAT HAVING learned how to determine the measure of a plane figure, we would turn to space geometry and try to devise some means of computing the measure of a space figure. Our first objective will be to establish an appropriate unit for determining this measure. With this as a tool, we can then turn our attention to certain special solids and develop theorems that will enable us to compute their measure in terms of this unit.

Of the many space figures that exist, perhaps the most important of these are solids such as those in Figure 18-1.

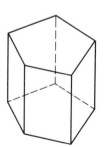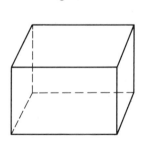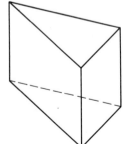

Figure 18-1.

Each of these solids is called a *prism*. Before a pyramid was defined, it was necessary that the pyramidal surface first be defined. So, too, before the prism can be defined, the *prismatic surface* will have to be defined.

DEFINITION 107: A prismatic surface is a surface that is generated by a line that moves so as to always be parallel to a fixed line and always intersect a fixed polygon. The fixed line does not lie in the plane of the fixed polygon. (Note the similarity between this definition and that of a pyramidal surface.)

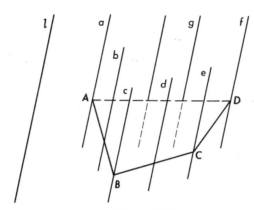

Figure 18-2.

In Figure 18-2 the fixed line is the line *l*, while *ABCD* is the fixed polygon. The lines *a*, *b*, *c*, *d*, *e*, *f*, and *g* are various positions of the moving line.

DEFINITION 108: A prism is a solid bounded by a prismatic surface and two parallel planes.

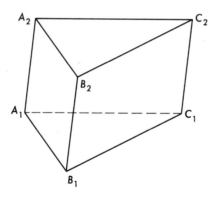

Figure 18-3.

The lines A_1A_2, B_1B_2, C_1C_2 are called the *lateral edges* of the prism. Since they represent the moving line in various positions, they must be parallel to each other, for lines in space that are parallel to the same line are parallel to each other.

THEOREM 149: The lateral edges of a prism are parallel.

The intersection of a plane and a prismatic surface is called a *section*. In the prism above, the sections $A_1B_1C_1$ and $A_2B_2C_2$ are the *bases* of the prism. If the section is made by a plane parallel to the bases, then this section is a *cross section* of the prism. If the section is made by a plane perpendicular to a lateral edge, then it is a *right section* of the prism.

The polygons $A_2A_1B_1B_2$, $B_2B_1C_1C_2$, and $A_2A_1C_1C_2$ are called the *faces* of the prism. The common perpendicular to the bases of a prism is its *altitude*. Should a lateral edge be perpendicular to the bases, then the prism would be a *right prism*.

Prisms are also classified by the polygons that form their bases. Thus, a *triangular prism* is one in which the bases are triangles. The prism on page 611 is a triangular prism. Were it an *equilateral triangular prism*, the bases would be *equilateral* triangles.

EXERCISES

A number of the statements to be proved in the following group of problems should be considered as theorems, as they will be used in the proofs that are to follow. Each of these statements will be marked with an asterisk.

1. The faces of a prism are parallelograms.*
2. The lateral edges of a prism are congruent.*
3. The bases of a triangular prism are congruent triangles.*
4. A cross section of a triangular prism is a triangle congruent to either base of the prism.*
5. A cross section of a prism is a polygon congruent to either base of the prism.* (Hint: See the definition of congruent polygons and then use the information in Problem 4.)
6. The lateral area of a prism is equal to the product of the perimeter of a right section and the measure of a lateral edge.* (The lateral area of a prism is the sum of the areas of the faces.)
7. If a plane is passed through two nonadjacent lateral edges of a prism, the intersection of the plane with the prism will be a parallelogram.
8. The faces of a right prism are rectangles.
9. If a plane is passed parallel to an edge of a triangular prism, the intersection of the plane with the upper and lower bases of the prism will be congruent line segments.

10. Given: Prism *ABC–DEF* is a right
equilateral triangular prism.
Plane *QRS* ∥ plane *DEF*
Plane *PRS* contains $\overline{RS}$.

Concl.: △*PRS* is isosceles.

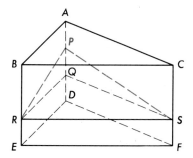

11. Given: *ABCD–EFGH* is a prism.
Concl.: If $\overline{DF}$ and $\overline{HB}$ are drawn,
they will bisect each other.

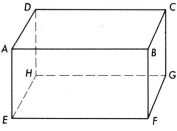

12. Use the same diagram as in Problem 11.
Given: Right prism *ABCD–EFGH*
EFGH is a rectangle.
Concl.: $(HB)^2 = (HE)^2 + (EF)^2 + (BF)^2$

B

Each of the problems in this group will depend upon the
theorem you proved in Problem 6 of the exercises in Group A.

1. The base of a right prism is an eight sided equilateral polygon, one
of whose sides is 5. Find the lateral area of the prism if the lateral
edge is 12.

2. A side of the base of a right equilateral triangular prism is 10. If the
lateral edge of the prism is 15, what is the lateral area of the prism?

3. The base of a right triangular prism is a right triangle whose legs are
18 and 24 respectively. If the lateral edge of the prism is 38, what is
the lateral area of the prism?

4. The lateral area of a prism is 448. If the lateral edge is 7, what is the
perimeter of a right section?

5. The lateral area of a prism is 684, while the length of a lateral edge
is 12. If a right section is an equilateral triangle, what is the length
of one of its sides?

6. The base of a right triangular prism is a right triangle whose legs are

24 and 32 respectively. If a lateral edge is 14, what is the total area of the prism? (The total area of a prism is the sum of the lateral area and the areas of the bases.)

7. A side of the base of a right square prism is 16. The length of a lateral edge is 24. What is the total area of the prism?

8. A side of the base of a right equilateral triangular prism is 4. If a lateral edge is 6, what is the total area of the prism?

9. A right section of a prism is an equilateral triangle, one of whose sides is 12 inches. The prism's altitude, whose length is 8 inches, makes an angle of 45° with a lateral edge of the prism. What is the lateral area of the prism?

10.* The right section of a prism is a rhombus whose diagonals are 6 inches and 8 inches respectively. The lateral area of the prism is 140 square inches. If a lateral edge of the prism makes an angle of 45° with the altitude of the prism, what is the length of the altitude?

■ Volume of a Prism

Perhaps the most commonly observed prism is the simple "box." Since its base is a rectangle and its lateral edges are perpendicular to the base, it could be called a right rectangular prism. It is, however, known as a rectangular parallelopiped.

DEFINITION 109: A parallelepiped is a prism whose base is a parallelogram.

DEFINITION 110: A rectangular parallelepiped is a right prism whose base is a rectangle.

In what two ways does a rectangular parallelepiped differ from the general parallelepiped?

DEFINITION 111: A cube is a rectangular parallelepiped whose edges are congruent.

Figure 18-4 shows the general rectangular parallelepiped, while Figure 18-5 is a drawing of a cube. In terms of the letters of these diagrams what are some of the properties of these solids?

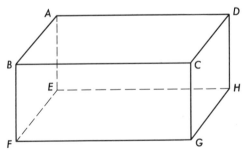

Figure 18-4.

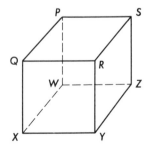

Figure 18-5.

Each of these definitions brings us somewhat closer to the objective of this chapter: to determine a means of expressing the measure of a solid.

There were a number of units available to us at the time we were seeking a way to express the measure for the region enclosed by a plane figure. The unit selected was one that was, possibly, the "simplest" polygon that enclosed a region of the plane. It was the square unit. So, too, in selecting the unit through which the measure of a solid can be computed, we reach for a solid that appears to us to have the "simplest" form. This solid is the cube. Thus, a cube, each of whose edges is one unit in length, is called a *cubic unit*.

DEFINITION 112: The volume of a solid is the number of cubic units contained by the solid.

Let us examine what this will imply in terms of the rectangular parallelepiped. By actual count we find that there are 24 cubic units in the

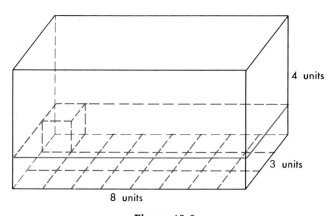

4 units

3 units

8 units

Figure 18-6.

bottom layer of this box. Since this box is 4 units high, there will be a total of 4 layers, or 96 cubic units, within the box. The *number* of cubic units in the first layer could have been determined by finding the area of the base of the rectangular parallelepiped, for there exists a one-to-one correspondence between the cubic units in the first layer and the squares in the region of the base. To find the volume of this solid would then be a matter of simply multiplying the area of the base by the measure of the altitude.

POSTULATE 47: The volume of a rectangular parallelepiped is equal to the product of the area of the base and the measure of the altitude.

It is important to realize that "volume," like "area," "measure of a line segment," and "measure of an angle," is simply a *number*. It is the number assigned to a solid dependent upon the number of cubic units that the surface of the solid bounds.

To determine the volumes of other solids will necessitate assuming the statement known as *Cavalieri's Principle*.

POSTULATE 48: If there exist two solids and a fixed plane such that every plane parallel to the fixed plane intersects the solids in sections that have equal areas, then the solids have equal volumes.

This principle can be illustrated by examining a deck of playing cards. Whether they are stacked vertically or ruffled slightly and placed on the table such as in Figure 18-7b, the volume of the deck will not be altered.

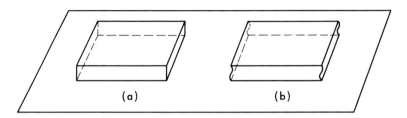

(a)   (b)

Figure 18-7.

No matter how we may twist or distort the position of the cards, just so we do not separate the cards, the volume of the deck will always be the total volume of the individual cards.

This same conclusion can be justified in terms of Cavalieri's Principle. Were a plane passed parallel to the table on which the cards were lying, it would intersect each of the decks in a single card. As the decks are identical, the cards of intersection will have equal areas. Since every plane parallel to the table and cutting both decks must always do the same, then Cavalieri's Principle grants us the right to say that the volumes of the decks will be equal.

In this illustration the polygons or cards happened to be congruent. This is not of importance. What is vital, though, is that the sections made by each plane parallel to the fixed plane always be equal in area. Below, one of the sections of equal area is a quadrilateral, while the other is a triangle.

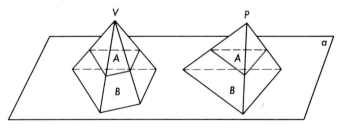

Figure 18-8.

POSTULATE 49: For any given polygon there exists a rectangle of equal area.

THEOREM 150: **The volume of a prism is equal to the product of the measure of its altitude and the area of its base.**

Given: Prism with base C and altitude h
Concl.: $V = Ch$

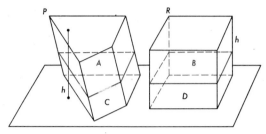

Figure 18-9.

PROOF STATEMENTS	REASONS
1. Prism with base C and altitude h	1. Given
2. Let rectangle D have the same area as the base of the prism and be in the same plane as the base of the prism; thus, $C = D$.	2. Postulate 47
3. At each vertex of the rectangle let the lines in the diagram be the perpendiculars to the plane that exist at those points.	3. There exists only one line perpendicular to a given plane at a given point on the plane.
4. At a distance h from D let the plane drawn be the one that is parallel to the plane of the base.	4. Why possible?
5. Let any plane be passed parallel to the plane of the base intersecting the prisms in A and B.	5. Same as 4
6. $B \cong D$, $A \cong C$	6. A cross section of a prism is a polygon congruent to the base. (See Problem 5, page 612.)
7. $\therefore B = D$, $A = C$	7. The areas of congruent polygons are equal. (Prob. 7, p. 593.)
8. $\therefore A = B$	8. Why?
9. Hence, volume of prism $P =$ volume of rectangular parallelepiped R	9. Cavalieri's Principle
10. But volume of $R = Dh$	10. Postulate 45
11. Volume of prism $P = Ch$	11. Substitution postulate

EXERCISES

1. The altitude of a prism is 12, while its base is a right triangle whose legs are 24 and 10 respectively. What is the volume of the prism?

2. The base of a prism is a square 15 on a side. What is the volume of the prism if the altitude is 25?

3. A side of the base of a right equilateral triangular prism is 8. What is the volume of the prism if a lateral edge is 14?

4. The base of a right triangular prism is an isosceles triangle whose leg and base are respectively 15 and 24. If a lateral edge of the prism is 16, what is the volume of the prism?

5. The base of a right prism is a parallelogram in which two adjacent sides are 8 and 12 respectively. The angle between these sides is 45°. What is the volume of the prism if the altitude is 17?

6. A prism whose altitude is 18 has a base with an area of 72. The volume of a rectangular parallelepiped is equal to the volume of the prism. If the dimensions of the base of the rectangular parallelepiped are 8 by 6, what is the length of its lateral edge?

7. (a) If the volume of a cube is 64, what is the length of one of its edges?
   (b) What is the length of a diagonal in a face of the cube?
   (c) What is the length of the line segment that joins a pair of opposite vertices of the cube? (This is called a diagonal of the cube.)

8. A diagonal of the base of a cube is $5\sqrt{2}$. What is the volume of the cube?

9. How many cubic feet of water could be stored in a tank such as the one shown in the diagram at the right?

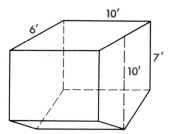

10. The front yard of the Evans home was rectangular, having dimensions of 100 feet by 45 feet. In planning his front lawn Mr. Evans decided to cover the area with top soil to a depth of 9 inches. If the cost of top soil is $3.50 per cubic yard, what was the total cost of the soil?

11. A watering trough for horses has an end that is in the shape of an isosceles trapezoid whose lower base is 2 feet and whose upper base is 3 feet. The distance between the bases is 18 inches. If the length of

the trough is 8 feet, what is the weight of the water when the trough is full? (1 cu. ft. of water = 62.4 pounds)

$$\boxed{B}$$

1. If two prisms have equal bases, then the ratio of their volumes is equal to the ratio of the measures of their altitudes.
2. If two prisms have congruent altitudes, then the ratio of their volumes is equal to the ratio of their bases.

■ Volume of a Pyramid

To develop the theorem concerning the volume of a pyramid, we again fall back upon Cavalieri's Principle. It is not possible, though, to prove this theorem without paving the way with two prior theorems and a postulate.

POSTULATE 50: If the intersection of two solids is a region of a plane, then the volume of the solid formed from these two solids is equal to the sum of the volumes of the two solids.

THEOREM 151: **If two triangular pyramids have equal bases and congruent altitudes, then their volumes are equal.**

Given: B_1 and B_2 lie in the same plane a.
$B_1 = B_2$
$h_1 = h_2$
Concl.: Volume of V = volume of P

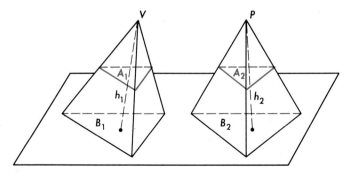

Figure 18-10

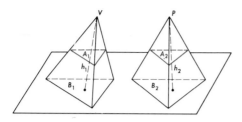

Figure 18-10.

PROOF	STATEMENTS	REASONS

STATEMENTS	REASONS
1. Pass any plane parallel to a that intersects the two pyramids.	1. Why possible?
2. $B_1 = B_2$, $h_1 = h_2$	2. Given
3. $\therefore A_1 = A_2$	3. If two triangular pyramids have equal bases and congruent altitudes, then sections made by planes parallel to the bases and equidistant from the vertices are equal. (See Problem 8, page 601.)
4. Hence, volume of V = volume of P	4. Cavalieri's Principle

THEOREM 152: **The volume of a triangular pyramid is equal to one-third the product of the measure of the altitude and the area of the base.**

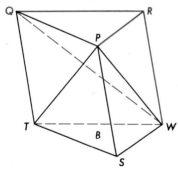

Given: Pyramid P–STW
Concl.: Volume of P–STW = $\frac{1}{3}Bh$

Figure 18-11.

ANALYSIS: A prism is constructed around the given pyramid. Our objective then becomes one of showing that the given pyramid is one of three equal pyramids in this prism. Perhaps the most difficult part of this proof is visualizing the three pyramids in the prism. They will be P–STW, W–PQR, and P–TQW. The pyramid W–PQR will have to be observed from two different points of view: once with vertex W and base PQR; the second time with vertex P and base QRW.

PROOF	STATEMENTS	REASONS
1.	In plane SPW let $\overleftrightarrow{PR} \parallel \overleftrightarrow{SW}$ and $\overleftrightarrow{WR} \parallel \overleftrightarrow{SP}$.	1. Why possible?
2.	In plane SPT let $\overleftrightarrow{PQ} \parallel \overleftrightarrow{ST}$ and $\overleftrightarrow{TQ} \parallel \overleftrightarrow{SP}$.	2. Why possible?
3.	Through P let plane PQR be parallel to plane STW.	3. Why possible?
4.	PQR–STW is a prism.	4. Why?
5.	$\triangle STW \cong \triangle PQR$	5. The bases of a triangular prism are congruent triangles. (See Problem 3, page 612.)
6.	$\triangle STW = \triangle PQR$	6. If two triangles are congruent, then their areas are equal.
7.	Altitude of P–STW = altitude of W–PQR	7. Reflexive property of equality (Both altitudes are the altitude of the prism.)
8.	$\therefore P$–$STW = W$–PQR	8. If two triangular pyramids have equal bases and congruent altitudes, then their volumes are equal.
9.	$\triangle TQW \cong \triangle RWQ$	9. S.S.S. theorem on congruence (Prove the triangles congruent.)
10.	$\triangle TQW = \triangle RWQ$	10. Same as 6
11.	Altitude of P–TQW = altitude of P–RWQ	11. Reflexive property of equality (The altitudes of both pyramids is the perpendicular segment from P to plane $QTWR$.)
12.	$\therefore P$–$TQW = P$–RWQ	12. Same as 8
13.	But W–$PQR = P$–RWQ	13. Reflexive property of equality
14.	$\therefore P$–$STW = P$–TQW	14. Transitive property of equality
15.	P–$STW + P$–$TQW +$ W–$PQR = PQR$–STW	15. Postulate 48, page 619.
16.	P–$STW + P$–$STW +$ P–$STW = PQR$–STW	16. Substitution postulate
17.	But PQR–$STW = Bh$	17. The volume of a prism is equal to the product of the measure of its altitude and the area of its base.
18.	Hence, $3P$–$STW = Bh$	18. Same as 16
19.	$\therefore P$–$STW = \frac{1}{3}Bh$	19. Division postulate

THEOREM 153: The volume of a pyramid is equal to one-third the product of the measure of its altitude and the area of its base.

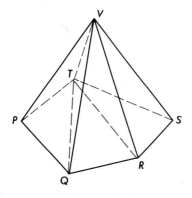

Given: V–$PQRST$ is a pyramid.
Concl.: V–$PQRST = \frac{1}{3}Bh$

Figure 18-12.

PROOF	STATEMENTS	REASONS
1. Let VTR be the plane that exists through V, T, and R.	1. Why possible?
2. Let VTQ be the plane that exists through V, T, and Q.	2. Why possible?
3. V–$TRS = \frac{1}{3}\triangle TRS \cdot h$	3. The volume of a triangular pyramid is equal to one-third the product of the measure of its altitude and the area of the base.
4. V–$TQR = \frac{1}{3}\triangle TQR \cdot h$ V–$TPQ = \frac{1}{3}\triangle TPQ \cdot h$	4. Same as 3
5. V–$PQRST = V$–$TRS +$ V–$TQR + V$–TPQ	5. If the intersection of two solids is a region of a plane, then the volume of the solid formed from these two solids is equal to the sum of the volumes of the two solids.
6. V–$PQRST = \frac{1}{3}\triangle TRS \cdot h +$ $\frac{1}{3}\triangle TQR \cdot h + \frac{1}{3}\triangle TPQ \cdot h$ or, V–$PQRST = \frac{1}{3}h(\triangle TRS +$ $\triangle TQR + \triangle TPQ)$	6. Substitution postulate
7. But $PQRST = \triangle TRS +$ $\triangle TQR + \triangle TPQ$	7. Postulate 42, see page 582.
8. Hence, V–$PQRST = \frac{1}{3}h \cdot PQRST$ or, V–$PQRST = \frac{1}{3}hB$	8. Same as 6

EXERCISES

1. Find the volume of a pyramid whose base is a square with 12-inch sides and whose altitude is 15 inches.
2. The base of a pyramid is a rectangle whose diagonal and one side are 35 inches and 28 inches respectively. If the altitude is 16 inches, what is the volume of the pyramid?
3. The solid at the right is a cube whose edge is 9 inches. What is the volume of the pyramid *A–EFH*?

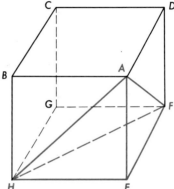

4. Find the volume of an equilateral triangular pyramid with 12-inch sides and whose altitude is 8 inches.
5. A pyramid whose base is a square has an altitude of 15 feet. If the volume of the pyramid is 180 cubic feet, what is the length of one of the sides of the square?
6.* A pyramid whose base is an equilateral triangle has a volume of $80\sqrt{3}$ cubic inches. If the altitude of the pyramid is 10 inches, what is the length of one of the sides of the base?
7. A pyramid has a base of 48 square inches and an altitude of 8 inches. A plane is passed parallel to the base and 6 inches from the vertex. What is the volume of the pyramid that was cut off the top of the original pyramid?
8. A plane is passed parallel to the base and 8 feet from the vertex of a pyramid whose base is 45 square feet and whose altitude is 12 feet. What is the volume of that part of the pyramid that remained after the top had been removed?
9. A pyramid has a square base, each of whose sides is 12 inches. A plane is passed parallel to the base and 2 inches from it. If the altitude of the pyramid is 8 inches, what is the volume of the pyramid that was removed?

10. In the pyramid at the right $ABCD$ is
a square. $\overline{VE}$, the altitude of the
pyramid, passes through the point
of intersection of the diagonals.
$m \angle EVC = 45$. If $CD = 6$, what is
the volume of the pyramid?

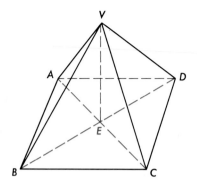

B

1. If two pyramids have equal bases, then the ratio of their volumes is equal to the ratio of the measures of their altitudes.†

2. If two pyramids have congruent altitudes, then the ratio of their volumes is equal to the ratio of their bases.†

3. If the bases of two pyramids are similar triangles, then the ratio of the volumes of the pyramids is equal to the ratio of the products of the measures of their altitudes and the squares of the measures of a pair of corresponding sides of the bases.

4. If a plane is passed parallel to the base of a triangular pyramid, then the ratio of the volume of the top pyramid to the volume of the original pyramid is equal to the ratio of the cubes of the measures of their altitudes.

5. A plane bisects the altitude of a triangular pyramid and is parallel to the base. The ratio of the volume of the pyramid above the plane to the original pyramid is $1:8$. (Hint: Use Problem 4.)

■ Surface Area and Volume of a Cylinder and a Cone

With but slight variations of the definitions that we already have, it is possible to extend the theorems developed for prisms and pyramid to theorems that apply to *circular cylinders* and *circular cones*. First, however, what are these latter solids?

DEFINITION 113: A circular cylindrical surface is a surface generated by a line that moves so as to always be parallel to a fixed line and always intersect a fixed circle. The fixed line does not lie in the plane of the fixed circle. (How does this definition differ from that of the prismatic surface?)

† These statements often appear as theorems.

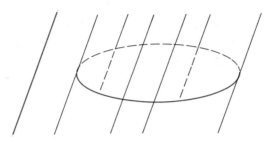

Figure 18-13.

DEFINITION 114: A circular cylinder is a solid bounded by a circular cylindrical surface and two parallel planes.

Terms such as *section of a circular cylinder, bases, cross section, right section, altitude,* and *right circular cylinder* have meanings similar to those used with the prism.

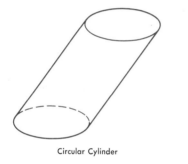

Circular Cylinder

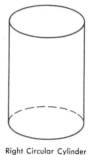

Right Circular Cylinder

Figure 18-14.

Applying methods similar to those employed in the proof of Theorem 147, it is possible for us to prove the theorems below. As honors work, you might want to determine what postulates will have to be assumed and how each of these theorems can be proved.

THEOREM 154: The volume of a circular cylinder is equal to the product of the measure of its altitude and the area of its base.

Since the base of a circular cylinder is a circle, then the area of the base is represented by $A = \pi r^2$. Hence, it follows that,

THEOREM 155: The volume of a circular cylinder can be expressed by the formula:

$$V = \pi r^2 h$$

where r is the measure of the radius of the base and h is the measure of the altitude of the cylinder.

The circular cone that we mentioned earlier has a definition much like that of the pyramid. And it, too, is derived from a surface similar to the pyramidal surface. Thus,

DEFINITION 115: A circular conic surface is a surface generated by a line that moves so as to always pass through a given point and always intersect a given circle where the given point is not in the plane of the given circle. (Figure 18-15.)

Again, such terms as *vertex*, *nappe*, and *element* mean much the same when related to the circular conic surface as they do in the pyramidal surface (p. 595).

DEFINITION 116: A circular cone is a solid bounded by one nappe of a circular conic surface and the plane of the circle used in generating the surface. (Figure 18-16.)

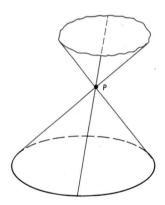

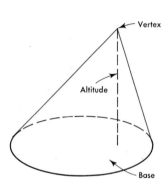

Figure 18-15.   Figure 18-16.

Theorems 142 and 153 apply equally well for the circular cone as they do for the pyramid.

THEOREM 156: If a plane is passed parallel to the base of a circular cone and intersects its surface, but not the vertex, then the intersection will be a circle.

THEOREM 157: The volume of a circular cone is equal to one-third the product of the measure of its altitude and the area of its base.

Since the base of a circular cone is a circle, then the area of the base can be found by the formula $A = \pi r^2$. Hence, it follows that,

THEOREM 158: The volume of a circular cone can be expressed by the formula,

$$V = \tfrac{1}{3}\pi r^2 h$$

where r is the measure of the radius of the base and h is the measure of the altitude.

The *regular pyramid* discussed in problem 13 on page 605 finds its counterpart in the *right circular cone*.

DEFINITION 117: A right circular cone is a circular cone in which one endpoint of the altitude is the center of the base. (Figure 18-17.)

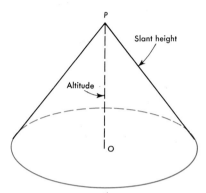

Figure 18-17.

The slant height of the regular pyramid which is an altitude of one of the faces now becomes the *slant height of the right circular cone*.

DEFINITION 118: The slant height of a right circular cone is the set of line segments whose endpoints are the vertex of the cone and a point of the base.

Notice that the slant height has been defined in terms of a right circular cone only. Why was this definition not broadened to include all circular cones?

With this as a background, Theorem 159 below appears to be a natural extension of problem 6 on page 606.

THEOREM 159: **The lateral surface area of a right circular cone is equal to one-half the product of the measure of the slant height and the circumference of the base.**

Needless to say, the circumference of the base is $2\pi r$. Hence, one-half of this becomes πr and therefore, Theorem 159 becomes,

THEOREM 160: **The lateral surface area of a right circular cone can be expressed by the formula,**

$$A = \pi r l$$

where r is the measure of the radius of the base and l is the measure of the slant height.

Should we now add the area of the base to that of the lateral surface, we come up with,

THEOREM 161: The total surface area of a right circular cone can be expressed by the formula,

$$T.A. = \pi r^2 + \pi r l$$
or $$T.A. = \pi r(r + l)$$

where r is the measure of the radius of the base and l is the measure of the slant height.

Our work would not be complete if we failed to consider the area of the surface of a right circular cylinder. As an outgrowth of problem 6 on page 624 we can say that,

THEOREM 162: The lateral surface area of a right circular cylinder is equal to the product of the circumference of the base and the measure of the altitude.

THEOREM 163: The lateral surface area of a right circular cylinder can be expressed by the formula,

$$A = 2\pi r h$$

THEOREM 164: The total surface area of a right circular cylinder can be expressed by the formula,

$$T.A. = 2\pi r^2 + 2\pi r h$$
or $$T.A. = 2\pi r(r + h)$$

Illustration 1:

In a right circular cone, the altitude forms an angle of 30 degrees with the slant height. If the slant height of the cone is 12 inches, find **(a)** the total surface area **(b)** the volume

METHOD: Using the diagram, we can determine the measures of the altitude and the radius of the base. Hence,

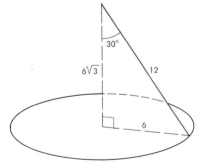

(a) $T.A. = \pi r(r + l)$
$$= \pi 6(6 + 12)$$
$$= 108\pi \text{ square inches}$$

(b) $V = \frac{1}{3}\pi r^2 h$
$$= \frac{1}{3}\pi 6^2 \cdot 6\sqrt{3}$$
$$= 72\pi\sqrt{3} \text{ cubic inches}$$

Illustration 2:

A rectangle whose dimensions are 6 feet by 8 feet is rotated about its longer side. Determine

(a) the volume **(b)** the total surface area of the solid generated.

METHOD: In the diagram at the right
we perceive that the solid generated
is a right circular cylinder whose radius
and altitude have measures of 6 and 8
respectively. Hence,

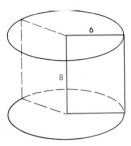

(a) $V = \pi r^2 h$
          $= \pi 6^2 \cdot 8$
          $= 288\pi$ cubic inches
(b) $T.A. = 2\pi r(r + h)$
          $= 2\pi \cdot 6(6 + 8)$
          $= 168\pi$ square inches

EXERCISES

(Leave all answers in terms of π unless otherwise stated.)

1. Find the volume of each of the following circular cylinders.
   (a) $r = 7''$, $h = 5''$ (b) $r = 12'$, $h = 4\frac{1}{2}'$
   (c) $d = 18'$, $h = 6'4''$ (d) $d = 24'$, $h = 5'3''$

2. Find the volume of each of the following circular cones.
   (a) $r = 6$ cm, $h = 8$ cm   (b) $r = 15$ yards, $h = 5$ yards
   (c) $d = 8$ feet, $h = 4$ feet 6 inches (d) $d = 3$ yards 2 feet, $h = 6$ yards

3. Find the lateral surface area of each of the following right circular
   cylinders.
   (a) $r = 10'$, $h = 4'3''$ (b) $d = 14'$, $h = 5'6''$

4. Find the total surface area of each of the following right circular cylinders.
   (a) $r = 5''$, $l = 8''$ (b) $r = 6''$, $l = 4\frac{1}{2}''$
   (c) $r = 6$ cm, $h = 8$ cm   (d) $d = 10$ feet, $h = 12$ feet

5. A right circular cylinder has a lateral surface area of 168π square inches.
   The altitude of the cylinder is 14 inches. What is the area of one of the
   bases?

6. A right circular cone has a lateral surface area of 32π square inches.
   The slant height of the cone is 8 inches. What is the total surface area
   of the cone?

7. The volume of a right circular cone is 96π cubic inches. If the altitude
   of the cone is 8 inches, what is the lateral surface area?

8. The altitude of a right circular cone makes an angle of 45 degrees with
   the slant height. If the radius of the base is 6 feet, what is the volume
   of the cone?

9. (a) If the altitude of a right circular cone is doubled while the radius of the base remains the same, what happens to the volume of the cone?

   (b) If the radius of the base of a right circular cone is doubled while the altitude remains the same, what happens to the volume of the cone?

   (c) If both the altitude and the radius of the base of a right circular cone are doubled, what happens to the volume of the cone?

10. A plane is passed parallel to the base of a cone and 6 inches from the base. The altitude and radius of the base of the original cone are shown in the diagram.
    (a) What is the radius of the upper cone?
    (b) What is the volume of the upper cone?

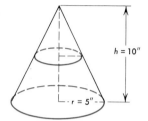

11. A pile of sand is in the shape of a right circular cone where the radius of the base is 10 feet and the altitude is 6 feet. A board is passed parallel to the ground removing all the sand within 2 feet of the vertex. What is the volume of the sand that remains?

12. The bases of a circular cone and a circular cylinder are exactly the same and the vertex of the cone lies in the same plane as the upper base of the cylinder. Compare the volumes of the two solids.

13. The area of the base of a circular cone is equal to the lateral area of the cone. How does the radius of the base compare to the slant height?

14. An isosceles right triangle is rotated about its hypotenuse. If the measure of the hypotenuse is 14, what is the volume of the solid that is generated?

15. A hot water tank is designed in the shape of a right circular cylinder large enough to hold 75 gallons of water. If the diameter of the tank is to be 2 feet, approximately how high will the tank have to be? There are $7\frac{1}{2}$ gallons in 1 cubic foot. (Use $\frac{22}{7}$ as an approximation for π.)

16. (a) Show that the ratio of the area of the base of a right circular cone to the lateral area is equal to the ratio of the radius to the slant height.

    (b) Show that if two cylinders have equal altitudes, then the ratio of their volumes is equal to the ratio of the squares of their corresponding radii.

■ Volume and Surface Area of a Sphere

In developing the theorem for determining the volume of a sphere we fall back on Cavalieri's Principle. Hence it is necessary for us to find a solid where every cross section of that solid has an area that is equal to the area of the corresponding cross section of the sphere. To do this we work with half the sphere rather than the total one. Therefore, when the proof is completed we will have to double the volume found to determine the volume of the sphere.

To create the solid needed, we construct a right circular cylinder where the radius of the base and the altitude of the cylinder are both congruent to the radius of the sphere. We then construct a right circular cone whose base is the upper base of the cylinder while its altitude is the altitude of the

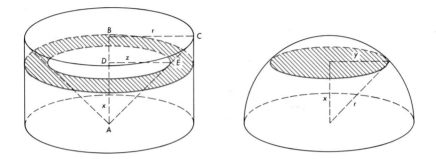

Figure 18-18.

cylinder. It is the solid at the left above to which we are referring.

Specifically, our objective is to prove that the volume bounded between the cone and the cylinder is equal to the volume of the hemisphere (half-sphere). To do this we will show that the areas of the shaded regions in the two solids are equal. Since they represent sections formed by any plane parallel to the plane containing the bases of the two solids, then by applying Cavalieri's Principle we can conclude that the solids have equal volumes.

For the shaded region of the hemisphere:
Since this is a circle its area will be,
$$A_1 = \pi y^2$$
but,
$$y^2 = r^2 - x^2$$
therefore,
$$A_1 = \pi (r^2 - x^2)$$

For the shaded region of the solid at the left:
Since
$$\triangle ABC \sim \triangle ADE,\ x:AB = z:r$$
But, AB is the measure of the altitude of the cylinder and hence it is the same as the measure of the radius.

Therefore,
$$x:r = z:r \quad \text{or} \quad x = z$$
The area of the shaded region at the left is,
$$A_2 = \pi r^2 - \pi z^2 \quad \text{or} \quad A_2 = \pi (r^2 - z^2)$$
Since
$$x = z$$
The area is,
$$A_2 = \pi (r^2 - x^2)$$

Thus, the areas of the shaded regions are equal and hence the volumes of the solids are equal. But the volume of the solid at the left is the difference between the volume of the cylinder and that of the cone. Hence,

$$V_h = \pi r^2 \cdot r - \tfrac{1}{3}\pi r^2 \cdot r$$

or
$$V_h = \pi r^3 - \tfrac{1}{3}\pi r^3 = \tfrac{2}{3}\pi r^3$$

Therefore, the volume of the hemisphere is,

$$V_h = \tfrac{2}{3}\pi r^3$$

And, in turn, the volume of the sphere is,

$$V = \tfrac{4}{3}\pi r^3$$

THEOREM 165: The volume of a sphere can be expressed by the formula,

$$V = \tfrac{4}{3}\pi r^3$$

where r is the measure of the radius of the sphere.

The proof of the last statement we would like to develop is somewhat beyond the scope of this course. However, it is possible to justify it intuitively by making use of Theorem 164.

Consider the possibility of cutting up a sphere as shown in Figure 18-19 below. Each of the solids resembles a pyramid except for the fact that the

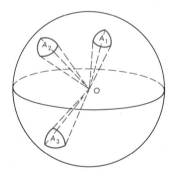

Figure 18-19.

base is a region of the surface of a sphere rather than a polygon. However, should each of these regions be taken small enough, then for all practical purposes the areas of the bases of these solids could be considered to be the same as the areas of the bases of pyramids. By accepting this, we can find the volume of the sphere by adding the volumes of all the "pyramids." Hence,

$$\text{Volume of sphere} = \tfrac{1}{3}A_1h_1 + \tfrac{1}{3}A_2h_2 + \tfrac{1}{3}A_3h_3 + \ldots + \tfrac{1}{3}A_nh_n$$

But the altitude of each of the "pyramids" is the radius of the sphere. Therefore,

$$V = \tfrac{1}{3}A_1r + \tfrac{1}{3}A_2r + \tfrac{1}{3}A_3r + \ldots + \tfrac{1}{3}A_nr$$

And by factoring,

$$V = \tfrac{1}{3}r(A_1 + A_2 + A_3 + \ldots + A_n)$$

However, $(A_1 + A_2 + A_3 + \ldots + A_n)$ represents the surface area of the sphere which we call A. Hence,

$$V = \tfrac{1}{3}rA$$

The volume, though, can be replaced by $\tfrac{4}{3}\pi r^3$. Thus,

$$\tfrac{4}{3}\pi r^3 = \tfrac{1}{3}rA$$

And finally we can conclude that,

$$A = 4\pi r^2$$

In view of the above, the following postulate appears justifiable.

POSTULATE 51: The surface area of a sphere can be expressed by the formula,

$$A = 4\pi r^2$$

where r is the measure of the radius of the sphere.

Illustration:

Liquid storage tanks are frequently constructed in the shape of a sphere. How many gallons can a spherical tank hold if it has a diameter of 21 feet? (Use $\tfrac{22}{7}$ as the approximation for π.)

METHOD:
$$\begin{aligned}
V &= \tfrac{4}{3}\pi r^3 \\
&= \tfrac{4}{3} \cdot \tfrac{22}{7} \cdot (\tfrac{21}{2})^3 \\
&= 4{,}851 \text{ cubic feet}
\end{aligned}$$
$$\text{Number of gallons} = 4{,}851 \times 7\tfrac{1}{2} = 36{,}382\tfrac{1}{2}$$

EXERCISES

(Leave all answers in terms of π unless otherwise stated.)

1. Find the volume and surface area of each of the following spheres.
   (a) $r = 4''$ (b) $r = 2\tfrac{1}{2}''$
   (c) $d = 4'6''$ (d) $d = 6$ yds. 2 ft.

2. The surface area of a sphere is 100π square inches. Find the volume of the sphere.

3. The volume of a sphere is 288π square feet. Find the surface area of the sphere.

4. A circle of radius 6 inches is rotated about a diameter.
   (a) Find the surface area of the sphere that was generated.
   (b) How does the surface area of the sphere compare with the area of the generating circle?
   (c) Is the conclusion found in (b) true of any sphere and its generating circle? Justify your answer.

5. A spherical balloon is inflated to the point where the measure of its radius is three times its original measure.

   (a) How does the new surface area compare with the original surface area?

   (b) How does the new volume compare with the original volume?

6. (a) Show that the ratio of the surface areas of two spheres is equal to the ratio of the squares of their corresponding radii.

   (b) Show that the volumes of two spheres compare as the cubes of their corresponding radii.

7. Two glass marbles having diameters of 4 inches and 6 inches respectively are melted down and then the molten glass is reshaped into a single marble. Determine the diameter of the new marble. (Leave answer in radical form.)

8. A hollow plastic ball has an inner diameter of 12 feet and an outer diameter of 18 feet. If a cubic foot of the plastic weighs 6 ounces, what is the total weight of the ball? (Use 3.14 as the approximate value of π.)

9. A sphere is inscribed in a right circular cylinder.

   (a) Show that the volume of the right circular cylinder is $1\frac{1}{2}$ times the volume of the sphere.

   (b) Show that the lateral surface area of the cylinder is equal to the surface area of the sphere.

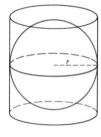

10. The upper and lower bases of a right circular cylinder are circles of a sphere. The radius of the sphere is 15 inches while the radius of the base of the cylinder is 12 inches. How much of the volume of the sphere lies outside the cylinder?

11.* In the diagram at the right, how does the surface area of the sphere compare with the total surface area of the right circular cylinder?

12.* How does the volume of the sphere in the adjacent diagram compare with the volume of the right circular cone?

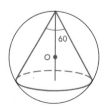

■ Test and Review

1. The base of a right prism is a triangle whose sides are 4, 5, and 7. If the lateral edge of the prism is 12, what is the lateral area of the prism?

2. (a) The base of a right prism is a rhombus whose diagonals are 10 and 24 respectively. If the lateral edge is 8, what is the lateral area?
   (b) What is the total area of this prism?

3. The base of a right prism is a quadrilateral whose sides are 3, 4, 7, and 8. If the lateral area of the prism is 132, what is the measure of a lateral edge?

4. A right section of a prism is a right triangle with legs of 9 and 12. The altitude of the prism makes an angle of 45° with the lateral edge. If the measure of the altitude is 10, what is the lateral area?

5. The volume of a rectangular parallelepiped is 105. If the dimensions of the base are 3 and 7, what is the total area of the parallelepiped?

6. The base of a right prism is an equilateral triangle that is inscribed in a circle of radius 6. If the lateral area of the prism is $90\sqrt{3}$, what is the measure of a lateral edge?

7. The dimensions of the base of a rectangular parallelepiped are 6 and 5 respectively. If the total area is 412, find the volume of the solid.

8. The length, width, and height of a rectangular parallelepiped are in the ratio of 2:3:4. If the volume of the solid is 648, what is the total area?

9. If the measure of the diagonal of a cube is $\sqrt{75}$, find the volume of the cube.

10. Two cubic feet of liquid plastic is poured into a rectangular mold whose base is 20 feet by 10 feet and allowed to cool. How thick will the sheet of plastic be?

11. The base of a right prism is an isosceles right triangle whose hypotenuse is 4. If a lateral edge of the prism is 7, what is the volume of the prism?

12. The base of the prism is a square with diagonal $4\sqrt{2}$. A lateral edge whose measure is 8 makes an angle of 60° with the altitude. What is the volume of the prism?

13. One of the great Egyptian pyramids has a square base, one of whose sides is approximately 233 meters, while its height is approximately 145 meters. If the average weight of the material from which it was constructed is 2.8 tons per cubic meter, what is the approximate weight of the pyramid? (Assume that it is a solid.)

14. The base of a pyramid is an equilateral triangle with a side whose measure is 8. The altitude of the pyramid is 10. A plane is passed parallel

to the base and 5 units from the vertex, removing a pyramid off the top. What is the volume of the remaining solid?

15. Find the volume and lateral surface area of a right circular cylinder that has a diameter of 8 cm and an altitude of 7 cm.

16. Find the volume and total surface area of a right circular cone where the diameter of the base is 24 inches and the altitude is 16 inches.

17. Find the volume and surface area of a sphere that has a diameter of 10 feet.

18. If an object sinks when placed in a basin filled with water, then the amount of water that spills out of the container is equal to the volume of the object. An iron ball having a diameter of 3 inches is lowered into a hollow right circular cone that was filled with water. If the radius of the base of the cone is 8 inches while the altitude is 6 inches, how many cubic inches of water remain in the cone?

19.* Two cubic feet of metal is drawn into a wire having a diameter of $\frac{1}{4}$ inch. How many inches of wire will there be?

20.* The base of a right circular cone is the base of a hemisphere while its vertex is a point of the hemisphere. Show that the volume of the hemisphere is twice the volume of the cone.

Prove each of the following statements:

1. Two right sections of a triangular prism are congruent triangles.

2. If a plane is passed through two diagonally opposite edges of a parallelepiped, these edges and the intersections in the two bases will form a parallelogram.

3. If a plane is passed through two diagonally opposite edges of a parallelepiped, it will divide the solid into two equal triangular prisms.

4. If a line segment contains the point of intersection of the diagonals of a parallelepiped and terminates in the bases, then that point is the midpoint of the line segment.

■ Try This For Fun

Mathematicians seem to go out of their way in order to throw obstacles in their path. To illustrate, earlier we had learned that although they have many instruments at their disposal, they insist that geometric constructions be made with the use of but the straightedge and compass. To limit the scope of their movement even further, they will frequently lay aside one of these two instruments and attempt to seek out the solution to their problem with the aid of the other alone.

Thus, in the two intersecting circles below the objective was to find the center of each circle by using only the straightedge. To do this, a point P

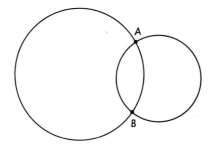

was selected on the circle at the left. $\overleftrightarrow{PA}$ was drawn and extended until it intersected the second circle at Q. This was followed by drawing $\overleftrightarrow{QB}$ and extending it to the point of intersection with the circle at R. A second point

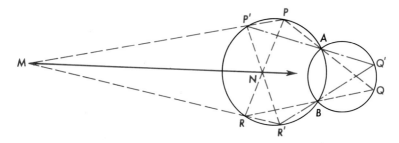

P' was then selected and the process was repeated. This, in turn, was followed by finding the points of intersection of $\overleftrightarrow{PP'}$ with $\overleftrightarrow{RR'}$ and $\overleftrightarrow{PR}$ with $\overleftrightarrow{P'R'}$; these being M and N. Now, were we to draw $\overleftrightarrow{MN}$, this line would pass through the center of the larger circle.

(a) Can you prove this?
(b) What further construction is necessary to find the center of the larger circle?

Index

Numerals shown in *italic* indicate page numbers of definitions.